NEW
HOME WORKSHOP
ENCYCLOPEDIA

PREPARED *by*
THE EDITORIAL STAFF *of*
POPULAR SCIENCE MONTHLY

WITH OVER 1500
WORKING DRAWINGS, DIAGRAMS
AND ILLUSTRATIONS

POPULAR SCIENCE PUBLISHING CO., INC.
353 FOURTH AVENUE • NEW YORK 10, N. Y.

NEW
HOME WORKSHOP
ENCYCLOPEDIA

Building Model Planes Without Balsa

DOMESTIC SUBSTITUTES SERVE CRAFTSMEN AS MODEL MATERIALS MARCH OFF TO WAR

By FRANK ZAIC

WHEN war was thrust upon us, it became evident that model builders would have to do without many of the materials they normally took for granted. Rubber became very precious, and in January, 1942, the manufacture of rubber thread for model use was suspended. Steel, aluminum, and copper, used in making motors and electrical equipment, were severely restricted. Japanese manufacturers of covering tissue became our enemies. Balsa wood—so desirable in model construction because of its lightness and strength—was classed as a vital war material, and existing stocks were frozen last August.

The search for substitutes, then, is on! Luckily, domestic paper mills have been turning out satisfactory covering tissue for several years. But new rubber is definitely unobtainable, and unless you can use strips from old inner tubes for powering your craft, your modeling urge will have to vent itself in gliders and gas designs.

The restriction on balsa, however, is much more serious. One can best judge the importance of this wood to the model industry by noting that about 4,000,000 board feet of balsa were hitherto used per year. It weighs from 4 to 20 lbs. per cubic foot, as compared with 30 lbs. for domestic light woods—our best available substitutes.

Spruce, white and sugar pine, poplar, basswood, and hemlock may be placed in this class, and of these, sugar pine seems to be the best now available for model making. It has many of the characteristics of balsa. It lacks the stringy grain that seems common to most woods, and can be crosscut without difficulty. Furthermore, it does not necessitate any variation from the aerodynamic design you used in balsa construction. As for tools, a good, sharp penknife is most important, as well as a jig saw or a coping saw with a fine-tooth blade. A block plane is essential also.

Of course, the select grade of sugar pine is now also on the priority list, but it is believed that other grades will remain available, and there will no doubt be stocks on dealers' shelves for some time to come. Most home workshops and school manual training departments, too, will have some of this material on hand. It can be ripped into suitable strips on a small power saw if a sharp blade is used and a wooden table insert with a very narrow slot is substituted so that the stock is supported right up to the blade.

Basswood promises to be the next best choice to sugar pine. It is slightly heavier—in the neighborhood of 35 lbs. per cubic foot as compared to 30 lbs. for pine. It is equally easy to work and should prove quite satisfactory. However, pine has larger "pores" than basswood, and its medullary rays (the lines radiating from the center outward) are much more pronounced, so that sheets cut along them are extra stiff and make excellent ribs.

The use of sugar pine or basswood involves no radical changes in structural design. In time we may find better ways of using it, but for the time being standard practice seems to work out very well. Pine spars and longerons will have to be smaller than those we made from balsa if their weight is to be within reasonable limits. However, the reduction should be in the thickness and not in depth, so that the beam strength will be preserved.

A wing design that proved to be good is shown on the drawing. The sheet covering the leading edge need not be more than 1/64" thick for models up to 200 sq. in., while 1/32" sheet takes care of all other sizes. This system makes possible the use of a small leading-edge spar. If the wing is small, one additional spar on the lower camber will be enough. Larger wings such as for gas jobs should have additional spars. Be sure to use sizes which have generous depth proportions. The trailing edge should have the standard tapered section. Unless the spar is placed close to the trailing edge, the covering will warp it. Some manufac-

turers supply trailing edges already shaped. If you have to cut one, be sure that it has a true taper and not just a round corner.

Most present-day designs have wings with an aspect ratio of about 8 to 1, so you can copy balsa models fairly closely in working with pine or basswood, simply making structural members one half as thick, but as deep as specified for balsa. Ribs may be cut from 1/32″ sheets, provided the chord is not more than 5″ and that there are several spars to prevent the ribs from weaving. Sheets 1/20″ thick will do for most "B" gas designs and large gliders, while 1/16″ material will take care of large "C" gas models. Some may think of lightening the ribs by punching holes in them. I do not recommend this practice, as the saving of weight will be small and the loss of strength great.

Fuselage construction, too, can be kept to established standards by the use of smaller longerons and stringers. For example, if ⅛″ square hard balsa is specified, 3/32″ square pine will do. It has about one half the area of a ⅛″ cross section, so the weight will remain almost the same as that of the balsa member. However, the smaller pine strips will require a greater number of uprights to keep them from bending under load. To prevent buckling of longerons, the spacing of uprights should not be more than eight times the square dimension; that is, spacing for ⅛″ square longerons should be 1″. This can be increased, however, if the longeron is curved; therefore fuselage outlines should have a curve all along them. The covering will then keep the strip under compression, whereas if the longeron is straight the covering subjects it to tension, with resultant wrinkles and structural failures, as shown in the drawings. Note, too, how the segments of round bulkheads should be made to overlap, with deeper stringers at these points.

When using pine or basswood for longerons or spars, always consider the forces that will be placed on it, and remember that the resistance against bending is squared when the depth is doubled.

If a builder designs his own model, the ideal wing would be tapered as shown. Note that some of the spars do not run the full span. For the time being we are using simple tips that can be shaped from trailing-edge stock. Regular round or elliptical tips can be built from sections as is done with balsa, but the stock will have to be quite thick to prevent warps. Since we are only beginning to use pine, and the chief problem is to keep weight down, such fine points can well be left for later decision.

At the very outset of the search for a balsa substitute, the need for rib-making material was most pressing. Hardwood spars and longerons can be purchased ready-cut, and no work other than trimming to length is needed. But ribs have to be cut to a curved outline. I tried to cut wide sheets from sugar pine, and found that the regular balsa-sawing equipment did the job well, and that the sheets had smooth surfaces. I cut the stock to quarter grain as is done for balsa sheets intended for rib work. The crucial test came when I tried to cut the ribs out with a razor blade. I found that sugar pine up to about 1/16″ thick can be readily cut this way for making ribs, bulkheads, and other flat shapes.

At first I was worried about the ability of model cement to join pine, but actual trials have shown that it can be safely used. It is, however, necessary to be generous and to go over the joints several times, extending the coating over a larger area than on balsa to obtain good anchorage. When this is done, the dope by which the covering is held in place will soften the cement at the

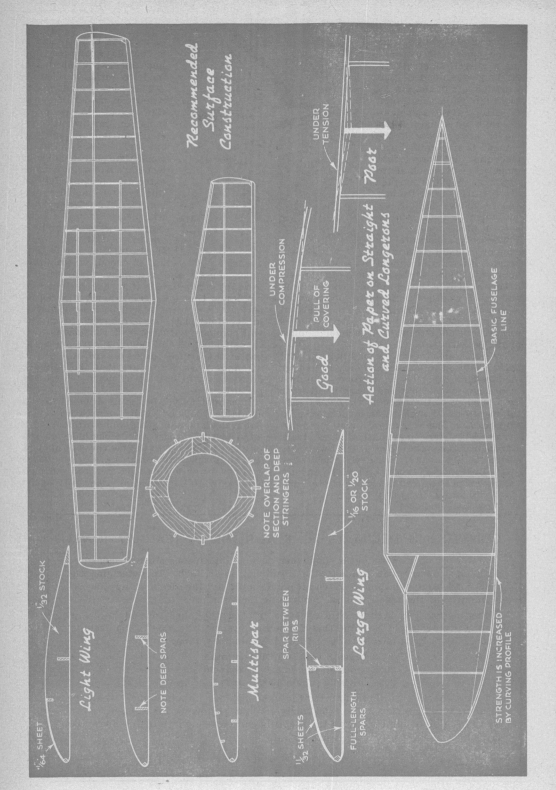

Recommended Surface Construction

Light Wing

1/32 STOCK

1/64 SHEET

NOTE DEEP SPARS

Multispar

SPAR BETWEEN RIBS

NOTE OVERLAP OF SECTION AND DEEP STRINGERS

UNDER COMPRESSION

UNDER TENSION

Good

Poor

PULL OF COVERING

Action of Paper on Straight and Curved Longerons

Large Wing

1/16 OR 1/20 STOCK

1/32 SHEETS

FULL-LENGTH SPARS

BASIC FUSELAGE LINE

STRENGTH IS INCREASED BY CURVING PROFILE

joint and make it soak into the paper, thereby forming a gussetlike structure. It is recommended that work be left in the pin jig overnight while the cement is setting. Pine has more life than balsa and it is liable to break loose if the cement is not quite hard. One must not forget that model cement needs air to dry and that the surface always dries first, leading one to believe that it has set when it may still be soft inside.

The only substitute for cement, should this also become unavailable, would be casein glue. Ordinary fish glue seems never to set to a model maker's satisfaction, and damp weather is likely to loosen it up. Just what you will do for dope depends on what your paint shop has to offer. Lacquer thinned out 50 percent with lacquer thinner might be satisfactory.

To get a good idea of just how helpful balsa has been to us, one has only to look at models built by boys in Europe, who had to use hardwood all these years because of the tendency of their countries toward self-sufficiency. Although these models may be examples of fine workmanship, their aerodynamical layout makes them poor flyers and their actions remind us of our own early efforts of about 1927, when we knew very little about model aerodynamics. To our advantage was the fact that it is easy to build or repair a balsa model in a few days and try out new ideas. A hardwood model requires more time.

This is the challenge to American model builders: Can we tackle the problems of hardwood construction, and in spite of our inexperience, do better work than European boys who have had a much more extensive background in this type of model building? I feel that our work will have many advantages. A good example is our use of thin white-pine sheets for ribs, while they use plywood, which takes much longer and requires greater effort. Perhaps they tried thin sheets but did not know that quarter-graining was necessary. At any rate, it will be most interesting to note just how our hardwood models will compare with those of Europeans. Although most of our older builders are serving in the armed forces or are at work in war industries, I am sure that the younger craftsmen will not let us down in our expectations.

It cannot as yet be foretold which of the available woods will gain the greatest favor. Some dealers will stress pine while others may feature basswood, depending on the grades produced and the nearness of supply. Although this article may have dealt almost exclusively with pine, the methods outlined also apply to basswood or other softwoods.

CONVERTING DECIMALS TO FRACTIONS   [CALCULATIONS]

MANY occasions arise in the shop when decimal dimensions must be measured with an ordinary rule graduated in fractions of an inch. To determine the fractional equivalent of a given decimal, multiply the decimal by the denominator of the fraction most convenient for your use.

For instance, in laying out a sheet of light metal to be formed into 6¾" diameter pipe, it will be found that the circumference is 21.2058". The decimal, .2058, may be multiplied by any of three denominators, thus:

.2058 times 8 equals 1.6464 eighths.
.2058 times 16 equals 3.2928 sixteenths
.2058 times 32 equals 6.5856 thirty-seconds

Using the last of these figures, for example, the circumference would be measured as 21 inches and 6.5856 thirty-seconds. Allowing for a slight reduction in the pipe diameter when the metal is curved, the width of the piece you lay out may be 21 7/32", exclusive of lap.

POPULAR SCIENCE MONTHLY SHOP DATA

Hop sacking or cretonne makes a colorful lid cover and bag for this light, sturdy wash-day clothes hamper

When folded, the hamper takes up little space in the laundry, and it can be easily carried back to its closet when washing is done

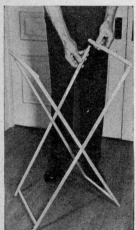

Collapsible Clothes Hamper

THIS attractive folding clothes hamper is easily carried to the laundry for sorting clothes before they are washed. The simple frame is made of dowels, while the cloth bag is so designed that the framework holds it open rigidly and, at the same time, allows it to be folded easily.

The lid consists of a piece of ¼" plywood covered with the same material as the bag and attached to the framework as indicated in the drawing below.

To empty its contents, the hamper is inverted. This is easy to do because of its extreme lightness.

Dowels are used throughout in building the frame, which is put together with glued mortise-and-tenon joints and pinned pivots, as shown above and in the drawings

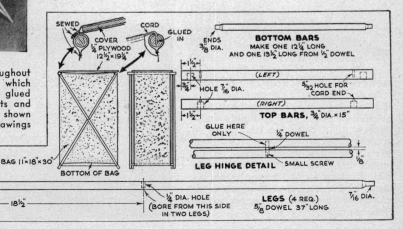

SEWED
COVER
¼ PLYWOOD
12½ × 19¼
CORD
GLUED IN
ENDS ⅜ DIA.

BAG 11 × 18 × 30
BOTTOM OF BAG

BOTTOM BARS
MAKE ONE 12¼ LONG
AND ONE 13½ LONG FROM ½ DOWEL

(LEFT)
HOLE ⁷⁄₁₆ DIA.
⁵⁄₃₂ HOLE FOR CORD END
(RIGHT)

TOP BARS, ¾" DIA. × 15"

GLUE HERE ONLY
¼ DOWEL
LEG HINGE DETAIL   SMALL SCREW

⅜ HOLE
1½
18½
¼ DIA. HOLE
(BORE FROM THIS SIDE IN TWO LEGS)
LEGS (4 REQ.)
⅝ DOWEL 37" LONG
⁷⁄₁₆ DIA.

MIDGET DOOR STOPS that slip under the pinhead of a door hinge take the place of more elaborate ones. They can be installed in a moment by lifting the hinge pin out of the hinge, inserting the pin through the hole in the door stop, and replacing the pin. The devices can be adjusted to stop doors at a 90-deg. or a 180-deg. angle. They can be removed at any time.

BLACKOUTS ARE CAMOUFLAGED from the inside through the use of the decorative shade above. Made of heavy black paper and absolutely opaque, it looks like a Venetian blind by reason of a design applied to its interior surface. It may be hung in place or rolled up for storage in a few seconds, and is available in four convenient sizes designed to fit almost any window in the home.

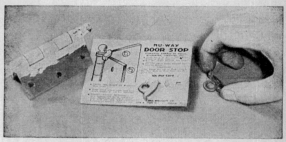

TILE BATHTUBS, built on the job, may save hundreds of tons of steel and iron that would otherwise go into the making of ordinary ones. The tub shown below was constructed on a wooden framework reinforced with wire mesh. It is roomier, easier to clean, and offers a surer footing than the old type, while the wide seat at the front is a distinct improvement. The interior is composed of pieces of unglazed ceramic tile, which is available in attractive color combinations. Such built-in tubs eliminate many transportation problems, and can sometimes be installed where others could not.

HERE'S WALL PROTECTION in the form of a transparent film that prevents dust and dirt from penetrating painted surfaces and washable wallpapers. The colorless flat finish is applied directly and dries in about twenty minutes. When walls become soiled, the film is washed off with water—no soap or cleaner is necessary—and a new coat is applied. A gallon of the fluid will cover about 1,500 sq. ft.

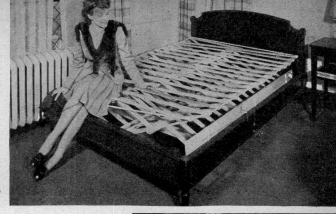

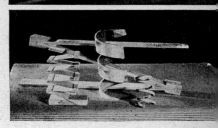

The full-size box spring above requires only 5 lbs. of steel. Instead of coil springs, there are ten birch slats, each 3" in width, suspended from double helical springs held by wire clips

Above, bedspring made of hickory slats, rope, glue, and nails! Right, spring band-sawed from one piece of wood. Right, below, four experimental types of springs. The large spiral one shown is of plywood

WOODEN FURNITURE SPRINGS may solve the problem raised by restrictions on the use of steel for such purposes. Experiments are being made with various types, one of these being a wooden bedspring which can be adapted to couches, chairs, and so forth. The resilient members are made of hickory, treated with a wood preservative, but not steamed or bent in any way. Oak, ash, and maple springs also are being tested. One manufacturer has combined wood with steel to make a full-size box bedspring, containing ten birch slats suspended from helical springs at both ends. The total amount of steel used, including that for the wire saddles or clips by which the slats are attached to the springs, is only 5 lbs.

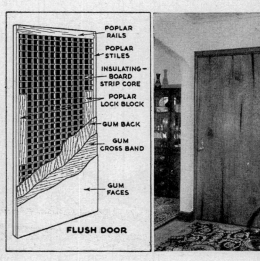

FLUSH DOORS add new modern beauty to any home. A honeycomb grid between the faces is said to make the type shown below unusually sturdy. The grid consists of strips of insulating board halved together to form a rigid, nonwarping core. Frame corners are made with wedged dovetail joints. The faces are composed of three-ply gum veneer, and completely seal in the core. All parts are fabricated with water-resistant resin glue, which fixes the two faces firmly to the frame and core.

Below and at extreme right, flush doors displaying the clean-cut lines and simplicity so desirable in modern homes. In the drawing, a cross section of the door shows the honeycomb core and the frame and face construction

POPLAR RAILS

POPLAR STILES

INSULATING-BOARD STRIP CORE

POPLAR LOCK BLOCK

GUM BACK

GUM CROSS BAND

GUM FACES

FLUSH DOOR

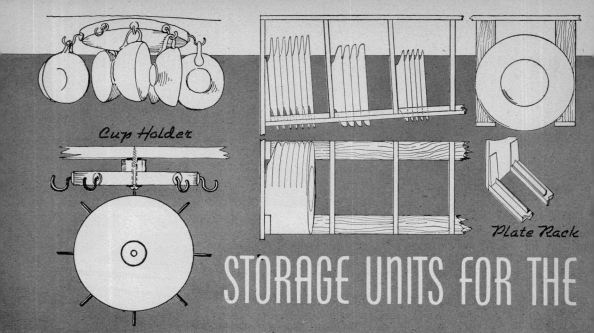

Cup Holder

Plate Rack

STORAGE UNITS FOR THE

Pot Closet

HOOK   RACK FOR COVERS

By JOSEPH ARONSON
Interior Designer

FOR complete modernization of a kitchen, a systematic method of storing equipment in use every day must be provided. Whether you are making a fresh start by remodeling, or already have some up-to-date units installed, it will pay to give additional thought to timesavers of this nature. Here are suggested designs, adaptable to the space you have available, for a pot closet, spice shelves, tray rack, revolving cup holder, and plate rack.

Pot closet. The old method of storing pots and skillets in low cupboards necessitated stooping and searching. A narrow closet taking less floor space will hold all ordinary pots in open view and within easy reach. One 15″ deep by 24″ wide and reaching to the ceiling will be sufficient. Put it near the stove. To plan the hanging arrangement, cut a plywood panel at least ⅜″ thick to fit into the back of the cupboard. Lay it on the floor, and group the utensils in staggered order to utilize all space. Ball-tip screw hooks are the best hangers.

Pot covers may be kept in racks on the inner side of the door. Strips ¼″ by 3″ are screwed to tapered cleats, leaving about ½″ open at the bottom. The covers wedge themselves in and will not rattle.

Spice shelves. Disorderliness of small articles in a deep cupboard can be avoided by fastening shallow shelves to the inside of the cupboard doors. One of the sketches shows a type suitable for small packages and shakers of spices and small bottles of condiments and sauces. End-pieces shaped as suggested may be sawed out to support two or three shelves. Both the shelves and fronts may be of ¼″ plywood. Rabbet the

DINNER PLATES | BREAKFAST PLATES | SALAD PLATES

SAUCERS | CEREAL DISHES | SOUP PLATES | DESSERT PLATES

THIS SPACE MUST BE GREATER THAN PROJECTION "A"

HOLES FOR MOUNTING SCREWS

RABBET FOR FLOOR

Spice Rack

MODERN KITCHEN

Tray Rack

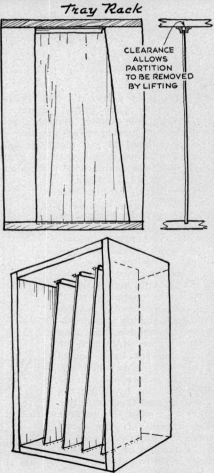

CLEARANCE ALLOWS PARTITION TO BE REMOVED BY LIFTING

floors into the endpieces, nail or screw the fronts on, and screw the assembled rack to the door. Size is best determined by arranging all the articles to be stored in rows according to height. The most important detail is to cut back any cupboard shelves that may otherwise interfere with the closing of the doors.

Tray rack. Trays may be stored vertically, thus occupying some odd corner of unused space either high or low. The dimensions should be based on the largest tray in your collection. All trays should be kept separate by partitions of ¼″ plywood or composition board, each set loosely into a groove in the floor of the rack and supported at the top by two short pieces of molding. Do not let the partitions go all the way back. They are easily removed for thorough cleaning.

Revolving cup holder. Eight cups may be stored in a small space on a 6″ diameter revolving disk of ¾″ plywood. Attach the cup hooks horizontally to the rim of the disk. Then fasten the disk to the underside of a shelf, using as a pivot a long screw passed through a small wooden collar and two iron washers as shown.

Plate rack. A system of storing plates on edge instead of flat not only saves space but reduces the danger of chipping. The usual way of piling plates means china on china, while in this rack we have the weight of the china resting on wood. Into the dish compartment, fix a pair of parallel stretchers at an angle of about 10 deg. and about 5″ apart. Partitions should not be vertical, but at right angles to the stretchers, so that the dishes may lean against them. Space the partitions after measuring your dishes, but make allowances to avoid tight fits.

A 1⅛″ cove molding placed to support the dishes at the edges as shown is helpful, as is also the use of weatherstripping as padding.

Colonial Plant Boxes

WALL HOLDERS MADE FROM A CHOPPING BOWL

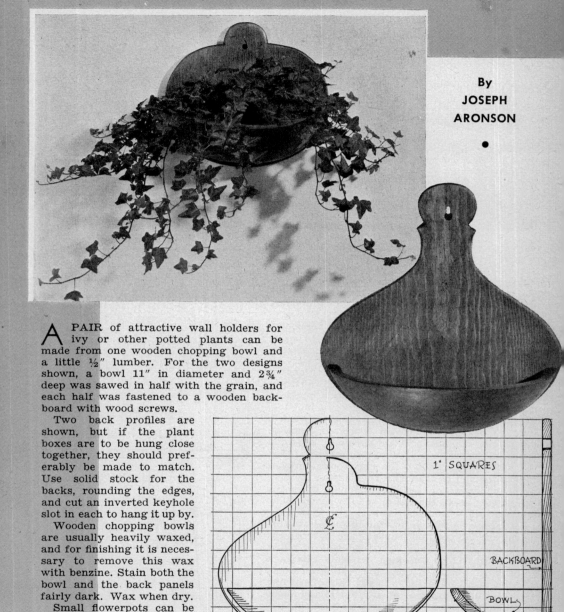

By
**JOSEPH
ARONSON**

•

A PAIR of attractive wall holders for ivy or other potted plants can be made from one wooden chopping bowl and a little ½″ lumber. For the two designs shown, a bowl 11″ in diameter and 2¾″ deep was sawed in half with the grain, and each half was fastened to a wooden backboard with wood screws.

Two back profiles are shown, but if the plant boxes are to be hung close together, they should preferably be made to match. Use solid stock for the backs, rounding the edges, and cut an inverted keyhole slot in each to hang it up by.

Wooden chopping bowls are usually heavily waxed, and for finishing it is necessary to remove this wax with benzine. Stain both the bowl and the back panels fairly dark. Wax when dry.

Small flowerpots can be kept in place by filling the space around them with fine gravel or sand. To protect the inside of the bowl against dampness, coat it with paraffin or fit a metal liner of tin-can stock.

Lay out the backboards on 1″ squares, following either of the two attractive designs above. Saw out the outline, and round the edges all around. Saw a chopping bowl in half with the grain, and attach each of the halves to a back by means of countersunk wood screws

PLAQUES ★ ★ ★ ★ ★ ★ ★ ★ ★ ★ ★ ★ ★

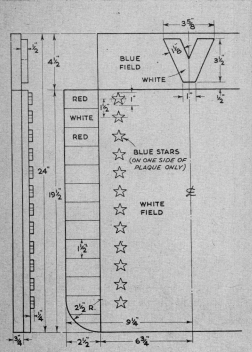

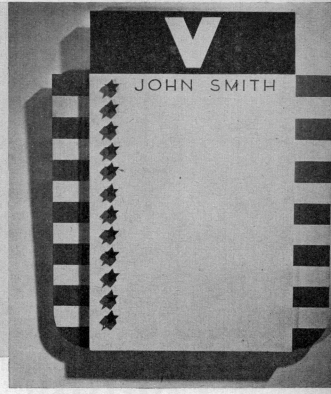

★ ★ ★ BY JUAN OLIVER

FROM thousands of American homes, offices, shops, and factories, men have gone forth to join the armed services of the United States. "Let's not forget them" is the slogan of those who stay behind, and to this end service flags and plaques of various kinds are displayed.

In a letter to POPULAR SCIENCE, R. J. Lamberth, of Chicago, Ill., writes that he is kept constantly busy in his home shop turning out wooden service plaques for clubs, fraternal organizations, and business houses, and he suggests that a suitable design for such pieces might be of interest to many readers. Illustrated on this page are two attractive plaques in modern styles appropriate for home display or as company honor rolls.

The plaques give an interesting relief effect, yet are easy to make either with or without power tools. Working to the dimensions shown, cut the back of the smaller one from ½″ stock, saw the raised middle section out of ¼″ material, and glue or nail

these together. The "V" and stars are jig-sawed from ¼″ stock. Finish separately before mounting these with brads. Stars can be made any size desired and spaced according to the number to be mounted.

Use ¾″ stock for the back of the large plaque. To this, glue and nail the ½″ thick center section. Cut the large "V" also from ½″ material, the stars from ¼″ stock. The names can be lettered on or cut from ⅛″ stock. Pressed composition board is excellent for small cut-out letters, as it does not splinter.

Clear white pine or plywood is suitable for such plaques, but for outdoor use plywood must be the waterproof resin-bonded type. Use a good quality of red, white, and blue enamel. Masking tape will be of help in painting the stripes.

The five-pointed stars, which add to the decorative effect of these plaques, can be laid out on ¼″ stock in accordance with the diagram shown on the opposite page, and cut out with a jig saw.

A stand like this is a useful accessory for your home. You can build it of wood to match other room furnishings, or finish it with a contrasting enamel.

The stand when compactly folded, ready to be tucked into a closet. Notice how little space it takes up

Folding Luggage

Holds a Guest's Suitcase for Easy Packing and Unpacking

SOLVING the problem of where to put suitcases for packing and unpacking, this sturdy luggage stand saves wear and tear on bedspreads and furniture, and folds so compactly it takes up little room in a closet when not needed.

Although the one shown was made from walnut, any strong, durable wood can be used. The bottom spreaders are turned to the dimensions shown, with ½" dowel tenons at the ends. Note that the top turnings are alike in length, and that the dowel holes are spaced 18" apart in one, but only 15⅞" apart in the other. Both bars have blind grooves or saw kerfs cut in them to take the webbing, and these are at right angles to the dowel holes.

Band-saw the four legs all to the same pattern from 1" by 2" stock. Bore a 1⅛"

hole through the upper end of each; then saw across the diameter of the hole, rounding the cut slightly. Be careful in boring the ½" dowel holes for the hinge pins and bottom spreaders. In two legs these are bored from the same side of the piece, but in the other two the hinge hole is bored from one side, that for the spreader from the other.

Assemble the inner frame with glue, insert the hinge dowels, place the outer legs upon them, and assemble the outer frame. Be sure the top bars are glued on with the slots facing out. Finish the wood as desired.

Cut three 18" lengths of 2" wide webbing, which can be bought at large hardware and upholstery shops. Push the ends into the saw kerfs, and secure them with small hardwood wedges 1/16" thick driven in alongside.—BENJAMIN NIELSEN.

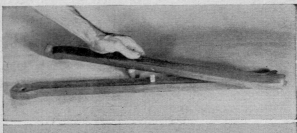

Above, how a pair of legs is joined by means of a hinge pin slipped into blind holes. These are bored in the two pieces so that they face one another

Below, legs are doweled to blind holes in the top spreaders. Webbing is wedged and glued into grooves

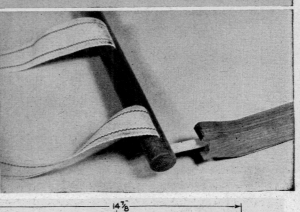

After a hole is bored into the upper end of the leg, the stock is sawed across to form a semicircular socket

Stand

The slits or kerfs in the top bars are ½" in depth, and should be wide enough to secure strong canvas webbing by 1/16" thick wedges

WEDGE, 1/16" × ½" × 2" FOR SECURING WEBBING (6 REQ.)

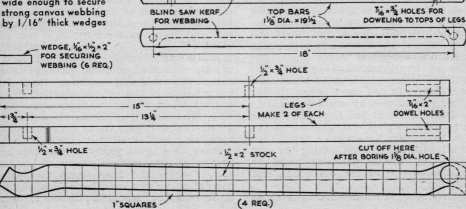

14⅞"
1"
3/4"
1"
7/8"
½" × 3/4" TENON

17"
1"
3/4"
1"
7/8"

15⅞"
BLIND SAW KERF FOR WEBBING
TOP BARS 1⅛" DIA. × 19½"
7/16" × 3/4" HOLES FOR DOWELING TO TOPS OF LEGS

18"

½" × 3/4" HOLE

15"
13¼"
LEGS MAKE 2 OF EACH
7/16" × 2" DOWEL HOLES

1¾"

½" × 3/4" HOLE
½" × 2" STOCK
CUT OFF HERE AFTER BORING 1⅛" DIA. HOLE

1" SQUARES
(4 REQ.)

Bindings, sports equipment and all leather articles respond favorably to good treatment and will reward their owner with longer wear and fine appearance

Heat supplied by a reflector lamp allows the oil to work itself into the leather without burning. Use an infrared type therapeutic lamp or radiant·heater

9 LIVES FOR YOUR

IF A SOCIETY for the prevention of cruelty to leather were formed, there is no doubt that many of us would be found guilty of abuse and neglect. These days, however, careful maintenance is the watchword for all goods that cannot be conveniently replaced, and leather—one of the oldest and most useful materials known to man—may have its life multiplied many times over with proper treatment.

Leather articles will, in spite of all care, become dirty. In the days when it was plentiful, rubber cement could be used to remove some kinds of dirt from fine leather surfaces. The cement was painted on the leather, left to dry for an hour or so, then rolled off with the fingers, taking the dirt with it. The rubber particles could be saved, dissolved in carbon bisulphide, and used again.

A wide variety of leather articles such as gloves and belts may be cleaned by washing them with water and saddle soap, Castile, or any similar mild soap, then rinsing well, and drying. However, drying leather calls for a word of caution. Did you ever get your shoes wet, dry them on the radiator, and then wonder why they felt like wooden clogs the next time you wore them? A quick way of ruining leather is to dry it rapidly with heat or direct sunlight. Heat causes stiffening and cracking. The safest procedure is to place the wet article where a draft of air strikes it—in an open doorway, for example, or in the air stream of a fan. After drying, it is a good idea to applying polish or other dressing.

Some time ago a group of scientists and library experts made a study of leather-bound books, and they found that those handled every day lasted much longer than those that remained undisturbed for long

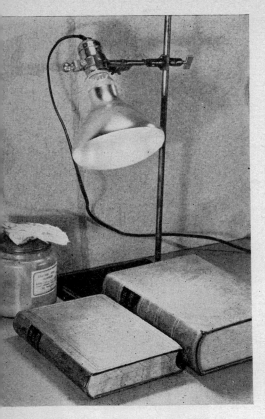

rather than to polish it, a dressing that consists essentially of oils and greases is most suitable. Dealers in shoe supplies usually handle such grease, but you can make your own preparation. A paste that I have used for a number of years on book bindings and other leather articles consists of 3 oz. of neat's-foot oil and 2 oz. of lanolin, by weight. Warm the mixture until the lanolin is distributed evenly through the oil, and use it warm. Apply it to the leather with a cloth, but do not put it on too heavily. Then place the article in a warm (but not hot) place to drive the preparation into the leather.

Another lubricant used in libraries consists of a mixture of castor oil and paraffin. Enough for a considerable number of books is made by heating 3½ oz. of castor oil and adding 1½ oz. of paraffin chips. Stir until the wax melts and blends with the oil. Apply lightly about once a year. The castor oil may be of the odorless variety.

A third leather lubricant is ordinary petroleum jelly. All of these dressings can be used on other leather articles as well as on book bindings.

The committee that investigated the preservation of leather bindings unearthed a lot of other facts. Books last longer if stored in open shelves not placed against the wall. Gas fumes, which create sulphuric and sulphurous acid in leather, are injurious. Likewise harmful is tobacco smoke, which contains ammonia. This provides sound reason for those "No Smoking" signs in libraries. Books kept in a damp place are likely to mildew. Those kept in closed cases should be removed and aired occasionally on dry days.

LEATHER GOODS

periods. The reason was that oil transferred from the hands to the book bindings —an insignificant amount—acted as a dressing for the leather.

Leather must be "fed" at intervals with oil or grease if it is to give maximum service. The oil added to it in the manufacturing process will in time disappear through evaporation or other action; if it is not restored, the leather becomes dry and stiff, cracks, and often disintegrates into powder. After cleaning leather by washing or some other process, application of a dressing is always advisable.

There are numerous leather dressings on the market. Any good shoe polish will keep leather in good shape. However, leather authorities recommend that only a polish that dries to a dull finish be used, or one that has to be buffed to a luster.

When it is desired to feed the leather

One man who hates to wear rubbers uses a commercial leather paste to waterproof his shoe soles. He smears the grease liberally on the sole and drives it in by baking, being careful to heat the leather no more than necessary. He used a soldering torch until he discovered recently that the new drying lamps and the older infrared therapeutic lamps would do the job without the danger of scorching the leather. Two or three treatments make his shoe soles water resistant for several months and improve their flexibility and wearing qualities.

Other lubricants used for making shoes and other leather goods water resistant are neat's-foot and sperm oil. The leather, particularly the soles, is well impregnated with one of these oils; then the shoes are set aside until the oil dries, after which they are polished. Neat's-foot oil dries a little

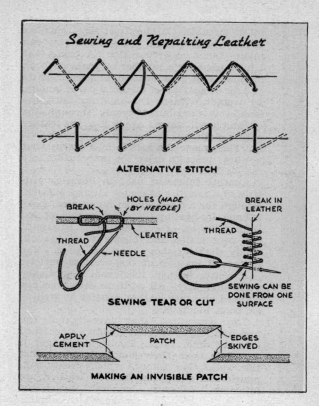

Sewing and Repairing Leather

ALTERNATIVE STITCH

BREAK — HOLES (MADE BY NEEDLE) — BREAK IN LEATHER

THREAD — LEATHER — NEEDLE — THREAD

SEWING TEAR OR CUT — SEWING CAN BE DONE FROM ONE SURFACE

APPLY CEMENT — PATCH — EDGES SKIVED

MAKING AN INVISIBLE PATCH

A brief case is refinished with a leather dressing that will dye as well as polish

Tags of shoe leather are cemented down to prevent them from being torn off

Shoes may be waterproofed on uppers and soles. A commercial solution is used

If the leather at the lap joint of a belt loosens and rises, cement it immediately

Liquid dressing applied to the back of a belt soaks through to provide lubrication

more slowly than sperm oil. There are on the market various waterproofing preparations that can be used in a similar way.

One of the best methods of prolonging the life of leather shoes is simply to polish them frequently. Use a good liquid or paste shoe polish that has to be buffed to produce a shine. Work it thoroughly into all cracks and seams, and particularly into the space between the soles and uppers. An old toothbrush is good for this.

When two pieces of unlubricated leather rub against each other, they cause a squeaking noise. In shoes the trouble is usually between two layers of leather forming the soles. One remedy is to make a small opening at the edge of the layers and introduce through it a mixture of castor oil and powdered soapstone. The opening is then closed by cementing or sewing.

A leather article may often be given a new span of life by patching it. If the damage is a mere slit, sewing with linen thread may be all that is required. For a larger hole, a cemented patch that can be made almost invisible may be used. Cut a paper pattern to cover the spot; then lay out a patch about ¼″ larger all around. It should be of the same kind of leather as the article being repaired. With a sharp knife, bevel the edges of the patch.

Lay the patch over the hole and dust around it with dressmaker's chalk or talcum powder. Remove the patch and, following the chalked outline, skive around the hole, beveling the leather to match the patch. Use pyroxylin household cement, waterproof leather-belting cement, or a good rubber cement to fasten the patch in place. If a hairline shows around the edge, use ink of appropriate color to cover it. Finally, polish the area in the usual way. This technique may be used to repair the tiny cracks or slits that often appear in shoes where the leather bends in walking. Use slivers of leather of a size and shape to fill the crack, and apply ink or leather dye to color them before polishing.

Many companies in war production have installed line shafts because of the scarcity of electric motors for individual drives. Since rubber belting is also hard to get, a good many leather belts are being used. The care of these leather belts differs according to their use and surroundings. In one plant, where lubricating oil gets on them frequently, they have to be taken down and cleaned often. The secret of good belt performance is proper lubrication to keep the leather soft and supple without making it slippery. A soft, pliable belt, combined with good pulley design and belt tension, requires no sticky, friction-producing dressing to make it efficient. Heat generated by pulley friction dries out a belt, so a lubricating dressing has to be applied each week or so.

Belt manufacturers can provide prepared dressings suitable for any variety of belt, but good lubricants can be prepared right in the shop. One consists of about equal parts of castor and neat's-foot oil. Like all such dressings, it should be applied to the outside of the belt and permitted to soak through to the pulley (hair) side of the leather. Another dressing sometimes recommended is a mixture of about 7 oz. of tallow and 3 oz. of cod-liver oil, by weight. Rub this on the pulley side of the belt.

When a belt slips because it has become coated with metal dust and oil, it should be dry-cleaned. Any well-equipped belting supply company can clean it, but sometimes the job can be done in the shop by washing the leather in a standard dry-cleaning fluid or in a gasoline-turpentine mixture (about twice as much gasoline as turpentine). After the belt is dry, apply a dressing.

Mounting Stripped Bicycle Pedal

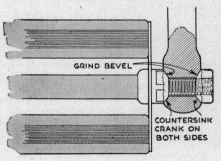

GRIND BEVEL

COUNTERSINK CRANK ON BOTH SIDES

WHEN the threads of a bicycle pedal are stripped at the end, the pedal can still be made to serve by countersinking the crank on both sides, and beveling the pedal spindle on the grinding wheel, as shown in the drawing, so that good threads will project far enough through the crank for the nut to get a firm grip. Grind a bevel on the nut also, leaving about half of it untouched to provide a secure hold for the wrench employed to tighten it.—AXEL E. OGREN.

DRAWING ELLIPSES TO EXACT SIZE   [SHOP METHODS]

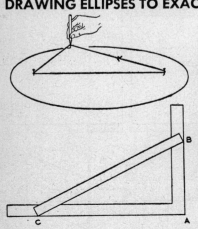

THE method of drawing a perfect ellipse with a pencil and a loop of string placed around two brads or thumbtacks, as shown in the diagram at the left, is frequently used in laying out work. An easy way to find the proper spacing between the brads and the correct length of string to be used is as follows:

Measure the breadth of the desired ellipse on one leg of a steel square, or any other right angle. This breadth is *AB* on the diagram. Now measure off the length of the ellipse from *B* to the intersection at the other leg of the square—*BC* on the diagram. The distance *AC* laid off on the leg of the square is the correct distance between the two brads. The sum of the distance *AC* and the length *BC* is the proper length of string in the loop.

POPULAR SCIENCE MONTHLY SHOP DATA

POPCORN CART

Holds Four Individual Servers

Cheer your guests with popcorn from a charming, hand-lettered wagon

By ELMA WALTNER

HOT buttered popcorn, that perfect snack for frosty evenings, will be welcomed even more enthusiastically, by children and grownups alike, if served in this attractive cart.

The four scoops, which are lifted out by handy finger holes, make convenient individual servers for guests.

Make the cart of ¼″ plywood, or, if this material is unavailable, of any well-seasoned ¼″ stock. The sides of an apple box, if planed smooth, will do nicely.

The cart and the scoops are put together with ½″ brads. Note that there is no back to the cart. This makes for easier removal of the popcorn boxes.

The axle blocks have holes slightly larger than the ¼″ dowel axles, which pass through them and are glued into 4″ plywood wheels. If desired, dummy wheels may be nailed directly to the body of the cart. Glue the handle into holes bored into the sides.

Finish both the cart and the scoops with two coats of clear shellac. The lettering on the sides of the cart is painted over the shellacked finish.

Wood stock, glue, brads and a little time are all you'll need to build this cart from the drawing below

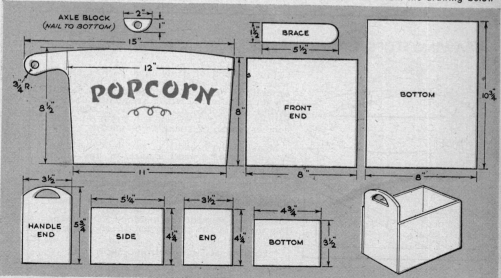

NEW
SHOP
IDEAS

QUICK-GLANCE SPEED CHARTS mounted on machine tools having step pulleys tell instantly how to obtain the nearest correct speed for working various materials, and do away with constant thumbing of the instruction book. The speeds obtainable on a drill press, for example, may be typed or lettered on paper and glued to the belt-guard, as in the photograph at left. On lathes, speeds for both motor and countershaft belt positions may be posted in the same way, together with detailed information on direct and back-gear drive, as shown at the right. Varnish, transparent cellulose tape, or wax will protect the paper and prevent it from being loosened.—R. HANSCOM.

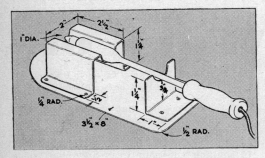

A STAND to hold your electric soldering iron while it is still hot but not being used will protect your workbench top from the heat and prevent accidents. The parts for the one shown in the drawing were cut out of 23-gauge sheet metal, although tin-can material may be used if no other is available. Bend the supports to shape in a vise, forming the rounded portion by hand or over a pipe. Holes are drilled for screws in the places indicated, and the holder may be fastened to a wooden block or permanently mounted on the workbench by means of these screws joining the parts. The sheet-metal base shown is optional.—M. ROSENFELD.

BURNED-OUT HEATING ELEMENTS can be repaired efficiently with powdered iron cement of the type sold at most hardware stores. Raise each end of the parted resistance coil, clean the first two or three loops with sandpaper, and interlock them. Do not join more than two or three loops of each end because this might reduce the resistance too much and cause the coil to burn out again. Mix a little iron cement with water, and apply the paste to the interlocked loops, filling and covering them, and smoothing down the top surface below the groove in the insulation. Let the cement, which is a fairly good conductor, set thoroughly before turning on the current.—W. C. WILHITE.

HOLES IN WELDING-TORCH TIPS or in the generators of gasoline blowtorches can be cleaned with steel bristles cut or pulled from a rotary scratch brush of fine or medium grade. Bristles of either of these sizes are fine enough to go through the holes without enlarging them. It will not impair the efficiency of a good wheel to have a few bristles cut from it, if an old wheel is not available at the time a cleaning wire is needed.—W. C. W.

1 "Here is that gear-blank job for you to start on, Roy," says the foreman as he hands the rough stock to the machinist. "As you see, it's already centered . . .

Turning Work of

From the U. S. Office of Education Training Film, "Turning Work of Two Diameters"

Whether you're preparing for defense work or already in it, your advancement will depend on what you know. "Learn more to earn more" is a good slogan these busy days. To train war workers in the fundamentals of machine-shop practice, the U. S. Office of Education has prepared a series of 16-mm. sound films, one of which provided the material for the following article. These motion pictures, distributed for the Government by Castle Films, are of inestimable value to the shop student and beginner. Don't fail to see them if they are being shown in your community or at the plant where you are employed.

ALL the power that drives America's mighty war machines is transmitted through wheels of steel. These must be carefully designed and skillfully machined. In making the spur gear and shaft of a U. S. Army "blitz buggy," for example, time is saved and strength and precision are gained when both the shaft and gear are turned from a single piece of steel, eliminating the use of fragile pins, keys, or splines, such as would be required to lock the gear on the shaft if the two parts were produced separately.

The blank for this unit must be turned on an engine lathe, after which the teeth can be cut by a milling machine. A piece of rough stock in the capable hands of the lathe operator and a drawing from the shop foreman's desk are all that is needed for the making of the blank. The lathe job requires

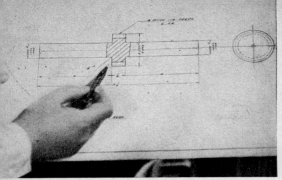

2 "Let's look at the drawing together," he goes on. "Notice that the collar diameter is 2¼", and that it is ¾" wide, with tolerances as shown . . .

3 "On the finished piece, both shafts are 1" in diameter and 4" long on each side. Be sure to finish up fillets where the collar joins the shaft."

4 Roy first measures the stock to make sure it is big enough. Then he studies the drawing, notes diameter tolerances, and decides the order of cuts

5 Using the right size of lathe dog is important. Roy picks one to fit the work closely, clamping it to one end of the stock with the tail facing out

Two Diameters

turning a piece of two diameters, and the collar that will later become the gear must be of a specified width and diameter and should be finished with fillets where it joins the shaft. The accompanying series of photographs shows step by step how the blank is turned.

The rough stock is a piece of machine steel, 2½" in diameter and 9" long, already centerdrilled. The foreman gives it to the operator and turns over a print of the drawing to him, pointing out the more important features of the work. As always, the machinist's first job is to study the drawing and determine the order of the cuts. Then he places the drawing on a blueprint board where he may refer to it conveniently, cleans and oils his lathe, sees that his tool rack is in order, and clears the floor of obstructions. As an efficient operator, he is dressed with due regard for his personal safety, with collar buttoned, sleeves rolled high, necktie tucked into his

shirt, and hair combed neatly and in place.

The machinist measures the stock, noting that the collar diameter must be brought down to 2¼" and the shaft diameter to 1", with tolerances of .004" on the collar and .002" on the shaft. The collar width is ¾", the shafts are 4" long from each collar face, and the piece is 8¾" long over all. He then selects a dog to fit the work—one neither too large nor too small—making certain that its tail is pointing to the headstock. He cleans the center holes, and lubricates the one to go on the tailstock center. Then the work is mounted in the lathe, and the tailstock spindle wheel is adjusted so that the piece turns freely but not loosely between centers.

Since the stock is rough, a truing-up cut must first be taken. The tool required for this must be sharp and properly ground so that it will remove stock rapidly. After a short trial cut is made, the piece is calipered and found to be 2½" in diameter. Now the

6 After carefully lubricating the center at the tailstock end, he mounts the stock between centers and brings the tailstock center up. The dog tail is in the slot of the faceplate, and the work should turn freely

7 A correctly ground roughing tool, used to make the first cut, is adjusted in the tool post; with the cutting point set just above the center of the stock. For safe turning, there must be a minimum of overhang

8 The tool post is turned to bring the tool bit at a right angle to the center line of the work, which is revolved slowly by hand to make sure that all is clear. With speeds correctly set, Roy makes a short trial cut

operator's problem is to bring the work down to the required 2¼" diameter of the collar, which is the largest part, plus about 1/32" allowance all around for the finishing cut to be made later. This may be accomplished by setting the depth of the rough cut at 3/32", or .093", thus reducing the total diameter by 3/16". This cut is made as near to the revolving dog as possible, but always out of danger of actual contact. Care must be taken to keep the tail center well lubricated and properly adjusted during the cut to keep the work from expanding and binding between centers as it becomes hot.

To obtain a reference point for the width of the collar and the length of the two parts of the shaft, one end of the work is next faced off. A rule is then used to measure from this end, and the tool is set for turning a nick or groove that marks one face of the collar. Several roughing cuts follow to bring the shaft down to rough size, leaving 1/32" for the finishing cut. Then the face of the collar is turned, leaving the same margin for finishing, as well as a 1/16" shoulder for the fillet.

A preliminary finishing cut can be made with the roughing tool to within .010" of the final size. Then a finishing tool is used to take a cut of .005" (remember that twice the depth of the cut is removed from the diameter of the work). For facing the collar—the operation that brings this end of the shaft to finished length—a radius tool is used. Only the fillet remains to be done on this end.

The work is now reversed between centers. Exactly the same operations follow as were used in turning the other end. Then, after a finishing tool has brought the shaft and the collar to their correct diameters, the collar is faced to the required width, again leaving only the fillet allowance. Afterwards the end of the shaft is faced with a finishing cut to the exact length specified in the drawing, the steel rule being used to measure from the finished face of the collar.

Finally the fillets, which add strength to the shaft where it joins the collar, are turned with a radius tool, which is set on center and used first on one side of the collar, then on the other. This completes the machining of the piece, and it is then checked against the drawing for possible errors.

When inspection is completed, the blank is ready to go to the milling machine to have the gear teeth cut.

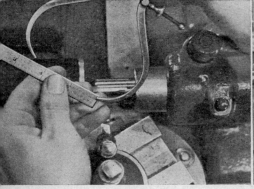

9 The cut is stopped after it has proceeded about 1/4". The diameter is calipered and found to be 2 1/2". The finished size is to be 2 1/4", but 1/16" more (1/32" all around) must be left for the finish cuts

10 Since the tool is set in only one half as much as the amount of stock to be removed, Roy will adjust the feed and speed for a rough cut of 3/32", or .093", which will remove 3/16" from the diameter

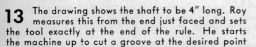

11 The new cut is checked with calipers, and, if correct, is continued up to a safe point from the whirling dog. Care should be taken to keep the tail center oiled, and set neither tight nor loose

12 Before accurate measurements of length can be made, the end must be faced off as a point of reference. For this, a facing tool is used, set so that the cutting edge is turned in toward the work

13 The drawing shows the shaft to be 4" long. Roy measures this from the end just faced and sets the tool exactly at the end of the rule. He starts the machine up to cut a groove at the desired point

14 This groove marks the face of the collar, but some excess will have to be left on this face for finishing, so the rough cuts that are to follow will be made only to the right of the groove's edge

15 The shaft is to be 1" in diameter, plus .002" tolerance. Roy makes rough cuts to begin the process of bringing it down. The last one must leave 1/32" all around for the finishing cut made later on

16 After this final roughing cut is started, it is checked with a micrometer to make sure that it is not too deep. If it is satisfactory, this cut is extended all along the shaft to the marking groove

17 The face of the collar is still uneven and has to be machined. The same roughing tool is fed in by hand against the face of the collar. Note the stock left for the 1/16" fillet to be turned later

18 Roy is now ready for the finishing cuts. The first one can be made with the roughing tool to within .010" of final size. After starting the cut, he again carefully checks with a micrometer

19 A finishing tool is now needed for the final cuts to the tolerances specified. Here below, from left to right, are bits ground for roughing, finishing, parting, threading, and radius forming

20 On this finishing tool the nose is flat and narrow, while the end relief angle, or heel clearance, is about 10 degrees. Note particularly the lip which gives the tool a fine cutting edge

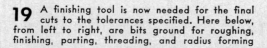

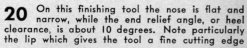

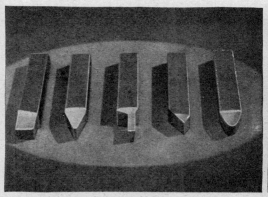

10 Degrees

21 As seen from the cutting edge, arrows show the sides of the tool without any side rake or relief angle. The nose must be set parallel to the work and on dead center, while the cut is .005″

22 A radius tool, set at a convenient angle, is used to face the collar. Measuring the length of the shaft from its trued end with a steel rule, Roy sets the tool against the collar by hand feed

23 The piece is taken out, and a smaller dog is clamped to the finished end with a thin band of soft metal to prevent surface marks. The work is remounted, and the other shaft end rough-turned

24 Finishing cuts bring the shaft and collar to correct diameter. Roy measures the width of the collar, and with a rough facing cut and a light finish cut brings it to size, plus fillet allowance

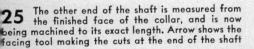

25 The other end of the shaft is measured from the finished face of the collar, and is now being machined to its exact length. Arrow shows the facing tool making the cuts at the end of the shaft

26 A radius tool is used to turn the fillets. The carriage feed is operated with the left hand, the cross-slide feed with the right. Finally, the work is once more checked against the drawing

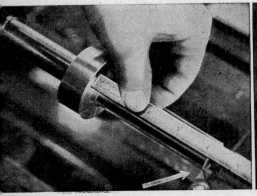

Many craftsmen have scraps of plastic left over from completed work. Here are three projects that can be made from such odds and ends. None calls for a piece longer than 4", yet all show off the beauty of this material to the full.

Made from clear plastic, maple, and walnut, this cigarette box is a handsome project involving several interesting operations

LID 3¼" LONG

WALNUT FILLER

WASTE

CUT

2½" DIA. PLASTIC TUBE

⅛"

2⁷⁄₁₆"

9⁄₁₆"

DRILL FOR ¾" BRAD

⅛"

³⁄₁₆"

³⁄₈"

5⁄₃₂"

1³⁄₁₆" R.

1⁵⁄₁₆" R.

⅛"

SIDE-MAPLE MAKE TWO

¼"

BODY 3½" LONG

⅞"

³⁄₈"

1⁵⁄₈"

³⁄₈"

¼" DOWEL

9⁄₁₆"

7⁄₁₆"

3¼"

PLASTIC LID

DRILL FOR ⅜"-2 FLAT-HEAD SCREW

7⁄₁₆"

WALNUT KNOB FITS CURVE OF LID

PIVOT HOLE FOR BRAD

⅛"

WALNUT HINGE PIECE

WALNUT KNOB

³⁄₈"

3¼"

³⁄₈"

PLASTIC LID

MAPLE

LID AND BODY MEET HERE

PLASTIC BODY

3½"

¼" DOWEL 3⅝" LONG

CIGARETTE BOX. Clear plastic, maple, and walnut are combined in this unique occasional piece, displaying both the plastic and the woods to good advantage. A clear-plastic tube 2⅛" in diameter and 3½" long is sawed apart as shown in the drawings at the left to form both the body and the lid. Lay out two maple endpieces, as shown, on ⅜" stock. Drill two ¼" holes 3/16" deep in each for the dowel rails, which are also of maple; then cut out the ⅛" by ⅛" circular groove with a circle cutter, and finally cut and sand the outside to shape. Use the circle cutter also to cut a ⅛" by ⅛" walnut ring, from which filler pieces can be made to close those portions of the grooves alongside the lid.

Cut the lid to 3¼" in length, saw off a strip ⅜" wide along

By
ERNEST R. DEWALT

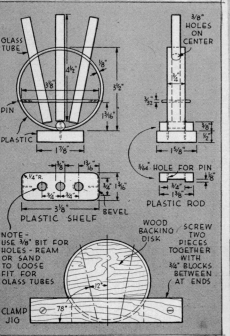

GLASS TUBE

4½"

⅛"

3/8"

3½"

PIN

1 3/16"

PLASTIC

1 7/8"

3/8" HOLES ON CENTER

¾"

3/32"

1 5/8"

3/8"
½"

3/64" HOLE FOR PIN

¾"
1 3/8"

PLASTIC ROD

⅛"

¼" R.

3/8"   1 3/16"

¾"   ¾"

¾" 1 3/16"

3/8"

BEVEL

PLASTIC SHELF

WOOD BACKING DISK

SCREW TWO PIECES TOGETHER WITH ¾" BLOCKS BETWEEN AT ENDS

NOTE— USE 3/8" BIT FOR HOLES - REAM OR SAND TO LOOSE FIT FOR GLASS TUBES

12"

CLAMP JIG

78°

one side, press the lid into a 3/16" deep groove in the walnut hinge piece, and attach a walnut knob with a small countersunk screw.

Assemble the ends, body, and dowel rails with cellulose or model-airplane cement. Fit the lid in place, and drill through the maple ends into the plastic—not the hinge piece—for pivot pins. Insert these, and fill the holes over them. Finish with three coats of wax applied to the wooden parts, rubbing well after each of the coats. Working time: 4½ hours.

THREE-BUD VASE. This triple flower holder provides a decorative touch on the table, mantel, or piano. Clear-plastic pieces are used. The dimensions given in the drawings may be altered to suit the material on hand. For the holder shown, a ¾" wide band, or ring, cut from 3½" diameter tubing was used, and three holes were drilled in it to support the vases, which can be small test tubes or vials.

A simple drilling jig will prevent break-ing of the edges of the holes. Band-saw a wooden disk to a snug fit inside the ring. Mark the middle hole, and with a flexible rule or a piece of paper bent to the contour of the tubing, lay off two other holes 1⅛" to either side. Secure the work with the backing disk in a clamping jig as shown. Drill the holes with a 3/8" bit, tilting the drill-press table 12 deg. for the two side holes.

Note that the shelf length is less than the ring diameter. Round the corners, and bevel the short edges to fit inside the ring. Ream or sandpaper the holes to a free fit for the vases. Line up the holes by a trial fit; then drill a slightly undersized hole through each side of the ring into the shelf and press in a ½" escutcheon pin.

The ring is held on a base by a 3/8" plastic rod 1⅜" long, in which a ⅛" by ¾" notch is cut. Drill both the rod and the base for escutcheon pins, file small notches in the ring where these pass, and assemble.

Sand all edges very smooth, and buff any scratches off the polished surfaces. The

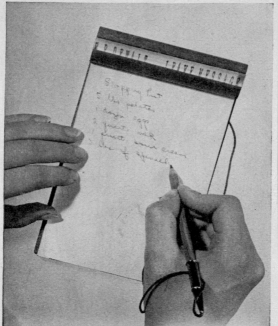

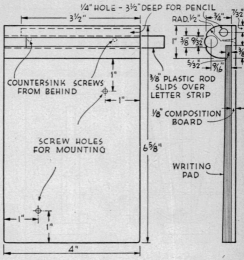

1/4" HOLE - 3 1/2" DEEP FOR PENCIL

RAD. 1/2"

3/8" PLASTIC ROD SLIPS OVER LETTER STRIP

1/8" COMPOSITION BOARD

COUNTERSINK SCREWS FROM BEHIND

SCREW HOLES FOR MOUNTING

WRITING PAD

edges may be left unbuffed for textural contrast. Working time: 4 1/2 hours.

MEMO PAD. This is handy for kitchen reminders, an office desk, or messages from callers. The over-all size, 4" by 6 5/8", fits a 4" by 6" stock pad slipped into a 5/32" by 3/8" rabbet in the molded hardwood strip. Use a 1" by 1" by 4" piece of walnut, mahogany, or maple. Drill the 3/8" hole through with a keen spur bit. Use fine sandpaper on a dowel to sand the hole so that a 1/4" wide strip of paper and a 3/8" clear plastic rod may be inserted together. Open out the hole with two saw cuts 9/32" apart, and then round off the outside to 1/2" radius. Drill a 1/4" blind hole in from one end to a depth of 3 1/2" for a pencil, which may be secured with string or fine chain. Screw the strip fast to a 1/8" composition-board back. Finish with two coats of clear lacquer, but apply none to the channel. Insert a typewritten strip and the plastic rod, which will magnify the lettering. Working time: 3 1/2 hours.

PLATING NONMETALLIC WORK [ELECTRICAL]

THE plating of nonmetallic articles is generally thought of in connection with baby shoes, but other objects that can be encased in electroplated metal include flowers and insects, leaves and fruit, plaster casts, pottery, textiles, wooden handles, buttons, drinking cups, and so forth. A small wooden box or drawer pull can be more uniformly covered with metal by electroplating than by working metal in sheet form.

It is necessary first to treat the surface of the work so that it will conduct electricity. A rough method consists in coating the surface with spar varnish, then, when this is tacky, laying pieces of thin metal foil on it much as sign painters apply gold leaf. It must be patted into close contact if detail of the work is to be reproduced.

A better way of forming the conducting surface is to give the work a thin coat of wax (paraffin) or electrotypers' varnish. These must not be applied so heavily as to obliterate detail. The conductive powder generally consists of finely powdered graphite (known as plumbago or black lead) as used by electrotypers. Copper bronzing powder is also used; carefully applied, it allows faster plating. All grease must be removed from the powder by shaking it in a bottle with acetone.

The conductive powder is applied with a soft brush. Particular pains must be taken to see that all crevices are coated. Brush off the surplus after the work has taken on a shiny, thoroughly coated appearance. The cathode connection is best made by slinging the work in fine copper wires. Rinse it well in water before transferring it to an acid copper-plating bath. After the article has been plated with copper, it may be plated with some other metal if desired.

POPULAR SCIENCE MONTHLY SHOP DATA

ADJUSTING THE CUT-OFF TOOL is generally considered one of the most difficult of lathe operations. The tool must be ground properly and adjusted to exact lathe center height. At the left is shown a quick and accurate way of doing this. A machinist's rule is used to measure up from the ways to exactly the height of either center, and the tool is set at precisely that height.—C. W. W.

NEW CUTTING OILS adapted to specific machine operations now eliminate in large part older trial-and-error methods of prescribing proper grades. They permit faster speeds and new methods of tooling, closer tolerances, and increased use of alloy steels with lower machinability ratings than metals normally used. The oils are higher in active sulphur than ordinary types and reduce the tendency of ferrous metal surfaces to fuse or weld, thus eliminating any bonding of the tool and the surface being cut.

Another step toward production efficiency is a newly perfected graphite lubricant for the dead centers of lathes. This is a compound of flake lubricating graphite and specially formulated ingredients which effectively controls overheating and protects dead centers against scoring and softening.

GROTESQUE WELDING MASKS. Fighting planes painted to resemble sharks may have inspired these welders at North American Aviation to apply war paint to their helmets — or perhaps it's an old Indian custom they've adopted to scare the Axis. Other workers have followed suit, and many weirdly decorated masks glower from the walls of the plant's locker rooms.

By
EDWIN
M.
LOVE

The hollow - ground planer blade cuts smoothly and is especially adapted to ripping and mitering. With dado sets, it is possible to do grooving, tenoning, and rabbeting

Special accessories enable one to get the fullest service from that most versatile power tool, the circular saw. Here Mr. Love discusses the use of planer saws and dado heads

Using Special Blades on the Circular Saw

SPECIAL accessories and jigs greatly increase the usefulness of the circular saw. Often they enable it to double for machines that may be lacking in the home workshop. Many useful attachments can be made of wood in the shop. Others must be purchased, and among the most important of these are planer saws and dado heads.

What is a planer saw? This is a stiff combination blade having groups of crosscut teeth alternating with single ripping teeth called rakers. It has no set; clearance is obtained by hollow grinding, which decreases the thickness of the blade from the teeth to the arbor washer. It is designed only for fine work. If kept sharp and

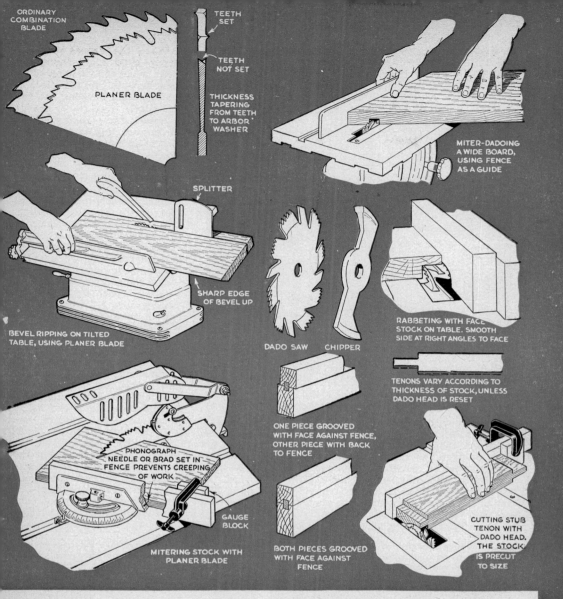

ORDINARY COMBINATION BLADE

TEETH SET

TEETH NOT SET

THICKNESS TAPERING FROM TEETH TO ARBOR WASHER

PLANER BLADE

MITER-DADOING A WIDE BOARD, USING FENCE AS A GUIDE

SPLITTER

SHARP EDGE OF BEVEL UP

BEVEL RIPPING ON TILTED TABLE, USING PLANER BLADE

DADO SAW

CHIPPER

RABBETING WITH FACE STOCK ON TABLE. SMOOTH SIDE AT RIGHT ANGLES TO FACE

TENONS VARY ACCORDING TO THICKNESS OF STOCK, UNLESS DADO HEAD IS RESET

ONE PIECE GROOVED WITH FACE AGAINST FENCE, OTHER PIECE WITH BACK TO FENCE

PHONOGRAPH NEEDLE OR BRAD SET IN FENCE PREVENTS CREEPING OF WORK

GAUGE BLOCK

MITERING STOCK WITH PLANER BLADE

BOTH PIECES GROOVED WITH FACE AGAINST FENCE

CUTTING STUB TENON WITH DADO HEAD. THE STOCK IS PRECUT TO SIZE

properly jointed, so that it is at all times perfectly round, it cuts with almost glossy smoothness, but when dull it can hardly be made to rip, and will usually wander off along the grain of the wood.

For what is a planer blade used? Its smooth cut makes it especially useful for ripping glue joints. Use only material that is reasonably straight, for wind (twist) will bind the blade, and the cut will not fit the joining member. The edge bearing against the fence must not be irregular, or the cut will be unsatisfactory. When the edge is to be beveled, as in ripping a side for a column, tilt the table to the correct angle and adjust the fence so that the far edge of the board slides against it. This enables the fence to carry the sliding thrust of the piece, and prevents pinching of the saw. If the piece is too wide for this, place the fence above the saw, so that the weight of the work below the blade will tend to open the kerf. On saws having tilting arbors, the tendency to slide is not present.

When several pieces are to be ripped to the same width, bevel one edge of each; then bevel the other edges after adjusting the fence to the desired width. Always slide the board along with the sharp edge up, for if this edge lies on the table it will wedge under the fence.

For a three-sided column, the bevel must

Dadoing a wide board to receive a shelf, with an auxiliary fence on the miter gauge. The ripping fence could also be used

face to the fence, with the upper edge high enough to clear such obstructions. It is necessary to rip the piece to width before beveling the second edge.

How is the planer saw used for crosscutting and mitering? Just like an ordinary blade, except that the feed must be slower. If there is objectionable splintering of the underside, make a wooden insert to replace the soft-metal one furnished with the saw, and slit it to fit the blade by lowering the table (or raising the arbor) as the machine runs. This insert will support the work up to the very edge of the cut.

Can the parts of a dado head be used separately? Yes. To cut a groove $\frac{1}{8}$" wide, use one saw of the combination; for a width of $\frac{1}{4}$", use both. Wider grooves are cut with chippers between the saws, arranged with the swaged edges opposite the openings between the teeth, and fanned out so as not to interfere with each other.

How is a dado head used? It must be accurately set for depth, and then used as if it were a thick blade. When grooving lengthwise of stock, set the fence as for ripping, measuring from the side teeth and making test cuts in scrap wood. Any ordinary groove is made in one pass, but dadoes wider than the head are cut in two or more passes with the fence reset or a strip of wood laid between it and the work to locate the second side.

be ripped with the stock edgewise on the table. After the cut has proceeded a little distance, the board tends to settle, which may damage the sharp edge and spoil the straightness of the work. This can be prevented by clamping or tacking a strip of wood to the back so that this strip rides on top of the fence, as shown in the photograph on page HW 32. If bolts or other projections interfere, attach an auxiliary wooden

Have the face side of each piece bear against the fence when grooving stiles and rails for a panel. All grooves will then meet in perfect alignment

Use of a clamping device when mitering prevents creeping. The reversed gauge allows full contact between the edge of the stock and the gauge head

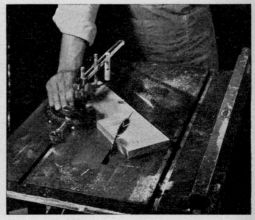

When grooving edges for a panel, as in stiles or rails, slide the face side of each against the fence so that the grooves in all pieces will be the same distance from the face. The same applies to cutting spline grooves, as shown in the drawings. If the material is bent, try to spring it flat against the fence.

Grooves across the grain on wide boards can be made with the end of the stock sliding against the fence. On narrower work, however, the miter gauge is used.

In making tenons, use

When beveling a second side, as with the tilting-arbor saw above, keep the sharp edge of the finished bevel up, or it may wedge under the fence

the miter gauge and cut a dado along what is to be the shoulder. Shift the piece and make a second cut beside it, and so on to the end. Then turn the miter gauge end for end to cut the other cheek. This keeps the face edge against the gauge head in cutting both tenons. The stock should be precut to exact length, and the tenon length located with a block clamped to the saw table. This method permits tenons of any length to be made. A disadvantage is that the tenon thickness varies according to the thickness of the stock, unless the depth of cut is changed.

How are rabbets cut with a dado head? Rabbeting is done much like grooving, but with one side of the dado head exposed. When the fence is used on long cuts, set it away from the saw a distance equal to the thickness of the flange to be left on the edge, set the head for depth of cut, and pass the work over edgewise. This results in a smooth side parallel to the face. For a smooth side at right angles to the face, lay the stock flat on the table, with the edge against the fence. If the fence is arched, or an arched auxiliary wooden fence is used, the lumber can be rabbeted edgewise with the flange outside, the unused portion of the dado head running without obstruction under the arch of the fence.

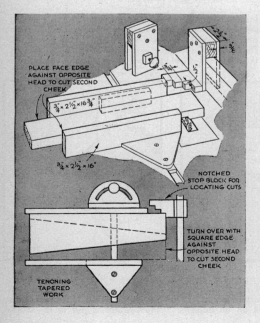

PLACE FACE EDGE AGAINST OPPOSITE HEAD TO CUT SECOND CHEEK

3/4 x 2 1/2 x 16 3/4

3/4 x 2 1/2 x 16"

NOTCHED STOP BLOCK FOR LOCATING CUTS

TURN OVER WITH SQUARE EDGE AGAINST OPPOSITE HEAD TO CUT SECOND CHEEK

TENONING TAPERED WORK

Tenoning Jig on Miter Gauge Provides Parallel Heads

THIS jig permits the miter gauge to be kept in one groove for tenoning, as the working edge of the stock bears against a second parallel guide for cutting the opposite cheek. Not only does this prevent any misalignment of shoulders due to the stock being not quite parallel, but it also allows tapering stiles to be tenoned. Screw one auxiliary head fast to the miter gauge, the other to a plywood base, which is attached to the gauge bar with machine screws fitting the tapped holes. Both heads must be squared with the bar.

The stepped stop block is attached to a saddle having plywood sides, and the latter clamped to the fence with a setscrew inserted through a small reinforcing block. Bore the hole slightly undersize and let the screw cut its own threads. This block is more readily adjustable than one clamped to the table, and can be raised if a pattern is used.

1¼"× 1¼"× 32"

¾"×6"×6"

1"×2"×2"
ANGLE
BRACKET

¾"× 3"× 3"

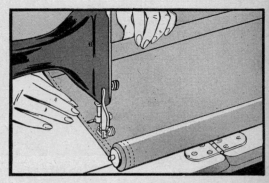

Two rows of machine stitching along each side of a paper window shade reinforce the edges and prevent tearing and fraying. Stitching may be done with the shade still attached to the roller by beginning at the top and rolling the shade as the work proceeds

Orderly habits in hanging clothes where they can be found the next day may be taught a child with a clothes tree built to his size. Use pine or scraps, apply a maple oil stain and wipe it off until the desired color is obtained, then finish with shellac. The height may be changed to suit

Ice trays can be kept from sticking in the freezing unit of a refrigerator by coating them on the bottom and sides with a thin film of cooking or salad oil. The oil film does not retard freezing, but prevents the ice from sticking fast to the metal tray surface

In order to use garlic sparingly, put it in a tea ball that can be fastened over the edge of the kettle for removal at any time

Food may be scraped off pots without danger of scratching by using a wedge-shaped piece of wood sanded well on all edges

Washing will not stretch pockets and buttonholes in a sweater if they are basted together before the sweater is put in the water

THE HOME SHIPSHAPE

Frozen pipes can be thawed out by using a portable hair drier with a tin can cut to fit the nozzle. Flatten the open end of the can to concentrate the heat

Paraffin rubbed into rough spots in the lining or seams of shoes lessens friction and prevents blisters. Repeat for several days, and sprinkle with talcum

Six cans on a wall in the form of a 2' circle, as above, make a garden-hose rack. Punch screw or nail holes. A solid rod will be of help in driving in nails

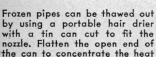

When the threads holding the cap on a fountain pen are so worn that the cap keeps coming off, stick a piece of transparent cellulose tape over the threads on the barrel to increase the strength of the grip

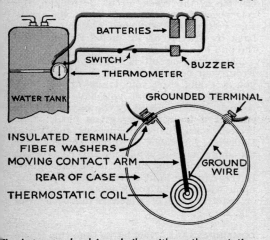

The hot-water level in a boiler with no thermostatic control can be signaled automatically by adapting a dial-type thermometer and connecting it to a buzzer. Pry the back off the thermometer, attach terminals as shown, solder a metal contact arm to the back of the thermostatic coil, and solder on a ground wire. Strap the unit onto the tank about 3' from the top

Discard the wire from a package handle, cover the wood with felt, and then shape a coat hanger for a handle to make a roller for painting screens

Two-Rail Operation

AUTOMATIC SIGNALING

By
David Marshall

CAN we have two-rail operation and automatic signaling, too? Only a few years back the answer would have been a flat *"no."* It was pretty well known, of course, that the trick was not altogether impossible—two-rail pikes, completely signaled, were already in operation. But the apparatus required was so expensive that the average model railroader could not even dream of it.

In the past two or three years, however, new methods have been evolved—simple, reliable, and quite inexpensive. Circuit for circuit, signal for signal, the cost today will not exceed what you would ordinarily spend for signaling a three-rail road; or at least the difference will not be great enough to matter one way or the other.

Although these new methods represent a distinct improvement over the tried and true systems of the past, they have, unfortunately, one drawback. For reasons that will presently become apparent, signaling a two-rail system imposes a burden upon the operating efficiency of your trains. This is true, however, only within limits, and the limits can be wide enough. Stated broadly, the situation is that a resistor in every car must limit the length of trains or rob the locomotive of necessary power. But if you keep this point in mind, and stick to a certain balance, you will find the following method not only simple, reliable, and cheap, but also quite satisfactory.

NORMAL TRACK CIRCUITS. To approach our problem the easy way around, let us begin by recalling all we know about track circuits and automatic signaling in general. Let us build a normal three-rail pike and signal it the normal way, and having done this, let us convert the whole job to a two-rail pike.

In Fig. 1 we have the orthodox three-rail main line, broken up into blocks according to standard model-railroad practice. Of the two running rails, the upper one is con-tinuous, serving as a ground for both power and track circuits. The lower one is broken up into insulated sections, each one extending the length of a block, which can be anywhere from 2,500 scale feet to three or four scale miles. The third rail is also sectionalized, to enable us to control trains in separate blocks separately. We have here three electric circuits, each one forever separate and distinct from the others, though all three may flow—never mixing—through common channels.

The power circuit is from the generator to the various controllers to the various third-rail sections, thence through the locomotive windings to the common running rail and so on back to the generator. The track circuit, on the other hand, is from the track battery to the common rail, where normally it is broken. Then, from every section of the control rail—the broken running rail—the track circuit is to a relay corresponding to that particular block, and from the relay back to the battery.

Thus the track circuit is normally open. But when a train—or a runaway box car, for that matter—enters a given block, it closes the gap between the common rail and the control rail; its own wheels and axles form a channel through which the electricity flows, and thus the circuit is completed. The track relay, normally inactive, is now energized, its armature drawn hard against the magnetic poles. That is the function of the track circuit—simply, under a given track condition, to energize a magnet. And, of course, when the track condition changes, when the train passes out of the block, the track circuit is broken, the relay becomes once more inactive, the armature returns to its normal position—drawn back by gravity or, on model railroads, by the pull of a spring.

The power circuit is under your control. From your perch before the operating panel you stop and start your trains at will. But over the track circuit you have no direct control. This is closed by the physical presence of a train in any given block; it is broken with the departure of the train. Likewise you have no direct control over the signal circuit, which in any case is not subject to interruption, but flows continuously through one light or the other depending upon whether the track relay is energized or inactive. All of which is made clear in Fig. 1.

COMBINING RAILS. Now let us take this whole setup, precisely as it stands in Fig. 1, and see what happens if we combine the third rail with the control rail which it so closely resembles. So far as the signal circuit is concerned, nothing at all will happen, for this is independent of all the rails, and it stands to reason that the signals will continue to flash red and green in response to the movement back and forth of the track armatures. So we can forget the signal circuit entirely, and concern ourselves from now on simply with the track and power circuits, confident that, if we can get the relays to behave properly, the signals can be depended on to do likewise. To keep things simple, therefore, the signal circuit is omitted from Fig. 2, though the tie-in is sufficiently indicated.

In changing over from three-rail to two-rail, we retain the common rail precisely as it is. And we transfer to the control rail all the functions of the third rail, as indicated. Then we cross out all the duplicating wires, and find the track relays neatly tucked away between the power controls and control rail (Fig. 2). The relay is thus in series with the locomotive—and here we have two distinct situations. The locomotive draws power through the relay, so the relay must be energized when the locomotive is under way. But the locomotive, as a result of the hookup shown in Fig. 2, also pulls a certain minimum of electricity even when standing still, and this, though it is not enough to move the locomotive, is sufficient to keep the relay energized. And so the signal shows red as long as the block is occupied and whether the locomotive is in motion or halted. In short, the power is never shut off completely, and the rheostats at your control board must be adjusted accordingly. To stop a train, you simply reduce the power to a point below the minimum required to keep the locomotive going.

HALF-AND-HALF WHEELS. So far, then, as the locomotive goes—and with certain reservations — we have an adequate setup for automatic signaling. If we next equip all the cars with half-and-half wheels (steel on one side of the trucks and plastic on the other), and place a light or other resistor on each car, we have whole trains

equipped for working the signals. The scheme is, of course, that the steel wheels of the forward truck shall ride on one rail, and the steel wheels of the after truck on the rail opposite, so that, even in the case of a box car, a current will forever flow from one rail through a resistor to the other rail. But since that can cause too great a drain on your power, it becomes expedient, at times, to cut out resistors by reversing one truck on each of several cars by having all the steel wheels ride on a single rail.

And so we have the beginning of an automatic system for a two-rail pike. As it stands, however, it is not perfect, though it may do for an HO pike. The trouble is, when we apply the scheme to an O-gauge road, that a relay sensitive enough to pick up on the minimum flow of current would burn out if sufficient power were shot through it to get the train really working. How this defect is remedied we shall explain later on.

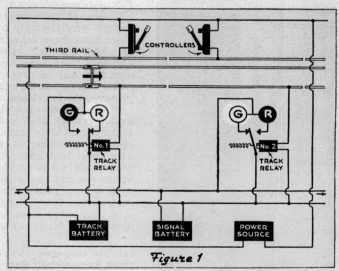

Figure 1

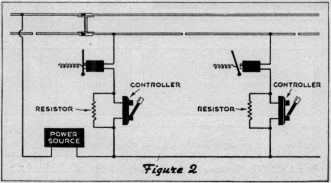

Figure 2

SIMPLE STORAGE RACK
for SKIS

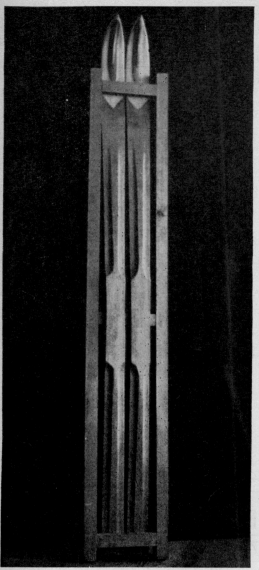

Sturdy Frame Prevents Warping

SKIS often present a difficult storage problem because of their length and shape. Although some experts prefer simply to tie them together and stand them in a corner, other skiers favor the use of a frame in which the skis can be clamped. Such a frame prevents them from becoming warped in the wrong direction, and so preserves their camber. If desired, extra clamps can be affixed to the tips of the skis to preserve the curvature of these parts.

The frame shown at the left can be built from any available stock such as 2" by 2" or 1½" by 2" lumber. Make the middle crosspieces just high enough to give the proper camber to the skis when they are placed over these and under the end pieces. Assemble the parts with mortise-and-tenon joints. One crosspiece at the toe end of the frame is removable and held in with wooden pins so that the skis can be put in the rack easily. The dimensions given are for a pair of 7' skis. For other sizes, simply build the rack in proportion.—R. H. JENKINS.

Left, the completed storage rack, showing skis in place. The strong frame protects them against being warped, scratched or otherwise damaged, and keeps them bent to the proper camber

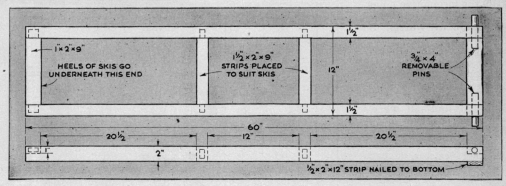

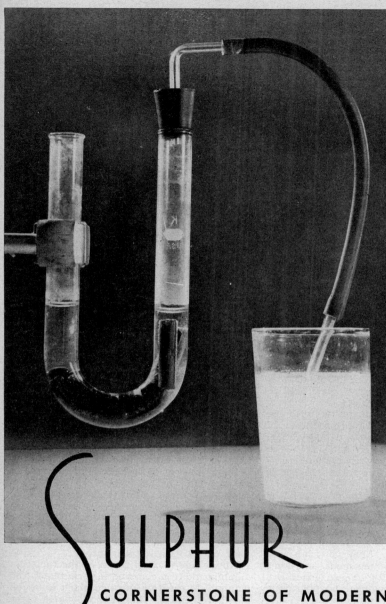

Commercial sulphur, produced first in Sicily, comes today from deposits under the earth of Texas and Louisiana. It is raised by melting it with hot water under pressure and forcing it to the surface by means of compressed air. Left, how a salt solution is analyzed by passing hydrogen sulphide through it. The white precipitate shows zinc is present

SULPHUR

CORNERSTONE OF MODERN INDUSTRY

TAKE sulphur from the chemist's kit of magic, and almost every manufactured article of daily life would either be altered or cease to exist. Sulphuric acid, which enters into more commercial processes than probably any other chemical, as well as other sulphur compounds, play important roles in many basic industries.

Called brimstone ("burning stone") by the ancients, sulphur was first found near volcanoes. Chemical theory has it that it forms in these regions due to the interaction of the gases hydrogen sulphide and sulphur dioxide. You can learn to generate these important compounds of sulphur, and to produce sulphur as a volcano does, with the simple chemicals and apparatus of your home laboratory.

Sulphur dioxide may be prepared by heating sodium sulphite and dilute sulphuric acid in a flask provided with a thistle tube and a delivery tube. You probably know its

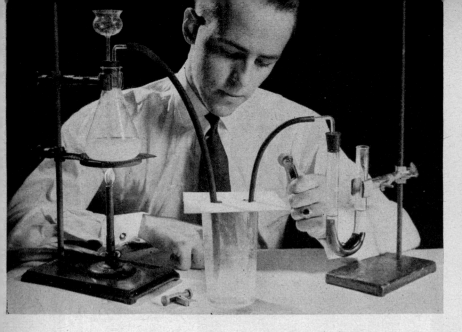

smell as the odor of burning sulphur. Hydrogen sulphide, recognizable by its "rotten-egg" smell, may be generated by an apparatus which stops production as soon as enough gas is obtained. This is made by filling the bottom of a U-tube with glass beads. In the outlet leg of this tube drop several pieces of iron sulphide, and pour in enough dilute hydrochloric acid to cover the sulphide.

As long as the acid is in contact with the sulphide, hydrogen sulphide is produced. If a pinchcock is applied to the delivery tube, gas pressure forces the acid away from the iron sulphide, and gas production automatically stops. Releasing the pinchcock starts generation again.

Set up these two generators together and lead a rubber tube from each to the bottom of a glass jar. Loose a little of both gases at once. As they mix, a cloud forms, and finely divided sulphur deposits on the sides and bottom of the jar. Keep your lab well ventilated during this experiment, and don't prolong it unnecessarily. These gases are evil-smelling, and may even be poisonous when breathed in large amounts.

An interesting characteristic of sulphur is that it can exist in three widely different physical forms. Dissolve some in carbon disulphide (keep this liquid far from any flame, as it is volatile and inflammable) and pour the solution in a dish to evaporate. The sulphur crystals that form are rhombic or octahedral in shape. This is the most common and stable form of sulphur.

Melt some sulphur, with the least heat possible, and pour it into a dish to cool. Now the crystals are thin, prismatic, and needle shaped. After standing, the crystals will change back to the rhombic form.

Melt sulphur and continue heating until it boils, however, and you temporarily change its basic characteristics. Pour some into water and it forms a tough, elastic mass resembling rubber. Gradually this too will change to the first crystalline form.

Powdered sulphur may be made by holding a cold plate in the vapors of boiling sulphur, which condense as the familiar fine powder.

An extremely active element, sulphur combines directly with all metals, except gold and platinum, on the application of heat. The result of the reaction is a sulphide. By dropping iron filings or a bit of steel wool on some burning sulphur, you may witness a vivid demonstration of one form of combination, the end product in this case being iron sulphide. So much heat is liberated that the iron sparkles and glows as it unites with the sulphur.

Advantage may be taken of the fact that sulphur and iron combine to form black iron sulphide to create a durable black finish on small iron parts. Immerse the parts to be blackened in a solution of sulphur in warm turpentine (heat the turpentine over a water bath, and keep it away from all open flame); then heat them in the flame of a Bunsen burner. By repeating the immersion and heating, the coating may be built to the desired thickness.

Raw rubber is a gummy mass, sticky and shapeless—completely useless for most of the products with which we are familiar. Sulphur is the chemical that gives this mass strength and life; the process is known as

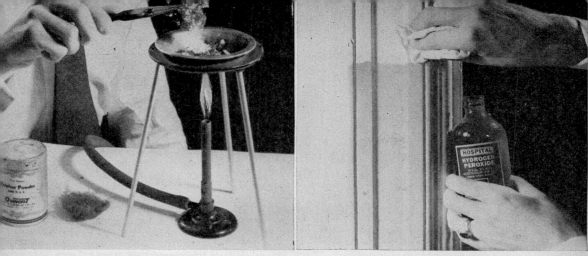

Left above, if sulphur is heated in an open tin until it blazes, and steel wool or filings are dropped into it, the resulting combination is iron sulphide. Right above, lead paint, darkened by the presence of sulphur in the air, may be whitened again by oxidizing the surface with a solution of hydrogen peroxide

vulcanization. By regulating the amount of sulphur and the temperature and length of time of vulcanization, the elasticity, toughness, and hardness of rubber may be accurately controlled.

The process of vulcanization originated in 1839, when Charles Goodyear accidentally spilled a mixture of rubber and sulphur on the top of a hot stove. The product formed was the forerunner of the entire rubber industry.

You can repeat this experiment with the aid of a little rubber cement and powdered sulphur. Heat a few drops of rubber cement over a small flame, and add a few grains of sulphur. When the mixture has been heated sufficiently to melt the sulphur and evaporate the solvent of the cement, the patch may be peeled from the tin. This new product displays the stretch and tensile strength of rubber.

Hydrogen sulphide gas is a great help in the laboratory in the detection of metals. When it is passed through salt solutions of various metals, colored sulphides may be precipitated. From the color and solubility of these sulphides it is possible to identify certain metals.

Pass some of the gas from your hydrogen sulphide generator into a solution containing some unknown salt. If the precipitate is white and will dissolve in hydrochloric acid, the metal is zinc. If it is brown-black and soluble, it is copper. If black and insoluble, it is mercury. If black and soluble, it is lead.

Minute amounts of hydrogen sulphide in the air turn silverware black, and often cause white-lead paints to darken due to the formation of lead sulphide. Paint so discolored may often be whitened by oxidizing the surface with hydrogen peroxide, changing the sulphide to *sulphate*, which is pure white.—KENNETH SWEZEY.

Two forms of sulphur are seen in the above photo. One assumes the shape of crystals; the other is a plastic, rubbery mass. Learn how sulphur acts on rubber by mixing powdered sulphur with rubber cement and heating the mixture over a small flame, as shown below

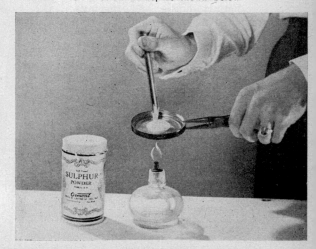

SHORT CIRCUITS and their effects can be demonstrated with two dry cells, a small battery bulb, and a battery-testing meter. First, connect the bulb in series with the dry cells and the meter. Now scrape a bare spot on the wires leading to the bulb and away from it. Short-circuit the bulb by connecting these bare spots with a metal object. The resistance of the bulb gone, the hand of the meter jumps ahead. What had been a harmless, controlled current, now becomes an excessive one that will soon exhaust the cells. In the case of house current, it might cause a fire.

RADIO STATIC is caused by atmospheric electricity and by radiations and fluctuating magnetic fields from doorbells, telephone equipment, streetcar lines, X-ray apparatus, and so forth. How static can affect your receiving set can be demonstrated with the simple setup shown at the right. Make a loop of several turns of bell wire, to represent your radio aerial, and connect the ends to a pair of headphones. Set up a similar coil a few inches away, and parallel to it. Connect one end of the second coil to one terminal of a dry cell, scrape the other end over the second terminal, and distinct clicks and raspings will be heard in the headphones. Connect a bell or buzzer in series with the second coil, and you will hear a buzzing in the phones. In both cases the noise in the headphones is caused by electrical currents induced in the "aerial." Similarly, electric wires running parallel to your radio aerial cause induced currents every time a switch is opened or closed or a bell is rung, even though the wires and aerial are insulated from one another.

WHY BATTERIES "PICK UP" after a rest is illustrated at the right, with a transparent experimental cell. Arrange a rod of carbon, and another of zinc, in a glass containing a strong solution of sal ammoniac. If you connect a small 1½-volt bulb to the two terminals the bulb will light brightly at first, but will gradually lose its brightness until it goes out completely. Observe the carbon rod carefully, and you will see just what causes the diminution in current. As soon as the bulb is connected in the circuit, bubbles of gas begin to collect on the carbon, clinging to the rod until it is almost completely covered. These bubbles are filled with hydrogen, and their effect is the dual one of partly insulating the carbon from the solution and of creating a contrary potential in the cell. Together, they reduce the voltage of the cell and, consequently, the current. To prove that this is correct, merely scrape off the hydrogen bubbles, and the lamp will light brightly again. In dry cells, "scraping" of the gas bubbles is accomplished by chemical, rather than by mechanical action. It is brought about by a depolarizer, such as manganese dioxide.

MAGNETIC LINES OF FORCE around conductors carrying an electric current can be demonstrated with a coil of bell wire, two dry cells, and a small magnetic compass. It is a good idea to wind the coil as large as you can conveniently make it, since the magnetic fields are likely to interfere with each other if the coil is too small. By moving the compass about on the cardboard platform, placed as in the photograph below, the needle can be made to indicate both the direction and the arrangement of the lines of magnetic force, which can be drawn easily with a pencil. Reversing the battery connections will also reverse the direction in which the current enters and leaves the coil. The lines of force, and therefore the compass needle, will change accordingly.

IS MORE ELECTRICITY obtainable from dry cells in series, or from cells in parallel? An analogy answers this question. Fill two containers, both having a hole punched in the bottom, with water. Arrange them as below. The greater height of the upright one results in greater pressure, and the water flows out more quickly. The lower pressure of the horizontal one results in a slower flow, which continues longer. Similarly, two dry cells in series produce greater electrical pressure, causing more current to flow in a given time. Connect them in parallel, and only half the current flows, but for a longer time. In both cases the total amount of electricity is the same.

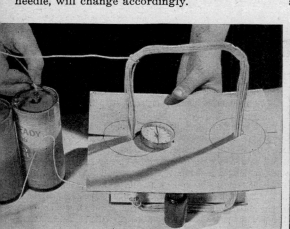

A portable testing instrument with a direct-
reading ohmmeter being employed to check
the insulation resistance of a large generator
Courtesy of James G. Biddle Company

PROPER MAINTENANCE METHODS INSURE TOP PERFORMANCE

By HAROLD P. STRAND

WITH most factories engaged in war production on a 24-hour schedule, it is more imperative than ever that the electric motors which drive their machinery should be given every care. A motor breakdown may slow up production or even close an entire department for a time.

Under present conditions, many motors must be run the clock around with no relief periods. This skyrockets their average working time from the normal figure of about 1,800 hours a year to over 8,700 hours. No wonder inspection, lubrication, cleaning, and adjustment must be quadrupled if motors are to last for the duration!

In the home workshop, motors are not likely to be overworked, but since new ones cannot be bought readily, the shop owner had better take good care of those he has. Dampness, acid fumes, dirt and dust, abrasive particles, and vibration are natural enemies of motors, as are overloading, misalignment, lack of lubrication, friction, and stray oil. Operating a motor with badly worn bearings is another form of abuse. In the box below are given some hints of value.

As most motor failures are electrical rather than mechanical, one of the most important pieces of equipment for the maintenance man is an insulation-resistance tester. This device consists of a hand-operated, direct-current generator capable of supplying a potential of 500 volts, mounted in a carrying case with a direct-reading meter calibrated in ohms and megohms. For testing apparatus rated above 750 volts, a 2,500-volt generator is available.

With such a tester, it is easy to keep a constant check on the insulation resistance of motors, generators, starters, and wiring so that breakdowns can be avoided. One test lead is connected to "ground" and the other, in the case of motors and generators, is clipped to a brush holder. By lifting or removing the brushes, the field can be tested separately from the armature.

All forms of both D.C. and A.C. apparatus and all wiring circuits should be tested periodically and charts kept of the meter readings. Motors that have been rewound should be given an insulation test before the usual dielectric-strength test with high voltage. If the reading is low on the insulation test, it is not good practice to use the high voltage until the windings have been dried or other measures have been taken to raise the reading, so as to avoid permanent damage. Following the application of high voltage, the insulation tester should be used again to make sure the insulation has not been strained to the point of puncture or breakdown.

The scale of a typical resistance tester reads from 10,000 ohms to 100 megohms, and is suitable for most maintenance work under 750 volts. It can be seen that this instrument starts where most bell-ringing magnetos leave off (10,000 ohms) and as one megohm equals 1,000,000 ohms, the condition of insulation can be quite definitely determined with a top limit of 100 megohms. The readings to be expected will vary with the type of apparatus, temperature of the machine, humidity and operating conditions. Motors, for example, when tested after a long run and consequently warm, will show a lower reading than when cold. Cleanliness of the parts also has a bearing on the case, and when readings are low and there are no serious defects otherwise, washing with a solvent and drying out may raise the reading considerably. Motors in

SERVICING HOME WORKSHOP MOTORS

- Keep commutators of both A. C. and D. C. commutator-type motors clean with fine sandpaper.
- If deep pitting or ridges are evident, turn commutator down in the lathe.
- Replace brushes worn too short to make good contact. Set tension springs to provide only enough pressure for nonsparking operation.
- Keep brush guides clean and free from oil.
- Should sparking persist after brushes are correctly adjusted, try undercutting the mica. If this does not end sparking, test the armature on a growler.
- Use the oil specified by the motor manufacturer. Avoid spilling it into or on the motor.
- Blow out dirt, dust, shavings, chips, or sawdust frequently.
- Cover idle motors to keep out dust.
- Keep mounting bolts tight to prevent vibration.
- Do not allow belt tension to be greater than necessary.

*I*F A MOTOR seems to run hotter than usual, check with a suitable thermometer and compare the temperature with that specified on the name plate as normal. If a commutator-type motor has run hot, examine the soldered commutator leads. Should solder "whiskers" be evident or solder be spattered inside the housing, resoldering would be advisable. Overheating of the commutator may be caused by using brushes of the wrong grade or poorly fitted brushes.

This motor on a wood shaper is covered with sawdust after a day's run, despite its shield. Damage is likely if such clogging dust is not blown out

Air cleaning of such shop motors as this should be a daily chore. A compressor or electric blower is ideal, but even a hand bellows can be employed

damp places are hard to keep dry enough to give a satisfactory reading unless given special care as described below.

The actual value on the scale in megohms is not so important as are comparative readings over a period of time, as noted from the charts. However, many engineers and practical electricians take the value of one megohm per 1,000 volts as a standard for a low limit. Some types of apparatus will show considerably higher tests and others operating under adverse conditions may be safely run at lower values, but any sudden or even gradual lowering in resistance is an indication that something is wrong. Unlike a bell-ringing magneto, which delivers alternating current, a D.C. tester of this type is not short-circuited by the capacitance of a large machine or a long cable, nor choked by inductance, as is often the case with an A.C. tester, resulting in a false diagnosis of the trouble. In using either machine, make sure the current is off on the line or apparatus under test.

Water, or dampness, is the cause of many electrical failures. Avoid spraying water on a motor or splashing water close to it. Keep a motor subject to spray or splashing covered with a protecting box or hood at all times or, better still, use a totally enclosed or splashproof motor. Make frequent tests with the resistance meter, and when the reading shows a decline, take steps to dry

out the motor before damage is done. This can be done in an oven under controlled temperature or by locking the rotor and sending a low-voltage current through the windings. Another method is to cover the motor with a tarpaulin having ventilation holes at top and bottom, and blow hot air through the motor. Make frequent resistance tests to avoid unnecessary loss of time and possible overbaking, which may cause insulation to become brittle and crumble.

Where shop motors are choked with sawdust, air pressure from either a compressor or a hand bellows should be applied to blow this waste matter out after each day's run. If allowed to remain, it will cause overheating of the motor and possibly a burnout. Totally enclosed, fan-cooled motors should be used for this class of service.

Overloading a motor willfully should be a punishable offense. The first indication of it is usually a decided increase in temperature and a blowing of fuses or overload relays. To determine whether or not overload is present, connect an ammeter in series with one lead while the motor is carrying full load, and note the reading in amperes. If this is not more than the normal current stated on the name plate, it can be assumed that the motor is not overloaded.

Several things other than the external load given a motor can result in overloading. Lack of lubrication can cause friction

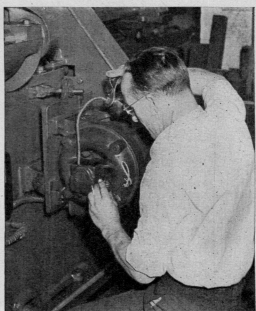

The contact fingers of magnetic controllers need inspection and cleaning at regular intervals for protection against burn-outs due to bad contacts

The lubrication of a 5-h. p. motor on a big power saw is being checked here. Oil is added to keep the cup at the side of the bearing nearly full

at the bearings. Worn bearings may allow the rotor to rub on the field poles. An overly tight belt can make a motor labor. Dirt and other waste matter inside the housing may have the same effect. Misalignment of pulleys, chain sprockets, or gears will cause friction, vibration, and inefficient operation. If after all these points have been checked, overload is still present, there is nothing else to do but substitute a larger motor for the work. Don't continue using an undersized motor by overloading it.

Lubrication is one of the most important factors in keeping motors on the job. In bearings that have oil rings, always use oil —never grease. Check the rings occasionally to make sure they turn freely. Drain the wells at intervals and refill with clean, fresh lubricant. Keep the level at all times just below the top of the overflow cup at the side, which level should be determined when the motor is at rest. Use an oil of the correct grade for the size of the motor. Too light an oil will be squeezed out from between the shaft and the bearing surface and allow metal-to-metal contact with resulting damage.

Waste-packed bearings also use oil, and this should be renewed occasionally. Antifriction bearings such as ball bearings require grease. This should be injected as required, for damage to the polished surfaces is sure to result if such bearings run dry.

When ball bearings wear to a point where play or shake is noticeable, new ones should be installed without delay. If any dirt or abrasive particles ever get into the bearings of a motor, stop the machine at once and thoroughly wash out the parts with carbon tetrachloride; then refill with new lubricant.

A point often overlooked in the maintenance of motors is the possibility of three-phase motors running "single phase" due to a blown fuse or dirty contacts in the control switch or breaker. When this happens, the motor will continue to operate, but with a gradual increase in temperature until fuses blow, relays open, or perhaps the motor burns out. To guard against this hazard, check fuses frequently and clean all contacts in both fuse panel and control switches regularly. Often it will be found that fuse clips are loose, making poor contact. Control contacts may be pitted and burned. They should be cleaned or new contacts obtained and installed.

Another source of trouble in motors is vibration. Many times the rotor is out of balance, especially following an armature repair. This can be checked by testing the rotor on parallel knife edges or bars. It should not come to rest at any particular point repeatedly. If it does, it has a heavy side. The usual remedy is to drill a few shallow holes in the armature core at this point until it balances.

FIRST STEPS IN ELECTRONICS

PART I — THE ELECTRON

By CHARLES I. HELLMAN

*Physics Instructor, Bronx High School
of Science, New York*

ELECTRONS, although the smallest particles in existence, are doing a big job in helping Uncle Sam win this war. The problem of producing them and putting them through their paces is a comparatively new branch of science called *electronics*.

Through this and subsequent articles, those readers with a general interest in science may gain an understanding of how electronics is helping in our war effort. Experimenters will discover in this most fascinating of modern sciences a ready field for new activities. And men and women who wish to expand their knowledge of electronic applications in war industry will find it essential to study and master the fundamentals.

Electrons are literally everywhere, for they are constituents of matter. Free electrons abound even in "empty" interplanetary space. Surcharges of electrons create the beauty of the northern lights and the flash of lightning. Electrons are also given off by radium and other radioactive substances.

We ourselves are constantly freeing electrons from ordinary matter, and putting them in motion. Comb your hair briskly with a hard-rubber comb on a dry winter day, and the friction strikes electrons loose from the atoms comprising your hair. These cling to the comb, which we then say is "electrified."

An electric current consists of electrons in motion. Snap an electric-light switch, and billions of electrons flow through the filament. Millions crowd upon the negative terminal of the dry cell you buy for a dime, and are ready to flow forth, through the bulb of your flashlight, and back to the positive terminal, at the touch of your finger on the button.

Early in the science of electricity it was rather arbitrarily decided that the flow of current was from the positive to the negative. Today it is known that the electron flow constituting the current is exactly opposite to this—from the negative to the positive. It is an excess of electrons that constitutes a negative charge. Matter that has been stripped of some of its electrons is said to have a positive charge, and will attract electrons from whatever source it can. The electron flow is thus always from the negative to the positive.

A source of electrons most of us are familiar with is the cathode or filament of a vacuum tube. As electronics has made perhaps its greatest contributions in the field of radio communication, it is interesting to note that our modern knowledge of the electron began with an accidental discovery made during the first demonstration of wireless waves.

In 1864 James Clerk-Maxwell, in attempting to explain how a magnet would pick up a piece of iron at a distance, or how an electrified rubber rod could attract pieces of paper at a distance, propounded a startling theory. By mathematical calculations he found that the speed with which a magnetic disturbance traveled was nearly that of light, and he therefore concluded that light itself was an electromagnetic disturbance.

Since light can be reflected, focused, and transmitted through space, and since electromagnetic disturbances seemed to be of the same nature as light, Clerk-Maxwell's discovery indicated that it might be possible

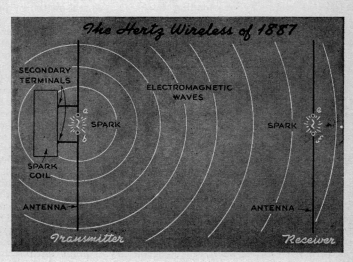

The Hertz Wireless of 1887

SECONDARY TERMINALS

ELECTROMAGNETIC WAVES

SPARK

SPARK

SPARK COIL

ANTENNA

ANTENNA

Transmitter

Receiver

to produce an electromagnetic wave having somewhat the same properties as light. As a consequence of this work, many physicists were stimulated to experiment along these lines, and in 1887 Heinrich Rudolph Hertz, after painstaking work, succeeded in producing waves that completely confirmed Clerk-Maxwell's theories. The apparatus he used for some of his experiments is shown on the facing page. Using this equipment, he was able to duplicate with electromagnetic waves almost all the effects possible with light waves.

Let us examine Hertz's equipment in order to understand how, as early as 1887, he was able to produce radio waves. A spark coil like that in an automobile was connected to the two brass rods, as shown in the diagram. This apparatus was the transmitter of energy. The receiver was used to pick up the electromagnetic waves. When the receiver was tuned to the transmitter by using the correct length of antenna wires, Hertz found that whenever a spark was set up in the gap *ab* by the spark coil, a spark was received at gap *ef*. With this apparatus, simpler than the ignition system of an automobile, Hertz was able to establish the experimental foundations of radio communication.

An elementary explanation of the above experiment may be given in terms of electron movement. Whenever an electron is speeded up or changes its direction suddenly, it tends to radiate energy in the form of electromagnetic waves. If the oscillating motion of the electrons occurs at a frequency of 730 trillion times a second, then the electromagnetic disturbance will affect our eyes and be called light. If the frequency is in the range of 100,000 to 1,000,000,000 times per second, the energy radiated will be picked up by a properly tuned set as a radio wave. The chart at right shows how the nature of electromagnetic waves depends on the frequency of electronic oscillation. Since the frequencies are extremely high, mathematical shorthand is used in writing large numbers. Thus 10^{13} is 1 with 13 zeros following or 10,000,000,000,000. For convenience, this may readily be reduced

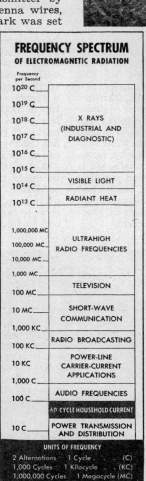

FREQUENCY SPECTRUM
OF ELECTROMAGNETIC RADIATION

Frequency per Second

10^{20} C	
10^{19} C	
10^{18} C	X RAYS
10^{17} C	(INDUSTRIAL AND DIAGNOSTIC)
10^{16} C	
10^{15} C	
10^{14} C	VISIBLE LIGHT
10^{13} C	RADIANT HEAT
1,000,000 MC	
100,000 MC	ULTRAHIGH RADIO FREQUENCIES
10,000 MC	
1,000 MC	
100 MC	TELEVISION
10 MC	SHORT-WAVE COMMUNICATION
1,000 KC	
100 KC	RADIO BROADCASTING
10 KC	POWER-LINE CARRIER-CURRENT APPLICATIONS
1,000 C	
100 C	AUDIO FREQUENCIES
	60 CYCLE HOUSEHOLD CURRENT
10 C	POWER TRANSMISSION AND DISTRIBUTION

UNITS OF FREQUENCY

2 Alternations	1 Cycle	(C)
1,000 Cycles	1 Kilocycle	(KC)
1,000,000 Cycles	1 Megacycle	(MC)

Modern version of the apparatus used by Hertz—a walkie-talkie radio that keeps Army patrols in close touch with their officers

to ten million megacycles. Directly above is a modern version of Hertz's apparatus. This walkie-talkie radio outfit used by soldiers keeps fast-moving patrols in constant touch with directing officers. A drawing on page HW52 shows graphically the mechanism of radiation.

An important phase in the development of electronics is the discovery of the photoelectric effect. In 1887, Hertz discovered that when ultraviolet light fell on the metallic knobs of the spark gap in his receiver, he could obtain a spark more easily.

A year later, Wilhelm Hallwachs, another physicist, studied the effect of light in producing a discharge from metal surfaces. As a result of

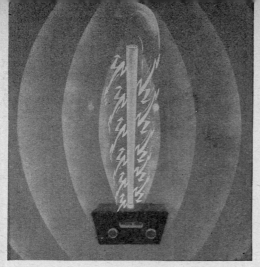

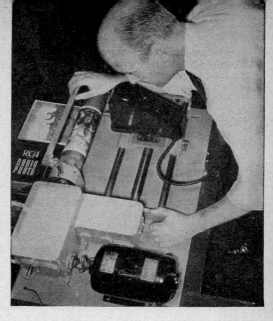

Electrons tend to radiate energy in the form of electromagnetic waves when speeded up or suddenly changed in direction. At right, transmission of pictures by radio—a new photo-cell application

his work, he is credited with the discovery of the photoelectric effect. His apparatus is shown just below. Ultraviolet light falling on the zinc knob caused the leaves of the negatively charged electroscope to lose their charge of electrons and collapse.

Photo cells are today used to transmit television images, to help guard defense plants, to convert sound-track densities into talking movies, in plane de-icers, and in a vast array of other applications. One new use is the sending of photographs by radio.

A diagram of the action of a photo cell is also shown below. The electrons emitted from the light-sensitive surface are picked up by the collecting rod and are conducted to an outside circuit. This stream of electrons constitutes an electric current.

The best way to learn electronics is to handle electronic equipment. However, due to the fact that almost all electrical equipment is being diverted to military channels, such apparatus will no longer be available to the experimenter. Fortunately, there is a source of equipment that most of us can tap at little or no cost. Every old or obsolete radio set is a veritable gold mine of parts. If you can get your hands on one that has outlived its usefulness, you can still make use of its components.

A few of the electronic devices that can be made from them are a radio-frequency oscillator, an audio-frequency oscillator, a wave-trap, and a phonograph amplifier. How to build these and other useful devices will be told in a later article.

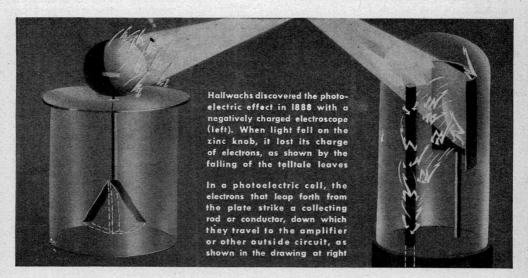

Hallwachs discovered the photoelectric effect in 1888 with a negatively charged electroscope (left). When light fell on the zinc knob, it lost its charge of electrons, as shown by the falling of the telltale leaves

In a photoelectric cell, the electrons that leap forth from the plate strike a collecting rod or conductor, down which they travel to the amplifier or other outside circuit, as shown in the drawing at right

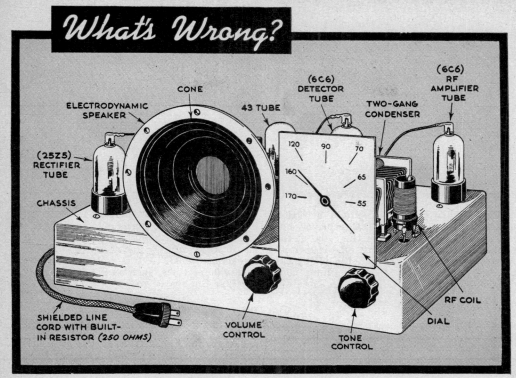

What's Wrong?

CONE
(6C6) DETECTOR TUBE
(6C6) RF AMPLIFIER TUBE
ELECTRODYNAMIC SPEAKER
43 TUBE
TWO-GANG CONDENSER
(25Z5) RECTIFIER TUBE
CHASSIS
RF COIL
DIAL
SHIELDED LINE CORD WITH BUILT-IN RESISTOR (250 OHMS)
VOLUME CONTROL
TONE CONTROL

CAN YOU FIND EIGHT ERRORS?

How much do you know about radio? In the sketch of a four-tube A. C.-D. C. TRF receiver above, the artist has made eight intentional errors. Can you find them? As a clew, look for omissions and unnecessary inclusions, and study the parts themselves and their position on the chassis. Take as much time as you require; then turn this page upside down to check your answers.

ANSWERS: 1. A 6C6 is never used as an RF amplifier tube. In a four-tube TRF receiver, the first tube is always a 6D6 super-control RF amplifier tube. The 6C6 is a detector tube. 2. The RF coil is never mounted on top of the chassis; it is the antenna coil that is mounted in this position. The RF coil is mounted underneath the chassis for shielding purposes. 3. The 25Z5 rectifier tube should not have a grid cap on top of the bulb. 4. The resistance in the line cord is too high for the tubes used. It should be between 165 and 180 ohms. 5. Line cords on A. C.-D. C. sets are never shielded. 6. There is no dial-control knob shown. With only volume-control and tone-control knobs, there would be no way of selecting stations. 7. All the tubes have the wrong shape, since the 6D6, 6C6, 43, and 25Z5 types all have dome tops. The shapes in the sketch are those for the newer GT/G-type tubes. 8. The speaker is too close to the dial for practical use in a cabinet.

Pocket-Size Kit Contains Dial and Knob Parts

A COMPLETE assortment of knob springs, setscrews, dial pulleys, idler pulleys, and drive rubbers is contained in a radio kit, at left, equipped for repairing dials and knobs. The kit is convenient to take on jobs, since it measures only ⅞" by 2¾" by 4¾". Two models are available, one containing 70 pieces, the other 150, and replacements may be obtained. Either kit will service any type knob or dial.

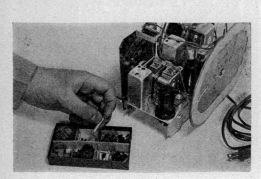

Servicing Your Radio

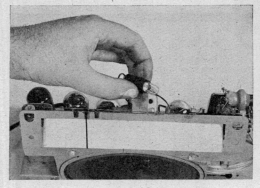

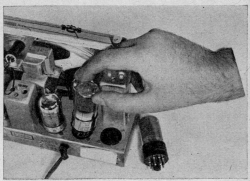

CHANGING PILOT LIGHTS is a simple operation in servicing a small A.C.-D.C. receiver, but be sure that you disconnect the radio at the wall socket—don't just turn off the switch. A serious short can occur if the pilot-light bracket and holder drop on the tuning condenser or chassis.

INCREASED HEATER VOLTAGE may be necessary if the rectifier tube burns out quickly on an A.C.-D.C. radio having a new high-voltage heater tube and no line-cord resistor. Try replacing the 35Z5-GT/G rectifier tube with a 45-volt rectifier, such as a 42Z5-GT/G, to increase the heater voltage to 120 volts.

THE PAPER TUBULAR CONDENSER connected between the power pentode tube and chassis, as shown in the diagram below, may be shorted if an A.C.-D.C. radio has gone dead except for the heater glow inside its tubes. This is especially true if, upon testing, the D.C. voltage to the tubes shows only about 20 volts. Remove the power pentode tube (a 43, 25L6, 50L6, or similar tube) from its socket, and test the condenser by placing an ohmmeter across it. If the needle on the meter swings over, the condenser is shorted and a new one must be installed.

SQUEALING AND WHISTLING that make it impossible to tune in a station clearly on a small A.C.-D.C. receiver may mean failure of one or both of the filter condensers shown in the photograph above and the diagram below. The noise is usually accompanied by a noticeable loss in volume. If defective, the condensers must be replaced.

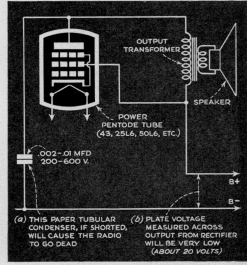

(a) THIS PAPER TUBULAR CONDENSER, IF SHORTED, WILL CAUSE THE RADIO TO GO DEAD   (b) PLATE VOLTAGE MEASURED ACROSS OUTPUT FROM RECTIFIER WILL BE VERY LOW (ABOUT 20 VOLTS)

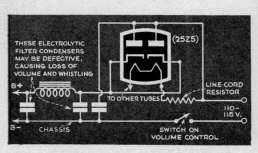

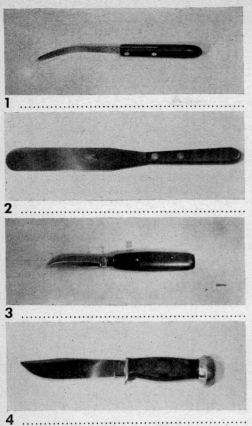

1 ....

2 ....

3 ....

4 ....

Question Bee

A SHARP shell or bit of flint was probably the first knife, so the origin of this tool undoubtedly dates from the dawn of human history. There is no tribe today, even among the most primitive peoples, that does not use knives of some kind. War, hunting, fishing, manufacturing, and the arts have all developed their special types, and at least seven different kinds of steel are used in the manufacture of modern knives. Can you name the ten common knives shown here? After writing your answers on the dotted lines, turn the page upside down to find your score.

ANSWERS

1. Grapefruit knife
2. Spatula
3. Sloyd manual-training knife
4. Sheath knife
5. Shoe knife
6. Clam knife
7. Jackknife
8. Fisherman's knife
9. Slicing knife
10. Linoleum knife

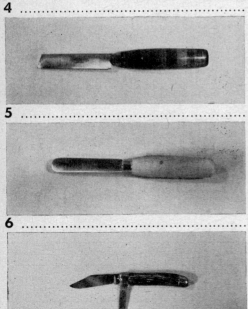

5 ....

6 ....

7 ....

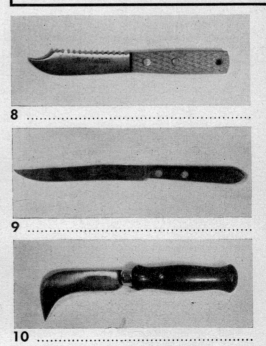

8 ....

9 ....

10 ....

Dear Workshop Editor:

Most home craftsmen need some kind of lumber rack badly. I know I do. Stock left on a damp floor is likely to warp or split, and if it's stacked up in a corner you may fall over it and you always have a hard time finding the piece you want. How about a plan for a simple rack that can be placed against one wall, with some way of keeping different kinds or thicknesses of stock separate? *C.E.V.*

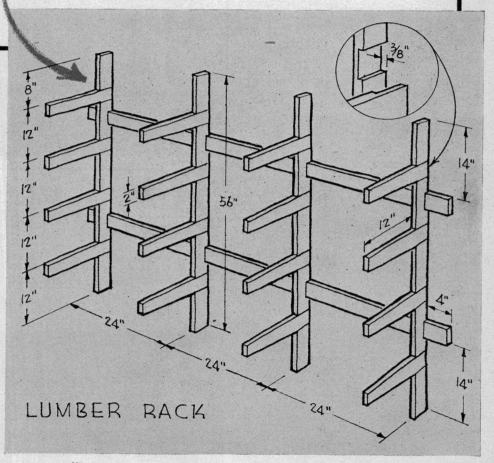

LUMBER RACK

Clear white pine ¾" by 3" is used for this rack designed by James N. Larson, but 4" stock would add strength, if desired. The four uprights are notched for lap joints with two cross supports and 16 lumber holders. These holders are alike, and can be made quickly on the bench saw by using a jig for cutting the bottom tapers. Assemble with nails, screws, or bolts, and mount on a wooden wall or, if the wall is concrete, make the uprights long enough to nail to overhead joists

Clock Spring Replaces Shop-Apron Strings

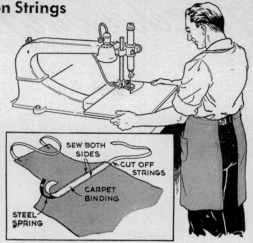

AN OLD clock or phonograph spring sewn around the waist of your shop apron will eliminate bothersome strings and hold the apron firmly in place.

Cut the spring to a length equal to the width of the apron. It is wise to use the innermost part of the spring, since it has more tension, and will cling more closely to the body. Sew a strip of ordinary carpet binding across the apron with strong thread and insert the spring in the opening between the two rows of stitches.

If you do not have a spring suitable for this purpose, you can purchase one for a small sum from almost any jewelry or clock-repair shop in your neighborhood.

When the apron is to be laundered, it is a simple matter to pull the spring out, and to replace it afterwards.—FRANK LAMBERT.

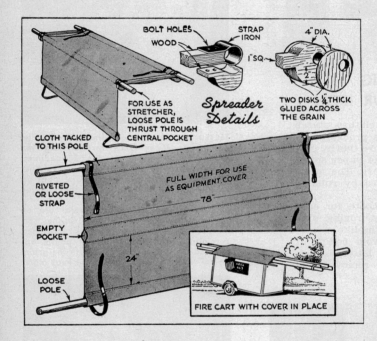

Detachable Bag Catches Litter from Workbench

A bag attached at the end of a workbench as shown below is useful for catching sawdust or shavings. A straight piece of wood as wide as the bench, with a curved piece of stock bent around it and screwed fast at each end, forms the bag frame. A burlap bag is fitted into this curve. Keyhole slots hook over screws so that the bag may be detached for emptying.—J. H. WILSON.

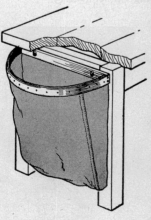

Stretcher Doubles as Cover for Fire Cart

HEAVY, unbleached muslin—waterproofed and cut out to cover civilian-defense equipment, such as a mobile fire cart—can also serve as an emergency stretcher.

If the cover is wider than a standard 27″ stretcher, a third pole pocket should be stitched in. The length of the stretcher fabric should be approximately 78″, and the poles should protrude far enough at both ends for an easy carrying grip.

Two alternative spreaders are shown in the drawing, one built entirely of wood. Straps will be needed for fastenings when the unit is used as a tarpaulin.—BLAINE KLUM.

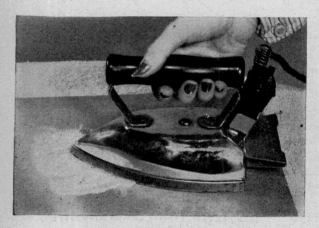

ALL-GLASS PRESERVING JAR. This has a reclaimed-rubber gasket that can be used again and again. The jar is opened by indenting the gasket with a sharp instrument through a special slot in the side

PROLONGING
THE LIFE OF YOUR IRON

IF YOUR iron sticks to the clothes, starch or other foreign material has probably collected on the sole plate. Remove this by rubbing the hot iron on a piece of paper sprinkled with salt, as shown above. The metal surface should then be waxed by rubbing it with beeswax or paraffin.

The sole plate must be smooth for easy ironing. Don't scratch it by ironing over buttons, snaps, zippers, and the like.

Never kink the cord. Avoid coiling it around the iron while the latter is hot. Detachable cords should be removed and hung up separately.

TESTED RECIPES are contained in this file, which has index dials for locating the cards quickly. Each of the 22 sections, from appetizers to desserts, is tabbed. Touch one of the tabs and a dial pops up to tell you all the recipes in that section

A FURNITURE POLISH for general use on varnish, shellac, or lacquer finishes removes spots and covers minor scratches. A cloth is moistened with the polish, applied to the spot, and rubbed with the grain. Removes liquor, water, and even heat marks

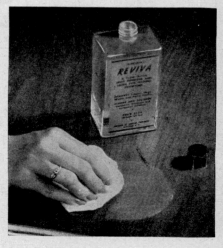

OFFICERS' BUNK BAGS provide ample space for two uniforms (or uniform and overcoat), plus all other essential clothing and military accessories. The garments travel on hangers, shown above, inside cellulose-film envelopes. The bags are covered with water-repellent sailcloth in olive drab or navy blue

PREPARING CORN DISHES, such as corn fritters, succotash, creamed corn, and the like, is made easy by this stainless-steel scraper with specially designed teeth that split the kernels and cut them off the cob in one motion, leaving only the hulls. The wooden handle is enameled green or red to match other utensils

COOKING ODORS are dispelled with an air purifier that can be attached to any fan. The unit clamps upon the guard of the fan, and a wick arrangement dispenses the liquid inside the bottle onto a fibrous pad from which it is volatilized into the room. Feed can be altered by varying the number of wicks in the bottle

EXTRUDED PLASTIC takes the place of rubber in this kink-preventing jacket, which is easily placed on any ordinary telephone cord. Translucent and lighter than rubber, the spiral jacket is already coiled and will retain its shape for an indefinite time

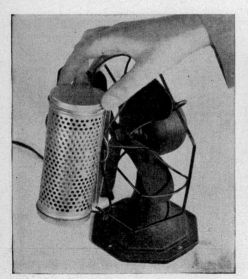

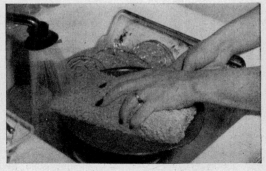

GENUINE SPONGE is sewn inside the soft tufted sack shown above, creating a very absorbent cleaning sponge for all household purposes. It will not scratch or shrink, and dries to a thick, fluffy pile. The sponges are available in three useful sizes

Frame Is Bowed at Center to Pull Wire Screening Taut

WIRE screening can be made taut by bowing the frame ½″ or so at the center while the ends of the screening are being tacked on. Place the ends of the frame on saw-horses, and fasten a C-clamp at the center of each side. Lay a sturdy board under the clamps, nail one end to the floor, and attach an eyebolt to the board midway between the two clamps. Through this eyebolt and the clamps stretch a wire or cord, fastening it so that the free end of the board is about 2″ off the floor. Then press the board down, working it under a cleat, as indicated in the drawing. This will bow the frame sufficiently for the screening to be attached to the ends. Release the tension on the frame when you wish to tack the sides down.—E. M. WOODEN.

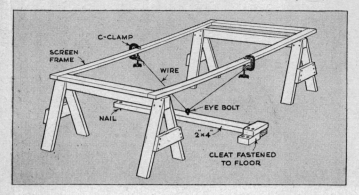

Angle-Painting Problems Solved with Adjustable Brush

HERE'S an adjustable-angle brush for painting inaccessible corners on cameras, recording instruments, and similar equipment. Saw off an ordinary brush about two thirds of the way up the ferrule. Drill corresponding holes in the metal ends, and join the two parts with a machine screw and nut, as shown. Set at the most convenient angle, and tighten the nut.—CHARLES HOMEWOOD.

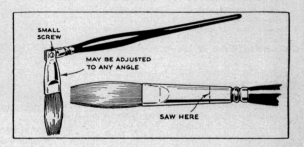

REMOVING UPPER WINDOW SASH   [SHIPSHAPE HOME]

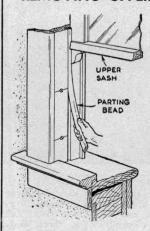

Upper sash cords do not often need replacement, but when they do, a stop must first be removed and the lower sash taken out and laid aside. Then pry out the parting bead from the same pulley stile. This member, sunk in a groove, is often held by a nail near the center, and if the runs are painted, may be stuck tight. Drive the edge of a wide chisel into the bead at various points from behind, raising or lowering the sash as required, and pry against the bevel until the parting bead is loose. A knife point passed along each side may help.

Raise the sash to the top and pull the strip out of the groove, twisting it forward to clear the notch in the end of the check rail. It may be easier to lower the sash and pull out the bead from above. Replace the sash cord, swing the sash into place, and put back the parting bead. Rehang the lower sash and install the stop.

Sabotage under Your Roof

HOW CONDENSATION CAUSES A HOUSE TO DETERIORATE
. . . AND WHAT YOU CAN DO TO CORRECT IT

IN THOUSANDS of loyal American homes, sabotage is going on. This sabotage is unintentional, but scarcely less severe than if it were enemy inspired. When paint blisters and peels or brown stain appears on the outside walls of a new home—look for sabotage.

People who pride themselves on maintaining healthful living conditions are most apt to be unwitting partners to the crime. For the offender—the saboteur—is condensation or uncontrolled moisture in the home. Like a stealthy enemy agent, it performs its destructive work unsuspected and unseen.

Ironically enough, condensation rarely gets the blame. If the paint has failed, we sue the painter. If the woodwork is stained, we blame the carpenter. The surface evidence is against them, and they have to make good the damage. Yet underneath, the true culprit, condensation, goes unrecog-

nized and is left free to raise havoc again.

Condensation is a national problem. So prevalent has it become in recent years that many scientific building authorities have delved into the subject, among them the National Bureau of Standards, Forest Products Laboratories, the University of Minnesota, Iowa State College, and the Canadian National Research Laboratories. They all agree on a common cause and a common cure.

Back in grandfather's day, homes were drafty. In winter you could feel the chill wind blowing in around the doors and windows, and the walls were cold to the touch. Escaping heat melted snow on the roof almost as soon as it fell. Just as the cold air crept in and the heat escaped, moist indoor air easily found its way outdoors. Grandfather had a serious fuel problem, but no paint troubles worth mentioning.

His grandsons live in much more comfortable homes. Heat loss and wind infiltration have been reduced by insulation, weatherstripping, storm sash, and tighter construction. Cracks and crannies through which moist indoor air might escape have been largely eliminated. For health and comfort, modern homes are often provided with furnace humidifiers or some other means of increasing indoor humidity. It is

Introducing:

The little man who WAS there— if things happened when they shouldn't. He's the Household Gremlin, grounded cousin of the sky pixy who's the bane of air pilots. How he loves mischief!

in these homes where high humidities are maintained that most condensation difficulties occur. And the grandsons have paint trouble aplenty.

What is condensation? When water is evaporated, it changes into an invisible gas or vapor which mixes readily with air. This water vapor in the atmosphere we call humidity. As a gas, water vapor exerts a definite pressure that is part of the total pressure exerted by the atmosphere. Vapor, therefore, tends to expand to areas where the pressure is less, much as gas leaking from a kitchen stove will quickly spread throughout the house and force its way outdoors.

The amount of vapor that the air can carry increases as the temperature rises, and decreases as the temperature drops. When vapor-laden air is for any reason cooled—by striking a cold surface, for example—it can no longer retain the moisture it has taken up, and what we call condensation sets in.

In our homes we are seldom aware of water vapor until condensation has set in. A vast quantity of it is drawn into the air

VITAL SPOTS IN YOUR HOME WHERE CONDENSATION CAN CAUS

MOISTURE STAINS SIDING

MOISTURE BLISTERS PAINT

MOISTURE ENTERS AROUND DEFECTIVE FLASHING

MOISTURE MAKES DOORS AND WINDOWS STICK

MOISTURE BREAKS MORTAR BOND

from new plaster, furnace humidifiers, air-conditioning equipment, and rooms where heated water is in use—the bathroom, laundry, and kitchen. The air exhaled from our lungs and moisture evaporated from our skin surfaces contribute more air-borne moisture.

Acting under pressure, this vapor moves as a rule from warm to cooler areas entirely independent of air currents. It passes readily through plaster and other unprotected wall coverings on its way to the outside air. Gathering in the stud spaces within the wall and cooling there, the vapor condenses into water, and destructive action begins. The moisture works through the sheathing and siding to the paint film, where it forms blisters and causes the paint to peel.

Certain woods commonly used for siding contain large percentages of water-soluble coloring matter. Moisture passing through the siding from within leaches out this coloring matter and deposits it on the painted exterior in dirty brown streaks resembling tobacco juice. If used promptly, a solution of one half painters' alcohol and one half water will remove the ugly stain, but if the stain has become oxidized the surface must be scraped and repainted.

Lumber used in homes normally contains from 12 to 20 percent moisture. When condensation water soaks into the wood and forces the moisture content above that range, there is bound to be trouble. The wood will swell and warp or even split. Doors and windows will stick. Excessive moisture working through the siding may encourage dormant fungus spores to develop in the wood and discolor the paint film with a dirty blue stain.

In homes of brick or stone, moisture from within, after freezing a few times, may break the mortar bond, leaving little but gravity to hold the masonry together. As moisture passes through the wall, it leaches out alkali salts, which on evaporation are left on the surface as a disfiguring white deposit known as efflorescence.

Moisture condensed in the walls may also do considerable damage to home interiors by soaking through the plaster and discoloring the wallpaper. High humidity invites decay in wood, permits corrosion of metals. In warm weather moisture condensing on cold-water pipes may drip on the woodwork and cause serious localized decay. In winter there may be so much condensation on window panes that water will run down over the sash or sills and soak into the wood.

Now, what can be done? Authorities agree that the relative humidity in homes should be controlled according to the outside temperature. In below-zero weather the indoor relative humidity should not be more than 20 percent; between zero and 20 deg. F., not more than 30 percent, and in temperatures over 20 deg., not more than 40 percent.

Lowering the relative humidity indoors as the outside temperature drops may be accomplished with exhaust

COSTLY DAMAGE

MOISTURE DISINTEGRATES CHIMNEY MORTAR

MOISTURE COLLECTS BEHIND HEAVY PLANTING

MOISTURE CAUSES EFFLORESCENCE

The owner of this new home bragged about the high humidity he maintained—and look what happened. Condensation is the cause of many paint failures

Four types of paint deterioration near a bathroom window—peeling on the casing, blue stain on the sash, and brown stain and blisters on the siding

fans, and ventilating louvers may be installed to assure frequent changes of air. When moisture gathers on walls, windows, or mirrors in the kitchen, laundry, or bathroom, open the windows and let the saturated air escape. Regulate the furnace humidifier or shut it off entirely in below-zero weather.

These precautions, although helpful, are not sufficient. The outside walls and top-floor ceilings are still permeable to vapor. The problem is, therefore, (1) to stop the vapor from entering the outside wall and top-floor ceiling spaces, and (2) to allow any vapor within these spaces to escape outdoors. In other words, a "vapor dam" is needed on the warm side of the outside walls or top-floor ceiling to retard vapor travel, and a "vapor gate" on the cold side to carry off any overflow from the "dam."

In new construction this is easily accomplished by installing an asphalt vapor barrier underneath the plaster, and by avoiding the use of any materials in the outside part of the wall which too greatly retard the escape of vapor. For homes already completed, two coats of a good oil or varnish-vehicle paint on the interior of all outside walls and top-floor ceilings will provide an effective vapor barrier. There must be no gaps. Protect the backs of cupboards and bins in the kitchen, bookcases and window seats in the living room, cabinets and buffets in the dining room, and all other built-in features, and don't forget the closets or the area underneath and behind the bathtub where it adjoins an outside wall. Above all, make sure that no vapor can escape from the basement into the stud spaces. Here a reinforced duplex building paper will provide an excellent vapor seal. Remember that any appreciable gap in the vapor barrier may result in condensation trouble.

Moisture difficulties may arise from other sources. Moisture may enter the wall through improper flashing at interior angles,

Repair YOUR HOME Now

eaves, or over doors and windows, and it may also seep in through cracks or gaps in the siding. Look for loose joints at the corners of the house, around door and window openings, and between the boards themselves. Any good caulking will correct this.

Excessive moisture in the basement may be due to ground water or unusually damp surrounding areas, such as those caused by heavy shrubbery planted close to the house. Slope the soil up to the foundation so that water will drain away from the house, and make sure there are no low spots near the wall where water can gather.

If trouble persists, it may be necessary to dig a trench around the house and lay drain tile next to the foundation and just below the basement floor level. Before filling in, give the foundation wall a good coating of asphalt. Check downspouts and leaders for breaks below the ground level.

For slow leaks in foundation walls, any good concrete waterproofing compound applied on the inside should prove a corrective.

Natural gas, when burned in open heaters, produces a vast amount of water vapor. During a single heating season a five- or six-room home—for example, one in Oklahoma City, Okla., where much natural gas is used—may burn 80,000 cubic feet of gas, and in the process some 800 gallons of vapor will be released, with possibilities of condensation damage. To prevent condensation, gas heaters should be vented directly to the outside so that the water vapor produced in combustion will not be added to the air in the house.

Chimney failures from disintegrating mortar may be due to moisture caused by poor capping or originating within the flue. In converting a heating plant from coal to gas, reduce the diameter of the flue to 5" or 6", or the extra moisture from gas combustion will be chilled to the dew point before escaping. An acid- and corrosion-resisting slip-in liner should also be inserted in the flue.

NAVAL BOMBING GAME

. . . . . Features Ingenious Bombsight

By MYRON FLEISHMAN
Toy and Game Designer

ENEMY fleet sighted! . . . On target! . . . Bombs away! . . . Here's a realistic naval bombing operation brought to your parlor floor in miniature, and a fascinating game that's bound to make a direct hit with everyone who plays—and anyone can. All the thrills of an actual aerial attack are present; the bomber "flies" over the formation of warships below, selects a carrier, battleship, or cruiser for blasting out of the sea, gets into position over it, and releases the bombs over the target.

The bomber is made almost entirely of wood and cardboard, painted olive drab, and decorated with insignia and representations of pilot's cabin, ailerons, elevators, gunner's turret, cannon, and so forth. The fuselage, wing, stabilizer, and rudder are cardboard, while the nose, tailpiece, motors, turret, wheel assemblies, and bombs are made of wood. The bombsight is an ingenious device consisting of a mirror, guide lines, and a miniature plumb bob. The only other materials needed in the construction are some small pieces of celluloid.

To make the fuselage, cut a 1⅜″ o.d. cardboard mailing tube

to a length of 7½″. Cut out a 1″ hole with its center ⅞″ from one end, and glue a celluloid strip, on which the bombsight pattern is inked or painted, over this hole, securing it also with small screws and nuts. Punch a small hole in the precise center, and through this, thread a plumb line ¾″ long with a small weight on its end. Cut a 7/16″ by ⅞″ opening for the bomb bay, measuring 1⅝″ from this same end of the fuselage, as shown in the drawing. For the bomb rack, extend a ¼″ wide slot on a direct line with the bombsight center to a length of 2½″. To complete the fuselage, make the wing slots, as shown, and glue on the rear gun turret, which is shaped to fit the tube.

The nosepiece is made of wood, shaped as indicated, with a small mirror fastened to it at a 45-deg. angle. For the tail, a piece of wood of the same diameter as the fuselage is shaped to size and a ½″ hole is bored through it for sighting. Slots are made to receive the vertical fin and stabilizers, which are cut from cardboard, and a hole is then bored diagonally in the bottom for the tail wheel.

Cut a 12″ long wing from cardboard, insert it in the slot in the fuselage, and glue it in place. The twin motors are 1″ in diameter, tapered to a length of 2″,

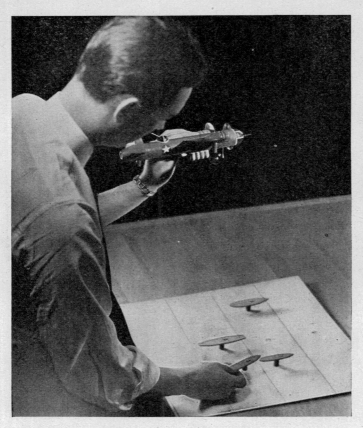

"Enemy" warships are set up in the first area on the target board, as directed below, and five bombs dropped. Surviving ships are moved and bombing is repeated over the other areas

slotted for a snug fit on the wing, and bored diagonally underneath for the ⅜" dowel that supports the landing-gear assembly. Celluloid disks 2¼" in diameter are fastened to the motors to simulate spinning propellers.

The bombs are made from ⅜" dowel, grooved to hang in the bomb rack, while the bomb release is fashioned from ½" wood dowel, formed as to slide along the bomb-rack slot. This arrangement makes it a simple matter to release one bomb at a time.

Ships are of thin wood, with a ½" wood dowel as support. They are cut to the three shapes and sizes indicated, then painted battleship gray, and numbered as follows: cruisers, "3"; battleship, "2"; carrier, "1."

DIRECTIONS FOR PLAYING THE BOMBSIGHT GAME

1 The target board is placed on the floor or on a low table, and the "admiral" arranges his fleet in the area marked A.

2 The "bombardier" loads his bomb rack, sights through the tail of the plane, and approaches the ships, holding the bomber on a level with his eyes. Both hands should grasp the wing, while one thumb should be ready to push the bomb release forward. When he sees a ship focused in the reflector, the player maneuvers his plane until the indicator is directly in the center of his bombsight. He then releases a bomb by sliding the trigger forward and, if his aim is true and his hand has been steady, the ship should be toppled on its side and "considered sunk."

3 When all five bombs have been dropped, the score for area A is tabulated. The number on the ship indicates its scoring value, to which four points are added for each ship sunk.

4 The "admiral" shifts his remaining warships into area B, and again the "bombardier" attacks. For the score in this area, three points are added to the value of each ship sunk, and the total is added to the previous score.

5 The action is repeated in areas C and D if any ships are left, with two points being added to ships turned over in C and only one point for ships sunk in D. The "bombardier" then takes command of the ships, the "admiral" flies the bomber, and when action is completed, contestants compare scores.

6 If no ships are left afloat after the bombing of area A, the "bombardier" receives the highest possible score, or a total of 32 points.

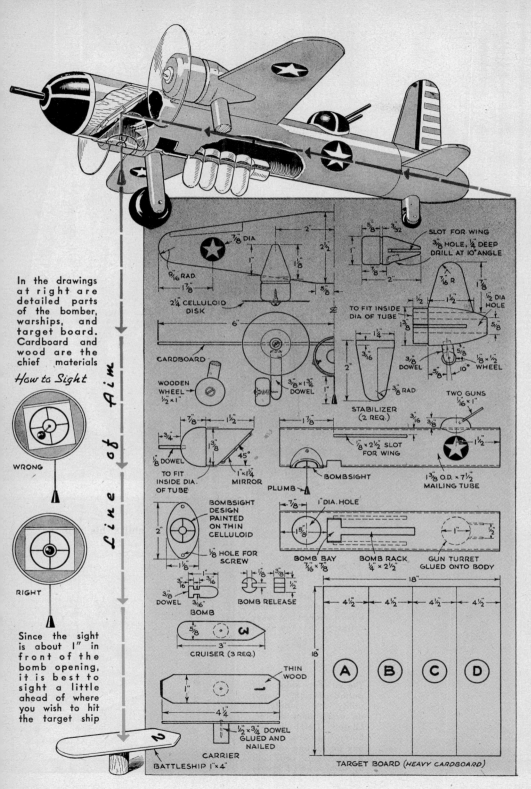

In the drawings at right are detailed parts of the bomber, warships, and target board. Cardboard and wood are the chief materials

How to Sight

WRONG

RIGHT

Since the sight is about 1" in front of the bomb opening, it is best to sight a little ahead of where you wish to hit the target ship

Line of Aim

7/8 DIA

2

2 1/2

1

1 1/8

5/8

9/16 RAD.

1 7/8

2 1/4 CELLULOID DISK

5/8 3/32

1"

7/8

2"

SLOT FOR WING
3/8 HOLE, 1/4 DEEP
DRILL AT 10° ANGLE

7/16 R

1 7/8

1 1/2

1/2 DIA HOLE

5/8

6"

CARDBOARD

WOODEN WHEEL
1/2 × 1"

3/8 × 1 3/4 DOWEL

1"

TO FIT INSIDE DIA. OF TUBE

1 1/4

3/16

2"

3/8 RAD.

STABILIZER (2 REQ.)

1/2

1 1/2

1 3/8

5/8

3/8 DOWEL

5/8

5/8

10°

1/8 × 1/2 WHEEL

TWO GUNS
1/16 × 1"

3/4

7/8

1 1/2

1 3/8

1/8 DOWEL

45°

TO FIT INSIDE DIA. OF TUBE

1" × 1 1/4 MIRROR

PLUMB

1 3/8

BOMBSIGHT

3/16 3/8

1/8 × 2 1/2 SLOT FOR WING

1 1/2

1 3/8 O.D. × 7 1/2 MAILING TUBE

BOMBSIGHT DESIGN PAINTED ON THIN CELLULOID

2"

1/8 HOLE FOR SCREW

1 1/8

7/8

1 3/8

1" DIA. HOLE

BOMB BAY
7/16 × 7/8

BOMB RACK
1/4 × 2 1/2

1"

1/2

GUN TURRET GLUED ONTO BODY

3/16

3/8

1/8

1"

3/8

3/8 DOWEL

3/16

BOMB

1/2

BOMB RELEASE

5/8

3

3"

CRUISER (3 REQ.)

1"

THIN WOOD

1

4 1/4

1/2 × 3/4 DOWEL GLUED AND NAILED

CARRIER

2

BATTLESHIP 1" × 4"

18"

4 1/2   4 1/2   4 1/2   4 1/2

18"

A B C D

TARGET BOARD (HEAVY CARDBOARD)

A busy housewife will find that the cabinet shown open above will often save her a tedious search for needed items when a sewing emergency arises in the household

The cabinet, which is of period design, blends utility and beauty to an exceptional degree. Closed (left) it will harmonize with almost any decorating scheme. Right, doors are built up with doweled frames

Period Cabinet

HOLDS ALL HOUSEHOLD SEWING MATERIALS
AS WELL AS DRESS PATTERNS AND KNITTING SKEINS

By FRANK HEGEMEYER

A PIECE to gladden the heart of any homemaker, the Colonial cabinet shown at the left keeps in one neat, compact unit all the sewing materials and accessories found in the average household. It will harmonize with almost any type of room decoration. Standing 34¼" high, it is 20¾" wide and about 10" deep. The insides of the doors are fitted with racks to hold 40 spools of thread, while two scroll-sawed panels form racks for dress patterns and fashion magazines. Space is also provided for shears, thimbles, needle booklets, and so forth.

Perhaps the most interesting feature of the cabinet is the quadrant-shaped drawers, which swing out for ready accessibility. These have glass fronts for the user's convenience in identifying their contents quickly, and may be easily removed in case it is necessary to empty them completely or to replace the glass. The center bin also swings

out and can be used for storing articles to be mended, while the handsome cabinet-width drawers provide ample accommodation for a great many other items.

Maple is an excellent wood to use in building this piece, but any other fine cabinet wood will serve equally well. Birch is a good choice if the cost must be kept down. The best figured stock should be used for the doors, top, sides, and base, in that order of preference. The remaining stock can be used for the drawer and bin fronts. Both door fronts are single panels, with 2" wide hinge pieces doweled to them at right angles. They are equipped with ball-type friction catches at the top.

Dado the two sides of the cabinet for the rails, which are glued and doweled in. Cut a ¼" by ⅜" rabbet in each sidepiece for the back. Both the top and the baseboard are joined to the sides with ⅜" dowels. The base has mitered joints with maple splines and is fastened to the baseboard with screws. The lower three-compartment bin is fastened

The hole for the pivot pin has been bored in the upper rail. Because of its length the pin must be permanently inserted before the top is doweled on

Stop block in vise aids in cutting glass fronts for the button boxes. The curved parts (below) can be made from thin veneer or a discarded radio cabinet

in place, but the upper yarn bin is free to slide out. A short piece of ¼" dowel is fitted loosely in the sides to act as a stop for this bin. The bin fronts are grooved for the partitions.

Underneath the lower drawer is an apron. This is glued to the baseboard and serves as a door stop. The doors are hinged with three pairs of loose-pin butts. To relieve their otherwise plain corners, run beads along the fronts and sides ¾" from the edge. Both door handles are made as one piece and cut apart later. Attach them with screws.

The parts for the eight button boxes can be cut eight at a time with the exception of the bottoms. The only difference is in the grooves for the glass, which are reversed in four of the bottoms. Corner posts are cut from a quarter-round strip which has been grooved on the two flat sides. The boxes are opened by pressing sideways on the pivot edges with the thumb.

Each button box has under it a shim or spacer ⅛" thick. This is placed on the dowel pivot with the flat edge against the side of the cabinet. A hole is drilled through the upper rail for the pivot pin. Because of its length

Below, a useful jig for cutting miters and spline grooves in the base parts. This jig is held against the head of the miter gauge

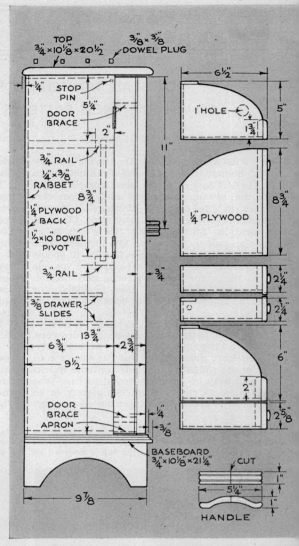

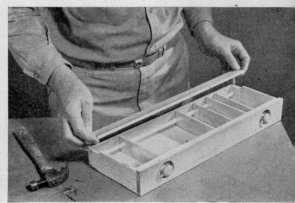

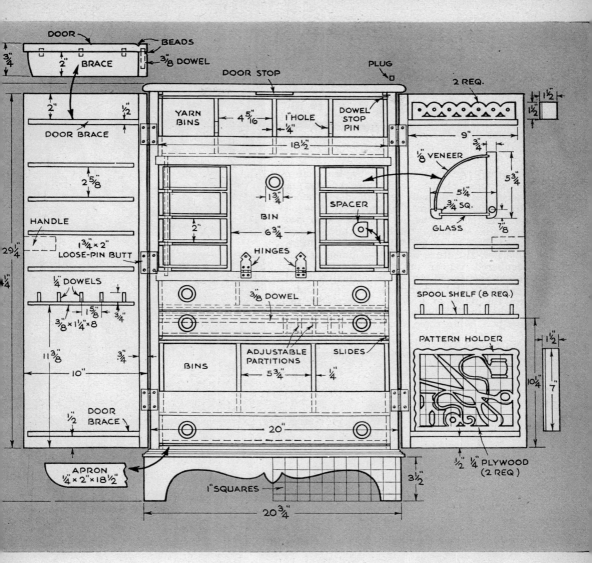

the pin must be inserted and brought to rest in the blind hole in the lower rail before the top of the cabinet is doweled on. The vertical strip shown inside the back in one photograph on page HW 69 acts as a stop to align the button boxes when they are closed.

The lips of the extra deep drawer fronts will conceal the two drawer slides between. It is advisable to build the drawers slightly undersize so that they will move freely. All drawer and bin fronts have ¼" by ⅜"

The photo at the left shows adjustable partitions in one of the drawers. These form compartments of various widths and are kept in contact with the bottom of the drawer by a narrow strip at the back

rabbets on the ends and bottom; all floors and backs are made of ¼" plywood.

The recessed drawer pulls are made by boring a 1¾" hole ⅜" deep with an expansive bit and fastening the knob inside it with screws. Be sure the knobs on the lower drawer clear the door brace and that all the spool shelves are doweled to the doors.

If the cabinet is made of maple or birch, it is advisable to procure a maple stain of the penetrating type. This stain will give the attractive mellowed finish which is characteristic of this type of furniture. If it is desired to highlight the wood for an aged effect, let the stain set about ten minutes and rub it off lightly with a soft cloth.

IDEAS for HOME OWNERS

FURNITURE PACKED IN CARTONS. Tables, chairs, beds, even cradles, come packed flat in pieces that are easily assembled into modern, livable furniture. The parts are grooved so that they can be put together with two or three screws. Cupboards and chests come already assembled. Extremely light, this new furniture is made of limed oak or lacquered veneer on plywood. The only metal parts used are screws. Flexible wood replaces metal bedsprings. At right above are the parts of a chair. Directly at the right a small table is being assembled. Below is a living room straight from cartons.

CORRUGATED ASPHALT SIDING, rigid, lightweight, and waterproof, has been designed for wartime application on industrial, commercial and farm buildings as a substitute for corrugated steel sheets. The new product, shown at left, consists of two sheets of heavy felt saturated with a resino-bituminous compound, bound together with asphalt adhesive and corrugated under high pressure. The finished sheets retain their stiffness in summer weather because of the high melting point of the resins used.

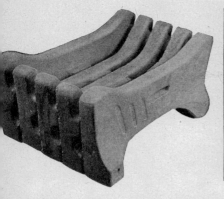

NEW FIREPLACE GRATES. The sectional ceramic grate shown directly above will stand any reasonable thermal shock, since each grate is fired for fourteen days up to 2,280 deg. When the grate has cooled, it is easy to separate the sections and clean them with a soft brush. Good combustion is produced with a minimum of smoke, since air is preheated, before entering the fuel bed, by passing first over the hot section. The latticed moss-colored grate at the right above is made of ground bottle glass, pressed until it has acquired the strength of cast iron. This grate has been tested to withstand 2,750 deg. without cracking and is said to burn coal, charcoal, and coke with equal efficiency. Both grates must be handled with care when they are out of the fireplace.

THE FIRE EXTINGUISHER shown at the left also serves as a decontaminator for three major war gases. The ever ready, free-flowing chemical contained in the extinguisher will not harm fabrics or machinery, and it is adapted for use in the home, office, or factory. The tubelike container is held in a horizontal position, and the fire is dusted with a sweeping left to right motion from edge to center.

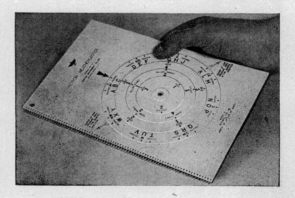

A DIAL-TYPE FORECASTER that, with the aid of a barometer, will make reasonably accurate weather predictions from 12 to 24 hours in advance, is shown above. Four concentric dials are set according to wind direction, barometer reading, barometer change, and present weather conditions. As the dials are set, numerals align themselves underneath the large arrow at the top of the forecaster. These numerals, along with their corresponding letters, are translated into probable weather conditions by referring to tables in the back of the booklet.

GLASS MAIL BOXES may replace tin and other metal types. The supports and the strip at the top for holding newspapers are the only metal parts. The heavy glass is strong and durable; it will withstand all kinds of weather and will harmonize with any background.

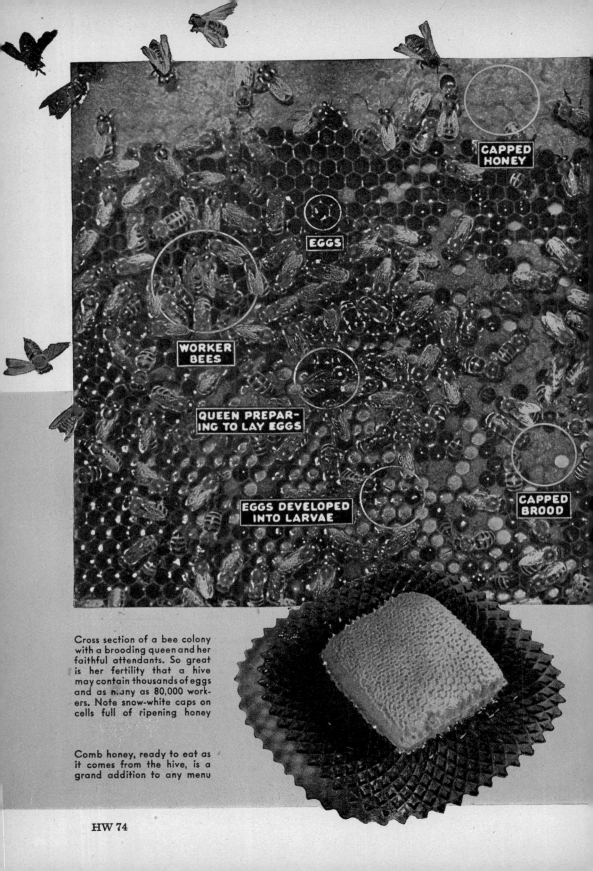

CAPPED HONEY

EGGS

WORKER BEES

QUEEN PREPAR-ING TO LAY EGGS

EGGS DEVELOPED INTO LARVAE

CAPPED BROOD

Cross section of a bee colony with a brooding queen and her faithful attendants. So great is her fertility that a hive may contain thousands of eggs and as many as 80,000 workers. Note snow-white caps on cells full of ripening honey

Comb honey, ready to eat as it comes from the hive, is a grand addition to any menu

ANYONE looking for an interesting and productive outdoor hobby might well consider beekeeping. Honey is a natural, wholesome sweet that may profitably be substituted for war-rationed sugar in many instances—as a spread for bread, in candy making, in baking and cooking, and for use in beverages. You'll have no trouble giving away or even selling any surplus. The investment required is small—it is possible to start with one or two hives, set up in a corner of the back yard or the roof top.

But that is only half the story. Few hobbies are so inherently fascinating. You will find it a real thrill to open a hive and see the busy, purposeful life of the bees going on before your eyes.

Many people are timid about working with bees, but by observing a few common-sense precautions even the novice should have no trouble.

The first step is to assemble the hive. It is possible to build your own, but the beginner will find it easier to buy a hive. Full directions for assembling the accurately made parts usually come with the hive.

It is wise to give it two or three coats of outside-white paint. The frames too must be fitted together and the wax foundations then inserted.

Now you are ready to supply your little factory with workers. You can do so by catching a swarm of bees, but unless you have had previous experience in beekeeping, this is rather unwise. It is best to order package bees. Caucasian bees are bred for gentleness, as are Italian bees. A common size is a 2-lb. package. You ought to have the bees delivered at the beginning of the fruit-blooming season so that they can get the full benefit of the blossoms.

Bees are shipped in a screen cage with the queen confined in a smaller cage suspended in the center. They are supplied with a can of sugar sirup on which they feed. Upon arrival, the caged bees should be taken to a cool place, where, at intervals during the day, they should be sprinkled with sugar sirup and allowed to gorge themselves. Sugar sirup can be made by mixing equal parts of sugar and warm water. Sugar for feeding bees may be

Beekeeping-

How to Start a Hive for Honey Production in Your Own Back Yard

The beekeeper at the right is removing a bee-laden frame for examination. Smoke from the device at the lower right is blown into the hive to confuse the bees temporarily, so that they may be safely handled. It is always a thrill to open a hive and study its teeming activities

Hives come ready to assemble. When put together according to instructions, the parts will be found to fit accurately. The frames must also be assembled, and supplied with wax foundations. Lower photo shows hive ready for bees, with five frames added

Sugar sirup is sprinkled over the cage of package bees before it is put in the hive. A bottle with a clothes sprinkler is being used here. In the lower photograph the beekeeper is placing the bees in their future home, where they will begin their work

obtained by applying to your rationing board.

Toward evening the package should be taken to the hive, which should be permanently installed in a sunny spot facing south or southeast. Remove half the frames from the hive and insert the cage in this space. Pry off the wooden cover of the cage and remove the feeding can. The queen cage is taken out next, the small cardboard strip at one end removed, and a match pushed through the candy at the end of the cage. The bees will eat their way through this opening, releasing the queen in a day or two. The queen's cage is laid in the position shown in the photo. If the bees have had plenty of sirup, they will remain docile while all this is done.

Perforate the lid of a gallon pail of sugar

sirup and invert this over the frames. Next, place an empty hive body over the frames and cover the top. Turn the entrance cleat to its smallest opening and leave the bees completely alone for a week.

By then the bees should have drawn out some of the wax foundation into the cells, and the queen should have begun to lay. If she has, your colony is successfully established. Those combs removed at the installation of the bee package are now replaced, and the bees left to their own devices for another week, at which time the sirup in the pail should be replenished. The colony should build up and draw out the wax foundation by the time nectar-bearing plants bloom.

The next step in producing honey is to

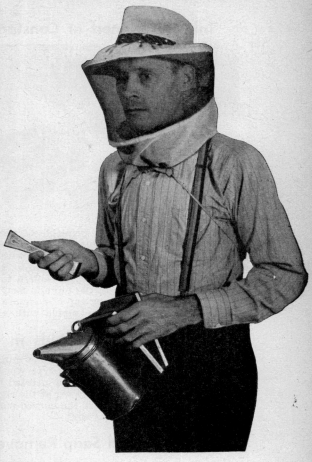

The beekeeper has placed an inverted pail of sirup on the frames, and above is covering the hive. Note how bees are swarming out to devour the sirup and free the queen, imprisoned in the small box on top. Below, section comb honey, choice of most beginners

When handling bees, beginners should wear a veil of fine netting slipped over a wide-brimmed hat and be armed with a smoker and hive tool. This beekeeper has taken all necessary precautions, but timid souls can wear gloves for added protection

add a previously prepared super (the removable upper story of a beehive) in which the bees can store their surplus. Several supers should be prepared, so that when space in one is almost filled, another may be added.

Beginners will find it easiest to produce section comb honey, as it requires no special handling, being served in the comb as it comes from the hive. For extracted honey to be put up in bottles or jars, larger combs are used. A machine is needed to extract the honey by centrifugal force, after which the empty combs are put back in the hive. They are used year after year.

The beekeeper should wear a bee veil of fine net slipped over a wide-brimmed hat as a protection to the face. A bee smoker is also necessary to keep bees under control.

The common practice in the colder sections of the United States is to destroy all of the bees in the fall and buy new ones in the spring. When this practice is adopted, the bees get a new young queen each year. There is also a saving in honey, for if the bees are kept through the winter, a considerable amount is consumed.

Some beekeepers prefer to keep their swarms through the cold weather, and if the bees have plenty of stores and a good windbreak they will as a rule come through in good condition. Information on wintering and other matters of interest to the beginner will be found in the many excellent textbooks and Government bulletins on the subject.—BENJAMIN NIELSEN.

Ink Maintained at Constant Level in Draftsman's Bottle

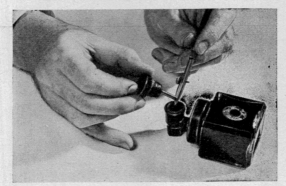

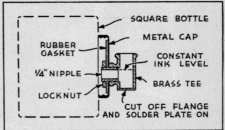

SQUARE BOTTLE
METAL CAP
RUBBER GASKET
CONSTANT INK LEVEL
1/4" NIPPLE
BRASS TEE
LOCKNUT
CUT OFF FLANGE AND SOLDER PLATE ON

The drawing above shows the bottle in cross section. At the left is the completed inkwell. It will hold an extra large quantity of ink

UTILIZING the familiar principle of the inverted water jar, this cleverly constructed inkwell will provide the tracer with an abundant supply of ink, maintained at a constant level. Bore a hole large enough to take a 1/4" brass nipple in the top and near one edge of the metal screw cap of a square ink bottle. Secure the pipe nipple with a locknut, using a rubber gasket on the inside to prevent leakage. Fit a standard-size brass tee to the nipple and cut off the flange on the bottom of the tee. Solder on a plate to close this. Cap the receptacle thus formed with a quill-cork from an ordinary India-ink bottle, and turn the dispenser on its side for use.—R. L. WHITMAN.

Spring Clothespin Aids in Gluing Ship-Model Bulwarks

BULWARKS at the stem of a ship model can be clamped together with an ordinary spring-type wooden clothespin while glue is setting. Pins are inserted through the jaws, as illustrated in the drawing at the right, in order to hold the bulwarks against the curved surface of the bow.—WILLIAM S. LEIBBRANDT.

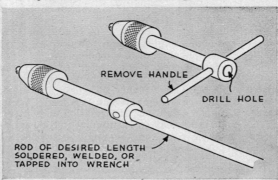

PINS

BULWARKS

Homemade Hand Soap Removes Grime

GREASY, grimy hands are no novelty these days. The problem of keeping them clean can be easily and inexpensively solved by making a soap solvent at home. Simply dissolve 1 lb. of soap chips in 1 gal. of boiling water. Remove this mixture from the fire, add 1/2 lb. of soda ash, 1 lb. of pumice stone powder, and 1/4 oz. of oil of citronella. This solvent is harmless to the hands, and does an efficient job.—P. A. B.

Tap Wrench and Length of Rod Form Handy Drill Extension

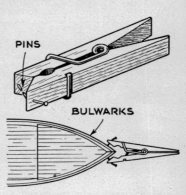

REMOVE HANDLE

DRILL HOLE

ROD OF DESIRED LENGTH SOLDERED, WELDED, OR TAPPED INTO WRENCH

A DIME-STORE tap wrench and a length of welding rod, drill rod, or similar stock 3/16" or 1/4" in diameter will make a convenient extension for use in an electric or hand drill. Remove the handle and drill a hole of suitable size down the center from the top. Insert the rod and weld or solder the joint. If you wish to use interchangeable lengths of rod, tap the hole and thread the rods for screwing into the wrench. Should the chuck prove too loose for holding small drills, file the slots slightly wider.—NORMAN F. WILLARD.

Old Drill Bits Are Easily Converted into Useful Woodworking Gouges

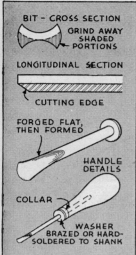

BIT - CROSS SECTION

GRIND AWAY SHADED PORTIONS

LONGITUDINAL SECTION

CUTTING EDGE

FORGED FLAT, THEN FORMED

HANDLE DETAILS

COLLAR

WASHER BRAZED OR HARD-SOLDERED TO SHANK

OLD straight-fluted drill bits can be converted into serviceable gouges. A simple method is to square the end of the bit, grind the sharp ridges to a C-shaped cross section, and sharpen the end to a cutting edge. Still another method is to heat the bits red, cooling them slowly, then reheating and forging the end to form a carving tool of the desired shape. Harden the gouge by heating it red and plunging it quickly into water. Polish the metal with an abrasive cloth; then temper by heating the end to a straw color, and again quenching.—W. E. B.

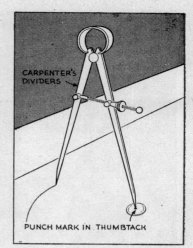

CARPENTER'S DIVIDERS

PUNCH MARK IN THUMBTACK

Tack Forms Pivot Point for Scribing Materials

IN MARKING soft, flexible materials with large dividers, it is very necessary to maintain a steady pivot point. To avoid wobbling or inaccuracy, make a small prick mark in the head of a thumbtack and shorten the point with nippers or a file so that it can be used on thin substances, such as asbestos or rubber sheeting. The dividers will then have a true center, and the circles scribed will meet at their starting points.—H. D. CHAPMAN.

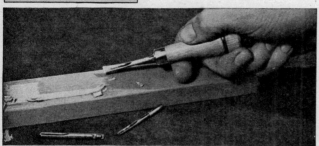

The gouge in use above was made from a drill of the type shown

---

CONVERSION FACTORS [CALCULATIONS]

The following table lists conversion factors useful in electrical calculations:

To Change	To	Multiply by
Circular Mils	Square Mils	.7854
" "	" Centimeters	.000005067
" "	" Inches	.0000007854
Centimeters	Inches	.3937
Square Centimeters	Square Inches	.155
Cubic "	Cubic "	.061023
Kilowatt-Hours	British Thermal Units	3415.
Kilowatts	Horsepower	1.341
Deg. Centigrade	Deg. Fahrenheit	(1.8 x Deg. C) +32

To Change	To	Multiply by
Square Mils	Circular Mils	1.27324
" Centimeters	" "	197352.
" Inches	" "	1273240.
Inches	Centimeters	2.54
Square Inches	Square Centimeters	6.452
Cubic "	Cubic "	16.387
British Thermal Units	Kilowatt-Hours	.0002928
Horsepower	Kilowatts	.7457
Deg. Fahrenheit	Deg. Centigrade	(Deg. F−32)÷1.8

POPULAR SCIENCE MONTHLY SHOP DATA

When a latch, like that at the left, sticks flush with the lock face, the spring is faulty and must be replaced. Remove knobs, spindle, and screws to pry the lock out of the door with a screw driver

Repairing

... AND HOW TO FILE KEYS THAT WILL FIT THEM

● ● ●

CYLINDER or pin-tumbler locks are now most commonly used as the safest for outside doors, but for every two of these in the average home, a half dozen or more of the older-type mortise locks will be found. These are the locks on the inside room doors, serving as latches even where the greater privacy of a lock is not required. It is these mortise locks, too, that are most often in need of repair, if for no other reason than that they are in almost constant use. Frequently the necessary servicing is a matter of simple adjustment or replacement of a part.

Take, for example, a door that will not stay latched when closed. This can be a nuisance, and the cause is usually a broken latch spring. The lock in the photograph at left is a case of this kind. The latch is back flush with the lock face, and there is no spring tension to force it out.

The first step is to remove the screw from

Take off the cover, and remove the broken spring, shown in the top left-hand corner of the lock at right

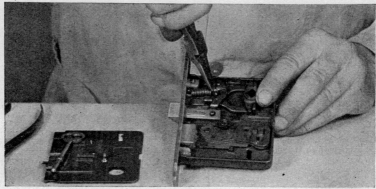

Insert a new spring, fitting it in with small-nosed pliers. Clean the lock; then oil and reassemble it

Ordinary Inside Door Locks

one knob, and either unscrew or pull off the knob. The other knob can then be pulled out from the other side with the spindle attached. Then remove the two wood screws holding the lock in the edge of the door, and pry the lock out with a screw driver.

Removing the lock cover reveals that a broken coil spring, shown in the photo at the top of this page, is causing the trouble. A new one from a hardware store or locksmith's shop is then installed with a pair of small-nosed pliers. Dirt in the lock is cleaned out, and a few drops of oil are applied to each working part.

This is a three-lever lock. The narrow flat springs attached to each lever should be inspected at this time, and broken ones replaced with some of the same spring stock. Drive out the broken piece from the side of the lever by using a thin piece of steel and a hammer. After breaking off a piece of stock to the approximate length, lay one end in the narrow slot in the lever and drive it in place. If it fits too loosely, a slight bend at the extreme end will cause it to bind when driven in. The new spring is then curved to the right shape, and the

lever replaced on its spindle with the spring end pulled down to rest against its stop.

After replacing the cover, put the lock back in the door mortise, reversing the steps taken in removing it. Do not make the knob adjustment too tight, as this will cause binding. With square, straight spindles, washers should be used if necessary to get this adjustment just right.

Lock construction varies widely with different makes and ages. Some manufacturers use coil springs, others flat ones, and some a combination of both. To repair a lock that has a broken flat spring, use the same gauge stock, breaking it off to the length of the two pieces of the old spring. One end is then bent so it will lock between the two projections cast on the inside of the case. The free end should have a good upward tension and bear against the part shown in the illustrations on page HW82. Try it in place with a pair of small-nosed pliers. It may be necessary to alter the shape to get the tension just right.

In making a key for a mortise lock, select a blank that will not require much filing to fit in the keyhole. Its barrel should

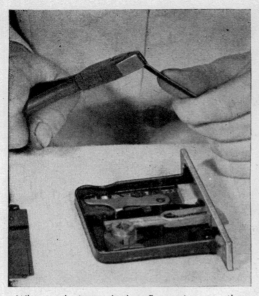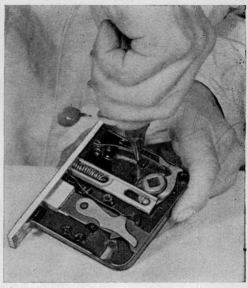

When replacing a broken flat spring, use the same gauge stock and measure it to the length of the broken pieces. Bend one end to lock it between the cast projections inside the case

There should be good upward tension at the free end for the spring to bear against the pivoted part shown above. Try the spring in place, and reshape, if necessary, to get the tension right

be a reasonably good fit for the round hole. The drawings on the facing page show a typical one-lever lock, a key filed for it, and also a key filed for a three-lever lock. After filing to allow the blank to enter the keyhole, hold it down with the shoulder against the case to determine the filing necessary for the width of the bit to fit inside the lock. In turning, the key will probably come against stops cast on the inside of the cover. Rocking it back and forth will make bright marks on the bit, indicating where to file a ward to clear. A ward should also be filed at a corresponding point at the other end of the bit to allow the key to be used from both sides of the lock.

The key will now turn further in the lock until it strikes the lever. Marks can be obtained the same way on the bottom edge of the bit to indicate the position of the lever and where the lever ward must be filed. A beginner may like to check on this point with the cover off, but it is better practice to make the key from marks.

It may be necessary to round the end of the bit slightly to allow it to pass smoothly in the V-cut in the bolt. When the work is correct, the lever will be lifted so that the square stud attached to the bolt will pass through a narrow slot in the center of the lever and permit the bolt to be thrown out with the key. The lever ward should be filed by careful stages to keep it from getting too deep. Make frequent trials in the

lock, and observe bright marks that will indicate where further filing is necessary. All sharp edges should be rounded off slightly.

Making keys for three-lever locks is similar, except that three levers must be lifted varying distances until their center slots are in line, as shown in the bottom drawing, so the bolt can pass out. Levers are indicated by dotted lines in the drawing to illustrate how the wards are used on the levers when the key is inserted from opposite sides of the lock. The lock for this key has a projection on one side of the keyhole instead of stops on the inside of the cover, and a groove is filed across one side of the bit to clear this.

Sometimes it is not the fault of the lock when a door refuses to latch. A latch plate or strike with a worn band may show that the latch hits it too low to enter its opening. Tightening the screws of the top hinge may raise the door enough to remedy this condition. Otherwise, the strike will have to be lowered or a longer opening filed. If the cause is a warped door, move the strike out until the latch catches. Sometimes a door will shrink in width so much that the latch will not touch the strike at all, in which case a strip may be nailed along one edge of the door to increase its width. As a rule, this involves some refitting of the lock or hinges, and it may be easier to build out the strike with some thin wood placed back of it.—HAROLD P. STRAND.

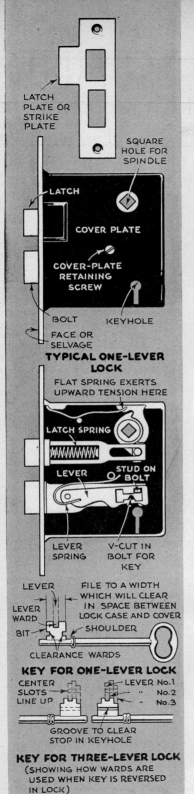

LATCH
PLATE OR
STRIKE
PLATE

SQUARE
HOLE FOR
SPINDLE

LATCH

COVER PLATE

COVER-PLATE
RETAINING
SCREW

KEYHOLE

BOLT

FACE OR
SELVAGE

**TYPICAL ONE-LEVER
LOCK**

FLAT SPRING EXERTS
UPWARD TENSION HERE

LATCH SPRING

LEVER

STUD ON
BOLT

LEVER
SPRING

V-CUT IN
BOLT FOR
KEY

LEVER

FILE TO A WIDTH
WHICH WILL CLEAR
IN SPACE BETWEEN
LOCK CASE AND COVER

LEVER
WARD

SHOULDER

BIT

CLEARANCE WARDS

KEY FOR ONE-LEVER LOCK

CENTER
SLOTS
LINE UP

LEVER No.1
" No.2
" No.3

GROOVE TO CLEAR
STOP IN KEYHOLE

KEY FOR THREE-LEVER LOCK
(SHOWING HOW WARDS ARE
USED WHEN KEY IS REVERSED
IN LOCK)

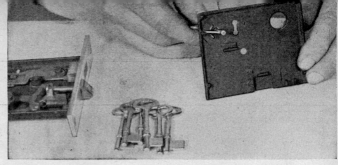

Stops are usually cast on the inside of a lock cover (shown removed above) and wards are filed in the key to clear them

Wards must also be filed in the bottom edge of the key bit to lift levers just enough to clear the stud and throw the bolt

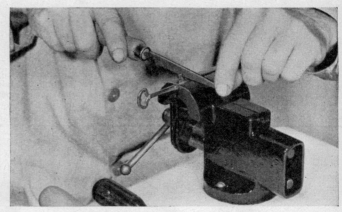

Filing of the lever wards should be done a little at a time, and the key tried often, to avoid getting them too deep

At right, the worn band shows that the latch is missing the plate hole. Tightening on the upper hinge may raise the door enough for it to catch

MACHINE

STURDY WOODEN STAND

By C. W. WOODSON

This stand for a circular saw is equally suitable for other power machines

DURING the last few years many home workshops have been equipped with machine tools by owners who appreciate their labor-saving qualities and wish to turn out a wide range of work on a production basis. But as more machines have been introduced, the mounting of the equipment has presented an increasingly difficult problem. Although suitable steel stands for such power tools have been available as optional equipment, the mechanic who takes as much pleasure in building his own shop accessories as he does in using them has often preferred to make his own stands of wood. These men will be interested in the homemade bench illustrated.

This bench is used as a mount for a small circular saw, but it would serve as well, if the dimensions were altered slightly, for a variety

BENCH FOR YOUR SHOP

PROVIDES HEAVY-DUTY SUPPORT FOR POWER TOOL

of other machines. It is heavily and staunchly built and will easily support any equipment found in the average home shop. With the addition of shelves its roomy interior can be used for the storage of attachments or other tools, and will be especially convenient for those accessories that the operator must use frequently.

The bench is simply constructed, with no attempt at fine cabinetwork. Top and bottom rails are cut to length and the tenons formed exactly alike by working to gauges set up on the saw table. The legs are mortised with a brace and bit, and the holes squared up with a sharp chisel to receive the tenons of the side and end rails. The outside corners are rounded as indicated.

All top and bottom rails, with tenons cut, are shown along with the heavy bench legs in Fig. 1 at the bottom of the facing page. Figure 2 shows these parts assembled and gives an idea of their strength, while in Fig. 3 the back and ends as well as the two doors, with their modern handles, have been added. In Fig. 4 the bench top has been put on. This top is built up by making a framework of two-by-fours, covered with 7/8"

pine boards. Wide 2" stock, as indicated in the drawing just below, will look as well as the built-up top and perhaps be even more substantial, although the built-up method of construction will be found adequate.

The finished bench may be stained and varnished or enameled in a color matching other shop equipment.

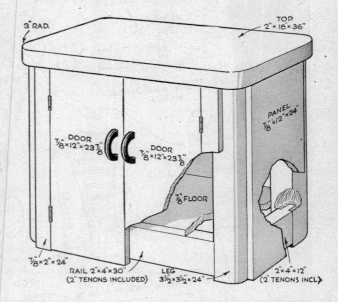

A Dutch treat for your garden or lawn can be made in the form of a model windmill spinning in the breeze. Follow the simple construction details on the drawing

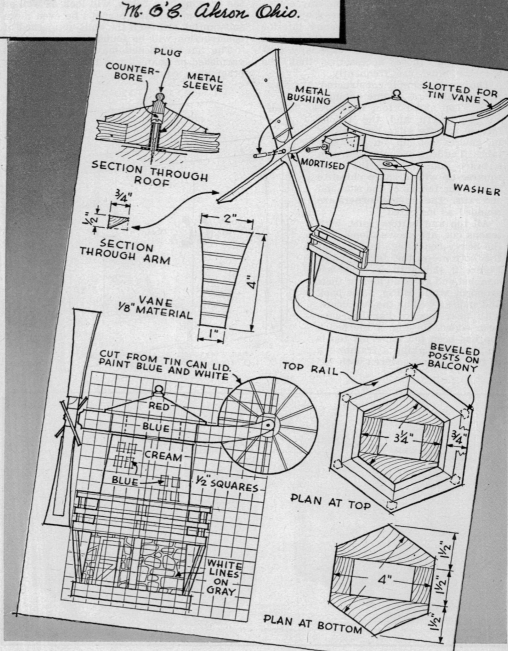

SECTION THROUGH ROOF

COUNTER-BORE · PLUG · METAL SLEEVE

METAL BUSHING

SLOTTED FOR TIN VANE

MORTISED

WASHER

3/4"
1/2"

SECTION THROUGH ARM

2"
4"
1"

VANE
1/8" MATERIAL

CUT FROM TIN CAN LID. PAINT BLUE AND WHITE

RED
BLUE
CREAM
BLUE

1/2" SQUARES

WHITE LINES ON GRAY

TOP RAIL

BEVELED POSTS ON BALCONY

3 1/4"
3/4"

PLAN AT TOP

1 1/2"
1 1/2"
4"
1/2"

PLAN AT BOTTOM

NEW SHOP IDEAS

SHARPENING WIRE SCRATCH WHEELS can be done with a simple jig. After prolonged use, such wheels get dull and fail to cut properly, and while reversing the wheel on its arbor will help somewhat, the best remedy is to sharpen and true up the wires. Do this by making a simple jig, as shown, which holds the wheel against the grinder so it can be turned while held on a true axis. Turn the wire wheel slowly by hand with a light pressure against the grinding wheel, preferably contrary to any curve of the bristles.—H. P. S.

Easily Built Telescoping Support Has Numerous Uses

WITH a 48″ length of 1¼″ pipe, a 54″ length of 1″ pipe, and an old automobile jack, preferably of the screw type, you can construct an adjustable support that will give valuable service around the shop and home. It will support a pipe vise for threading pipe, hold long lumber being cut on a circular saw, keep sheet metal or wallboard against the ceiling while one is nailing it on, serve as an auxiliary clothesline pole, and so forth.

Drill a ½″ hole 4″ from the end of the 1¼″ pipe. Drill ½″ holes 4″ apart in the 1″ pipe, starting 10″ from one end. The smaller pipe, inside the larger one, protrudes 6″ to afford a grip for adjusting the setup. A ½″ bolt will serve to hold the pipes at approximately the setting desired, and the jack screw will take up the slack.

Weld the 1¼″ pipe solidly to the top of the jack. Bend the handle near the jack at a right angle and cut the other end off to suit. This adjustable support, with a piece of angle iron bolted to the smaller pipe at the desired hole, will serve also as a carpenter's clamp, as shown in the photo directly below.—URIAH HILLEGAS.

At left, how the support, set up in a doorway or in a cellar between floor and joist, will hold a pipe vise

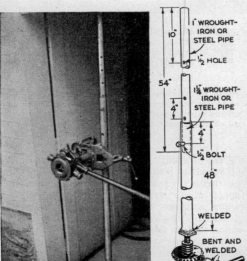

1″ WROUGHT-IRON OR STEEL PIPE
10″
½″ HOLE
54″
1¼″ WROUGHT-IRON OR STEEL PIPE
4″
4″
½″ BOLT
48″
WELDED
BENT AND WELDED
CUT TO SUIT

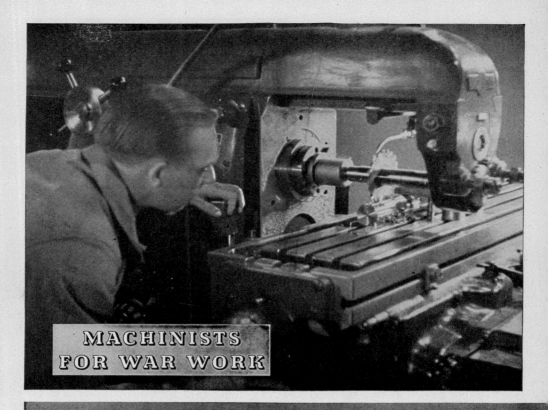

MACHINISTS FOR WAR WORK

Using the Modern

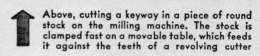

Above, cutting a keyway in a piece of round stock on the milling machine. The stock is clamped fast on a movable table, which feeds it against the teeth of a revolving cutter

As in all machine work, the operator's first duty is to thoroughly brush all dirt and abrasive grit off the working parts, and to lubricate all of these parts and their controls

THE milling machine is an extremely versatile power-driven machine tool, and performs a great variety of operations with speed and accuracy. It is particularly useful when a large number of interchangeable parts must be cut to exactly similar dimensions, and its adaptability is such that it can handle large castings and forgings as easily as small pieces of intricate design.

The two basic elements of the milling machine are (1) a movable table and (2) a revolving cutter. The table carries the work to a multitoothed rotating cutter, instead of revolving it, as does a lathe, or reciprocating it, as in the case of a planer. The cutter remains in a fixed position, but its speed is adjustable. Cutters of various shapes and sizes are used to suit the job to be done. In the milling machine shown on the facing page, a slotting cutter is being employed. Speeds of cutters may range from 20 to 500 revolutions per minute.

After carefully brushing the bed of the machine and lubricating its working parts, the operator secures the rough stock to the table, which can be brought up or down, sideways or across, as may be necessary to manipulate the work under the cutter. These movements can be made under power by means of rapid-traverse controls on the front of the machine, or by duplicate hand controls at the sides. For precision adjustments, however, the work is fed by manual controls equipped with calibrated dials on which each division represents .001″ of table movement.

With the work in place, the operator is ready to adjust the revolving cutter. First, he fits an arbor shaft into the power-driven spindle. Spacing collars are used to locate the cutter at any position on the arbor, while additional collars and a key hold the cutter in place when the arbor nut is tightened and lock it on the arbor to provide a positive drive. A large collar is then set on the end of the arbor to act as a bearing for the overarm bracket, which is slid out and locked in place to support the shaft.

The selection and mounting of the cutter depend on the construction of the machine and the type of work to be done. Before it is placed on the arbor, it is necessary to ascertain the relation of the headstock to the table, whether right or left, and to determine the direction of cutting movement and rotation of cutter teeth. In general, the cutter to be used should be as small as the job permits, since a shorter cut will allow for greater feed speeds and requires less power.

When the motor is started up, the cutter is set in motion by engaging a quick-acting clutch. The work is then carried up to the cutter and is secured against vibration through various levers which lock the knee, saddle, and cross feed. A selective feed indicator, graduated in inches per minute, is set to govern the speed at which the work is fed.

Successful milling depends upon the flexibility of movement of the table, the accuracy with which the work is adjusted in relation to the cutter, and the use of the correct tools at the proper speeds. Excessive speeds should be avoided, as they dull the cutter and produce a coarse surface. [CONTINUED]

Milling Machine

1 In setting up the milling machine, the work and fixtures must be held securely. The table can be moved up or down in a vertical plane, back and forth horizontally, or in a cross-feed manner

2 The arbor shaft is fitted into a tapered hole in the power-driven spindle, and is secured by a draw-in bolt that passes through the hole in the spindle from the rear. Drive lightly with a mallet

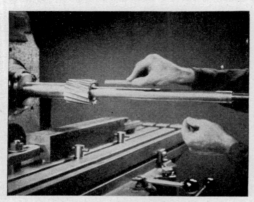

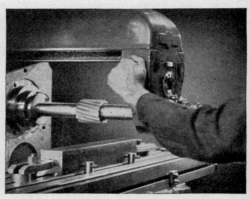

3 The cutter to be used is placed in position on the arbor and is keyed to the shaft. Collars to hold it in place are then added, and a binding nut is tightened. A larger collar fits on the arbor end

4 The overarm is slid out to support the arbor. It is adjustable along its axis and is moved to any desired position and locked by clamps. An outer bearing prevents chatter and steadies heavy cuts

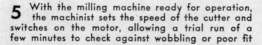

5 With the milling machine ready for operation, the machinist sets the speed of the cutter and switches on the motor, allowing a trial run of a few minutes to check against wobbling or poor fit

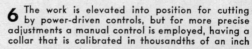

6 The work is elevated into position for cutting by power-driven controls, but for more precise adjustments a manual control is employed, having a collar that is calibrated in thousandths of an inch

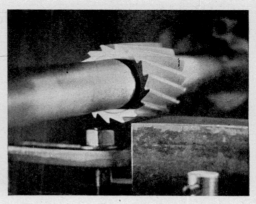

7 If it is not desirable to bring the work up by electric power, these duplicate hand controls may be fitted to the feed levers. The table pivots on the clamp bed and can be swiveled to any angle

8 The revolving cutter is now ready to bite into the rough stock. The speed at which the work is fed is governed by a selective indicator and varies with the material being milled and the cutter used

9 The job proceeds with the work being faced, as shown. A continuous flow of oil applied to the cutter keeps it cool, and washes away chips. Milling compounds differ according to the metals machined

10 Milling cutters are usually grouped into four classes: facing, radial, angular, and formed. Above is shown a straddle, or heading cutter of the radial type machining two surfaces simultaneously

11 Below, an involute gear cutter of the formed class is cutting grooves in a gear blank. A fly cutter may also be used for this kind of work, but its single cutting edge requires a finer feed

12 A plain slitting saw cutter makes a keyway in a shaft. If the slot is to extend along its entire length, the feed must not be eased off until the axis of the cutter passes the shaft end

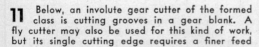
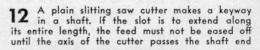

Matching Heart-Shaped Pendant and Pin Carved from Wood

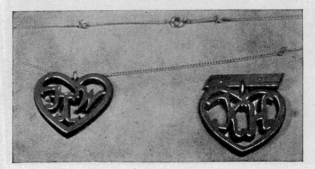

Above, the pendant and pin ready to grace milady's costume

THIS monogram pendant and pin set makes a distinctive personal gift. Any craftsman, with the aid of a jig saw, can turn it out in a comparatively short time. The set shown was made of padouk, a dark-red wood that takes a glossy polish, resembling plastic when finished either with ordinary white shellac or varnish.

Use wood about ¼″ thick, well planed and sanded. Begin by drawing an outline of the heart, with the outer edge about 3/16″ wide. Inside this outer rim, arrange the initials. Either two or three may be used. The two pieces illustrated do not match, as they were made with different initials.

The letters of the script alphabet may have to be altered slightly for best arrangement by lengthening their protruding parts. Lay out the letters on ⅛″ squares just as they appear on the squares below, and cut with a fine fret-saw blade.

For the necklace, use a discarded chain or a silk cord. The pin on the bar consists of a safety pin set into the groove with double-strength casein glue. Fasten the heart to the bar with a small loop of wire or thread.—ELMA WALTNER.

The letters and the heart outline are laid out on ⅛″ squares exactly as shown in the drawing below

FASTEN PIN INTO SHALLOW GROOVE WITH CASEIN GLUE

ABCDEFGHIJKLM
NOPQRSTUVWXYZ

⅛ SQUARES

LAYING OUT SPIRALS [SHOP PRACTICE]

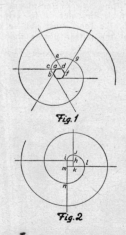

Fig. 1

Fig. 2

A SPIRAL is a curve about a fixed point that will make any number of revolutions around that point without returning into itself. The two easiest ways to construct a spiral are to make it the involute of either a circle or a square. To use the circle method, divide the circumference of a circle (the primary, or "eye" of the spiral) into six equal parts, forming a hexagon. Extend the sides outside of the primary, as shown in Fig. 1. With *a* as a center, describe the arc *bc;* from *d* draw the arc *ce,* from *f* the arc *eg,* and so forth, increasing the radius at each step to continue from the part of the spiral last drawn.

To lay out a spiral from a square, draw the square and extend its sides as shown in Fig. 2. With *h* as a center, draw quadrant *ij.* From *k* draw *jl,* from *m, ln.* Continue with as many successively larger quadrants as necessary.

While the square method is simpler, it may be found to be less accurate than the circle system. In fact, the greater the number of divisions, the more precise will be the spiral.

POPULAR SCIENCE MONTHLY SHOP DATA

ACCENT ON UTILITY

THREE CRAFTWORK PROJECTS

DESIGNED BY
ERNEST R. DEWALT

HANDY REFRESHMENT SERVER. This project is a combination of birch and plywood comprising an attractive and useful server for four glasses of iced drinks. It is based on the use of a minimum amount of material with hardly any waste. Two pieces of ⅜″ birch plywood, 3⅜″ wide by 10¼″ long, are required for the two arms of the base and for the legs, and another piece, 3½″ by 3¾″, is needed for the ring in the handle, while the handle stem is a turning from ⅞″ by ⅞″ maple stock 4 11/16″ long.

The two pieces for the base are half-lapped, as shown in the drawing, with a 3 7/16″ overhang on all four sides to form arms. The holes are cut out with a circle cutter, and the disks are saved for use as the legs, which also serve to join the base halves. All holes are centered on the crosspieces with ⅜″ rims at ends and sides.

In making the legs, lay out a ⅜″ notch on the disks as shown in the drawing, and cut out all four at the same time so that they will be uniform. Glue these legs on the arms after all the holes and rims have been smoothed and rounded. The holes in the arms are made to fit woven grass casters, but the diameter may be changed to suit. The glasses shown have a bead to hold them; tapered glasses also would serve.

The handle is also cut with the circle cutter. It has a ⅜″ rim that widens out to ⅝″ at the bottom to provide a section for joining to the maple turning. The maple

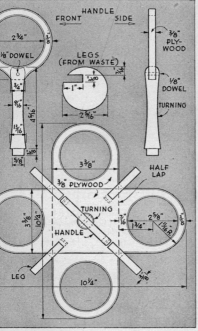

Clocked Project
Average Time 4 hours

part of the handle is turned to the diameters shown in the drawing, with a ⅝" peg left at the bottom for insertion in a hole bored in the center of the base. This should be a good tight fit so that the handle and base can be held together with glue. Notch the top of the turning to a width of ⅜" to receive the handle ring, and bore both the turning and bottom section of the ring for a ⅛" dowel, which is inserted and glued after the inside and outside of the ring have been properly rounded.

Three coats of clear lacquer, rubbed well between coats with fine sandpaper or steel wool, will give a handsome natural finish.

ADJUSTABLE SHOE TREE. Since metal shoe trees are difficult to find, here is a welcome project using nothing but wood. The trees are easily adjusted by removing and reinserting a small peg, and are designed for use with shoes within a range of three half sizes. The wooden construction provides sufficient strength for all ordinary demands, and has the added advantage of having no parts that will tend to rust with frequent use.

The fork and blade of the shoe trees are of maple, although birch may be used, and the toe piece and heel knob are of whitewood. The hinge joint in the toe piece is either dadoed or formed by repeated saw cuts in a 3 9/16" by 4¼" block. The ¼" hole is then drilled for the pivot peg, after which the block is carved to the shape shown in the drawing.

Shaping of the toe piece is done best by first bandsawing the block to the approximate dimensions and then finishing with rasp, plane, and sandpaper. Make free use of paper templates. These may be cut in any way that is most convenient, one method being to cut them to the outside dimensions of a shoe, and then to reduce them somewhat to allow for the thickness of the leather. Although the trees may be

shaped for right and left shoes, this is not necessary, and time may be saved by making them interchangeable.

The fork and blade are of ⅝" square stock. Cut out the middle section of the fork to a width of ¼", leaving two 3/16" sides. Drill two ¼" holes 9/16" on centers in the fork, and two similar holes 7/16" on centers in the blade. These provide for adjustment for shoes of sizes 8½, 9, and 9½ when the other dimensions in the drawing are followed. The length of the blade and fork and the position of the holes in them may be altered slightly, however, to fit shoes of smaller or larger size.

The heel piece is turned on the lathe to a 2" diameter, and flattened on the sides. Join the blade into the heel by rounding off the square to a ⅜" by ⅝" peg joint. Dovetail a finger-grip arm into the blade. Bore a ¾" hole in the upright after a ⅝" upper portion has been strengthened with a 1/16"

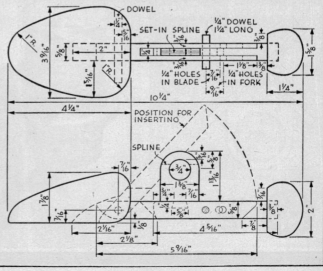

spline. Have the grain of the spline at right angles to that of the grip arm for added strength. The shoe tree is removed by pulling upward, and inserted in a shoe by folding it up and then pushing down at the center. Finish with three coats of lacquer.

MORTAR AND PESTLE. This double-decker woodturning project is intended for use in preparing salads, gravies, dressings, or sauces that require spices or like seasonings to be ground or pulverized before mixing with the other ingredients. Select well-seasoned walnut (either crotch or stump wood), and bandsaw a 3¼" by 4¾" block to a cylindrical shape as a preliminary step.

Turn the top portion, the mortar, first on a faceplate or in a wooden chuck turned to fit it. The mortar is 1½" deep, and is turned to a template having a 2 3/16" radius. Finish the piece smooth on the lathe, rounding the mortar well to the sides. The ledge on the bottom is for closure with the bottom container, and has a 3/16" shoulder; it is tapered 1/16", thus coming to a diameter of 4 1/32" at the bottom. After finishing the piece, cut it off with a parting tool.

The bottom portion is 1¼" over all, and has a well 1 1/16" deep, large enough to hold garlic, cloves, spices, or other seasonings. The outside diameter is turned to the same size, 4⅝", as the mortar. Fit both turnings snugly, but not so tight that they cannot be separated when desired by twisting and pulling them apart.

Turn the pestle from 1½" by 4¼" stock, and finish on the lathe to the dimensions known in the drawing below.

Apply three coats of lacquer, rubbing between each coat, right on the lathe. Put no finish on the well of the mortar or bottom container, and use none at the bottom end of the pestle, as these come into contact with the spices being ground.

TURNED MORTAR AND PESTLE ARE USEFUL CULINARY ACCESSORY FOR PULVERIZING SEASONINGS NEEDED IN THE HOME KITCHEN

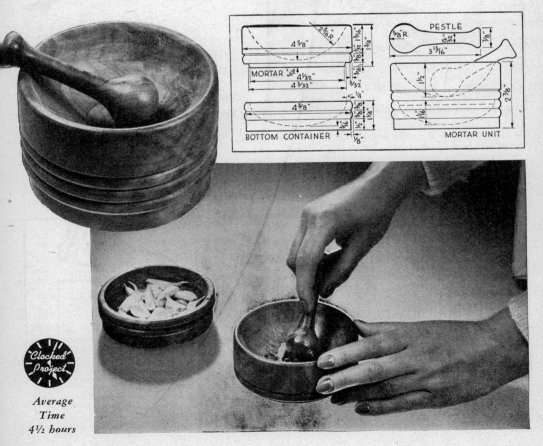

Average Time 4½ hours

KEEPING THE HOME

Knit a woolen cover for a hot-water bottle, and you'll not only improve its appearance, but increase the comfort of the user. Add a gay pompon, as shown, in a contrasting color

A drawer attached to the underside of a rocking chair will hold sewing needs, books, magazines, or stationery. It is handy for use on the porch, or in a summer cottage where drawer space is limited. Paint or finish drawer to harmonize with the chair

Tongs for removing hot potatoes from the oven can be simply made by riveting two tablespoons to the two parts of a spring-type clothespin

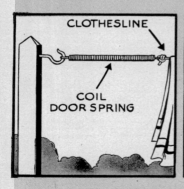

Fixed to one end of a clothesline, a coil door spring keeps the line taut, and prevents it from breaking due to shrinkage

Keep knives sharp by protecting them with the cardboard sheath above. Nicked fingers are also less likely with such a covering

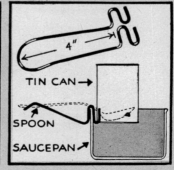

Wire from a clothes hanger, bent and hooked over the lip of a saucepan, holds a spoon or a tin can placed there to drain

SHIPSHAPE

RUBBER SAC

RUBBER CEMENT

Repair leaking fountain-pen sacs by placing the sac over the pen, as shown, and applying rubber cement. Turn inside out and coat the inside also

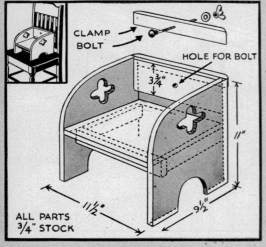

CLAMP BOLT

HOLE FOR BOLT

3¾"

11"

ALL PARTS ¾" STOCK

11½"

9½"

TOP DRESSING

For the youngster who has outgrown a high chair, the seat shown above is ideal. A clamp bar at the back holds it firmly to an ordinary chair, and it is readily portable. The parts are simply assembled with glue and reinforced with screws

A garden hose can be effectively repaired by first painting the break with auto-top dressing, then wrapping it strongly with cloth, followed by stout twine. This stops leaks, and the hose remains fairly flexible

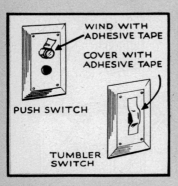

WIND WITH ADHESIVE TAPE

COVER WITH ADHESIVE TAPE

PUSH SWITCH

TUMBLER SWITCH

Adhesive tape, placed on light switches as shown in the drawing above, prevents lights from being turned on in blackouts

STAPLES DRIVEN INTO BACKS OF FRAMES

For keeping stepped pictures in alignment, staples bent from pins are driven in, joining the pictures before they are hung

Twisting a stubborn cap lid with a trouser belt and ruler, as shown, will loosen it. Increased leverage does the trick

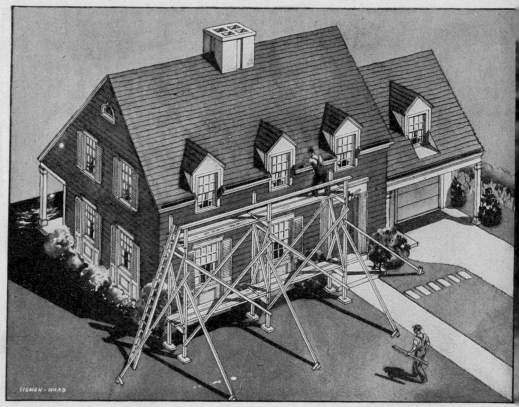

For repairs along the whole side of the house, a built-up scaffold is used with well-braced double uprights

PROFESSIONAL TRICKS AID

SCAFFOLDS

FOR

HOME REPAIRS

How Any Handy Man Can Erect
Substantial Temporary Staging

•

By HAROLD R. TERPENY

NEEDED repairs on the outside of houses frequently require a temporary staging, or scaffold. Therefore erection of safe and sane structures of this nature is of special importance to the home owner.

When the entire exterior is to be painted or shingled, for example, stationary or built-up scaffolding is recommended. Spruce is a first-class wood to use for this because it is tough-fibered and will bend without breaking. Suitable boards can generally be rented from a lumber yard for a small sum, the undamaged wood being returned after the work is done. Any cut or broken lumber, will, of course, have to be paid for.

The uprights are 2″ by 4″ lumber, and the crosspieces upon which the planks rest, commonly known as ledger boards, are 1¼″ by 7″ lumber. Upright bracing is 1″ by 3″ stock. Planks are 2″ by 9″ hard pine. For more foot room and greater safety, use two planks side by side and cleated underneath, as in Fig. 1.

For nailing, use regular double-headed staging nails, as shown in Fig. 2. If these cannot be obtained, ordinary No. 10 nails will do, provided you leave the heads sticking out ¼″ or so for easy removal when dismantling the structure. The 1″ by 3″ braces are nailed to the uprights and to stakes driven in the ground. Wherever the braces cross each other, a nail is driven through to prevent them from jiggling back and forth, and to make the scaffold a much stronger unit. Ledger boards, which the planks will rest upon, are secured to the uprights with not less than five nails at each point of nailing, as in Fig. 3. On soft ground the uprights are prevented from sinking into the earth by means of short squares of board, as shown. Double uprights should be not more than 12′ apart, since a greater distance allows too much spring to the planks.

The 2″ by 4″ uprights should be not less than 3′ above the highest plank on the staging. At this level, a 2″ by 3″ guard rail should be nailed on horizontally, as shown in a drawing on the facing page. This is important, as it takes very little to throw a person off balance when working above the ground. A built-up scaffold, with double uprights connected by ledger boards, is good because it does not require fastening ledger boards directly to the house. However, Fig. 4 shows how single uprights can be used by nailing the inner end of the ledger boards to vertical supporting boards nailed to the shingles. When working alone on a hard surface where stakes cannot be driven into the ground, you can erect the uprights by bracing them against a couple of big rocks. Otherwise, use stakes as in Fig. 5.

Another type of scaffolding, using the push brackets of Fig. 6, is shown in the lower corner of the opposite page. This is easy to erect and is especially adapted for use where work is to be done at just one particular spot on the house or barn.

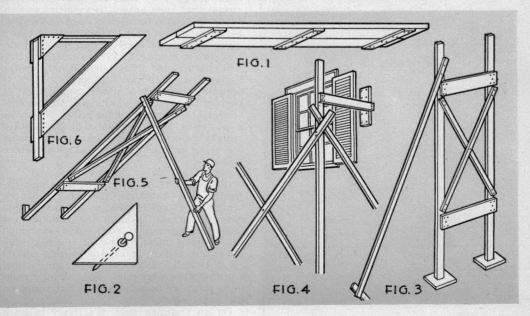

FIG. 1
FIG. 6
FIG. 5
FIG. 2
FIG. 4
FIG. 3

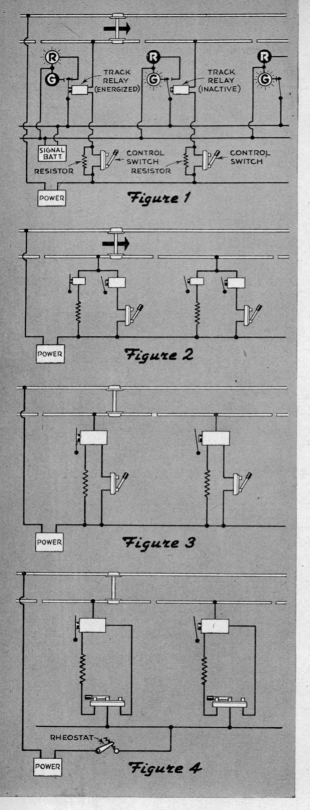

Figure 1

Figure 2

Figure 3

Figure 4

AFTER examining the main characteristics of two-rail operation, in our last article, we began to wire a two-rail pike for automatic signals, carrying things to the point shown in Fig. 1. Here the left-hand block is occupied, and the signal guarding it is at the *stop*, while the right-hand block is vacant, and the signal protecting it is at the *clear*. In each instance the signal is controlled by a track relay. In the occupied block, the mere presence of the train establishes a flow of electricity from the generator to the common rail, through the motor of the locomotive (or through a light on board a passenger coach) to the control rail, and thence through the relay back to the generator. The relay is thus energized, the armature freezes to the magnet, the green-light circuit is broken, and the red-light circuit is closed.

In the vacant block, the green light shows because the track relay is not energized, since there is no train to close the gap between the common rail and the control rail.

TWO-WAY CIRCUIT. What is rather special about Fig. 1 is the fact that the track relay is in series with the locomotive; that is, the power that drives the locomotive must pass through the relay. This is the distinguishing feature of two-rail automatic signaling.

The first objection to it is that when you shut off power and bring your locomotive to a stop, the relay becomes inactive resulting in a false *clear*. But we have solved that in Fig. 1 by inserting a resistor in a circuit that runs around the control switch. When the control switch is open—as in Fig. 1—there is no train movement within a given block; but there is still, through the resistor, a minute flow of electricity that will energize the relay but will not stir the locomotive. Thus, as long as any block is occupied, there is a never-ending flow of current through the windings of the locomotive and the winding of the relay. It may be a powerful flow, driving a double-headed freight train, or it may be too weak to budge a 6-wheel switcher; but it will always work the relay.

DIVIDING THE RELAY. There is a second objection. As it stands, the relay must be sensitive enough to pick up on the minute flow of current through the resistor, yet husky enough not to burn out when trains are working under full power. Such a relay is not unheard of; and if you operate an HO or an OO pike, with a spread of only a few volts between your minimum and maximum flow, you may be able to get what you need inexpensively.

On an O-gauge pike, it's likely to be a

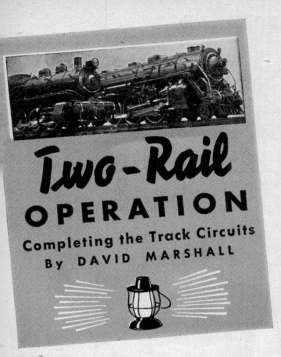

Two-Rail
OPERATION
Completing the Track Circuits
By DAVID MARSHALL

different matter. Let us consider the average O-gauge layout with good locomotives that start rolling (dead speed) on 8 volts and reach their maximum speed and pulling power on 20 volts. That is a spread of 12 volts through the control switch alone. It becomes greater if the current through the resistor runs to as little as 4 volts. In such a case the relay would have to work on anything from 4 to 20 volts. Such relays are not unobtainable, but they are costly—so much so that the average model railroader could not think of buying them.

To get around that difficulty, we divide the relay, and get, as in Fig. 2, a little fellow and a big, husky one. The little one is the more sensitive; it operates on 1 volt and does not get too hot on 4 volts. We hook this one up in series with the resistor. The big fellow operates on 8 volts and can stand 20—at least for as long a time as any train, working on full power, takes to run through the block. And this husky relay, which is not hard to get and not too costly, we hook up in series with the control switch.

Thus far, then, we have solved the cost problem, and we have one relay to pick up on a suboperating flow of current and another to pick up on a much heavier flow.

RECOMBINING THE RELAYS. An obvious fault with this arrangement is that both relays do not work together. In Fig. 2, the left-hand block is occupied, the control switch open, and the train standing still. The little relay

has picked up on current passing through the resistor, while the big relay has not, and we must assume that the effect of this (see Fig. 1) must be to cause both red and green lights to show.

You can get around that by wiring the signal differently, but an easier way is to take the coils of these two relays and wind them separately around the same core. Wind both wires in the same direction and keep them insulated from each other throughout the winding, but bring them together at the rail end to form a single wire. In this way we combine the two relays of Fig. 2 in a single relay. (See Fig. 3.)

This new relay differs from others only in having two separate coils. Its action is the same. It picks up when the requisite current flows through either of its coils—2 volts through its high-resistance coil, or 20 through its low-resistance coil.

CUT-OUT SWITCH. But if we leave the thing as it stands in Fig. 3, we complicate our operating problem by adding to the load. If the train in Fig. 3 were actually running, the control switch would be closed, and power would be passing through both coils of the relay at the same time. Nothing would be gained by that; indeed, there would be a loss of power which, multiplied a few times over, would amount to something worth considering.

So it becomes important to cut out the high-resistance circuit once the low-resistance circuit is established by the closing of the control switch. How this is done by a single-pole double-throw knife switch is illustrated in Fig. 4. On your control board you would not have anything so crude, but you must have what will do precisely the same job—a single-pole double-throw toggle switch. With one of these, either circuit must always be closed, the other always open. Then, as long as the block is occupied, the relay will be energized.

Figure 4 also shows the position of the rheostat, close to the power source. This controls the voltage that goes to this or that block separately through the various control switches. It delivers to the locomotive through the low-resistance coil a maximum of 20 volts, and is so adjusted that it must deliver a minimum of 6 volts. That, passing through the low-resistance coil, is too little to move a locomotive; passing through the resistor, it is still enough to operate the relay.

To meet demands, the resistor ought to reduce 20 volts to 4. In that case, the minimum flow of 6 volts from the rheostat would be cut to a little more than 1 volt. Your relay will have to be sensitive enough to pick up on that.

Carved leaves are attractive

Hand-Carved Fruit Tray

THIS attractive tray appeals to both the beginner and the experienced wood carver. Make it of a piece of fine-grained wood such as mahogany, walnut, gumwood, or even poplar or whitewood, about ⅞" by 10" by 15". The finished tray will be 9½" wide by 14" long.

Use a piece of thin cardboard exactly 4¾" by 7" for the outline pattern. This must be square along one edge and one end. Draw one quarter of an oval on this paper and cut it out, leaving the edge and end square as in Fig. 1.

Draw center lines on the surface of the wood, both lengthwise and crosswise, at 90 deg. to each other. Align the pattern accurately on these and trace around the outside of it four times to draw the oval wanted (Fig. 2).

Trim the pattern along the curve about ⅜" from the edge, but square the end across inside, leaving approximately 1" for the handle part, as in Fig. 3. Now trace the reduced oval on the wood for rough carving.

Rough out the entire inside of the tray to about ½" in thickness at the bottom. Cut

Balance and symmetry depend to a large extent upon accuracy in fitting and tracing the pattern

only within the inner oval and trim the edges out concavely (Fig. 4).

Decide on your design (see Fig. 6), lay out one fourth of it as a pattern, and transfer it to the work. Natural forms such as leaves may be adapted by copying them on a heavy paper pattern.

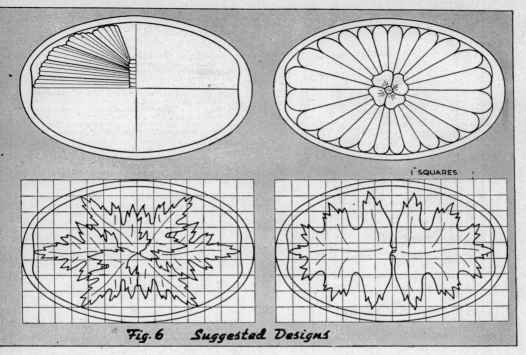

1" SQUARES

Fig. 6 Suggested Designs

In selecting your pattern, keep the general shape of the tray in mind so the carved area will conform

When the carving is finished, sand very lightly—a few chisel marks left in the design add to its looks—and bandsaw to the outside line. If a power saw is not available, use a handsaw and trim to the line with a file, plane, or spokeshave.

Undercut the outside as shown in Fig 5.

Be careful to follow the line of the inside as much as possible so that you will not cut through into the design. Gouge out the underside of each end to form the handles, and sand smooth. Finish with stain, wood filler, shellac, and one or two coats of well-rubbed varnish.—LEONARD F. MERRILL.

USING WOOD FASTENERS   [WOODWORKING]

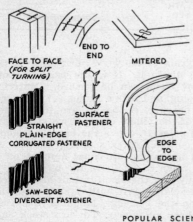

FACE TO FACE
(FOR SPLIT TURNING)

END TO END

MITERED

STRAIGHT PLAIN-EDGE CORRUGATED FASTENER

SURFACE FASTENER

EDGE TO EDGE

SAW-EDGE DIVERGENT FASTENER

There are two kinds of metal joint fasteners in general use—corrugated nails, and surface fasteners. Both can be used regardless of the direction of the grain in the work, and both hold very securely. Best known are the corrugated fasteners. Specialized uses for them, modifications of those illustrated in the sketch, are constantly being found. They may be used either with or without glue. For good work, fit joints well and drive the corrugated fasteners much like ordinary nails, but be sure to strike them on the ends as well as on the centers to prevent distortion. Underneath shelves, or in other hidden places, simply drive them home; but on exposed surfaces and on work to be painted, set them with an ordinary nail set, and putty. Corrugated fasteners tend to draw the joint open on the opposite side; therefore, hold the joint flat until the glue dries, or use fasteners on both sides. Surface fasteners, unlike corrugated fasteners, cannot be set.

POPULAR SCIENCE MONTHLY SHOP DATA

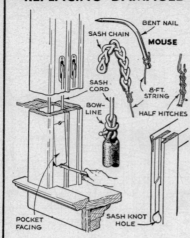
Steady Rest on Lathe Increases Production

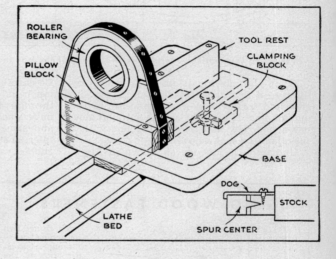

THIS homemade "traveler" or roller-bearing steady rest for a small woodworking lathe gives the same advantage as a hollow-spindle lathe but will take work of larger diameter. I have used it for turning wheels as large as 1½″, cutting each off and starting on the next without the usual delay involved in remounting or recentering stock.

The stock is first turned between centers to the required diameter, care being taken to keep it as uniform as possible. Then the tailstock is backed up and the traveler mounted on the lathe bed. The stock is passed through the roller bearing and fastened to the spur center with a lathe dog, then turned as required and used up to the roller bearing. After that, the wing nut is loosened and the traveler slid up toward the headstock, bringing more of the material into use.

To line up the roller bearing with the headstock, turn a plug on the screw center to make a snug fit for the inside of the bearing. Then mount a piece about twice the thickness of the bearing and turn a hole to the outside diameter of the bearing. Remount both plug and bearing on the spindle and slip the turned pillow block on with the grain of the wood horizontal. Slide the base up to it. Now the base line of the pillow block can be scribed. Centering in the plug, and with a radius ⅝″ greater than the bearing, scribe an arc to outline the top of the pillow block. Two straight lines to a point 1″ above the base line complete the outline. After shaping, trim to thickness by taking an equal amount off each side down to 1″ above the base line. Then simply saw the block in half and fasten the upper part down with a strip of metal to clamp the bearing. Mount a tool rest on the base as shown. To turn stock smaller than the inside of the bearing, make a wooden bushing.—E. W. MARSTON.

The Element with a Dual Personality

ALUMINUM, INDUSTRY'S LIGHTWEIGHT CHAMPION,
ACTS CHEMICALLY AS BOTH AN ACID AND A BASE

WITH a bit of aluminum from a discarded pot, plus some alum and a few chemicals found in any home laboratory, you can demonstrate several interesting and little-known facts about this useful metal. You can make aluminum salts that react both as acids and as bases, learn how aluminum helps make fast colors in the dye industry, account for some odd reactions of aluminum utensils to food and cleaning compounds, and show what role aluminum plays in baking powder.

Oddly enough, this light, silvery-white element now so seriously needed for airplane and other machine parts is the most abundant and widely distributed metal in the earth's crust. Almost all soils, clays, and rocks contain aluminum in some form, and a great many minerals, including rubies,

sapphires, bauxite, and feldspar, are aluminum compounds. It is only the difficulty of releasing the pure metal from its various compounds that prevents aluminum from being the cheapest and most commonly used metal in the world.

Because of its tremendous affinity for oxygen, aluminum is never found uncombined in nature. That is why the surface of aluminum is always thinly and invisibly coated with a film of oxide which, luckily, inhibits further oxidation. A simple chemical stunt, which prevents this oxide from forming, will show you vividly how active aluminum really is.

Clean a scrap of aluminum with steel wool; then rub a few grains of mercuric chloride briskly over the cleaned spot with a cloth or cotton wad moistened with water,

In dyeing cotton, aluminum hydroxide is used to make the dye adhere better. At left, the cloth, after being dipped into solutions of aluminum sulphate and aluminum hydroxide, is finally placed in the dye

until the aluminum becomes coated with metallic mercury. Now rinse and dry the aluminum. Almost immediately, thin filaments or "whiskers" of aluminum oxide begin to rise from the metal. These continue to grow until they are an inch or more long, sometimes until the metal beneath has been entirely eaten away. This rapid oxidation would also attack aluminum utensils and even streamlined trains and airplanes, if the thin coating of oxide that first forms did not protect them!

Caution: As mercuric chloride is very poisonous, be sure to clean up any spilled grains and wash your hands thoroughly after this experiment.

As you know, bases neutralize acids, and acids neutralize bases, in each case producing compounds known as salts. However, there are also certain chemical elements and compounds which are amphoteric, or dual-natured, acting as weak bases in the presence of acids, and as weak acids in the presence of bases. Aluminum hydroxide is one of these, as can be proved by a simple experiment.

First, make some aluminum hydroxide by dissolving a little common alum (which is a double sulphate of aluminum and potassium) in half a glass of water, and adding ammonium hydroxide (household ammonia will do). A white, almost insoluble precipitate of aluminum hydroxide forms which slowly settles to the bottom of the glass. Continue adding ammonia until no more precipitate forms. Then let the glass stand until the smell of ammonia has gone.

To prove the dual nature of aluminum hydroxide, add a little of the clear upper liquid in the glass (which contains a small amount of the hydroxide) to a universal indicator solution that has been made slightly acid with dilute hydrochloric acid. The aluminum hydroxide neutralizes the acid. Now add a little hydroxide to a similar indicating solution that has now been made slightly basic, or alkaline. Again the solution becomes neutralized!

Aluminum shows its dual nature in still another instance by liberating hydrogen when acted upon by either acids or strong alkalies. Aluminum scraps in hydrochloric acid yield hydrogen readily. It is not so well known that they will also yield hydrogen in a strong solution of sodium hydroxide, or lye. Put a little lye solution in a flask, as shown in one of the accompanying photographs. Add small pieces of aluminum and heat the flask gently until a strong reaction begins. Thereafter the reaction will continue without further heating. You may prove that the gas is hydrogen by blowing

Aluminum resists corrosion because of an invisible, thin coating of oxide which forms on its surface. Above, this coating is prevented from forming to show how active aluminum really is. Rub a few grains of mercuric chloride with a dampened cloth over a clean bit of aluminum. Rinse and dry the aluminum, and almost immediately thin filaments of aluminum oxide begin to rise from the metal, as seen in photo below

Aluminum has the strange property of being able to liberate hydrogen from acids or strong bases. Above, aluminum scraps gently heated in a solution of lye generate hydrogen. The bubble shown, filled with hydrogen, will rise to the ceiling

⟵ How aluminum reacts in two ways is easily demonstrated. Just a few drops of aluminum hydroxide added to an indicator solution made acid will neutralize the acid; a like quantity added to indicator solution made basic neutralizes the base

bubbles with it that will rise to the ceiling.

Ordinarily, aluminum should never be cleaned with alkalies such as soda or lye, which attack the metal. However, there is a trick whereby you can clean aluminum with alkalies and prevent these substances from corroding the metal. Add only 1 percent as much sodium silicate as washing soda to a 5-percent solution of the soda in water, and the alkali will clean harmlessly.

Animal fibers, such as silk and wool, readily take up most dyes and hold their color. Vegetable fibers such as cotton, however, are seldom color fast when dyed by direct processes. These almost always need chemical assistants. Here again, aluminum hydroxide becomes a helper.

Dip a strip of cotton cloth in a dye bath made of diluted ink. Rinse the strip, and you discover that most of the color washes away. Now dip a similar strip first in a solution of aluminum sulphate (alum will do) in water, and then in a solution of ammonium hydroxide. Dip this treated strip in the ink solution as you did the other strip. The color will be darker, and very little of it can be rinsed away.

What happens is this: the aluminum sulphate on the cloth is changed into aluminum hydroxide when it is dipped into the ammonia, and this hydroxide is precipitated into the fibers of the cloth, where it assimilates the dye. Since the aluminum hydroxide is insoluble, the dye cannot be washed away easily.

Aluminum, in the form of potassium alum or sodium alum, is often used in baking powder, where it acts as a harmless acid salt. Mixed with baking soda and water, it generates carbon dioxide bubbles which cause the bread or cake dough to "rise". Mix a little alum with baking soda, and add water. The mixture immediately effervesces. Mix flour with the two dry ingredients, stir in water, and the mixture swells like dough.—KENNETH M. SWEZEY.

THE VOLUME OF AN IRREGULAR BODY, such as a stone, a piece of coal, or the like, can be easily determined with a spring balance and a jar of water. First, weigh the object in air; then weigh it in water. According to the principle discovered centuries ago by Archimedes, the difference in weight of a given object will be equal to the weight of an amount of water of the same volume as the object. Since fresh water weighs a little more than ½ oz. per cubic inch, or one gram per cubic centimeter, a simple calculation will determine the volume of the water, and thus the volume of the object. At the same time, you may quickly determine the specific gravity of the object by dividing the weight of the object in air by the weight in air minus the weight in water. For example, if an object weighs 15 oz. in air and 5 oz. in water, the specific gravity would be 15 divided by 10, or 1.5.

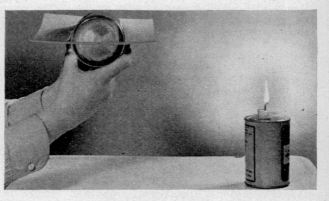

HOW WATER PRESSURE increases with depth, yet exerts an equal force in all directions at any given depth, is vividly demonstrated with the apparatus shown at the left. Connect a piece of bent glass tubing to a thistle tube having a thin rubber membrane stretched over its mouth. Colored water is poured into the open end of the glass tube to serve as an indicator. If the thistle tube is then lowered under the surface of water in a jar, the liquid in the outer leg of the tube will rise, continuing to do so as the thistle tube goes deeper into the water. If, however, the thistle tube is swung around at various angles, while kept at a given depth—mouth down, mouth up, or mouth to the side—the liquid will remain at the same height, indicating that the water pushes upward, downward, and sidewise with equal pressure at any fixed level.

IS THE SUN WHERE WE SEE IT? The answer to this seemingly simple question is—no. The sun is often seen before it has reached the horizon in the morning, and after it has passed the horizon in the evening. This phenomenon can be explained by the fact that in this case light is bent, or refracted, by our own atmosphere. The effect can be duplicated on a small scale by using a candle to represent the sun, and a soda bottle filled with water to represent the earth's atmosphere. A piece of cardboard marks the horizon. Arrange the bottle and candle as shown in the photograph, then look above and along the "horizon." The candle, which is actually far below the

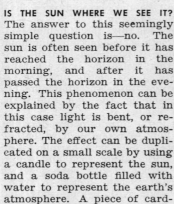

card, will seem to be above it. Furthermore, as sunlight must travel about 8 minutes to reach us, we never see the sun as it is, but always as it was 8 minutes ago.

home EXPERIMENTS

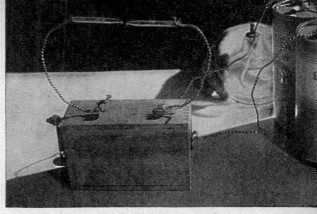

GLASS CONDUCTS ELECTRICITY. Although a good insulator when cold, glass becomes a fair conductor of electricity when heated. You can demonstrate this quickly and simply in your home lab. Draw out a short length of glass tubing in a flame so that its central portion has a bore of only a few millimeters. Into the ends of the tube place leads from the secondary of a spark coil, or a small neon-tube transformer. Now excite the coil. If sparks do not immediately jump through the tube, heat it with the flame from an alcohol lamp. As soon as the tube is hot enough, sparks will leap through it. The sparks will, under favorable conditions, continue to jump even after the flame has been removed, and may finally melt the glass in the small part of the tube, thus producing two sealed glass electrodes. If the spark has been hot enough, it will still continue to jump between these two glass electrodes!

FLUORESCENT LIGHTING. The reason for the great efficiency of fluorescent lamps can be readily demonstrated with some fluorescent paint and a small argon bulb. The paint can be made by mixing a paste of quinine sulphate and dilute sulphuric acid. Coat half the bulb with paint and, when it dries, turn on the current. The coated side will give out considerably more light than the uncoated side. The paint, upon being bombarded by ultraviolet rays from the plates in the bulb, gives out visible rays of great intensity. In regular commercial tubes, the fluorescent coating is on the inside of the tube, rather than the outside. This protects it, and at the same time utilizes those ultraviolet rays that cannot pass through the glass.

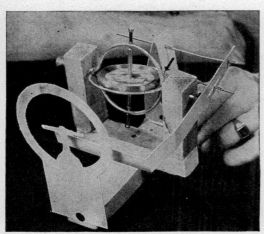

ARTIFICIAL HORIZON. How does a pilot, flying blind, know whether his plane is ascending or descending? His instrument board has an artificial horizon—a gyroscopic device that indicates the plane's relation to the real horizon. Mount a toy gyroscope in a U-shaped frame to tilt freely at right angles to the wheel axis. Solder a stiff wire to the gyroscope frame as indicated by the arrow. Let this project into a slot in a cardboard lever that is pivoted at one end and bent at the other. If the base is now tilted as a plane is in climbing or diving, the spinning gyroscope will not tilt with it, but will continue spinning parallel to the earth. When the plane is climbing, the horizon bar will be below the indicator; in descending, the bar will be above it.

REBUILDING THAT OI

Expert Reconditioning in the Home Workshop Can Restore to Further Use Many Appliances and Other Electrical Machines That Have Long Been in Discard

By
HAROLD P.
STRAND

MAKE it do, or do without! To these alternatives that are daily becoming apparent to more and more Americans, there can be added a third. Rebuild it! This is particularly true of a worn-out vacuum cleaner. No matter how old it may be, or how long it has lain in dusty discard, it probably can be made to work almost like new. Electric mixers, drills, and other machines having universal-type motors can be rebuilt in much the same way.

The first step in reconditioning your vacuum cleaner is to remove and discard the bag, saving the clamping ring at the bottom and the spring-clip bar at the top for use with a new bag. The procedure of disassembling will differ with various

STEPS IN RESTORING A WORN-OUT

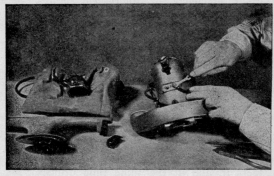

1 Remove the front suction housing by swinging the top clamp to one side and tapping the unit off its pin. Then disconnect the wires from the binding posts

4 The two parts of the motor unit are separated to give access to the inside of the motor and its armature and other parts that may be in need of repair

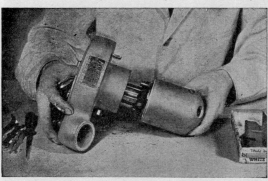

VACUUM CLEANER

makes, but in general should follow the order described for the cleaner shown.

Remove the front suction housing by swinging its top clamp to one side and tapping it off its hinge pin. Then disconnect the wires as in Fig. 1. Take off the handle by loosening two machine screws (Fig. 2). If the spring that keeps it upright is broken, replace it. Bending will probably suffice to restore lost tension.

In taking out the fan, first remove the three screws in the cover. Some fans are locked on the shaft with a nut and may be threaded on as well, in which case a small wrench thrust through a housing opening may be used to grip a square part of the shaft or to bear against the inner motor-

cooling fan. A setscrew locks the fan shown. Back of the fan are two machine screws holding the motor unit to the fan housing. These are removed next (Fig. 3), and the two parts are separated, as in Fig. 4, for access to the inside of the motor.

Inspect the armature to see that no wires are unsoldered from the segments, and check the insulation for char indicating burned-out windings. The only effective test is to place the armature on a growler, as in Fig. 5, to test for shorts, opens, and grounds that may require rewinding or exchanging the armature for a rewound one. Any electric shop will make the tests if you have no growler available.

The commutator probably will be grooved

VACUUM CLEANER WITH THE USE OF FEW NEW PARTS ➤

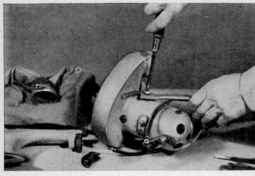

2 The handle is taken off by removing two screws. If spring that holds the handle up is broken, replace it. Bend it to restore lost tension

3 After removing the cover and taking out the fan carefully, remove the two screws behind it. These hold the motor unit to the fan housing

5 An armature can be tested effectively only on a growler. Look for shorts, opens, and grounds. Defects here may mean a rewinding job

6 Turn down the commutator in the lathe if the surface shows grooves made by the brushes. Take only light cuts and finish with fine sandpaper

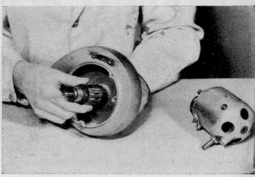

7 All parts should be cleaned thoroughly of grease and dirt. Those containing no wires may be washed in carbon tetrachloride or kerosene

8 Test the armature shaft for play at both of its bearings. Any worn bearings must be replaced or made to fit with emergency repairs

9 Connect a jumper across the brush guides to get a through circuit in the field windings, and then make tests for open circuits and grounds

10 Draw the wires out of the handle along with the switch. If the cord is broken near the handle, cut it off at the break and reconnect it

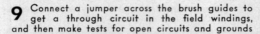

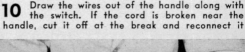

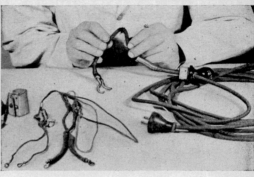

from the brushes, and it should be turned smooth in a lathe as in Fig. 6. Make several light cuts, and finish with sandpaper. Slightly undercut the mica separators between the segments, using a special tool or a piece of hack-saw blade with the "set" ground off until it makes a cut the width of the mica. Hold it to cut as you pull it toward you. Cut the mica down a little further than the copper surface, taking care not to cut into the copper; then sand.

Clean grease and dirt off all parts, washing those that contain no wires in carbon tetrachloride or kerosene (Fig. 7) and drying with clean cloths. Clean the motor-field unit with a round bristle brush; then wipe the exposed inside metal parts with a small piece of cloth dampened in the solvent.

Pass the armature shaft through its bearings (Fig. 8) and test for play, being sure there is no lost motion at either bearing. If wear is evident, new bearings should be obtained or some stopgap measure taken. You might press the bearing sleeves out, using a shoulder arbor in the

vise, and then press them into a hole of slightly smaller diameter that has been drilled into ½" steel. When pressed out again, the sleeves will have holes reduced in size. Build the outside surface back with solder, and finish with a reamer.

Another method is to make a hack-saw cut lengthwise of the bushing, squeeze the cut together in the vise, and wrap a piece of thin shim stock around the bearing without letting the ends overlap. This can be pressed in the hole as before, and a reamer used to finish the inside.

The field windings should be tested with a series lamp (Fig. 9) for open circuits and grounds. Connect a jumper across the brush guides to get a through circuit of the two field sections. The lamp should light when the test prods are touched to the binding posts, but not when they are touched to the aluminum casing and either post.

Removing the screws in the top knob and switch will allow the wires to be pulled out of the handle (Fig. 10). The switch toggle lever is removed by loosen-

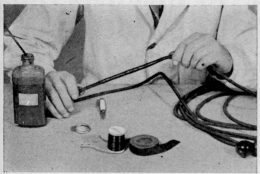

11 To patch the braided covering, apply one layer of friction tape, wind heavy thread over it, tie the ends, and finish with shellac

12 Polish the aluminum parts on a cloth buffing machine, which will give a high luster. Use aluminum paint on parts that do not finish well

13 When reassembling the cleaner, bush wheels if they wobble, take up end play in the armature shaft, and replace worn carbon brushes

14 Before putting the switch and wires back in the handle, clean the switch contacts with sandpaper and make final tests with a series lamp

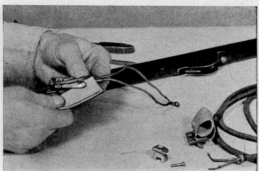

ing one screw in its face. Draw the wires out with it. If the cord is broken near the handle, which is the usual case, it can be cut off there and reconnected. Test for other breaks with the series lamp. Apply a single layer of ½″ friction tape over damaged spots in the outside braided covering, and follow with a close winding of heavy black thread, as in Fig. 11, and a coat of shellac. Minor damages on rubber cords can be patched with rubber tire putty or tape and thread. If the copper is brittle or the insulation badly worn, get a new cord.

Finish the handle by polishing the aluminum fork on a cloth buffing wheel and applying a coat of black enamel to the remainder. The other aluminum parts of the cleaner are also polished on the cloth wheel (Fig. 12). A fine scratch wheel will take rust and dirt off small parts.

In Fig. 13 the cleaner is being reassembled. Bush wobbly wheels, take up excessive end play in the armature shaft with thin fiber washers, and replace the carbon brushes if they are too worn. Clean the

switch contacts with fine sandpaper drawn between them, as in Fig. 14. Test the switch and wires again with the series lamp, and then draw them back into the handle with the aid of a fish wire. Attach the handle and the new bag; then refill oil or grease cups to complete the job.

A cleaner having a motor-driven brush is overhauled similarly. The brush wears too short in time and may need to be replaced. If the rubber belt is badly stretched and cannot be replaced, it may be necessary to remove the brush and use the machine as a suction cleaner only. Clean hair and lint from the brush and brush bearings, and test the latter with the belt off to see that they allow the brush to turn easily. If the belt is not put back on correctly, it may fly off the motor pulley, so look for markings or test it before reassembling. The underside of the brush should turn in to draw in dirt. Excessive wear may occur in the bearing near the pulley due to belt tension, but regular lubrication minimizes this. Test for lost motion with belt off.

FIRST STEPS IN ELECTRONICS

Part 2

ELECTRONS ON THE RADIO

IN ORDER to unfold the story of radio communication, it is necessary to roll back the curtain of time to a stormy day of 1901. On the rugged shores of St. John's, Newfoundland, a group of men had succeeded after a fierce struggle in sending aloft a large kite attached to a copper wire. The end of this wire was attached to an electrical receiving device. After several adjustments, the group gathered around the equipment and waited expectantly. Suddenly an electric earphone that had been making haphazard sounds buzzed three times, stopped, and again buzzed three times. The men cheered loudly. Long months of hard preparation had at last been crowned with success. The three dots of the letter "S" had traveled thousands of miles across the Atlantic from Poldhu in Cornwall, England, and had proved to a doubting world that almost instantaneous communication was possible over vast distances. Guglielmo Marconi, who transmitted the signals on his first attempt, is generally credited by the public with inventing radio communication. His contribution, however, was to make commercially successful the work of Clerk-Maxwell, Hertz, and other physicists.

In the comparatively short time that has elapsed since Marconi's colorful achievement, tremendous progress has been made.

A diagram of the important components of a modern broadcasting transmitter is shown at the top of page HW 116. At *A* is a graph representing an alternating current. Its amplitude (strength) is indicated by vertical displacement of the peaks above and below the axis. Its frequency is the number of cycles per second along the axis.

The oscillator, *by generating an alternating electric current,* makes electrons move to and fro at frequencies of from 550,000 to 1,600,000 times per second, depending upon the frequency at which the station is licensed to operate. The graph of the output of the oscillator is shown in curve *B* The feeble output of the oscillator is made stronger by the radio-frequency amplifier, and its effect on the oscillation is shown in curve *C*. Note that the distance the graph extends up and down—the amplitude of the signal—has been increased.

In order to transmit speech, the amplitude of the carrier wave must be modified by the modulator, in accordance with the sound variations of the voice. Sound waves strike the microphone and produce minute electrical currents varying at the rate of 16 to 16,000 times per second. These are called *audio-frequency* variations because they are audible. The graph of the audio-frequency output of the microphone is shown in curve *D*. The output of the microphone is increased by the audio-frequency amplifier with the result indicated in curve *E*. The output of the amplifier is used to modify, or modulate, the carrier wave from

WJSV

**By
CHARLES I.
HELLMAN**

Physics Instructor, Bronx High School
of New York

the radio-frequency amplifier, as in curve *F*. The modulated carrier wave is then fed to the antenna, and the oscillating motion of the electrons in the antenna sets up disturbances called *electromagnetic waves*.

Electromagnetic waves produce a modulated radio-frequency current of very small value in the antenna of a receiver. Look at curve *G*, Fig. 2. The radio-frequency amplifier builds up this feeble current to the strength of curve *H*. The modulation, or audio component, must be separated from the radio-frequency carrier wave before it can be made audible, and the detector performs this demodulating function as in curve *I*. The weak audio-frequency energy is amplified by the audio-frequency amplifier (curve *J*), and is fed to the loudspeaker which converts the electrical energy into sound. This completes the broadcasting cycle.

If the radio-frequency carrier is rejected in the

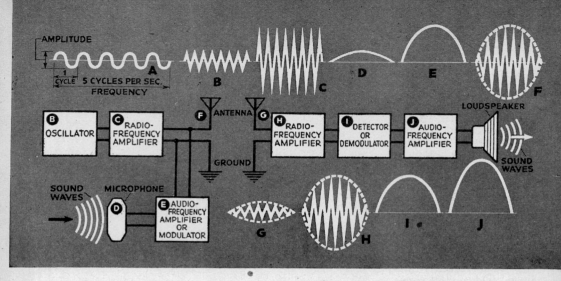

AMPLITUDE

1 CYCLE — 5 CYCLES PER SEC. — FREQUENCY

A

B

C

D

E

F

B OSCILLATOR

C RADIO-FREQUENCY AMPLIFIER

ANTENNA F G

H RADIO-FREQUENCY AMPLIFIER

I DETECTOR OR DEMODULATOR

J AUDIO-FREQUENCY AMPLIFIER

LOUDSPEAKER

SOUND WAVES

GROUND

SOUND WAVES

MICROPHONE

D

E AUDIO-FREQUENCY AMPLIFIER OR MODULATOR

G

H

I

J

process of modulation, you may ask, why not transmit the modulation energy directly? The answer lies in the fact that modulation is at audio frequencies and that radiation from an antenna is negligible at these frequencies, but is considerable at radio frequencies. Therefore, a radio-frequency (RF) wave is required to act as a *carrier* for the modulation.

An old radio may be disassembled and the parts used for many simple experiments in electronics. Remove the knobs by loosening the setscrews that hold them to the shafts. Carefully turn the set upside down and remove the screws holding the chassis to the cabinet. Occasionally some parts, such as switches or pilot bulbs, are fastened to the radio cabinet, as well as to the chassis of the set. These must be unfastened from the cabinet before removing the chassis.

Remove tubes and pilot bulbs. Care must be used in lifting off the screen-grid clips, or the grid terminals on the tubes may be pulled off.

You are now ready to begin disassembling the set. Turn the chassis over. Using a soldering iron, unsolder the small resistors. It may be necessary, when unsoldering connections, to twist one wire while the soldering iron is applied to the joint. Next, unsolder in order the small condensers, all connections to sockets, and connections from parts to the chassis called "ground connections." Be careful not to touch the hot soldering iron to paper condensers, coils, or other parts that may be damaged by heat. Do not dismount sockets from the chassis.

When the small parts have been removed and all connections unsoldered, you are ready to remove the larger pieces of apparatus with a screw driver. If any parts are riveted or welded to the chassis, it is preferable to leave them on it rather than risk damaging them. The tuned-radio-frequency transformer or oscillator coil, large fixed condensers, chokes, switches, volume and tone controls, and loudspeaker are the parts that will probably be dismounted at this point.

Save all the parts and hardware obtained from the receiver. A subsequent article will explain how you can make good use of them.

A, radio-frequency transformer; B, radio-frequency choke; C, switch; D, volume control; E, socket; F, small fixed condensers; G, carbon resistor; H, variable condenser

Servicing Your Radio

Yanking on a line cord often causes a break in the resistor wire. To avoid this, grasp the plug when removing it

LINE-CORD BREAKS, which occur most frequently in the built-in resistor in a cord of the type shown at the left, may be the reason a receiver goes dead. It is advisable to check this resistor if tests show that all the tubes are good. Sometimes it is possible to solder the thin resistor wire back to the prong, as shown in the sketch; if not, the whole line cord must be replaced.

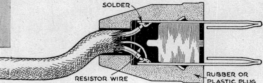

SOME TYPES OF DIAL POINTERS can be repaired easily with common liquid cement. If one cannot be set on the proper station indicator because it has come loose from the center plastic piece to which it was attached, remove the chassis from the cabinet and apply the cement as indicated in the drawing below. Best results can be obtained by removing the pointer assembly from the dial face and laying it flat, as shown. This will keep excess cement from spotting the dial face should any drip off the pointer during the application.

IF BATTERY OPERATION on a three-way portable is fuzzy, but reception is satisfactory on both A.C. and D.C., replacement of the battery pack is usually necessary. "B" batteries showing 75 volts on a meter have been known to have such high internal resistance that the voltage to plates and screens was reduced to as little as 35 volts.

BURNED-OUT BALLAST TUBES need not put a receiver out of service permanently even if the tubes cannot readily be replaced with new ones. Satisfactory results can be obtained by removing the old line cord from the set and substituting a new line cord having a built-in resistor of a resistance value matching the tube heaters.

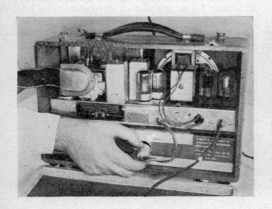

THIS PORTABLE MICROPHONE fits over the shoulders to leave both hands free. It is especially suitable for police and other call systems where the broadcaster must be engaged in writing or taking notes while using the instrument. At sports events, carnivals, and the like, it will be found highly portable; in addition, it permits the announcer to use both hands for moving other equipment. The unit is light in weight, and its shoulder harness fits snugly and comfortably. The mouthpiece, mounted on a flexible gooseneck-type column, can be held close to the mouth, and will give great volume without danger of feedback.

PLASTIC BASES FOR TUBES are being made to take the place of the customary porcelain bases heretofore used on tubes operating on ultrahigh frequencies. The new plastic is said to serve as efficiently as the ceramic material, and has one distinct advantage since it is not nearly as fragile as the regular porcelain. This is an extremely important point when it is considered that much of the equipment in use by the armed forces operates on ultrahigh-frequency bands and therefore requires tubes fitted with special bases for these bands.

REPLACEMENT VOLUME CONTROLS equipped with slotted attachments that automatically fit old shafts eliminate the problem of shaft sizes and knob fitting. Ten different types in the popular resistance values, tapers, and taps are available. Each control has a switch that can be put in operation only when a small lug on each side is removed, thereby enabling the control to be used without the switch when necessary.

INSULATION CAN BE STRIPPED automatically by placing the end of a wire in the new wire stripper below and pressing the handles together. One jaw clamps down on the insulation adjacent to that being stripped, while a second cuts through the insulation and removes it from the end of the wire. The tool can also be used for cutting copper wire and nickel-plated copper wire, but not wire made of iron or steel.

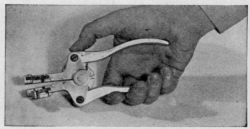

PRECISION RADIO-TIME CONTROL

Tuning-Fork Vibrations Amplified by Series of Vacuum Tubes Keep 200 Studio Clocks Synchronized

• •

ELECTRIC clocks in 200 studios and control rooms at Radio City, New York, are synchronized by a tuning fork vibrating in a vacuum chamber at 60 cycles a second. Developed and installed by NBC engineers, the system is now in the process of installation at other divisional headquarters. It assures synchronization of clocks within one third of a second a day.

The tuning fork creates infinitesimal pulses, which are amplified millions of times by a series of vacuum tubes until sufficient power is generated to operate the 200 clocks. An A.C. motor, driving a 60-cycle generator that actuates the system, draws current from the regular commercial power lines, but a battery-supplied D.C. motor on the same shaft is switched on automatically if A.C. power fails.

Two secondary tuning forks are included in the system for speeding or retarding the synchronized clocks each time the master clock is checked with the Naval Observatory. One vibrates at 65, the other at 55 cycles.

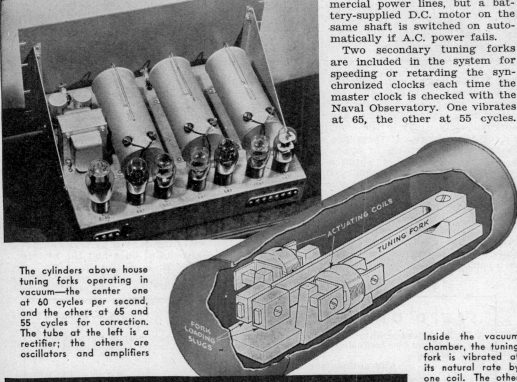

The cylinders above house tuning forks operating in vacuum—the center one at 60 cycles per second, and the others at 65 and 55 cycles for correction. The tube at the left is a rectifier; the others are oscillators and amplifiers

Inside the vacuum chamber, the tuning fork is vibrated at its natural rate by one coil. The other feeds back 60-cycle impulses to the vacuum-tube amplifier

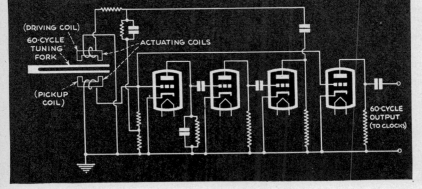

At left is a diagram of the pickup and amplifying circuit of the normally used 60-cycle fork. The output of the fork is amplified until power generated will operate 200 clocks

Double-Pole Switch Used to Control Two Motors

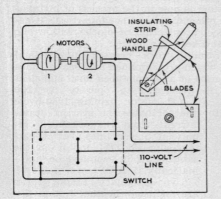

Above is a photograph of a switch controlling two ¼-hp. motors coupled together to power a metal-turning lathe

WHEN large electric motors are not obtainable, two smaller ones can be mounted end to end with their shafts connected by a coupling to form a power unit approximately equal to the combined output of the motors. If these are mounted so that they start up in opposite directions, the direction of rotation of the combined pair is determined by the motor that is started first. After this motor has reached a speed where the starting brushes of both motors are thrown out, the second one is cut into the circuit.

To accomplish this switching operation, you can use a double-pole, double-throw knife switch on which a minor operation has been performed. Remove the insulating strip connecting the two switch blades and replace it with a wider strip that will permit a slight staggering of the blades. Then, when the switch handle is moved toward a closed position, one blade makes contact first, and further movement brings the second blade into contact.

In use with the setup described, the first blade is closed to start the first motor; when the motor has gained sufficient speed to throw out the centrifugal brush mechanism, the second blade also is closed. Be careful not to close both contacts simultaneously. Watch the motors closely, and open the switch instantly if by accident you close both circuits at once and the motors "freeze."—W. E. B.

SPEED OF MOTORS   [ELECTRICAL]

THE speed of alternating-current induction motors depends upon the number of poles and the frequency. This can be figured for any motor from the following formula:

$$\frac{\text{Alternations per Minute}}{\text{Number of Poles}} = \text{r.p.m.}$$

As an example, if the frequency is 60 cycles, there are 120 alternations per second. Multiplying this by 60, we get 7,200 alternations per minute. If this is divided by 2, for a two-pole machine, the speed will be 3,600 r.p.m. Divided by 4, for a four-pole machine, the speed is 1,800 r.p.m. If the frequency is 25, by the same calculation, the alternations per minute will be 3,000. Dividing by 2 or 4 as before, the speed will be 1,500 or 750 r.p.m. respectively. This formula does not apply to direct current.

The following table gives the motor speeds obtained by this method for motors on 60-cycle lines:

No. of Poles	Synchronous speed (No Load)	Full Load
2	3600	3470
4	1800	1750
6	1200	1160
8	900	870
10	720	695
12	600	575

POPULAR SCIENCE MONTHLY SHOP DATA

Eccentric Disk Holds Work of Any Size Securely on Bench

THIS eccentric vise holds work on a bench securely, yet opens at a touch. The diameter of the disk can be made to suit your work. Drill several holes through it on a radius, and several holes in the bench to allow for holding stock of various widths. The bench has a removable piece against which the work wedges when the disk is swung around toward it. A heavy nail through a hole in the disk and one in the bench serves as a pivot. The width of the work will determine which of the holes are best to use.

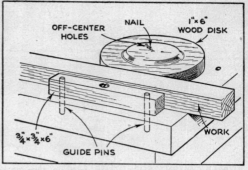

Safeguarding Your Checks

YOU can prevent alterations being made to a check by the use of an ordinary coarse mill file. Place the check face down with the portion on which the written amount appears flat on the surface of the file. Rub the back of the check carefully with a coin or piece of metal. The impression of the file will partly break through the paper and make it impossible to erase or alter the amount on the check.—W. S.

Outside Light Switch for Blackout Use

IF YOU desire to leave a light burning in your house, you can make it easy for your air-raid warden to turn it off from outside should occasion to do so arise while you are absent. On a light fixture which operates by a pull cord, attach a strong cord or fishline to the chain pull and run it along the ceiling, through a small pulley if necessary, to an outside window. In a strip of wood between the top of the upper sash and the window frame, drill a small hole slanting downward. Put the cord through this hole so it will hang outside the window within reach from the ground. On toggle switches, drill a hole through the operating arm, or notch it, and fasten a cord so a pull will flip the switch off. To avoid becoming the butt of practical jokers, keep the extension out of reach except when it is needed.—P. A. B.

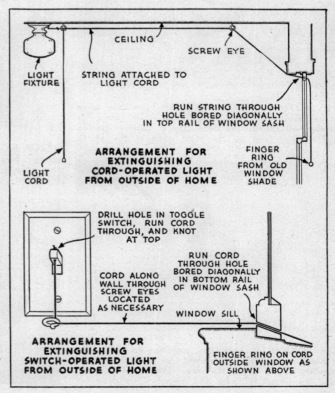

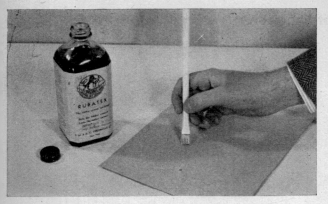

A RUBBER-CEMENT SUBSTITUTE now on the market is applied in exactly the same manner as regular rubber cement, and has the same adhesive qualities. The new cement contains neither crude nor reclaimed rubber, and is available in both pint and quart bottles

FOLDING LUNCH BOX. This container made of fiber board and available in blue or brown simulated leather is shown filled in photo above. Below, empty, it can be fitted easily into a man's jacket or coat pocket

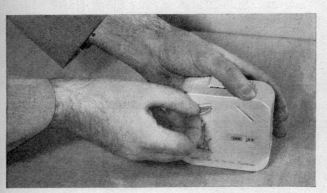

THIS NOVEL CALENDAR BANK lets you know when you're behind in your savings. A nickel, dime, or quarter will change the date, and a quarter inserted in the single slot on the right changes the month

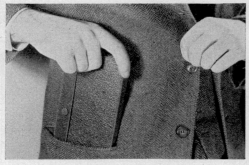

RAZOR BATH SETS save time and tempers. The special fluid, diluted with water and placed in the jar, will keep an undried razor free from rust for weeks. Cutaway view below shows razor in place

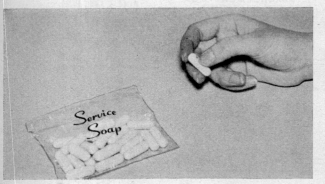

SOAP CAPSULES, each one sufficient to clean the grimiest hands, are convenient for motorists, train travelers, fliers, and the like. The celluloid capsules are about 7/8" long and about 1/4" in diameter

ANY QUART FRUIT JAR can be converted into a thermos bottle by fitting it into the container shown above. Made of heavy paper board with fiber insulation, such a jacket will keep foods hot or cold for several hours

PAPER-PLATE DISPENSERS are handy in the kitchen. The front perforations provide an opening for the removal of one plate at a time, and the flap fits back into place to keep dust out. An eyelet in the rear enables the package to be hung on the wall

FOLDING SPOOL RACK that's handy in the sewing room. When it is closed, as above, the spools cannot fall out or become tangled. Opened out, the rack forms a convenient spool stand, as below

THIS HANDMADE CIGARETTE BOX is as tricky as it is good looking. Simply turn the box on end and the lid automatically pops open, as shown in the photo above. Handsomely and sturdily made of walnut with maple inlays, it will fit into the most modern home, and makes an ideal gift for smokers

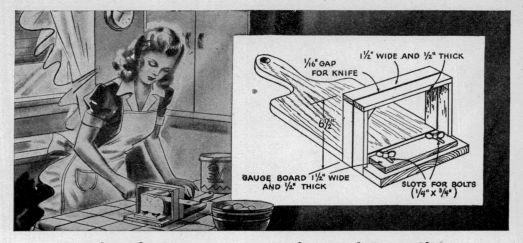

Labels on diagram: 1/16" GAP FOR KNIFE; 1½" WIDE AND ½" THICK; 6½"; GAUGE BOARD 1½" WIDE AND ½" THICK; SLOTS FOR BOLTS (¼" x ¾")

Bread-Knife Gauge Assures Thin and Even Slicing

HOUSEWIVES and those men who like to do a turn in the kitchen are now hacking away unfamiliarly with the bread knife after years of buying bread presliced at the bakery. For those who have lost the expert touch, here is a bread "miter box" to put an end to thick, jagged hunks and help toward the Government's goal of less waste. It not only assures even cutting, but also has an adjustable stop for making uniform slices of any thickness desired.

The base is an ordinary bread board, such as can be obtained at any store handling kitchenware. The knife guides are made from maple, built in two sections, as shown, and spaced 1/16" apart to allow free movement of the knife without wobble. Dado the edges of the baseboard and attach the frame with glue and countersunk screws. Blocks reinforce the upper corners. A 1/8" deep groove may be sawed across the board to receive the knife at the end of its stroke, so as to minimize dulling of the edge.

Drive square-shouldered carriage bolts for the thickness gauge into counterbored holes from beneath. They should be tight enough not to turn when the wing nuts are being tightened. A slice-thickness scale may be marked on the board.

In slicing bread, use a long, sharp knife with either a plain or scalloped edge, and cut with a sawing motion. Very fresh bread is likely to be soft and will give even with minimum pressure. This can be offset by turning the loaf on its side and slicing against the harder crust of the bottom.

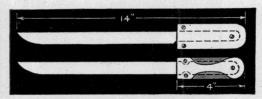

Labels: 14"; 4"

KNIVES THAT WILL STAY SHARP are often costly, but one can be made from a discarded power hack-saw blade that will cut through gristle and bone and still keep an edge keen enough for slicing hot bread. An old blade may be obtained from a machine shop, foundry, or large garage, but get one that is all hard, not one with a soft back. Grind off and taper one end, as shown; then grind the cutting edge slowly so that it does not burn. Grind the butt narrower or notch it for the handle rivets as shown, and sandwich the blade between two shaped pieces of wood, filling the crack with composition wood.

SHARPENING A KNIFE on an ordinary kitchen stone or steel requires a simple technique that is easy to learn. Keeping the cutting edge foremost and the blade tilted slightly, so that it will retain its bevel, start the stroke at the "heel" and sweep downward diagonally to cover the entire length from heel to point in one stroke. Alternate strokes from one side of the blade to the other, and do not use much pressure.

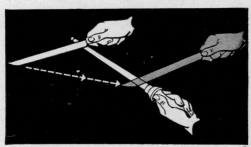

PHOTO IDEAS

Above, tank agitator ready for use. The tray fills with water until it is heavy enough to drop and lift the tank, falling to its original position as soon as the water spills from it

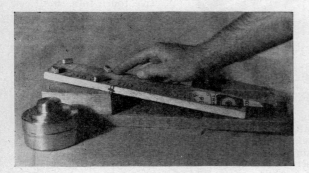

THIS HOMEMADE AGITATOR, suitable for any type of roll-film tank, works like a seesaw, with the tank at one end and a water tray at the other. A few small pieces of scrap lumber and a piece of tin cut from the side of a 2-qt. oil can are all you need to build it.

A block of wood 2" by 4" by 6" mounted on a baseboard will do for the fulcrum on which the movable board rests. Two small nails, placed near the edge of the fulcrum, fit inside corresponding screw eyes in the movable board to prevent it from creeping out of position when the agitator is in action. Four small blocks of wood hold the tank in place at one end of the board.

To find the correct position for the water tray, first fill the tank with water and place it on the board. It should be just far enough out to lift the fully loaded tank. When you find the position at which it operates most efficiently, fasten it to the board with small nails. Block the front up with a small piece of wood. It is advisable to coat the metal parts with waterproof paint or enamel, which will prevent them from rusting.—ROBERT SCOTT.

AMATEUR MOVIE FANS who would like to use the filters from their still cameras on their movie cameras can do so by a simple method involving very little labor and no cost. Simply enlarge the diameter of the movie-lens mount until it fits the larger filters. This is done by rolling a narrow band of light cardboard around the lens barrel, cementing it down as it is being rolled, until it is large enough to fit the filters neatly and snugly. This collar, shown in the photo at the left, can be left on the lens or removed when not in use. A further advantage is that such a collar arrangement will also permit the use of a still-camera lens shade for shooting pictures against the light.—L. HOCHMAN.

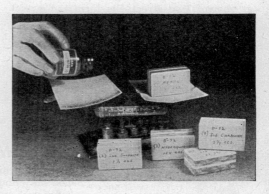

A NOVEL SYSTEM of measuring out photographic chemicals with "custom-built" weights is shown above. Such a method saves time, since all necessary information is printed on the boxes used as weights.

Using lead shot, pebbles, or some similar material, fill a small pillbox to the desired weight of each chemical required in the formula. Label the outside of each box with the name of the solution, the chemical it is to weigh, its weight, and the order-of-mixing number.—WM. SWALLOW.

Colorful Facing for a Chimney Made with Broken Pieces of Flagstones

WASTE pieces of colored flagstone left over from a job of paving a walk, terrace, or porch can be put to good use as a chimney facing if substituted for common brick or field stone. Fitted and cemented around the tile flue lining in the manner shown, the thin layers of flagstone form an unusual multicolored pattern.

Trim and lay flagstones so that regular bonds occur at corners

If you need a considerable quantity for facing a large house chimney, see your local building-supply dealer about buying up his stock of broken pieces. It takes only a few scraps, however, to add a distinctive touch to a small cottage chimney or an outdoor picnic fireplace.

Movable Pipe Arm Protects Electric Cable to Pump

WHERE a house water pump rests on a base set away from the cellar wall, the flexible cable supplying current to the pump can be protected from injury by running the cable through a supporting arm assembled from pipe fittings and screwed to the wall as shown. Two street ells form the swivel joint which permits the arm to be turned up out of the way against the wall whenever the cable must be disconnected for the purpose of servicing the pump. When in use, the free end of the arm rests on the motor. A short length of rubber hose, slipped over the end of the arm, serves as a cushion to eliminate noise due to vibration.—J. MODROCH.

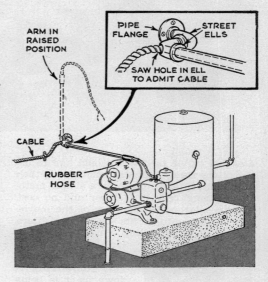

ARM IN RAISED POSITION

PIPE FLANGE — STREET ELLS

SAW HOLE IN ELL TO ADMIT CABLE

CABLE

RUBBER HOSE

Smoking Meat with Barrel and Stove Pipe

HOLES IN TOP
SMALL STICK THROUGH LOOP IN CORD
BARREL
WEIGHT
STOVE PIPE
SHEET METAL
FIRE PIT

THOSE wishing to smoke only a few hams or sides of bacon may find this simple method of interest. The tunnel insures cool smoke and eliminates the danger of overheating the meat.

Dig a trench about 12″ deep and twice the length of a piece of stovepipe. Bury the pipe in the middle of the trench. Over one of the open ends place a barrel upside down and bore a few holes in the top of it. Hang the meat with cords looped over small sticks.

In the other end of the trench build a fire with chips and corn cobs or hickory wood. Regulate the draft with a piece of sheet metal.—H. L. S.

EVEN ILLUMINATION, necessary when copying pictures or printed matter with a camera, is easily obtained by placing two or more silver-bowl lamps around the copy area, as shown in the photo above. The silvered globes direct light downward and also prevent direct rays from entering the camera lens. If each lamp socket is mounted on a block of wood, the lamps may be placed in any position quickly.—W. E. B.

TO KEEP A RECORD of film developer, showing how many times it has been used, paste a leaf from a small calendar on the bottle as shown below. Then, each time the developer is used, a number can be checked off. You will thus know when the developer has been used the prescribed number of times, and when to replenish it.

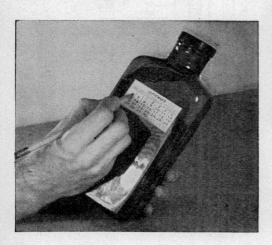

CURVED DRAWER HANDLES, such as are available for a few cents each, make it possible to move or adjust hot photoflood reflectors without waiting for them to cool. Two holes punched with a nail permit attachment of such a handle, and will not impair the efficiency of the reflector. The handles also help in carrying.—ANDREW M. LAVISH.

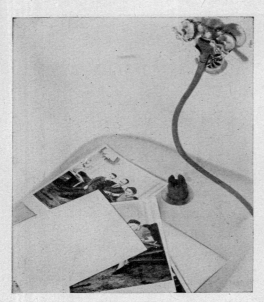

Print-Washing Drain Made from Auto Radiator Hose

FOR washing a number of large prints, a bathtub, wash tray, sink, or lavatory can be used if the drain is fitted with the device illustrated. This carries away the hypo-laden water from the bottom and allows the surplus to flow over the top.

The washer consists of a 4" length of automobile radiator hose of a diameter to fit into the drain snugly. A 3/8" hole is cut in it about 1/2" from the bottom, and three or four 3/4" deep notches are cut at the top. Push into the drain until the small hole is just above the bottom of the tub or sink.—W. L. BURKHARD.

Wetting Agent Causes Colors to Flow on Glossy Prints

ANYBODY who has tried to tint glossy prints with water colors knows how hard it is to make the color go on smoothly. It usually gathers into drops that defy the brush. To overcome this difficulty, I add 3 drops of wetting agent to 1 oz. of the water used. This decreases the surface tension so that the color spreads into a thin film wherever the brush guides it. It is not necessary to "work" it in. Any standard wetting agent, obtainable from photographic supply houses, will do.—SHIRLEY GADDIS.

Rocker of Shopmade Tool Post Cannot Fall Out of Slot

NEED an extra tool post? Here's a husky one you can make entirely of mild steel on the lathe itself. I have used this type for almost 40 years and still find it superior to commercial ones. The rocker cannot fall out or be mislaid, and the screw has a large flange and a fillet that prevent its bending if the wrench is accidentally hit.

After turning the body, drill a 25/64" screw hole right down to the bottom of the tool slot, which aids in finishing the slot. Clamp the body horizontally to the compound rest and drill a 1/2" hole through at either end of the slot. Then chuck a solid hand reamer in the lathe and use this as a milling cutter to finish the slot.

Turn the screw also from mild steel, stopping the thread about 1/4" below the fillet. Make the nut about one and a half times as high as the thickness of the wrench. The faces can be machined with a fly cutter held in the lathe chuck.

Leave the top of the rocker smooth. This will give it a firmer grip than if it is checkered and hardened. Drill a 1/8" hole at each end as shown and drive in tightly fitting pins, the second one after the rocker has been inserted in the tool slot. Caseharden only the screw.—HARRY L. ALLEN.

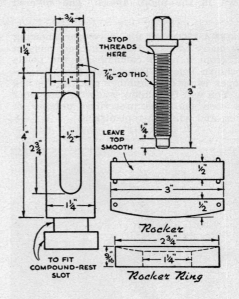

Taking a 4' hurdle, one obstacle on a course scientifically designed to help make boys physically fit

JUNIOR
Commando Course

OBSTACLES OF TYPE USED IN ARMY TRAINING ARE LAID OUT ON 100-YD. TRACK FOR TOUGHENING BOYS OF HIGH-SCHOOL AGE

HIGH-SCHOOL boys in many sections of the country are toughening up on junior commando courses similar to those used in the Army and at colleges to prepare soldiers and prospective soldiers for the rigors of battle. One such obstacle course, scientifically designed for boys of high-school age, is shown in the accompanying photographs and in the drawing on the following page. For comparison, a longer course used by soldiers in training at Fort Meade, Md., is shown on page HW 131.

The junior commando course at which the accompanying action pictures were taken was worked out principally by John M. Rowley, secretary and general custodian of the Board of Recreation Commissioners, East Orange, N. J. It is 100 yds. long and has a series of five different types of obstacles intended to give a good, stiff workout to all of a boy's muscles, particularly to those that do not get full exercise during the

average day's play. As an example of the speed at which the obstacles can be taken, the boy on the right in the photograph on the facing page and in the right foreground above was clocked when these pictures were shot, and he made the distance in 32 seconds, which is considered fast time. This will vary for boys of different ages.

All obstacles are easily built of lumber that should not be difficult to obtain. The hurdle, scaling wall, and balance beams are set in concrete to the depths shown in the drawing, while the low bridge and the stakes in the stake maze are simply driven into the ground. In these two cases, where the moisture in the ground is apt to have a deteriorating effect on the lumber, the portions that are to be underground should be impregnated with creosote to prevent rotting.

This course is built 12' wide to accommodate four contestants at one time, and is laid on a 100-yd. straightaway, although

Stay on the beam! So goes the watchword for this balancing act not unlike a circus tightrope walker's

there is no reason why it should not be curved to conform to the land available. If this is done, care should be taken not to have the curves too sharp, or too close to such obstacles as the hurdle or scaling wall, for which a running start is necessary. Their own momentum might otherwise carry the contestants off the course. One place where a curve might naturally fit, if convenient in the layout, would be in the stake-

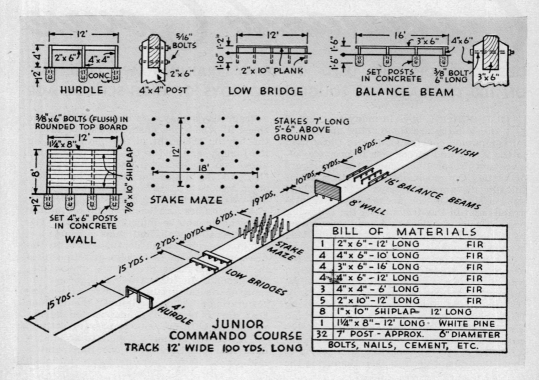

HURDLE

LOW BRIDGE

BALANCE BEAM

STAKE MAZE

WALL

JUNIOR COMMANDO COURSE
TRACK 12' WIDE 100 YDS. LONG

	BILL OF MATERIALS	
1	2"x 6" - 12' LONG	FIR
4	4"x 6" - 10' LONG	FIR
4	3"x 6" - 16' LONG	FIR
4	4"x 6" - 12' LONG	FIR
3	4"x 4" - 6' LONG	FIR
5	2"x10" - 12' LONG	FIR
8	1"x 10" SHIPLAP 12' LONG	
1	1¼"x 8" - 12' LONG	WHITE PINE
32	7' POST - APPROX. 6" DIAMETER	
	BOLTS, NAILS, CEMENT, ETC.	

This low bridge is no place for fat boys, but few will have excess pounds if they train in this way

maze obstacle itself, for here the stakes are so staggered and are at such unequal intervals that a curve would not add materially to the difficulty of passage.

It is a good idea to have at least a 15-yd. straightaway before the opening hurdle, one of 19 yds. before the scaling wall, and an 18-yd. straightaway at the end so that the contestants, if not already winded, can finish with a burst of speed.

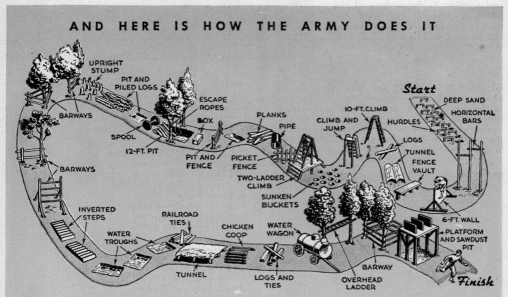

AND HERE IS HOW THE ARMY DOES IT

Start

UPRIGHT STUMP

PIT AND PILED LOGS

BARWAYS

ESCAPE ROPES

BOX

SPOOL

12-FT. PIT

PLANKS

PIPE

10-FT. CLIMB

CLIMB AND JUMP

HURDLES

DEEP SAND

HORIZONTAL BARS

LOGS

TUNNEL FENCE VAULT

PIT AND FENCE

PICKET FENCE

TWO-LADDER CLIMB

SUNKEN BUCKETS

BARWAYS

INVERTED STEPS

WATER TROUGHS

RAILROAD TIES

CHICKEN COOP

WATER WAGON

6-FT. WALL

PLATFORM AND SAWDUST PIT

TUNNEL

LOGS AND TIES

BARWAY

OVERHEAD LADDER

Finish

At Fort Meade, Md., this winding obstacle course is looked upon as "600 yds. of sore muscle." It is typical of toughening-up tracks for training Rangers and others in the Army to stand up under the rigors of battle. These obstacles will bring into play every muscle in a man's body

Adapted from *Yank*, the Army weekly. Original drawings by Privates Kraftsow and Ruge.

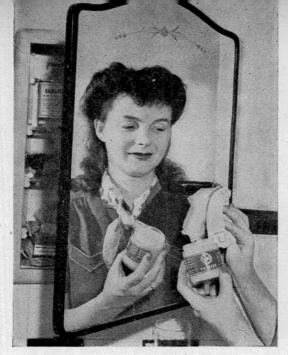

FOG ON MIRRORS can be prevented by applying a special new cream that spreads an invisible protective coating over the glass, causing all moisture to be dissipated. This cream is very convenient for shavers, for it does away with the annoying need of having to wipe off the shaving mirror several times when steam has collected there after the bath or shower. It can also be used to great advantage on kitchen windows, car windshields, and goggles. One application will keep the glass clear for approximately three to four weeks. The cream is put up in jars and comes in two handy 1-oz. and 4-oz. household sizes

COLORED WAX is now available for use on linoleum. It comes in red, blue, green, black, and clear, and can also be used as a filler for areas which are scratched or scuffed. Some of the matching wax is placed on a clean, dry cloth and applied to the surface of the linoleum. After it has dried, the floor is polished. The same product can be used on bric-a-brac, or anything that requires a coat of wax

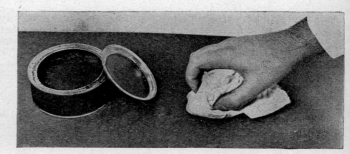

GLASS RING MOLDS now take the place of metal ones. Being ovenproof, they can be used in baking, as well as in molding gelatins, fruit desserts, and the like. A hole in the center enables one to get a strong grip when the mold is to be inverted. It measures 8¾" in diameter. The inside ring is 4" in diameter

THIS THERMOMETER is easy to read from any angle—left, right, or head-on. Because of this side-view advantage, it can be placed outside a window and can be read very easily from the inside. It can also be used in the office or the car. Two models of this handy gadget are available. One is finished in brass and the other in glistening chrome. Each one is 5½" high

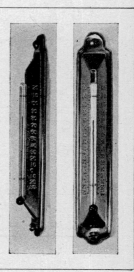

TWO NEW WOODEN GADGETS. Directly below, an ingenious all-wood hanger for skirts is shown. Constructed of plywood, it will not warp and is said to be exceptionally sturdy. The shoe rack at the right can be placed on the floor or hung on the closet door. Light in weight, it is made entirely of wood without the use of nails, screws, or any other metal parts. The rack comes knocked down, but with easy instructions for assembling. It will hold from six to nine pairs of men's or women's shoes

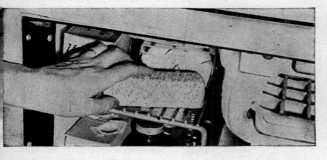

A REFRIGERATOR DEODORIZER that looks like pumice stone is shown at the left. It will eliminate the mingling of food odors, keep butter sweet and ice cubes fresh. The bar will revitalize itself if removed from the refrigerator while you are defrosting or cleaning. The chemical products it contains are of a type harmless to all foods and liquids. This deodorizer is said to last about one year if cared for as directed

PLASTIC POT CLEANERS to be used in place of steel wool and other types are now on the market. They are easy to clean after use and have an added advantage over metal cleaners in that they will never rust

FABRIC CLEANER. This fluid will remove grease spots and other stains harmlessly and efficiently. It can be used on glazed chintz, velvet, leather, and the like, and demoths the fabrics as they are cleaned

HANG YOUR IRON in this wall bracket, and it will be out of the way and safely removed from children. It is made of enameled metal, and has twenty glass balls against which the sole plate of the iron rests

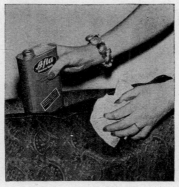

For the Period Room...

CHEST AND SECRETARY CAN BE BUILT OF PINE OR MAPLE

By JOSEPH ARONSON

EARLY American furniture was both sturdy and functional, particularly the cupboards, desks, and chests. This especially attractive piece of furniture, made up of two separate parts to form a secretary suitable for living room, bedroom, library, or den, pleasingly adheres to its American heritage.

The desk section has the advantage of having its drop front firmly supported when open by the top of the chest section, although the drop projects out far enough to provide knee room and toe space.

Generous space is provided in the drawers for storage of clothing or other articles, de-

pending on the use to which the piece is to be put, and pigeonhole compartments in the top hold writing equipment.

The construction of the chest unit is not difficult, although it takes accurate fitting. Solid lumber $7/8''$ thick was used for the most part. The secretary shown in the photograph was made of pine, but maple or another wood may be used. If the choice is a hardwood, which may not be fully $7/8''$ thick, the dimensions will vary somewhat.

After gluing up and preparing the top, sides, and drawer partitions, begin to form the case by doweling the frames into the sides. Note that only front and back rails and stretchers are glued to the sides. Side rails and cleats should be left free of the sides—that is, not glued—in order to permit the solid wood to expand and contract without cracking. The top back rail is set upright in order to stiffen the case.

Provide oversize screw holes all around the top stretchers and cleats, as the top of the chest should be held by screws passing through these holes to permit expansion of the solid top. The molding of the top is so simple that it can be planed off and sanded if no shaper is available. The base front member likewise is round-edged, and glued to the edges of the lowest rail and the ends of the sides. Secure this member further with small glue blocks under the lower front rail.

The drawers may be dovetailed or built with rabbet-and-dado joints. The dimensions given are for the latter type. In

Handsome and sturdy, this serviceable desk is built in two sections. Construction details for the desk portion are shown in the drawing on the facing page. Note the knuckle joint at the hinge

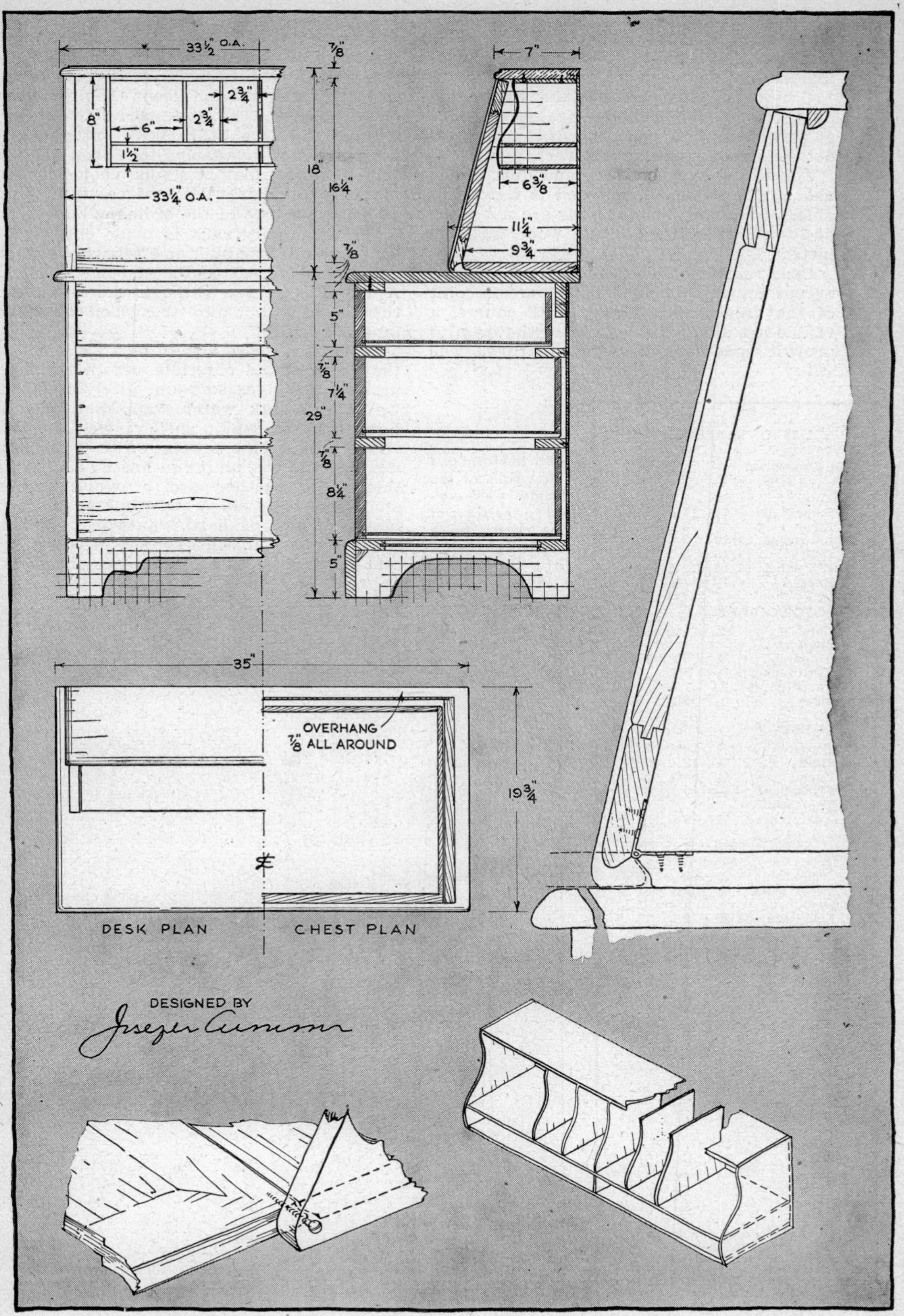

33½" O.A.
8"
6"
2¾"
2¾"
1½"
33¼" O.A.
7/8"
18"
16¼"
7/8"
5"
7/8"
7¼"
29"
7/8"
8¼"
5"
7"
6⅜"
11¼"
9¾"
35"
OVERHANG
7/8" ALL AROUND
19¾"
DESK PLAN
CHEST PLAN
DESIGNED BY

either case, it is advisable to set the sides in about ⅛" from the drawer ends, providing the lower edges with guide strips about ⅛" by ¾". This prevents the whole side of a drawer from rubbing against the side of the chest, and permits closer fitting to obtain smooth-running drawers.

For the drawer bottoms and dust panel, use ¼" hardwood if plywood is not available. If authentic metal pulls are not to be had for drawer handles, use wood turnings instead.

Construction of the desk section is simple except for the fitting of the knuckle joint of the drop front. There is, of course, a visible slit along the bottom of the drop to provide space for the edge to turn. The drop may be a plywood panel in a mitered frame of 3" wide members, or else solid pieces similarly framed. A quarter-round molding under the top keeps the drop from closing too far. The hinges should be preferably of the type called desk butts, but if they are not available, the back-flap or table-flap type may be second choice. These butts leave a fairly flat surface when open, which it not true of the ordinary butt.

The stationery rack is made entirely of ⅜" plywood. It is built as a separate section and then screwed to the top of the desk. A few fine screws through the back into the shelves will help to strengthen the whole inner structure.

Finish the secretary so as to emphasize the grain. Sand carefully before staining, making all edges soft and nicely rounded. Use a light-oak water stain first, then a light coat of white shellac, well rubbed. Next, antique the surface with a glazing mixture of burnt umber in linseed oil. After this, apply another coat of white shellac and sand to a silky smoothness. A final finishing coat of hard wax will complete the job, and you will have produced an excellent piece of Early American furniture.

LIST OF MATERIALS

No. Pc.	Description DESK	T.	W.	L.
1	Top	⅞	7	33½
2	Sides	⅞	11¼	17⅛
1	Floor	⅞	9¾	31½
2	Lid frame	13/16	3	31½
2	" "	13/16	3	17⅜
1	" panel	13/16	12⅛	26¼
1	Back	¼	17½	33⅜

PIGEONHOLES

1	Top	⅜	5¼	25
2	Shelf and floor	⅜	6¾	25
5	Partitions	⅜	5⅜	6⅜
1	Partition	⅜	1½	6¾
2	Sides	⅜	6¾	8

CHEST

1	Top	⅞	19¾	35
2	Sides	⅞	18	28⅛
1	Back	¼	28⅛	32¾
1	Front base	⅞	5	33¼
1	Top front stretcher	⅞	2½	31½
1	Top back stretcher	⅞	3	31½
2	Top side cleats	⅞	2	15⅛
3	Front rails	⅞	2½	31½
3	Back rails	⅞	2½	31½
6	Side rails	⅞	2½	13
1	Dust panel	¼	13½	27

TOP DRAWER

1	Front	⅞	5	31½
2	Sides	½	5	16¼
1	Back	½	4½	30¾
1	Bottom	¼	16¼	30¾

MIDDLE DRAWER

1	Front	⅞	7¼	31½
2	Sides	½	7¼	17
1	Back	½	6¾	30¾
1	Bottom	¼	17	30¾

BOTTOM DRAWER

1	Front	⅞	8¼	31½
2	Sides	½	8¼	17
1	Back	½	7¾	30¾
1	Bottom	¼	17	30¾

Note: All dimensions are given in inches

Both the front and back rails of the frames are doweled to the sides of the chest. Shown at the right below is a drawer joint

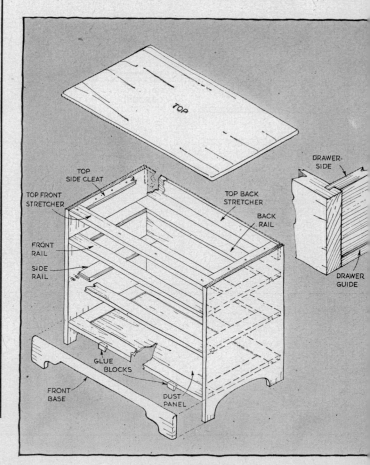

TOP

TOP SIDE CLEAT

TOP FRONT STRETCHER

TOP BACK STRETCHER

BACK RAIL

DRAWER SIDE

FRONT RAIL

SIDE RAIL

DRAWER GUIDE

GLUE BLOCKS

FRONT BASE

DUST PANEL

Storage Bins for Garden Food Utilize Garage Wall Space

YOU can keep garden fertilizers and soil builders in space ordinarily wasted in the garage by building these storage bins.

Detailed dimensions are not given, because these may differ slightly for various types of garage construction. The bottoms of the bins are made from 5/8" stock and toenailed to the sheathing and studs at a slight angle. If the lowest point of the bottom is 15" from the floor, the spreader can be filled directly from the bin. The bin front is plywood or wallboard 3' high and as long as desired.

Make the hole at the bottom of each bin by first boring three 1" holes, and then cutting out the center.

The covers are boards resting on the front panel and on cleats nailed to the studs.—H.W. DRYDEN.

Below, detailed construction of the storage bin with cutaway of one. Inset at left shows sliding door that closes bottom opening of bin. Note how neatly this utilizes garage space usually wasted

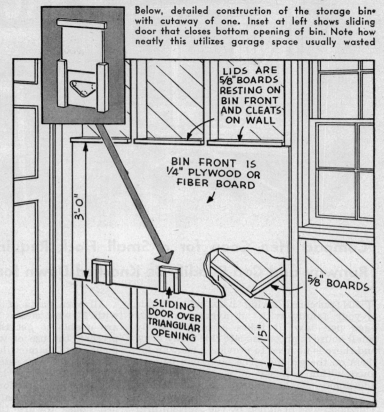

LIDS ARE 5/8" BOARDS RESTING ON BIN FRONT AND CLEATS ON WALL

BIN FRONT IS 1/4" PLYWOOD OR FIBER BOARD

3'-0"

SLIDING DOOR OVER TRIANGULAR OPENING

5/8" BOARDS

15"

Seedlings Are Easily Transplanted from Egg-Crate Fillers

SEEDLINGS will withstand transplanting better if they are raised in the compartments of an egg-box filler. One seedling is placed in each compartment, and it is an easy matter to slide out the tender plants, each with its own cube of earth, without disturbing the roots or soil. If a larger size is desired, a 36-compartment filler from an egg crate can be used, or you can make one by cutting card-board into 2" by 12½" strips and slitting them halfway through at intervals of 2". The strips are then fitted together to form the plant compartments. In making the flat, it is a good idea to have one side removable to aid in sliding out the plants more easily.—GEORGE MORASCH.

Seedlings set in egg-box fillers are easily transplanted. Wooden flat has been omitted for clarity

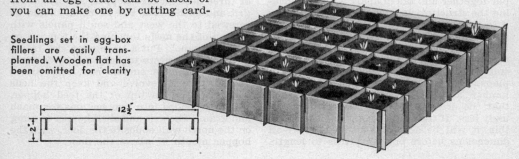

12½"

2"

Compact Hen Coop for a Small Flock Requires No Ground Runway and Can Readily Be Knocked Down for Easy Removal

TEN purebred laying hens will provide your family with an average of four eggs per day. It takes a comparatively small house to accommodate this many hens, and there is no need to provide a runway for them on the ground. The birds can be confined within a space of 5' by 6' plus an additional pen measuring approximately 2½' by 6', both areas 2' above the ground. This coop was designed by the Agricultural Department of the University of California.

The floors of the house and pen are covered with wire mesh, which eliminates the need of using litter on the floors and also makes the cleaning away of droppings a simple and not too annoying job. With this task in large part eliminated, the small amount of time consumed in the care of a few hens is amply repaid by having fresh eggs during the present food emergency.

While it would be less work to nail up the hen house on a site, the plans show how it can be built in sections so that it can be put together and taken apart without harming the structure as a whole. This will allow it to be moved from one location to another as circumstances may require. The use of lumber dressed on four sides is recommended because better-fitting joints will result with less work. All dimensions on the plans, as given, assume that dressed 1" lumber actually measures ⅞" thick and that the dressed width is also correspondingly less. If the lumber you use varies from this, it will be advisable to check over-all dimensions before cutting pieces to length.

All open parts of the house are covered with 1" wire mesh. If for any reason you are unable to get this size wire mesh at present, the use of wooden slats is recommended. Common lath will do for both floors and open sides of house and pen. Fasten the slats or lath on edge ¾" apart for the floors, and for open wall panels put them flat and vertical, 1½" apart. Face the hen house toward the south and put the open pen on the east end jutting out in front so the afternoon sun will reach it.

The hen house has a base, a floor section, four sides and a roof. The floor section fits into the top of the base, and the four sides are bolted to each other at the top and bottom corners, and also to the floor section on all sides midway between the corners. The sheathing for sides and roof is of 1" by 4" tongue-and-groove boards. Roof boards are nailed to three 2" by 3" cleats which extend about 2" beyond the sides.

Equipment for the house includes a group of three nests, a feed hopper, and a box for grit and shells. The row of nests should be screwed to the west and south panels with the top of the nests touching the top rail on the west panel. Put a triangular slat frame on top of the nests to keep the birds from roosting there. A tumble reel, constructed as shown, will revolve and keep the hens from standing on top of the feed hopper, which is divided into two sections for mash and grain. The grit and shell hopper is hung on the north wall opposite the door, with the hopper mouth 6" above the floor.

POULTRY HOUSE

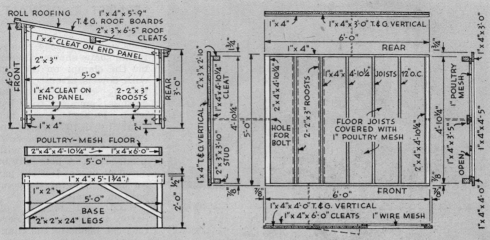

END VIEW

FLOOR PLAN AND SIDES

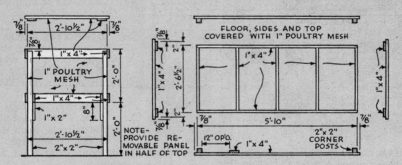

END VIEW — SCREEN PEN — FLOOR & SIDES

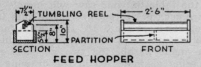

FEED HOPPER

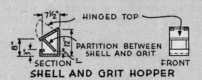

SHELL AND GRIT HOPPER

Dry ventilated quarters coupled with the right feed and clean water for laying hens will give maximum results in egg production. In severely cold or stormy weather the wire mesh of the house can be covered with burlap or muslin to keep the hens comfortable and in good health

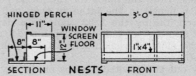

NESTS

Craftwork Projects Hit Keynote

DESIGNED BY
ERNEST R. DEWALT

tises and round the clamps to the shape shown. Assemble the clamps on the legs with dowels after trial fits, making certain that the springs engage the bar when pressed down and clear by 1/16" when upright. Then secure the dowels to the tongues with small brads. A hole may be bored at one end of the bar for use in hanging the compass on a wall.

Sand and smooth all parts, taking special care that the inside of the channel is smooth enough for free sliding. Brush with two coats of lacquer. Working time, 4 hours.

LOCKING TOY BLOCKS. Here is a model-making construction set with a wide range of possibilities for the juvenile builder. The blocks will form horizontal and flat patterns, animal forms, three-dimensional figures and spirals, such as shown in the photograph. A minimum set should contain at least 24 blocks and 48 lock strips.

To make the blocks, cut 1¾" by 1¾" pine or whitewood into 4' lengths, or longer if the table of your saw will handle them. Then set the rip fence so single cuts 19/32" deep can be made 3/16" from each face for the entire length of the piece. Eight cuts are made in all, the two at each corner crossing as indicated in the drawing. The corners are cut off at a 45-deg. angle to produce eight faces, each one 9/16" wide. Cut the piece into 1¾" blocks and sand to 1 11/16".

Make the lock strips of 21/32" by 21/32" maple. Eight rip cuts, set in 9/32" with the blade 9/32" deep, are necessary to leave 3/32" fins. Use a sharp blade and make the corners clean so they will fit easily into the mortises of the blocks. Cut the lock strips 1 11/16" long plus 1/32" allowance for sanding the ends. While pine or whitewood is

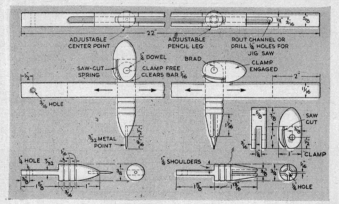

DRAFTING BEAM COMPASS. This all-maple compass, which has a bar ⅝" by 11/16" by 22", makes circles 34¾" in diameter on paper or plywood. It will prove much more convenient to use than a string on sticks or brads. The ¼" open channel, extending within 2" of either end, may be routed out or jigsawed from ¼" bored holes to gauged lines on opposite faces, and then sanded smooth.

Use ¾" maple dowel stock in turning the center point and pencil leg, allowing enough stock in the chuck on both pieces for 1⅝" tongues. Bore the holes for the metal point and the pencil in the lathe so they will be centered, taking the 3/32" hole to a depth of ½" and the ¼" hole to a depth of 11/16". Cut the slots and shoulders after finishing the lathe work.

Lay out the pivoted clamps on ⅝" by 1" maple stock, drill the ¼" holes, cut the spring line, and then cut out the open mor-

# of Ingenuity

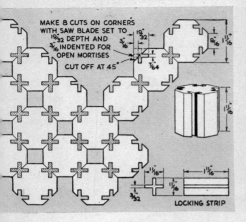

MAKE 8 CUTS ON CORNERS WITH SAW BLADE SET TO 19/32 DEPTH AND 3/16 INDENTED FOR OPEN MORTISES

CUT OFF AT 45°

LOCKING STRIP

satisfactory, hardwood is more substantial. Working time, 4½ hours.

A PARALLEL STRAIGHTEDGE is set up permanently on the drawing board, its length being optional depending upon the width of the board. Seasoned pine or whitewood is used for the body. Saw slots at a 10-deg. angle ¼" deep to take the strips of 3/16" by ⅝" clear plastic. These are fastened in with cellulose cement. True the edges carefully with a steel straightedge and a sharp plane to be sure they are parallel, round the four corners, and smooth with fine sandpaper.

The fillers are of 3/32" tempered composition board, cut to permit clearance of the cords which work on the four pulleys. Leave room between the fillers for the cords to cross at the center. Run the cords on diagonally opposite pulleys, pull them taut, and then fasten the ends at the corners of the board. Finally, cover the filler with composition board. This may be in two parts, and should overlap the edges to form a finger grip. Sand the cover and finish with three coats of lacquer, rubbed between coats. Do not apply lacquer to the plastic. Neat fitting and careful finishing will produce a useful drafting accessory. It can be pushed to the top of the board when not needed. Working time, 4½ hours.

CLEAR PLASTIC
STRINGS RIDE FREE IN GROOVES
STRINGS CROSS AT CENTER
CLEAR PLASTIC
COMPOSITION BOARD   COUNTERSUNK SCREWS
FINGER GRIP
RISER
DIAGRAM SHOWING PATH OF CORDS THROUGH STRAIGHTEDGE
Section A-A
ENDS ARE FASTENED TO CORNERS OF DRAWING BOARD

For War-Stamp Savings

NOVEL CARDBOARD BANK SEPARATES NICKELS, DIMES, AND QUARTERS

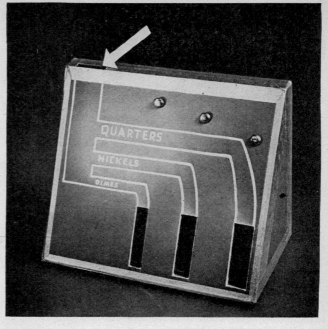

WATCH your War Stamp savings grow in this novel bank that automatically stacks nickels, dimes, and quarters in separate compartments as they are inserted through one slot at the top. Since the compartments are transparent, it is easy to see at a glance just how much money has been saved.

Draw the pattern on the right side of 14-ply showcard board, following the dimensions shown in the drawing; then cut with a knife and a brass-edged ruler. Where the board is to be folded, it is cut halfway through. The three rectangular openings are drawn on the reverse side of the front and cut out.

Next, the cardboard track down which the coins roll is cut out and glued, and the upper track for the glass slide likewise attached. The case is then folded, the left side glued in place, the glass slide inserted, and the lower track for the slide set in. The right side of the case is then glued in place.

Cut out the three boxlike compartments for the coins and attach them with split paper fasteners, propping them against cardboard stops at the bottom. Use gummed tape to finish the edges.—FRANK SHORE.

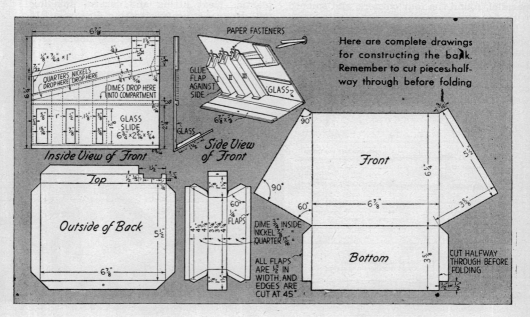

Here are complete drawings for constructing the bank. Remember to cut pieces halfway through before folding

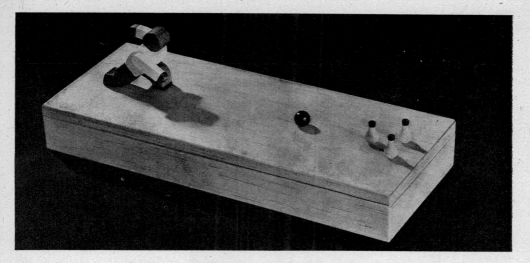

Bowling Motif Decorates Handkerchief Box for Man's Dresser

DESIGNED to hold handkerchiefs or collar buttons, cuff links, lodge insignia, and other small items, this unusual box will "strike" a sporting note atop a man's dresser. Make the box with butt joints or rabbet-and-dado joints. If it is built as a unit with the top and bottom glued in place, and then cut apart on a circular saw or band saw, lid and bottom will match perfectly. Bevel all edges and attach the lid with small hinges.

Draw the profile of the figure on a block 1⅛" by 2¼" by 2¼". Saw it to the outline; then cut back on both sides of the head to form the shoulders and cut to the halfway mark from opposite sides in front and back to form the two legs. Make the arms separately, attaching them with glue and brads. Hands, legs, and head may be stained brown, the feet black, and the upper portion of the body may be painted white.

Turn or carve the ball and three pins with a small projection on each for gluing into holes. Trim the ends flush with the inside surface of the lid. Accent the pins with black at the top and stain the ball black. A plain shellac and wax finish on the box will simulate the appearance of a real bowling alley.—JUAN OLIVER.

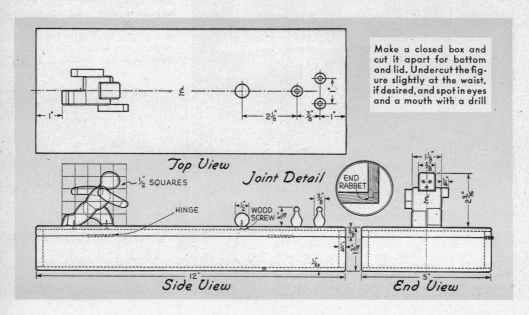

Make a closed box and cut it apart for bottom and lid. Undercut the figure slightly at the waist, if desired, and spot in eyes and a mouth with a drill

Butt Joints and Their Uses

By
EDWIN M. LOVE

A BUTT joint is formed when the end of a board is fastened to the side of another. The simplest and most easily made of all joints, it is probably more often used than any other. Carpenters, when framing a house, butt studs against plates and fire stops against studs. They nail shelves to cupboard sides, toenail drawer rails to the stiles, and butt baseboards against door casings. Wooden novelties and inexpensive furniture are often assembled by means of butt joints.

For such uses this joint is satisfactory. Its natural weakness is balanced by ample nailing and bracing in houses. In fact, butt joints are used throughout the framing of a house. In addition to studs, plates and fire stops, all diagonal bracing at corners is made with butt joints. Floor joists and the bridging that holds them rigid also rely upon this joint for stiffness. Walls offer a firm support to built-in cabinets constructed with butt joints. Novelties are usually rein-

To nail a square butt joint, as above, start the nails in one piece. Then, adjusting the joint with a forefinger, drive a single corner nail in first. A mitered joint, as shown at the right, is nailed with the top piece protruding slightly. It will draw into alignment as the nails are driven home

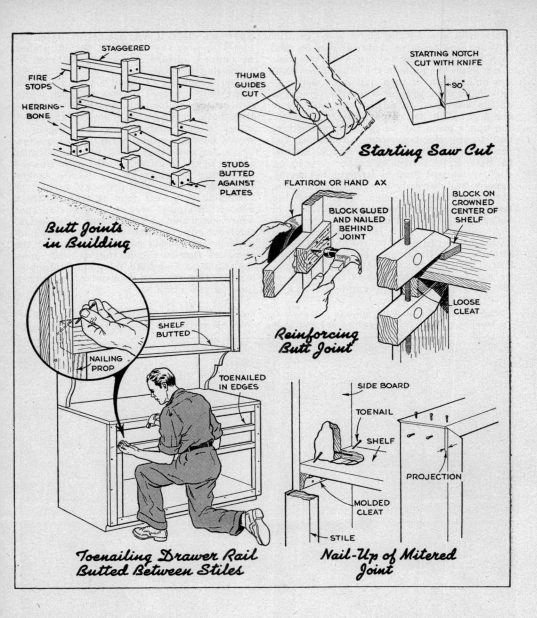

STAGGERED

FIRE STOPS

HERRING-BONE

STUDS BUTTED AGAINST PLATES

Butt Joints in Building

THUMB GUIDES CUT

STARTING NOTCH CUT WITH KNIFE

90°

Starting Saw Cut

FLATIRON OR HAND AX

BLOCK GLUED AND NAILED BEHIND JOINT

BLOCK ON CROWNED CENTER OF SHELF

LOOSE CLEAT

Reinforcing Butt Joint

SHELF BUTTED

NAILING PROP

TOENAILED IN EDGES

SIDE BOARD

TOENAIL

SHELF

PROJECTION

MOLDED CLEAT

STILE

Toenailing Drawer Rail Butted Between Stiles

Nail-Up of Mitered Joint

forced with glue. The home mechanic can make good use of butt joints in constructing fences, pergolas, garden furniture, and many pieces of household equipment.

As with all joints, the value of a butt joint depends much on the laying out and cutting of it. When new, mill-surfaced lumber is used, it can reasonably be assumed that the edges are parallel and square. If the end of the board is to be sawed, scribe a line across the face and edges, using a sharp, hard pencil, or better still, the point of a knife. However, a board that needs

cutting to size should be prepared with special care. First, plane one side and mark it for a working face. Next, joint one edge, checking it with a try square or bevel square. Guide against this edge to gauge the piece to width. Finally, gauge the board for thickness and plane the other side.

When starting the saw cut, extend the thumb to act as a guide, or notch the corner of the piece with a knife. Run the blade of the saw in the waste wood with the teeth splitting the line. The man who has trouble making a true vertical cut will find a guide block held against the blade to be helpful.

When one piece of material can be held in a vise, it is easy to nail a narrow butt joint. Start the nails in the other piece as it lies on the bench; then nail it as shown in one of the photographs, using the forefinger of the left hand to adjust the joint while the first nail is driven part way. Thereafter the upper piece can be pivoted on the first nail to the exact position for driving the second nail. Use a variation of this method to nail wide boards together, springing slightly warped lumber straight by prying against nails already driven. In such cases extra nails may be needed. Wide boards too large to hold in the bench vise can be held between the legs for nailing.

A clamp and a loose cleat can be used to flatten a warped shelf before nailing. Many kitchen cupboards are built with plain butted shelves, but strength can be added by nailing cleats to the side boards under the ends of shelves. If a simple molding is used as a cleat, it will not detract from the appearance of the cupboard. Should a shelf be cupped upward, it can be flattened by toenailing from above.

The shrinkage of wood across the grain must be considered in making butt joints. Wherever possible, join width to width, so that both members will shrink and swell alike. Avoid joining different species of woods having unequal shrinkage characteristics, for nails may work loose and cause failure of the joint. Should the nails succeed in holding the edges firmly despite uneven shrinkage, checks will probably appear.

Similar to a butt joint is that in which a board is lapped over the edge of another board, as when a cabinet stile is nailed to the front edge of a side board. In joints such as these glue holds well, and in all but the cheapest furniture construction will repay the slight time and labor involved in applying it. However, glue usually fails when used on end grain.

When nailing butt joints too large to put into a vise, the work can be held securely between the legs in a kneeling position, as below. Nail one end of the joint; then reverse the work to nail the other end

A simple miter joint, as shown in one of the photographs, is little more than a butt joint but has the advantage that it conceals the end grain. It is useful for applying trim such as a wainscot cap around a pilaster. Since the piece in which the nails are being driven generally slides down the slope of the joint, it should be allowed to overlap the other at first. Do not drive the nails home immediately, but wait until the joint is partly nailed from the other direction. Any inequality can then be adjusted by tapping nails alternately on one side and the other.

In places where miter joints are used and one or more pieces can be nailed in place before abutting pieces are put on, it is usually best to sand joints to a perfect fit before nailing the abutting pieces in place. Such places occur when fitting moldings or baseboards at both outside and inside corners of a cabinet or applying inside trim.

Kitchen Knife Rack Is Made Entirely with Butt Joints

THIS kitchen rack for bread and carving knives is assembled with butt joints. Trace a half pattern for the front piece and decoration by following the lines on ½" squares. Saw out the front and back and smooth them carefully. Prepare the partitions by accurately squaring the edges and rounding the upper ends. Lay the partitions in place on the front piece, separating them with strips of ¼" plywood; then mark and cut the bottom ends. Clamp the pieces together again in position and nail through the back. Remove the plywood separating strips and nail the partitions through the front. If figured hardwood is used for a stain and varnish finish, glue the front on instead. Weight or clamp it until the glue is dry.—E. M. L.

LIGHT GREEN
PINK
DARK GREEN

6½"
2¼"
10½"
8½"
¾" ¾" 1⅛" 1¾"
¼" ¼"

½ SQUARES

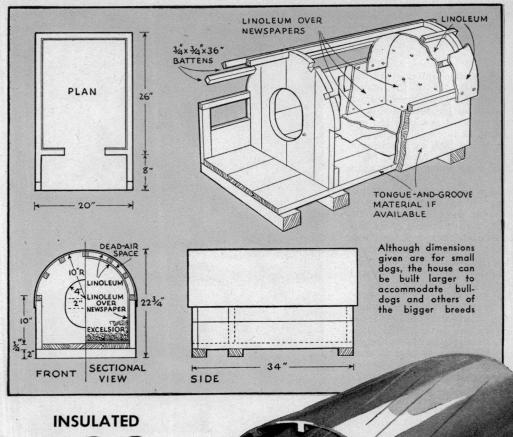

PLAN

26"

8"

20"

LINOLEUM OVER NEWSPAPERS

LINOLEUM

¾" x ¾" x 36" BATTENS

TONGUE-AND-GROOVE MATERIAL IF AVAILABLE

DEAD-AIR SPACE

10" R

LINOLEUM

LINOLEUM OVER NEWSPAPER

EXCELSIOR

22¾"

10"

¾"

2"

FRONT

SECTIONAL VIEW

SIDE

34"

Although dimensions given are for small dogs, the house can be built larger to accommodate bull-dogs and others of the bigger breeds

INSULATED

DOG HOUSE

LINOLEUM remnants and odd lengths of lumber are all the materials needed for this insulated dog house. The dimensions given are suitable for small dogs but can be increased to suit.

A floor of tongue-and-groove boards is laid on three 2 by 3's, and the sides and ends are erected upon this. The ends are cleated on the inside and notched for the roof battens as shown in the drawing. Walls, floors, and ends are well insulated with linoleum placed over several layers of dry newspapers. Be sure to warm the linoleum before bending it so that it will not crack. That on the roof is put on last and should come down a few inches over the side so as to give adequate protection in stormy weather. Place the smooth side uppermost and give it two coats of outdoor paint. Bed the floor of the house with excelsior.

The open doorway provides ample ventilation, while the front "porch" serves as a platform for water and food dishes, and keeps driving rain out.

"Peg Leg" Device Steadies Card Table on Uneven Surfaces

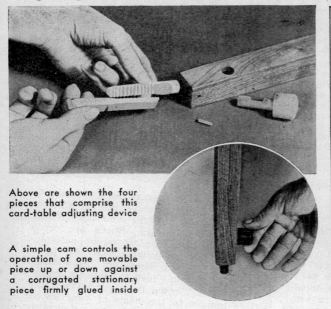

Above are shown the four pieces that comprise this card-table adjusting device

A simple cam controls the operation of one movable piece up or down against a corrugated stationary piece firmly glued inside

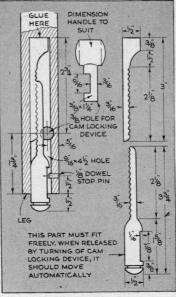

GLUE HERE
DIMENSION HANDLE TO SUIT

3/8 HOLE FOR CAM LOCKING DEVICE

1/8 DOWEL STOP PIN

9/16 x 4 1/2 HOLE

LEG

THIS PART MUST FIT FREELY. WHEN RELEASED BY TURNING OF CAM LOCKING DEVICE, IT SHOULD MOVE AUTOMATICALLY

A UNIQUE, easily made device eliminates the annoying wobble resulting when a card table is set on an uneven floor. Built into one leg, this extension permits the length of that one to be changed so that all four legs of the table will rest firmly.

Saw 1/2" off the bottom of the leg and bore a 9/16" hole up through the center to a depth of 4 1/2". Intersect this hole with a 3/8" hole bored horizontally through the leg at a point 1 3/4" from the bottom and, for a leg that is 1" square, 5/16" away from one edge. Drill a 1/8" hole in the side of the leg, and also at a right angle to the vertical hole, 1/2" from the bottom. Shape the two dowel pieces as shown and glue the station-

ary piece all the way up into the hole, with its notched face parallel to the 3/8" hole.

Make the cam pin and insert it in the side hole, turning it so that the movable dowel can be adjusted to protrude 1/2" from the end of the leg; then lock it in place. The stop pin is then glued into its hole with sufficient clearance to allow for easy adjustment of the lower dowel.

In operation, the movable dowel may be lowered or raised, depending on whether the table leg is to be shortened or made longer. A twist of the cam loosens the grip of the grooves, the card table is leveled, and the cam is turned once more to secure the setting.—BENJAMIN NIELSEN.

Party Favors Resemble Fans

GAY fan place cards that will add a sparkling touch to any dinner table can be made inexpensively in a few minutes.

Choose any color paper desired and fold it back and forth, accordion-pleat fashion. Holes are punched at one end of the pleats, and into these holes a poultry marker is slipped. The marker is spread wide enough to stand upright. Add a bright ribbon, as shown in the photo, paste a star or some other decoration to one end of the streamer, and stick the name card to the other.

The colors chosen for the favor pictured were red, white, and blue—an appropriate patriotic motif.

More Mileage from Shoe Leather

THREE pairs of shoes should be ample for the average person. Government officials have been backed up in this opinion by leading shoe-repair men, who say that a pair of good shoes properly taken care of should last not only four months, six months, or a year, but literally for years. But you can't be slipshod and be well shod! Here are several points that should be observed to make shoes give longer service and retain their looks at the same time.

SHOE TREES are as important to your shoes as hangers are to your clothes. Feel along the inside lining of your shoes. Do you notice any bumps, curves, sags? These come as a result of dampness, moisture, and perspiration, which cause the inner soles and linings of footwear to curl up or warp out of shape. If you place trees in your shoes promptly after taking them off, the shoes will be molded back into shape.

SHOEHORNS are another accessory too often neglected. The backs of your shoes are tender and have the least support of any part of the shoe structure. They will break down completely if you push your feet into them without the aid of a shoehorn. It is almost impossible to repair shoes with broken backs, but it is easy to avoid this.

THOROUGH CLEANING and polishing is a vital part of shoe care. Saddle soap or any other good leather soap should be used frequently in order to remove dirt from your shoes. Never polish over the dirt. After cleaning, give your shoes a high polish, for this keeps the leather soft and flexible. It is always advisable to use leather soap and polish after shoes have been exposed to wet weather.

THIN SOLES are a warning to have shoes resoled promptly. Don't wait until a hole appears. Shoes are much harder to repair satisfactorily when holes are present, especially men's shoes, in which the inner soles become damaged. The same advice applies to the heels of your shoes. Badly worn heels throw the feet out of position, strain the shoes, and cause uneven wear.

CORRECT SIZE is important. Be sure the shoes you purchase are large enough, for too-small shoes will soon be pushed completely out of shape and will wear much faster. Have your size checked frequently. Your feet may continue to grow even through middle age. A poor fit will harm your feet as well as the shoes. When you buy shoes, try on both of the pair.

HEAT dries out the leather, causing it to crack, split, and otherwise deteriorate. Therefore, keep your shoes away from radiators, fireplaces, and the like. Dry wet shoes in a cool place.

DON'T wear the same pair of shoes continually. Your shoes will last much longer if you change them often. Frequent vacations on shoe trees reshape and rehabilitate them.

Lawn Ornaments

Liven up your lawn with the figures shown in the drawing. They are scroll-sawed from ⅜" outdoor plywood, or else from ¾" solid lumber joined edge to edge with waterproof resin glue and doweled at all weak points

Designed by HI SIBLEY

RED AND WHITE

SASH CORD

TAN

BLUE

BROWN

BROWN BLENDING INTO FAWN BELOW

¼ DOWEL PAINTED WHITE

WHITE, YELLOW BILL AND LEGS

WIRE

YELLOW

RED ON WHITE

PINK

RED

DO NOT PICK THE FLOWERS

PUT EARTH MOUNDS EACH SIDE OF SHRUB

YELLOW

WHITE

BLUE

BRIGHT-COLORED PRODUCE

DARK BROWN

BLACK

DARK GREEN ON LIGHT

BLUE PANTS

ALL 2" SQUARES

THIS END PLUGGED

ADHESIVE TAPE

DELPHINIUM

NAME ON PAPER INSERT

CELLULOID OVER BLOCK ½" × ¾" × 3"

LIGHT YELLOW

BROWN

BROWN

BLACK

BRIGHT REDS AND BLUES

HARDWOOD STAKES ON LARGE FIGURES

(LAMB)

IRON ON SMALL ONES

TAN

YELLOW

(SHOULD HAVE A BRACE IN BACK)

BLACK

RED

BLUE

GREEN

BROWN

ODD PIECES OF ¾" MATERIAL GLUED TOGETHER AND FIGURE DOWELED WHERE MOST LIKELY TO SPLIT

WHITE WITH BROWNISH-GRAY LEGS AND FACES

MACHINISTS FOR WAR WORK

MILLING KEYWAYS

WHEREVER you find machinery, you are likely to see gears and shafts. Wherever a gear and shaft must rotate as one, they are locked together —often by a key fitted snugly into matching keyways. The accurate cutting of these keyways is one of the many important operations performed by the modern milling machine in producing the parts for America's heavy war weapons. Accompanying photographs show step by step how a typical keyway is milled.

The job starts with a blueprint calling for a keyway 3/16" deep by 5/16" wide by 3" long in each end of a 2" shaft 18" long. First of all the operator checks the shaft dimensions to make sure he has the right piece for the job.

When ready to set up the work, he brushes off the milling-machine table and wipes clean all parts that are fitted or clamped together so that they will line up accurately. Then he lubricates the operating mechanism and, in the slot on the table nearest the headstock, secures the shaft to be machined rigidly in place with two U-clamps and heel blocks. The arbor is inserted in the spindle and a draw-in bar is screwed in from the rear to set it solidly in position. Care is taken to see that both the spindle and arbor tapers are clean.

The machinist next selects a suitable slotting cutter with teeth 5/16″ wide—the width of the keyway—and places it on the arbor with the necessary collars. He slides out the overarm bracket to support the arbor, being careful to locate it far enough out to clear the table clamps when the shaft is run in for cutting.

How shall the operator center the shaft under the cutter? Using either the power-driven or hand controls, he raises the shaft alongside the cutter, leaving a space of .015″ between shaft and teeth, as determined by means of a .015″ feeler gauge. In this position, the distance from the center of the

cutter to the center of the shaft is equal to .15625″ (half the width of the cutter) *plus* .015″ (the thickness of the feeler) *plus* 1″ (the radius of the shaft). This totals 1.17125″ and represents the distance the table must be moved in toward the headstock in order to center the shaft precisely under the cutter.

To make this adjustment, the machinist lowers the table and sets the index dial on the cross-feed screw at zero. Since the dial is divided into 250 calibrations, each of which represent a table movement of .001″, a full turn advances the table .250″ or ¼″, and four complete turns plus .171″ will bring the shaft to the desired location.

With the table locked in this position, the operator is ready to calculate the cutting speed. Three factors enter into his selection: (1) the nature of the material to be cut, (2) the material from which the cutter is

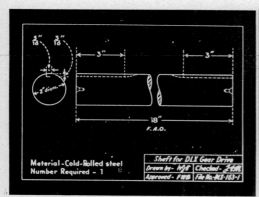

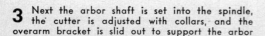

1 All jobs start with blueprints giving required dimensions. Note that each keyway is measured only to where the cut begins to leave the shaft

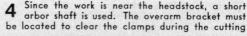

2 Brush the milling-machine table clean, and then clamp the shaft to it in the slot nearest the headstock, using two U-clamps and heel blocks

3 Next the arbor shaft is set into the spindle, the cutter is adjusted with collars, and the overarm bracket is slid out to support the arbor

4 Since the work is near the headstock, a short arbor shaft is used. The overarm bracket must be located to clear the clamps during the cutting

made, and (3) the diameter of the cutter. In this instance he is cutting cold-rolled steel with a 5" cutter made of high-speed steel, and according to the reference chart 100 surface feet per minute at the cutter teeth is a recommended speed.

The machinist now makes some rapid calculations. "Since the cutter is 5" in diameter," he reasons, "its circumference will be five times *pi*—that's 15.708" or 1.309'. The speed in feet per minute at the cutting teeth is to be 100. Dividing this speed by the circumference in feet gives me 76—the number of revolutions per minute I need. This setting does not appear on the spindle-speed dial, so I'll simply choose the nearest available setting, which is 74."

Having centered the shaft and established the cutter speed, the operator must now find the correct feed, or the number of inches per minute at which the work is brought into the cutter. For a 3/16" cut (the depth

of the keyway) each tooth should remove a chip about .002" thick. This chip thickness, times the number of teeth on the cutter—20 in this case—equals .040", or the distance the work is fed into the cutter in one complete revolution of the latter. To find the feed per minute, he merely multiplies .040" by the cutter speed, 74 r.p.m., which gives him a feed of 2.960" per minute. The nearest setting to this on the feed-speed dial is 2¾", so he sets it accordingly.

The milling machine is now ready for a short trial run, at the end of which the table is brought up by hand until the cutter just misses the shaft. The machine is then stopped, and the vertical feed index is set at zero. Now, the operator traverses the table manually until the cutter rests 3" from the end of the shaft, the specified length of the keyway. He locates the table stop to halt the table automatically when it reaches this position; then he runs the table

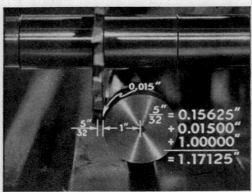

5 To center the work, bring it alongside the cutter with a .015" feeler gauge between. Add up half the cutter width, .015", and the shaft radius

6 Lower the table, set the cross-feed index at zero, and move the table over four full turns of the collar (which will equal 1") plus .171" more

7 Cutter surface speed of 100' per minute is taken from the reference chart and reduced to r.p.m. by multiplying the diameter by *pi* (3.1416)

8 Feed, or the rate at which the work is fed, is next established. For a 3/16" cut, each cutter tooth will remove a chip .002" thick . . .

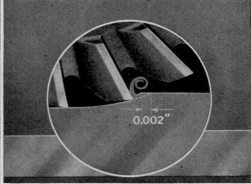

back and raises it to the height required for the cut.

The keyway is to be 3/16" deep, but milling the cylindrical shaft will produce a chord, and it is from this that the depth of the cut must be measured. Consulting a handbook, the machinist learns that the metal removed down to the chord is .0124". He raises the table, therefore, 3/16" or .1875" plus the thickness of the chord segment (.0124"), which gives him .1999" or roughly .200". Since one complete revolution of the vertical feed screw is equal to .100", two revolutions will provide the desired movement.

The operator locks the knee of the table in this position, starts up the milling machine, and cuts the keyway for about ¼". Stopping the machine, he runs the table back and measures the depth of the cut. This he finds is 3/16", as specified on the drawing, so he starts up the motor once more and finishes the keyway. In checking length, he measures to the end of the flat.

He now prepares to machine the other end in the same way. He lowers the table so the cutter clears the shaft and its clamps, and traverses it until the opposite side of the shaft is under the cutter. Since the cutter teeth must always travel into the work against the direction of feed, this cut is started from a point 3" along the shaft, rather than from the edge of the shaft as in the case of the first keyway. In other respects the procedure is similar.

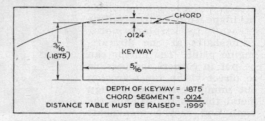

DEPTH OF KEYWAY = .1875"
CHORD SEGMENT = .0124"
DISTANCE TABLE MUST BE RAISED = .1999"

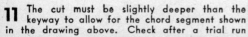

2.960"   20×0.002"=0.040"
         74×0.040"=2.960"

9 . . . Chip thickness times 20, the number of teeth, gives feed distance for one revolution. This is now multiplied by the r.p.m. setting . . .

10 . . . Thus, 74 r.p.m. (the nearest setting to 76 r.p.m.) times .040" equals a feed of nearly 3". The nearest setting to this is 2¾"

11 The cut must be slightly deeper than the keyway to allow for the chord segment shown in the drawing above. Check after a trial run

12 In milling the second keyway, the cut begins 3" from the end of the shaft. Steel rules are used to set the cutter at the starting point

NEW SHOP IDEAS

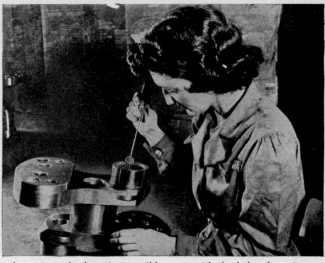

AN ORDINARY DENTAL MIRROR, a little chrome-backed reflector attached to a long handle, aids in inspection of the spline "teeth" in airplane-motor crankshafts at one aircraft-engine plant. The mirror can be put in corners inaccessible to direct vision for searching out minute grains of foreign metal that might damage the teeth and ruin a crankshaft when an engine is operated.

Inspectors check on inaccessible spots with the help of a mirror

Stepping Up Your War Production

WHETHER you work in a small shop or a large factory, you'll find you can contribute more to the war effort—and do it more easily—by following the suggestions listed below. Patriotic zeal is not enough. Precise workmanship is not enough. Ideas are not enough. A working combination of these three is necessary.

TOOLS AND MACHINES. These are important helpers. Treat them with care and respect. Keep machines scrupulously clean. Chips and dirt not only cause excessive wear—and therefore waste—but also inaccurate work. Micrometers and gauges should be checked frequently; they should not be left lying on the bench or table, but are to be kept in the tool chest. See that machines are well lubricated at all times.

ELECTRIC MOTORS. A motor breakdown can waste hours. Guard against overloading; check to see that drive belts are adjusted properly; keep chips and dirt out of motor housing.

WASTE. Help destroy this saboteur of production. Conserve all materials, tools, and machines, from the lowliest cleaning rag to the most powerful dynamo.

MORALE. Promote good spirits and fellowship by assisting in staging rallies and meetings. If it's possible, have officers and men of the armed forces speak. Music or community singing during rest periods is another good morale raiser.

GOSSIP. Don't! Honest facts are the best weapons against two dangerous enemies: rumors and idle gossip. If there's a bulletin board in your department, keep it supplied with news clippings and governmental bulletins. If you don't have a bulletin board, ask permission to put one up. Encourage other workers to bring in news items.

IDEAS. In most factories there are suggestion boxes in which you can drop ideas that will promote more efficient work. Use them! See that the contents are turned over to your foreman at intervals. If there is no such box in your department, have one put up, even if you have to build it.

REPACKING A PUMP BEARING can be made a leaktight job by using single-turn lengths of packing, each formed into a split ring, as shown at *A* in the drawing below. The assembled pack is uniform in shape, thus permitting even compression and proper bearing adjustment. Spiral winding, as at *B*, makes a lopsided pack against which even compression is impossible. Place the rings so that their breaks are offset, and fill grease cups with water-pump lubricant—not ordinary cup grease, which is unsuitable for this purpose.—J. MODROCH.

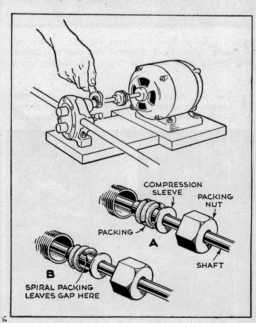

COMPRESSION SLEEVE

PACKING NUT

PACKING

A

SHAFT

B

SPIRAL PACKING LEAVES GAP HERE

AUTOMATIC SALVAGE of babbitt chips is accomplished with this pneumatic chip collector attached directly to a lathe used in machining the bore of babbitt-lined motor bearings. The lathe was originally piped for cutting oil, and this oil-piping system is connected with the shop compressed-air line. A sheet-iron pipe attached to the hollow spindle leads to a covered barrel into which the flying chips are blown when the air jet is in operation. Metal chips are thus kept free from floor sweepings and other contamination, and salvage is rated at 100 percent. The device can be adapted to any hollow-spindle lathe where salvage from boring jobs is desirable.

A BURNED SOLDERING IRON needed in a hurry can be cleaned quickly and efficiently by holding the tip against a coarse garnet sanding disk or belt. This rapidly cuts below the pits and leaves the faces perfectly flat for retinning.

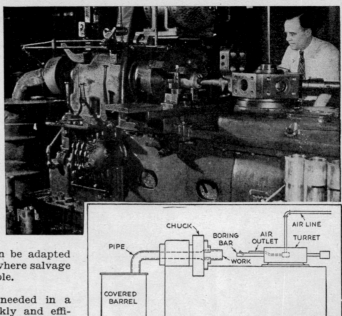

Metal chips, blown by compressed air, are salvaged as they are forced through the spindle into the barrel

PLASTIC-TUBE LAMPS that carry illumination to the end of their bent light-conducting stems will be found convenient for inspection of inside turnings while they are still chucked in the lathe. The tips of these lamps are so arranged that they can be put easily into small openings.—W. T. BAXTER.

A STANDARD LUBRICANT CODE is being drawn up by the American Standards Association to assist inexperienced workers. The grade of grease or oil to be used in a given place on a machine is indicated by color. Oil caps and containers both will bear corresponding markings for identification.

S. A. E. STEEL NUMBERING SYSTEM [*SHOP PRACTICE*]

Following are the basic numerals for the various types of S.A.E. steel. The first digit of the standard number indicates the type of steel; the second generally indicates the approximate percentage of the predominant alloying element in the case of the simple alloy steels; and the final two or three (represented by dashes in the table below) indicate the average carbon content in "points," or hundredths of 1 percent. For example, 2320 means a nickel steel of 3.50 percent nickel content and .20 percent average carbon. Sometimes the prefix X is used to denote variations in the range of elements.

Type of Steel	Numerals (and Digits)	Type of Steel	Numerals (and Digits)	Type of Steel	Numerals (and Digits)
Carbon Steels:	1---	1.75 percent nickel, 1.00 percent chromium	32--	Nickel molybdenum;1.75 percent nickel	46--
Plain carbon	10--	3.50 percent nickel, 1.50 percent chromium	33--	Nickel molybdenum; 3.50 percent nickel	48--
Free cutting (screw stock)	11--	Corrosion and heat resisting steels	30---	Chromium Steels:	5---
Manganese Steels:	13--	Molybdenum Steels:	4---	Low chromium	51--
Nickel Steels:	2---	Carbon molybdenum	40--	Medium chromium	52--
3.50 percent nickel	23--	Chromium molybdenum	41--	Corrosion and heat resisting	51---
5.00 percent nickel	25--	Chromium nickel molybdenum	43--	Chromium Vanadium Steels:	6---
Nickel Chromium Steels:	3---			1 percent chromium	61--
1.25 percent nickel, 0.60 percent chromium	31--			Silicon Manganese Steels:	9---
				2 percent silicon	92--

In some instances, particularly with reference to corrosion and heat resisting alloys, it has been found necessary to depart from this system by varying the second and third digits of the number.

Reprinted from the 1942 edition of the S. A. E. Handbook, by special permission of the Society of Automotive Engineers, Inc.

POPULAR SCIENCE MONTHLY SHOP DATA

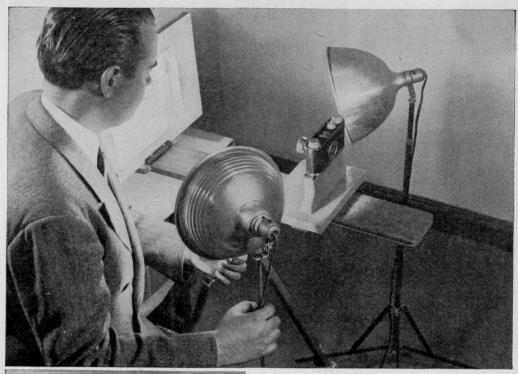

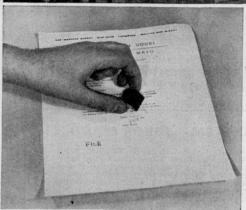

The making of small negatives sharp enough to be enlarged so as to reproduce the smallest of printing or line drawing may seem rather a difficult job, but if you rig up the right sort of equipment, shooting becomes so simple that anyone can learn how to do it in a short time.

One such unit for use with a miniature camera has been devised by Arthur C. Miller. It consists of an artist's easel, a 12″ by 17″ drawing board, and two blocks of wood for the camera support. All this came from an artists' supply store. The diagram shows how the items were put together to make the portable unit. That part of the easel normally used to hold the picture or canvas is clamped in a horizontal position, with the drawing board set upright and rigid at one end, and the blocks shaped into a holder for the camera that can be slid along the easel to various distances from the drawing board.

Mr. Miller's 35-mm. camera needs supplementary portrait lenses in front of the reg-

THE uses of microfilm are growing by leaps and bounds. Banks have long made photographic records of depositors' checks. Mail for service men abroad is now copied on film, so that a single reel bears hundreds of letters. Important documents have been filmed in England for safe storage against bombings. It may not be very long before a majority of business and professional offices will be keeping their records by this new method. The letter and record files that now take up considerable floor area will become a thing of the past. Tiny films will keep such records in a fraction of the space.

The two pictures on the opposite page show how lamps are used to illuminate the subject properly, and the relative sizes of a microfilm and the subject taken

Above is shown the upright part of an artist's easel clamped in a horizontal position to hold the drawing board and the sliding platform supporting the camera

Two photographs at the right show a simple method of constructing the camera support. A tripod screw holds the camera and a wing bolt secures the support

Copying Outfits
with Homemade Equipment Makes Permanent Photo Records

ular lens to allow for focusing at distances down to 10", and for covering a field from approximately 4" by 6" to 11" by 17". It takes a group of three lenses to cover this field, but for general work a No. 2 portrait lens will cover a field of approximately 6" by 9" to 10" by 14", which includes the average letter size of 8½" by 11". If you buy a portrait lens that does not fit your camera, get an adapter ring to fit your camera and the lens.

A chart may be had with each portrait lens showing the various focal distances, the lens setting for each, and the field the negative will cover at that distance. Adjustments consist of setting the focus scale in feet on your camera and sliding the camera support along the easel until it is the correct distance from the drawing board. For example, to microfilm a paper measuring 8¼" by 12", you will find on the chart that the closest corresponding field size is 8" by 12". You will also notice that the camera focus

scale is to be set at 10', and that the distance from the lens to the drawing board upon which the paper is thumbtacked is exactly 16⅞". It is important to have the settings accurate for clear and sharp results. Distances can be marked on the easel for quick reference, making actual measurement of them unnecessary thereafter.

The drawing board must be at right angles to a line drawn down the center of the easel from the camera support, which must also be at right angles to the line. If a line is drawn vertically down the center of the drawing board and another horizontally across it at the same height as the center of the lens, it will be easy to center the material to be copied on the drawing board. Use white thumbtacks to hold white paper, or ordinary white adhesive tape.

Lighting is done with No. 2 photoflood bulbs and reflectors placed at 45 deg. so as to prevent reflections from entering the camera lens and fogging or spotting the

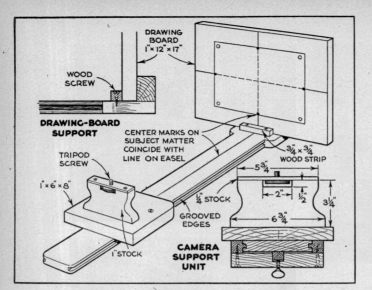

DRAWING BOARD 1"×12"×17"

WOOD SCREW

DRAWING-BOARD SUPPORT

TRIPOD SCREW

1"×6"×8"

CENTER MARKS ON SUBJECT MATTER COINCIDE WITH LINE ON EASEL

3/4"×3/4" WOOD STRIP

1/4" STOCK

GROOVED EDGES

1" STOCK

CAMERA SUPPORT UNIT

5 3/4"

2" 1/2"

3 1/2"

3 3/4"

6 3/4"

The construction of this portable and adjustable copying unit can be simplified greatly by the use of ready-made parts

negative. A photo shows this arrangement.

Another portable microfilm copying outfit has been designed and used by Willard Allphin, also with excellent success. This outfit takes the form of a carrying case that contains all of its parts when the setup is not in use. The four legs, which stand on top of the box and support the camera platform, are packed inside for carrying. They are then held in place by ordinary auto side-curtain fasteners, as is also the top platform which holds the camera, lens point-

ing downward, on top of the legs.

What becomes the bottom of the case when the outfit is being used has a piece of beveled 1/4" plate glass set in it. The glass protrudes just enough to hold the material to be photographed flat between its surface and that of the table upon which the outfit is placed. All parts of the inside of the case which the camera can see reflected in the glass are painted a dead black. Other areas are finished in white. A pocket is built on the inside of the lid into which fit the electric cord, lens tube, and extra films.

Into the top of the case holes are drilled to take two dowels set in one end of each leg. The upper end of each leg is fitted with a bolt, which goes through the platform that supports the camera. Wing nuts on these leg bolts hold the platform rigid. The two wood saddle blocks in which the camera rests have pins that go through the carrying-strap holes of the camera, thus keeping it in perfect alignment. A leather strap fastened to one block is pulled down tight over the camera and fastened to the other block with an auto-curtain fastener.

The over-all size of a microfilm outfit of this kind will vary with the size of the field to be covered. The outfit shown covers a field up to 11" by 16 1/2" in size, which is the

One portable copying outfit is completely contained within a case for ease in transportation

Demountable legs which support the camera platform above the box are doweled to the case lid

The picture below shows an operator putting a letter under the case for microfilming a copy

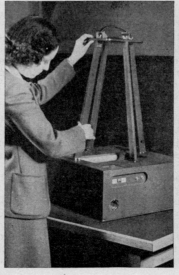

size of the plate glass. The distance from the bottom of the glass to the camera is 28". Two 14-watt, 15" fluorescent lamps are built in. The light is baffled to avoid high lights on the plate glass.

A wiring circuit for the two lights is shown in the diagram. It will be noted that the two lamps are wired for both A.C. and D.C. If it is attempted to start the lamps on A.C. with the toggle switch on the D.C. side —that is, open—nothing will happen. If, however, it is attempted to operate the lamps on D.C. with the toggle switch on the A.C. side, the lamps will burn out.

When the material to be photographed is on one side of the sheet only, an extra white sheet under it will increase reflection and contrast. If a paper has printing on both sides and the reverse side has a tendency to show through, a piece of black paper under it will help give a clearer result. Filters are not needed for ordinary work, but if special occasions arise, say to eliminate a color, use a filter which transmits that color. On the other hand, to emphasize or darken a color, use a filter which absorbs that color.

In general, it might be wise to standardize on one film and developer. There are special films

made for this purpose. The choice of developer will depend upon whether you copy photographs occasionally and want to maintain normal contrasts, or whether you are doing letters and drawings exclusively and want maximum contrast. An all-around film will give twice the contrast in one developer that it will in another, both developers being entirely suitable for the uses intended. Different films will take stops from f/6.3 to f/12.5, and exposures from ½ to 1 second.

Microfilming is done on either 16-mm. or 35-mm. films, and the negatives can be enlarged at will on photographic paper to provide individual copies, or the films can be thrown on a screen for temporary or group reading. Any kind of camera using small film can be adapted for this work.

At the right is a drawing showing how the case is constructed, and below the drawing is a picture showing how the legs and camera platform are carried. The picture directly below illustrates the camera in place on its platform

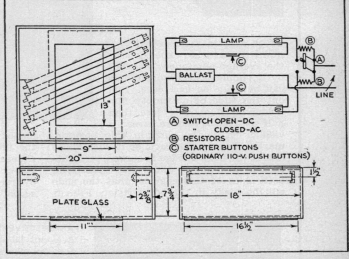

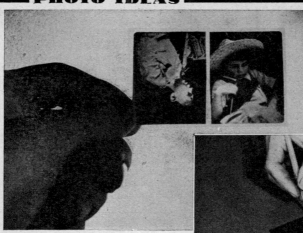

When two exposures are made on the same sheet of film, the pictures will be upside down to each other like this

After the slide is pulled about halfway out of the holder, a white line is drawn across the back side

COLOR FILM in professional cut-film sizes is rather expensive for the average amateur to use, but by a simple trick two pictures can be made on one piece. Pull out the slide of an empty film holder until slightly less than half of the exposure area is visible. With the slide in this position, mark a line on the back of it with white ink. If the bottom edge is curved, straighten it by grinding or filing. Put a radius on both sides of this edge so that the slide will fit easily in the bottom slot. Film is loaded into the holder with the notches in the upper right-hand corner. A picture is exposed by drawing the slide out to the mark; the film is then reversed end for end by reloading it in the darkroom, and the second picture taken.—FRANK McCARTY.

IN LOADING HOLDERS with different types of cut film, a good way to identify them is to snap a rubber band around each group and slip the instruction sheet from the film package under the rubber band. After exposure, the holders can be kept with a duplicate instruction sheet marked "exposed" to prevent errors in timing development and so forth.—LOUIS HOCHMAN.

AN EFFECTIVE film squeegee can be made in a few moments at very little cost from a pair of metal film tongs and a windshield-wiper blade. Make a lengthwise bend or crease in each side of the tongs and place half of the wiper blade in each crease. Hammer the creases around the two blades to hold them firmly in place. When the wet film is hung up to dry, a quick stroke with this handy squeegee removes all excess moisture. The better the wiper blade you use, the more efficient your squeegee will be. One with several edges is good.—ROBERT SCOTT.

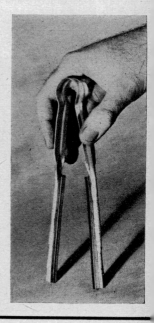

MOONLIGHT PHOTOGRA-PHY. The mellow glow of a full moon was the only light shining on this country home when the unusual photograph at the right was taken. A time exposure of seven minutes was made at a lens stop of f/5.6 on a high-speed panchromatic film. The shutter was closed whenever the gleam from car headlights passed before the camera, and opened immediately after to continue the exposure.

CUTTING PHOTOGRAPHIC PAPER in the darkroom is easier if white ink or luminous paint is used to touch-up the more commonly used markings on the paper-cutter board. The scored lines you will wish to point up will vary with your particular requirements, but for the average user, white lines at the 2½", 3½", 5" and 7" lines will be found most useful.—ED REYNOLDS.

FLASH BULBS are precious photo items these days, even to professional photographers. Now, more than ever before, the bulbs you have on hand should be tested in order to avoid wasting film and losing pictures. A simple tester can be made quickly by bending a wire clip to fit around a small flashlight cell and hold at its other end a 6-volt radio pilot bulb. Touch the center button of the cell to the bottom bulb terminal and the pilot-bulb terminal to the screw base. The small lamp will light with a faint glow if the flash bulb is good. Test the bulbs in a dimly lighted place.—L. H.

TIME is saved in filtering photographic chemicals when the funnel used is the plastic or glass upper bowl from a vacuum-type coffee maker (above). This enables you to pour a quart or more of the liquid into the funnel at one time. If you don't have one of these around the house, you can purchase the single piece at almost any department store. For filtering, a piece of absorbent cotton or a regular coffee filter can be used.—C. H. COLES.

KEEPING THE

To make one of these individual picnic trays, attach a 12" plywood square to a 22" broomstick, one end of which is pointed so it can be pushed into the ground

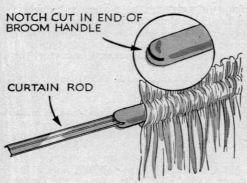

NOTCH CUT IN END OF BROOM HANDLE

CURTAIN ROD

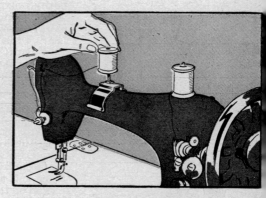

Curtains are placed on flat rods with a broomstick notched as above. If your rods are of the round type, bore a hole in the stick instead

An auxiliary spool holder that slips over the head of a sewing machine is made by attaching a 2" bolt to the spring clamp of a bicycle flashlight holder

MEDICINE DROPPER

WATER   SPONGE

You can lengthen the life of your precious rubber gloves by placing wads of cotton in the fingertips

A leakproof envelope moistener is easily made by tying sponge to a medicine dropper

For kitchen hot-dish mitts, cut several thicknesses of calico to shape; then quilt them together

HOME SHIPSHAPE

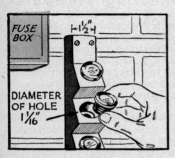

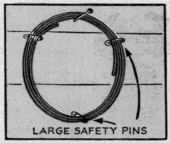

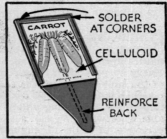

A fuse-plug rack is shown above. Cut the body in steps and bore fuse holes 1" in depth with an expansive bit or a fly cutter

Coils of wire can be kept from tangling or unwinding if large-size safety pins are placed as is shown in the drawing above

Garden markers of tin plate and celluloid are waterproof. Solder a tin strip to the back for reinforcement, and paint to suit

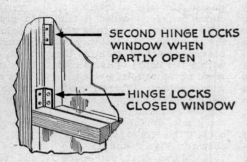

Small hinges make efficient window-sash locks. Screw one on each side of the inside face of the upper sash, with hinge joints close to the parting strip. To lock the window, open the hinges

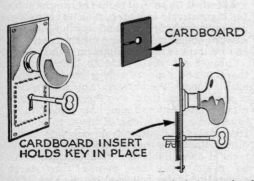

Keeping a key in place in a lock is simple if you remove the lock plate, insert the key in the keyhole, then slip a slit piece of cardboard directly behind the key and replace the plate

The convenient electric-razor holder above can be made of wood from a fruit crate, or any ordinary 1/4" stock. This holder also keeps the cord hanging free and prevents it from being kinked

Model Scenery and How to Plan It

Grading Railway Layouts from an Engineering Viewpoint

By DAVID MARSHALL

RAILWAYS must accept the world as they find it, dealing with every obstacle of nature in the most economical way possible. Every curve results from some irregularity of the land over which the railway operates, whether it be a ragged coast line, a mountain range, a winding valley, or an impassable waterway. We can set down as a first principle of railroad engineering the fact that curvature is determined by terrain.

The model railway, however, is built within the four walls of a room, and it curves simply because it cannot go through them.

JUSTIFYING THE LAYOUT. Having designed a satisfactory layout, you must now destroy the evidences of your four walls, and invent a completely different set of reasons why your track twists and turns as it does. You must get back of the layout and create geographical conditions that would have made your railway what it is had these conditions been created first. For example, if you wish to have your track curling through hills or following the winding course of a river, the hills and river must be drawn to scale upon the basic plan of your railway. In short, all scenery must be justified.

This involves a very close examination of the layout, a searching out of all the characteristics that provide clues to the lay of the land. On the grown-up railways, terrain determines curvature; on model railways, curvature determines terrain.

INTEGRATING TRACK AND TERRAIN. You must make certain that the rise and the fall of the land accords with your track elevations —roughly, of course, or else you can never have any cuts and fills or bridges. You will have to determine the way a hill slopes and exactly how steep the slope will have to be. The entire landscape must be allowed to develop naturally from your layout. Never introduce any single feature of the landscape gratuitously, but allow all to develop out of the stuff inherent in your layout, so that in the end you may have a terrain that is not only unified but integrated with the railway itself. Scenery cannot be improvised or haphazard. It has to be the inevitable conclusion drawn from the swing of your tracks.

Model-railway terrain consists of two parts: the foreground modeled in plaster, and the background painted on the wall, and these should be consistent with each other in order to form a logical whole. In other words, the painted background should "read out of" the modeled foreground; both foreground and background should be so well integrated that the whole character of one will explain and be explained by the whole character of the other.

CUT AND FILL. We start with the grading of the railway, the first element in model-railway scenery. We shall consider this only from an engineering viewpoint, leaving the structural problems and the modeling of plaster terrain to be dealt with later.

A grade is the prepared earth on which the ties are laid, or in a larger sense the vertical alignment of the railway. There are upgrades, downgrades, and level grades, and where two of them merge, the track passes through a leveling-off or vertical curve, which is called a transition grade.

The grade results from an equal balancing of cut and fill. Railway builders must of course take the terrain as they find it, but within the limits of their capital they seek more advantageous levels through hills and across valleys. Where the amount of earth to be excavated equals the amount required for the embankment work, at that level is the grade. In the words of the engineering book, "the grade splits cut and fill," as shown in Figs. 1 and 2.

It follows that you cannot build your model railway flat upon a table top, for the table top would represent water level, and if your grade lay there, you could not have a hilly terrain without immediately setting up a false engineering picture of cuts without corresponding embankments. Your average grade must lie several inches above the table top, figuratively speaking, thus leaving room not only for upgrades and downgrades but also for embankments, and for the inevitable concomitant of the embankment—the bridge.

Bridges we shall come to later on, but there is one type of bridge we must deal with at once—the culvert. Any bridge over a gap of less than 6' (Fig. 3) is called a culvert by railroad men. An embankment must have at least one of these, to allow a free passage of water from one side to the other; otherwise the embankment would become a dam, liable to be undermined or to be swept away the moment any large amount of water collected on one side of it. A bridge should be built for every valley, ravine, or gorge, and a culvert for every little fold and hollow the railway crosses.

Scenery, carefully planned and skillfully built to scale, adds a realistic touch to any model pike

The amount of earth excavated from the cut must equal the amount that is used in both embankments

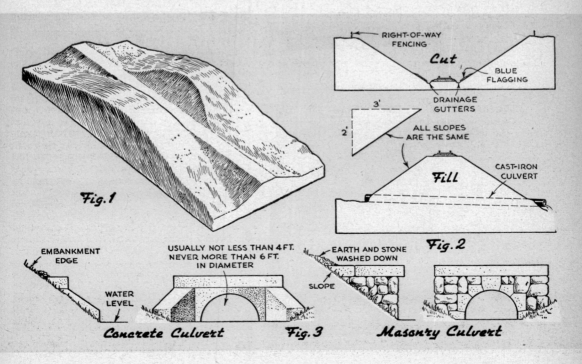

Fig. 1

RIGHT-OF-WAY FENCING

Cut

BLUE FLAGGING

DRAINAGE GUTTERS

3'

2

ALL SLOPES ARE THE SAME

Fill

CAST-IRON CULVERT

Fig. 2

EMBANKMENT EDGE

WATER LEVEL

USUALLY NOT LESS THAN 4 FT. NEVER MORE THAN 6 FT. IN DIAMETER

EARTH AND STONE WASHED DOWN

SLOPE

Concrete Culvert   Fig. 3   Masonry Culvert

1 ....

2 ....

3 ....

4 ....

5 ....

6 ....

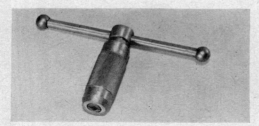

7 ....

8 ....

9 ....

10 ....

Question Bee

THERE is much evidence to show that wrenches in the 18th and 19th centuries were generally made of wrought iron and were hardly known to any but professional mechanics. It was not until after the middle of the 18th century and the introduction of agricultural machinery that wrenches came to be used universally. Little is known about wrenches before 1700, although there is no doubt that there must have been some contrivance existing that was at least similar to a wrench. Today, however, there are countless varieties of wrenches. Can you recognize the types shown on this page? After writing your answers, turn the page upside down and see how many you have named correctly.

ANSWERS

1. Self-adjusting wrench
2. Monkey wrench
3. Stillson or pipe wrench
4. Flat wrench
5. Allen wrench
6. Boos adjustable open-end wrench
7. Tap wrench
8. Alligator wrench
9. Tool-post wrench
10. Box wrench

HW 168

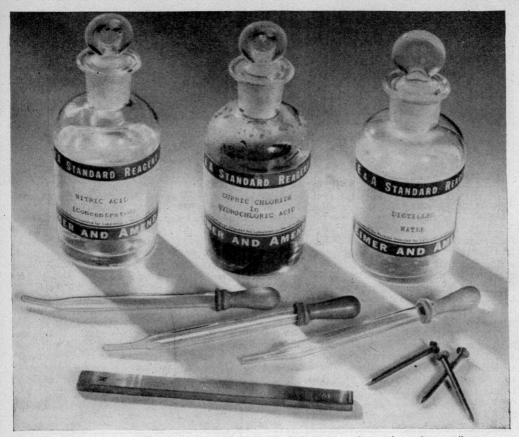

All that is required are three simple reagents, individual droppers, a few nails, and a small magnet

SORT YOUR SCRAP WITH A
Metal-Testing Kit

By KENNETH M. SWEZEY

WHAT YOU CAN
DO FOR VICTORY

FOR the householder who wants to know just what kind of scrap he has and how it might be used in the war, chemists of the International Nickel Company suggest a simple testing kit which should prove valuable also to manufacturers with scrap for sale, civic scrap-drive agencies, and dealers. It costs little to assemble a few ounces of concentrated nitric acid, a like amount of distilled water, and a solution of 10 grams of cupric chloride in 100 cubic centimeters of concentrated hydrochloric acid. For apparatus, you need only three droppers (one for each reagent), a few iron

or steel nails, and a small bar or horseshoe magnet.

With this simple equipment you can make a quick and positive identification of eight different metals and alloys, as shown in the table on the following page. Some of them look like others, but contain entirely different metals or the same metals in different proportions. Monel metal, for instance, is made up principally of about two thirds nickel and one third copper. Chromium-nickel stainless steel contains 18 percent and 8 percent of these same valuable metals, respectively.

Methods of carrying out the tests are as simple as the equipment. The first test is

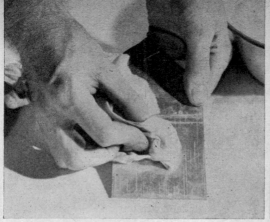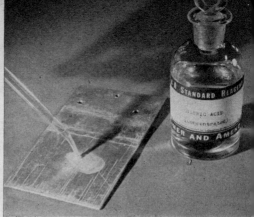

THE NITRIC ACID TEST. First clean the metal with an alkali, such as washing soda, to remove all grease. Apply two drops of nitric acid, and note the speed of the reaction. Now dilute the acid with water, a drop at a time, watch for any change in color, and compare it with the table below

for magnetic properties, which can be determined by suspending the magnet on a string, so that it is free to turn, and then bringing the metal toward it. Monel metal is usually magnetic at room temperatures, but if this quality does not show at once, a bath in ice water or a freezing mixture will cause it to be revealed.

Clean the spot where the nitric acid test is to be made, using washing soda or another alkali. Apply one or two drops of concentrated nitric acid, and wait a few minutes to note the reaction, if any, and the speed. Dilute the acid with three or four drops of distilled water, one drop at a time. If the solution turns green or blue, proceed with

the nail test for copper. Keeping the nail in contact with the metal, you rub the end of it in the nitric acid, which has been diluted with a few drops of distilled water. If copper is present in the alloy being tested, it will be deposited either on the nail or on the surface of the metal, under the acid solution.

The fourth test, in which a drop of cupric chloride in hydrochloric acid is applied, is described on the opposite page. Its purpose is to distinguish Inconel—an alloy containing 80 percent nickel, 14 percent chrome, and 6 percent iron—from those chromium-stainless steels mentioned before which contain only 18 percent chromium and 8 percent nickel.

QUALITATIVE TESTS FOR IDENTIFYING SOME COMMON WHITE METALS AND ALLOYS

| MAGNETIC TEST | NITRIC ACID TEST | | | | | |
Reaction to Magnet	Reaction to Conc. Acid	Reaction to Acid after Dilution	Color of the Solution	Iron Nail Test for Copper	Drop Test with Cupric Chloride in Hydrochloric Acid	Material Probably Is
Magnetic	Reacts Slowly	Reacts Slowly	Pale Green	No Copper Plates out	Not required	Nickel
Magnetic (slightly)	Reacts	Reacts Slowly	Greenish Blue	Copper Plates out	Not required	Monel
Non-magnetic	Reacts	Reacts	Bluish Green	Copper Plates out	Not required	Copper-Nickel Alloy containing less than 60% Nickel, e.g. Nickel-Silver
Magnetic	Reacts Slowly	Reacts	Brown to Black	Not required	Not required	Steel or Cast Iron
Non-magnetic	Reacts Slowly	Reacts	Brown to Black	Not required	Not required	"Ni-Resist"
Magnetic	No Reaction	No Reaction	Colorless	Not required	Not required	Straight Chromium Stainless Steel
Non-magnetic	No Reaction	No Reaction	Colorless	Not required	Copper deposits when drop is diluted	Chromium-Nickel Stainless Steels e.g. "18-8"
Non-magnetic	No Reaction	No Reaction	Colorless	Not required	No deposition of copper occurs	Inconel

When brought into contact with the concentrated nitric acid, the metal being tested will do one of three things: react swiftly, slowly, or not at all. If there is a quick reaction, it will appear as at right above. If, however, there is a slow reaction, or none whatever, it will appear as at left above

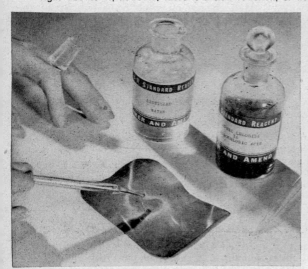

DROP TEST with cupric chloride in hydrochloric acid distinguishes between Inconel and chromium-nickel stainless steel. A drop of the reagent is applied to the cleaned metal surface and allowed to remain for two minutes. Three or four drops of distilled water are added, and the solution washed off. If sample is "18-8" stainless steel, copper is deposited (left, below); if Inconel, there is no deposit

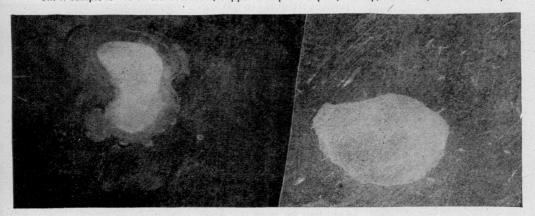

A PAPER BALLET. Put some bits of tissue paper in a dry glass bottle with a metal cap; then challenge your friends to make the papers dance without moving the bottle. For best results, the bottle should be no more than 3" high. To perform the trick, shuffle your feet about on the carpet; then touch the top of the jar with your hand. If sufficient static electricity has been produced by the friction of your shoe soles on the carpet, the accumulated charge on your body will make the papers leap from the bottom to the top of the jar several times.

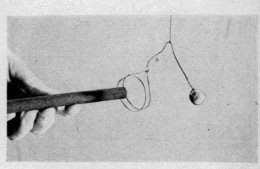

"REPELLING" MAGNET. Make a loop of several turns of copper wire, joining the ends together, and suspend the loop so that it hangs balanced, as shown. Now thrust a bar magnet or a straight electromagnet into the loop. The coil will be mysteriously repelled. The reason is that the magnet, by induction, sets up in the coil a momentary magnetic field of like polarity to that of the magnet.

WHY DOES A LIQUID STREAM TAPER? Pour any viscous liquid from a height, and the stream will taper from top to bottom. Since an equal amount of liquid must pass any point in the stream, how do you explain this difference in the size of the flow? The answer is that the thinner part of the stream is flowing faster, being accelerated by the force of gravity.

SURFACE TENSION can be demonstrated with a cork weighted so as to float in an upright position about one fourth out of a jar of water. Fasten a small ring of wire to it a fraction of an inch above the top. If you press the cork under water so that the wire is just submerged, the surface tension pulling down on the ring will keep it there despite the buoyancy of the cork. Now dip a piece of soap into the water near the side of the jar. The soap, on dissolving, lowers the water's surface tension, and up pops the cork.

HERE'S A MAGIC LIQUID that, unlike water, does not seek its own level. The U-tube shown in the photograph contains a colored liquid that rises an inch or more higher in one branch of the tube than in the other. You can prove to your friends by rocking the tube gently that there is no hidden partition holding the liquid in this odd state of unbalance. The secret of what seems a gravity-defying mystery is that there are two liquids colored alike in the tube. The heavier liquid is carbon tetrachloride, colored with a few iodine crystals. The lighter one is water, colored to match with crystals of potassium permanganate. These liquids will not mix. A few grains of sodium bisulphite dropped in will decolorize the potassium permanganate, as shown, and clearly reveal the relationship between the two liquids.

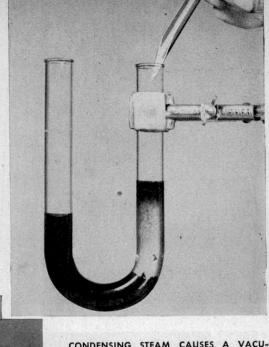

CONDENSING STEAM CAUSES A VACUUM, as can be seen by boiling some water in a flask until all air has been driven out. Pour the water out and insert a stopper with a glass tube drawn into a jet at one end. Invert the flask as shown below, placing the outer end in a tumbler of water. In a few seconds a fountain of water will spurt through the jet, continuing to rise in the flask until it is almost full. Since the steam has driven out all the air, the condensation of steam produces a vacuum.

ELECTROCHEMICAL RECTIFIER. To change A.C. to D.C., immerse a plate of pure aluminum and a plate of lead in 1 oz. aluminum phosphate dissolved in 8 oz. water. When these are connected in series with a 110-volt A.C. house line and a small argon bulb, A.C. will be allowed to pass first, as evidenced by the lighting up of both plates of the tube. However, one plate will grow dimmer and finally go out, indicating that half of each A.C. cycle is being cut off. Here is the explanation: a film of aluminum oxide is built up on the aluminum electrode, due to the liberation of oxygen about it. This film will not allow current to pass from the aluminum into the solution, but permits current to flow the other way into the plate.

THIS TANK PUMP and incendiary-bomb figh has been recently developed for effectiv combating fires. It has its own storage ta with a capacity of 5 gal. and will throw stream of water approximately 40'. apparatus is constructed almost entirely wood and plastic, is extremely light weight, convenient to carry, and can operated easily by just one person. synthetic hose is made of woven cotton-a paper fabric covered with a plastic sheeti The device has been subjected to tests leading laboratories, and the standards performance and durability revealed these tests were reported as being exce ingly high.

PAINTBRUSHES ARE RECONDITIONED with this brush cleaner that is noninflammable, will not evaporate, and is used as it comes from the can. Simply soak the brushes in the cleaner, then rinse them out in water. Harmless to bristles and settings, the brush cleaner can be kept for an indefinite period of time. It does not have the acrid smell of some other cleaners, and is economical, since only a small amount is necessary for cleaning each brush.

LONG LIFE FOR LINOLEUM is possible by painting the surface with a new, clear, gloss-finish fluid (not illustrated) which renders it impervious to stains, hot water, alcohol, or grease. It should not be used on new linoleum, since a "breaking-in" period of about three months is necessary before the coating may be effectively applied.

CLOGGED DRAINS can be opened with a new device that utilizes the water pressure at the faucet. It is simple to use and works automatically. One end of the cleaner is inserted in the drain and the other end attached first to the hot-water faucet. A small stream of water should be run through the tubing, and the flow gradually increased. The hot water expands the pipe, separating the grease and corrosion from the metal. The end of the cleaner is then attached to the cold-water faucet, and the water turned on full force. The cold water contracts and breaks up the grease and corrosion into small particles, and the water pressure forces these particles down the drain. This drain cleaner can be used effectively to clean bath tubs, kitchen sinks, laundry tubs, lavatories, and other appliances that may have clogged drains.

THE CERAMIC FAUCET shown at the right substitutes for prewar metal types. This new modernistic faucet operates similarly to a radio dial. You "tune in" on hot or cold water by turning the dial-like knobs on either side. The ceramic used in the faucet is heat resistant, so that it will not crack even when very hot water is turned on immediately after the cold water. The only metal part is a small brass spring employed in the control knobs. The rest of this unusual faucet is made of non-critical materials.

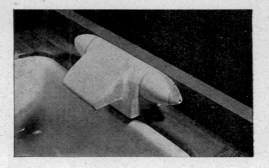

AN AWNING PRESERVATIVE in the form of a colorless liquid is simply rubbed into the canvas (below). So applied, the liquid impregnates the cloth fibers, and is said to strengthen them and to make the fabric repel water and resist sun and mildew. It can also be used on canvas auto tops, boat sails, tents, canvas furniture, and the like. Before using the preservative, the surface to be treated should be cleaned of all surface dirt.

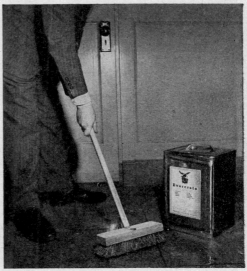

CONCRETE IS HARDENED by a transparent, penetrating liquid that can be put on with a broom or a brush. The product is said to make concrete waterproof and to prevent the formation of dust due to crumbling, besides increasing wear resistance. It can be used on brick, stucco, plaster, and unglazed tile as well.

FIVE-WAY NOZZLE. Attached to a hose, this nozzle produces five different streams, ranging from an 18' spray to a 40' flow. Made of rustproof metal, it has a spike that can be driven into the ground or used as a handle, and an adjustable disk against which water strikes to form a spray.

Wheel Mounted on Ladder Aids in Hooking It over Ridge

ONE MAN can hook this wheeled ladder over the ridge of a roof. The wheel and its axle can be taken from a child's discarded tricycle and attached to the ladder as shown. Set a ground ladder to reach above the roof and ascend this, carrying the other. Place the end of the wheeled ladder on the roof and roll it up the pitch until the wheel goes over the ridge. Then flop the ladder over so that the hooks catch.—A. D. S.

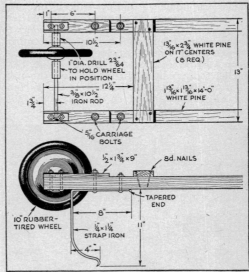

Sod Prevents Soil Erosion

JUST as straw is spread on newly graded road banks to prevent erosion by rain, so sod may be packed around the base of a large tree to keep rain rushing down the trunk from washing out a newly seeded lawn. In the photo, a protected section successfully weathered a heavy rain, while the unprotected area was ruined.—J. M.

REPLACING DAMAGED SASH CORD   [SHIPSHAPE HOME]

A GREAT many double-hung window frames are built without removable facings on the pockets. If a cord breaks, or if it comes loose from the sash or weight, the repair cannot be made without first removing a casing. This should be done after the stop is removed by prying the outer edge with a chisel braced against a strip of metal or thin plywood to prevent damage to the plaster. Loosen the lower end first, continuing to the top. The edge nailed to the pulley stile can then be worked loose easily. If the casing is mitered at the top, there may be nails driven in from the top and side edges, which will split the casing if care is not taken. Sometimes these nails can be driven all the way through with a fine nail set, so that the casing can be brought away at the top with a downward and outward prying motion. After the cord is replaced, pull the nails out from behind the casing and nail it back as if it were new material. Set the nails and putty the holes to match the paint.

Cleaning Your Warm-Air Furnace

ASH and soot can be readily removed from the radiator of a warm-air furnace by the use of a child's sand pail and a vacuum cleaner. The pail should be tapered and about 3″ in diameter at the larger end. A tenpenny nail hole is punched in the center of the bottom of the pail and in the center of the handle so that a length of No. 14 wire can be inserted and looped as illustrated. The top of the pail is squeezed to a slightly oval shape having the handle across the small diameter.

To operate this cleaning arrangement, tie the front clean-out door open and push a length of wire through to the check damper in the smoke pipe. Then fasten a rope to the handle of the bucket and to the wire, and a rope to the wire loop in the bottom of the bucket. Push the edge of the bucket down into the dust and pull it and one length of rope to the clean-out door. Remove the wire and repeat the operation several times with the ropes and bucket. The use of the suction nozzle of a vacuum cleaner at the clean-out door will avoid spilling the accumulation of dust into the basement.—ALFRED D. SLATER.

Cleaning out a furnace after the winter is over prevents corrosion during the summer

Lawn-Mower Grass Catcher Made from an Old Bushel Basket

Keeping a lawn in good appearance entails constant attention and considerable labor. A large portion of this is avoided by mowing with a grass catcher

MANY gardeners leave lawn clippings where they fall to add to soil fertility, but those who prefer to use a grass catcher can make a good one out of a bushel basket. Cut the basket so that one part is slightly the larger, with a handle at its middle. Nail a cleat across under the cut edge. Staple a semicircular-shaped No. 8 wire about 1″ from the bottom, bending the ends outward to engage the mower clips. Secure the handle of the basket to the lawn-mower handle by means of a coil screen-door spring after applying a coat of green paint.—B. N.

GETTING MOTORS OFF TO A

Push buttons (arrow) on the manual starter at left act mechanically to operate heavy-duty toggle mechanism. The unit has thermal overload relays

Shown below is a contactor of magnetic design. It is used on a conveyor for forward, reverse, and stop controls

How Special Control Devices Used on Machines in War Plants Guard Against the Burning Out of Costly Electrical Equipment

By HAROLD P. STRAND

STARTING controls for motors in war plants are likely to puzzle the home-workshop mechanic who comes into contact with them for the first time. They are encountered in a variety of designs, each serving the special need of the motor it controls. But their primary purpose is to overcome electrical overload and inertia when a motor is started.

Looking at them, the home-workshop owner may well wonder why a simple toggle switch suffices for the motor in his basement. The answer is that his fractional-horsepower motor uses so little current that elaborate switching is unnecessary.

There are some precautions that should be taken, however, even with small motors. The rating in amperes of each switch used should be high enough to carry the starting current without overheating—generally twice that of the running current, or a 10-amp. switch for a ¼-hp. motor taking about 4.8 amps. If 220-volt current is available, and the motor is designed to run on either that or 110 volts, the higher voltage will cut amperage in half and cause less light "dip" when the motor is started.

Polarity plugs and receptacles are safeguards for portable units having controls on the machine or in the cord. They can be plugged in but one way, and connections can be made so that the switch always opens the

GOOD START

This printing press has a repulsion single-phase motor that can be adjusted from 500 to 2,000 r.p.m. as the hand lever alters the position of the brushes. A toggle switch controls the motor

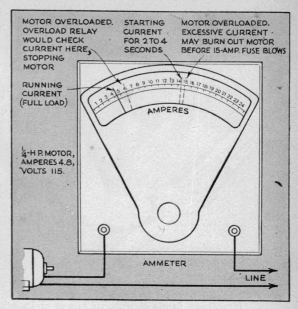

MOTOR OVERLOADED. OVERLOAD RELAY WOULD CHECK CURRENT HERE, STOPPING MOTOR

STARTING CURRENT FOR 2 TO 4 SECONDS

MOTOR OVERLOADED. EXCESSIVE CURRENT - MAY BURN OUT MOTOR BEFORE 15-AMP. FUSE BLOWS

RUNNING CURRENT (FULL LOAD)

AMPERES

¼-H.P. MOTOR, AMPERES 4.8, VOLTS 115.

AMMETER

LINE

Differences in running, starting, and overload current are illustrated by the ammeter readings

live side of the line. Some overload protection besides fuses, which are essentially short-circuit guards, should also be provided. Time-lag fuses give this protection to a certain extent. They contain thermal elements that will allow temporary overloading for the starting current. Better still is a small circuit breaker connected in each motor line, or a toggle switch with a built-in thermostatic overload relay, which permits momentary overload, but trips off the switch if the extra load continues.

The drawing at the top of this page shows the great difference in running current, starting current, and overload current, using as an example a ¼-hp. motor taking 4.8 amps. While the ammeter needle is at only 4.8 amps. when the motor is running under full load, it registers 14.4 amps., or 300 times as much, for two to four seconds during starting. The overload relay has been set to stop the motor at 6 amps., an overload of 25 percent, which is the maximum that should be permitted, and then only for short periods. Without this control, the motor might burn out before a 15-amp. fuse could blow.

This is particularly important for large motors. In the case of a 15-hp. three-phase 220-volt motor taking 38 amps. running current, for instance, the 300 to 500 times as much current it takes in starting would be tremendous. For this reason, one of the standard motor starters is usually selected for motors above 2 hp. These rugged controls may be either manual or magnetic in action. Manual starters are the cheaper and are satisfactory for motors rated as high as 5 hp. single phase and 7½ hp. polyphase at 550 volts. They have thermal overload relays, and their wire connections are simple. One starter of this type is shown in a photograph on the facing page. It has push buttons, but these are entirely mechanical in action, operating a heavy-duty toggle mechanism.

Ratings for magnetic starters run up to 50 hp. and more. The main unit is a contactor operated by the magnetic action of a coil. Push-button stations control the current through the coil, and these may be placed in the switch cover, under it, or any-

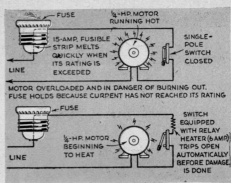

FUSE — ½-H.P. MOTOR RUNNING HOT

15-AMP. FUSIBLE STRIP MELTS QUICKLY WHEN ITS RATING IS EXCEEDED

LINE

SINGLE-POLE SWITCH CLOSED

MOTOR OVERLOADED AND IN DANGER OF BURNING OUT. FUSE HOLDS BECAUSE CURRENT HAS NOT REACHED ITS RATING

FUSE

½-H.P. MOTOR BEGINNING TO HEAT

LINE

SWITCH EQUIPPED WITH RELAY HEATER (6 AMP.) TRIPS OPEN AUTOMATICALLY BEFORE DAMAGE IS DONE

Some overload protection besides a fuse is needed on any motor, large or small. One safeguard is a thermostatic relay switch

At the left is a push-button station placed near a conveyor to provide instant control

where desired for local or remote control. If voltage drops sharply or power shuts off temporarily, the switch opens automatically, stopping the motor, and the operator must press the starter button to start it again. These starters are also equipped with overload relays which, added to undervoltage release, make them "tops" in controls.

The main contactor of a magnetic starter used with a floor-to-floor conveyor is shown in a photo on page HW 178. It is of the reversing type with twin contactors and has a stop and reset button in the face. Push-button stations for instant control are placed handy to the conveyor on each floor. One is shown in the photo on this page.

In some cities and towns, the power company or municipal authorities may not allow the starting of motors above 7½ hp. with across-the-line starters. This is because of line fluctuations and possible damage to power equipment caused by heavy starting current. In these places some form of reduced-voltage starting control, such as a primary-resistor or autotransformer starter, is necessary.

The former has a series resistance that permits 65 percent of the line voltage at starting. As the motor gathers speed, this is gradually cut out automatically until full voltage is applied. Some varieties are also used to provide a smoother start for machinery that, because of its construction, may be injured by the sudden application of full voltage. Ratings for reduced-voltage controls may run from 5 hp. to 30 hp. or more.

Autotransformer starters, commonly known as starting compensators, are useful for motors driving heavy loads, such as pumps, compressors, blowers, and similar

directly connected machinery. They have contacts operating in a bath of special oil that minimizes flashing. Taps are available on the transformer to permit a selection of starting voltage best suited to the load. Ratings often run as high as 150 hp. at 550 volts and several hundred horsepower at 2,200 volts. These starters have both overload and undervoltage protection.

There are a great number of other kinds of starting and controlling equipment, including many types of D.C. controllers, pressure and temperature switches, drum controllers, limit switches, solenoid valves, and photoelectric relays. Each has its special purpose for some type of motor. Of most interest are the speed controls as applied to A.C. motors.

Some forms of capacitor motors used on single phase are adaptable to limited-speed variations. Printing presses often use a repulsion single-phase motor, which can be adjusted from 500 to 2,000 r.p.m. by changing the position of the brushes. This is done by a hand lever, as shown in the photograph on the preceding page. A small toggle switch on the front of the stand controls the motor.

Polyphase motors are built in several types for variable speed, the most popular being probably the slip-ring wound rotor. In this design the armature has a winding, the ends of which are brought out to slip rings upon which the brushes bear. When a variable resistance with a special triplex rheostat is provided in the armature circuit, the speed can be reduced to 50 percent. There are also multispeed motors for polyphase that give two, three, or four fixed speeds.

Servicing Your Radio

TESTS ON BATTERIES from a portable receiver should always be made with a voltmeter—it is the only testing instrument that will show accurately the effective voltage of a battery. It is risky business to use any other device, including a flashlight bulb or an ammeter, since many of them are likely to affect the life of a battery materially. An ammeter —especially bad to use for this purpose— has a low resistance and will short a battery when placed across it. Invariably it will also give a high reading even when a battery is badly run down.

STRIPS CONNECTING THE LOOP ANTENNA inside the cover of some midget portable receivers are likely to wear and break off near the hinge as a result of frequent opening and closing of the lid. When such a break occurs, reception stops. These metal strips can be repaired, however, with short lengths of twisted metal cord like that used in repairing radio dials. Remove the broken part of the original metal strips at their connection with the two wires inside the set; then solder one end of the cord to each of these wires, and solder the other end to that portion of the strips connected to the antenna.

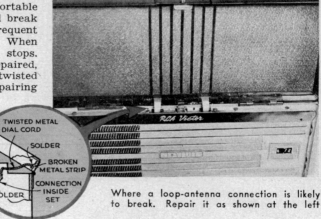

Where a loop-antenna connection is likely to break. Repair it as shown at the left

BATTERIES THAT DO NOT FIT TIGHTLY in their compartment will not knock about if wrapped in corrugated cardboard. A round hole cut in one piece of the material will permit insertion of the battery plug. To conserve your battery, turn off the receiver when it is not in actual use. If you have a three-way set, use electric current when possible. Batteries kept outside the case at 60-deg. temperature may last 18 months.

THREE SEPARATE PLUGS can be substituted for a single battery-pack plug, as shown in the drawing below, to permit use of separate "A" and "B" batteries with a portable if a battery pack cannot be obtained. In removing any plug from a battery, always grasp the plug itself. Never tug on the wire, for this may pull the insulation back, and a short caused by wires touching can render a battery useless in 15 minutes.

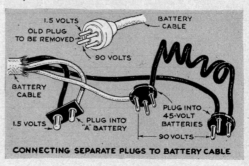

CONNECTING SEPARATE PLUGS TO BATTERY CABLE

AN ULTRAHIGH-FREQUENCY portable transmitter and receiver is said to provide two-way communication over distances of 5 to 30 miles, and to meet requirements for Civilian Defense service. It is powered entirely by self-contained dry batteries. A simple switch enables the user to change from transmitting to receiving operation instantly. The circuit employed makes possible the use of either a carbon or a crystal microphone. A vertical antenna rod telescopes into the cabinet when not in use.

PISTOL-GRIP SOLDERING IRON. The soldering tip of this iron consists of a loop of ⅛" copper wire shunted across the secondary terminal of a low-voltage transformer drawing about 80 watts from 110-volt A.C. lines. A trigger switch controls the primary current. The iron is unusually easy to handle. It reaches soldering temperature in 5 seconds, cooling again upon release of the switch, so that oxidation of the tip is minimized.

FLAT-TYPE RESISTORS mark a departure from the conventional tubular type, offering a higher wattage per unit, of space required, substantial reduction in depth behind the mounting surface, ease in mounting singly or in stacks, lower inductance, and light weight. Both resistor and mounting are an integral unit, and cannot rotate or become loose. The connecting terminals are of the standard type.

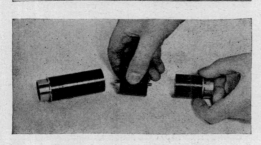

SECTIONAL RESISTORS are available in units that can be used singly or in combination for any desired resistance value. Individual sections consist of resistance wire wound noninductively on ceramic spools and adjusted to a rated current of 1 milliampere. Standard values range from .25 to 1 megohm. The units are locked together both mechanically and electrically with a small stud, and can be separated at will.

Suppressor Built from Junked Parts Reduces Man-Made Static

by
ARTHUR C. MILLER

●

Left, the unit connected to a midget A.C.-D.C. radio. It may be used with almost any receiver

A top view of the unit is shown in the first photo below. Few connections are necessary, as can be seen in second photo. Drawing shows how the static suppressor is hooked up to a receiver

OWNERS of sets ranging all the way from headphone "one-lungers" to 12-tube console models may find good use for this static suppressor. Easily attached across the output circuit, it will in most cases reduce severe man-made static by at least 50 percent. There is a slight loss of volume, but this can be overcome by turning the volume control.

The unit comprises a full-wave rectifier tube (such as the 6X5-GT/G or 50Z7-G), a push-pull output transformer, a 220-ohm line-cord resistor, a S.P.S.T. toggle or rotary switch, and a 4½-volt "C" battery. The secondary of the output transformer must have a high resistance. One of the old output transformers used with magnetic speakers will do admirably, and may be retrieved from the junk box. A class "B" interstage transformer might be tried, but make sure that the primary winding passes enough current. It is useless to attempt to use a transformer with an 8-ohm secondary.

Any kind of chassis, wood or metal, may be employed. The transformer, eight-prong tube socket, and switch are mounted on the top of the chassis. Drill ½" holes in the back for the line cord and the two leads to the "C" battery. The secondary leads of the output transformer (primary side if it is a class "B" interstage transformer) are connected to two plastic binding posts, which provide connections to the set.

Remove the radio chassis from the cabinet. Use leads not longer than 3' or 4' to make connections to the plate of the last tube and the B+ lead. Do not alter speaker connections.

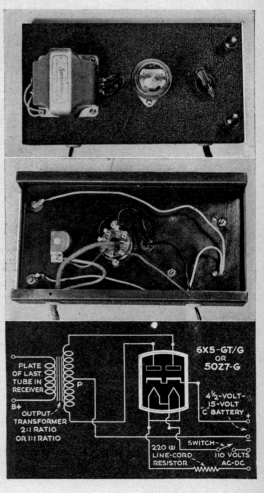

PLATE OF LAST TUBE IN RECEIVER

B+

OUTPUT TRANSFORMER 2:1 RATIO OR 1:1 RATIO

P

6X5-GT/G OR 50Z7-G

4½-VOLT-15-VOLT "C" BATTERY

220 (ω) LINE-CORD RESISTOR

SWITCH-

110 VOLTS AC-DC

LIST OF PARTS

Chassis, metal or wood
Full-wave rectifier tube 6X5-GT/G or 50Z7-G
Eight-prong octal wafer socket
Output transformer (see text)

Small "C" battery, 4½ volts
Line-cord resistor, 220 ohms
Binding posts (2)
Rotary or toggle switch, S.P.S.T.

FIRST STEPS IN ELECTRONICS

How Electrons Are Controlled

By CHARLES I. HELLMAN

BY FAR the tiniest particle yet put to work by man is the electron. With this mighty midget, science has wrought miracles as divergent as measuring the infinitesimal amount of light reaching the earth from a distant star and smashing an atom with force like that of a thunderbolt. Wartime research has so speeded the coming of the age of electronics that these minute particles of electricity are now used in X-raying high-speed bullets as they crash through armor, in killing germs, in heating molded airplane parts, in locating enemy airplanes, and in controlling machinery.

Electrons may be freed in several ways. In the vacuum tube they are evaporated from a hot filament; light falling on the sensitive metal in the photoelectric cell ejects electrons; and high-speed electrons striking a target may knock out secondary electrons of different energy levels.

One of the basic problems of electronics now being solved is the control of these electrons. It is through this control that the light of the distant star is measured and the atom smashed. In this article we shall demonstrate electron control by sim-

ple experiments which anyone can do at home, and then show a few of the applications of this control to today's problems.

First, it may be well to review briefly our knowledge of electrons, which can be stated simply in the electron theory of matter— the theory that all matter is made of electrical charges. According to this theory, infinitesimal, charged particles of electricity called electrons rotate around the nucleus of an atom to make up a miniature planetary system. The atom is the smallest division of matter that still has the chemical properties of an element. As long as it holds electrons in its orbit, these electrons cannot be put to work. The negative charge of the electrons is balanced by the positive charge of the nucleus.

To collect electrons, energy is necessary to pull them from the attracting force of the nucleus. This is demonstrated in the well-known experiment of the hard-rubber comb run through the hair. Some electrons are removed from the hair and added to the rubber, the excess giving the comb a negative charge. Their presence can be detected when a finger is brought near the charged comb, attracting a stream of electrons that gives off a crackling sound.

Giant insulators undergo high-voltage torture in photo at left. Cascades of sparks show they have reached the breakdown point in this strenuous test. Above, 300,000-volt high-speed X-ray tube with which millionth-of-a-second X-ray pictures can be taken through one inch of steel armor plate

parting to it a negative charge like its own. That the grain is repelled after both it and the comb are negatively charged demonstrates that *like charges repel*.

Suspend the rubber comb from a thread so that it balances, and charge it negatively by running it through the hair. Then charge a glass rod positively (a stirring rod or towel rod will serve) by rubbing it on a piece of silk, which robs it of some of its electrons, charging it positively. If you bring the glass rod near the comb, the latter will swing toward it, *because unlike charges attract.*

One application of electrons in industry can be demonstrated with two strips of newspaper about ½" wide and 20" long. Hold the two strips

Bring the negatively charged comb near some bits of paper, and it will pick up or attract the paper. Bring it or a negatively charged rubber rod near the top of a stream of water flowing gently from a tap, and the water will swing far over to the charged rubber, as shown in two photos on the next page. These experiments prove that *charged bodies attract neutral bodies.*

Now, to show the opposite effect, push a thread through a grain of puffed breakfast cereal, hold it so that the grain hangs free, and bring the charged comb near. The grain will be attracted to the comb at first, but the instant it touches the comb, it will be repelled violently. The charged comb gives the grain some of its excess electrons, im-

vertically by the top, and stroke each separately by running the fingers down the length. The strips, which originally hung straight down, now spread apart, as illustrated in an accompanying photograph. Since each strip was given the same charge by friction, they repel each other.

This principle is used in the electroscope, a device for detecting the presence of electrical charges and for determining whether they are positive or negative. Thin strips of metal foil are used in place of the paper.

Thus, through the principles demonstrated in these experiments, we come to the fundamental law of electrical charges: *Like charges repel, unlike charges attract.* Properly used, this knowledge offers such vast

The drawing below explains the principle of the precipitron. The heavy arrows point out the paths of dust-laden air. At the right, plates of a precipitron as used in an industrial plant

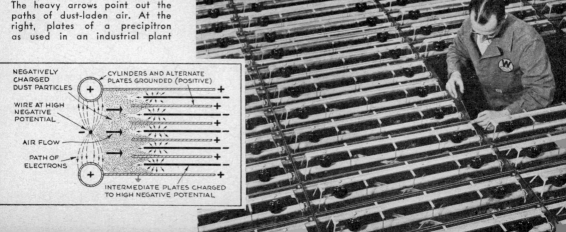

NEGATIVELY CHARGED DUST PARTICLES

CYLINDERS AND ALTERNATE PLATES GROUNDED (POSITIVE)

WIRE AT HIGH NEGATIVE POTENTIAL

AIR FLOW

PATH OF ELECTRONS

INTERMEDIATE PLATES CHARGED TO HIGH NEGATIVE POTENTIAL

  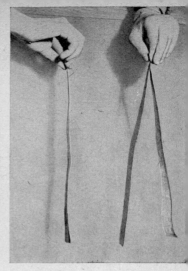

A stream of water flowing gently from a tap, at left above, can be made to swerve from its normal course if a negatively charged rubber rod is held near the top of the stream. This simple experiment shows how electrically charged bodies attract neutral bodies

When two newspaper strips are stroked downward, they spread apart as above, showing how like charges repel each other

possibilities in controlling electrons that it may well be likened to an enchanted wand. If we want the electron to move upward, it is only necessary to bring a positive charge over it. We may now increase the electrostatic force by placing a negative charge below the electron, thus repelling it from below as it is attracted from above.

This powerful electrostatic wand has many important military and industrial applications, among them the production of X rays. One of the drawings shows the construction of an X-ray tube. Electrons evaporated from the hot cathode come under the tremendous pull of the tungsten anode, which has a positive charge of hundreds of thousands of volts. As a result, the electrons are accelerated and strike the tungsten target with a terrific impact, giving up their energy to the tungsten, which

in turn radiates what we know as X rays.

Another ingenious electronic device guards many of our war industries from the sabotage of dust. This is the precipitron, shown in both a photograph and a diagram on page HW 185. It contains a series of plates charged with positive and negative electricity. A wire at a high negative potential gives off electrons in the path of a flow of air, and they impart a negative charge to dust and other foreign particles in the air. These negatively charged particles are repelled by the negative plates in the precipitron as they pass and are attracted and held by the positive plates.

Installed in the ventilating system of a film-manufacturing plant, this precipitron eliminates dust that might ruin the film. The same principle has been applied to precipitate soot from smoke in chimneys.

A positive charge placed near an electron will attract it. A negative charge placed on the side opposite accelerates the electron by repelling it at the same time the other charge attracts it

Below, an X-ray tube. The electrodes come under the pull of the positive tungsten anode, striking it with a terrific impact, the energy of which gives rise to the emission of powerful X rays

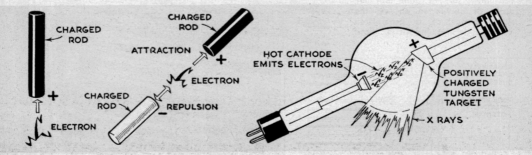

Detachable Pedal Extension for Child's Use

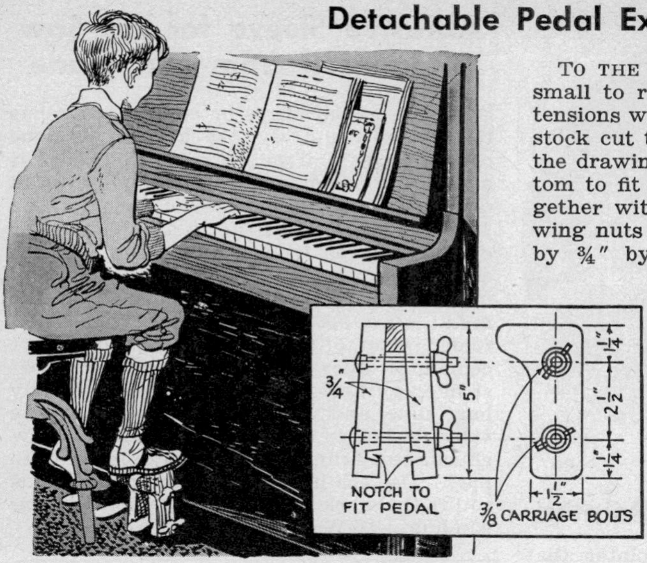

TO THE young musician who is still too small to reach the piano pedals, these extensions will prove a great help. Out of ¾" stock cut two pieces to the shape shown in the drawing. These are notched at the bottom to fit the piano pedal and fastened together with two ⅜" carriage bolts having wing nuts and washers. Glue or nail a ½" by ¾" by 2¼" filler strip along the top edge of one piece before assembly. This makes the tread wide enough at the top to accommodate a child's foot naturally. The height of the extension shown is 5", but this can be varied according to the size of the child. Finish the extensions to harmonize with the piano, preferably before assembling so that parts will not stick.—AXEL E. OGREN.

Linoleum-Block Cutting Tool

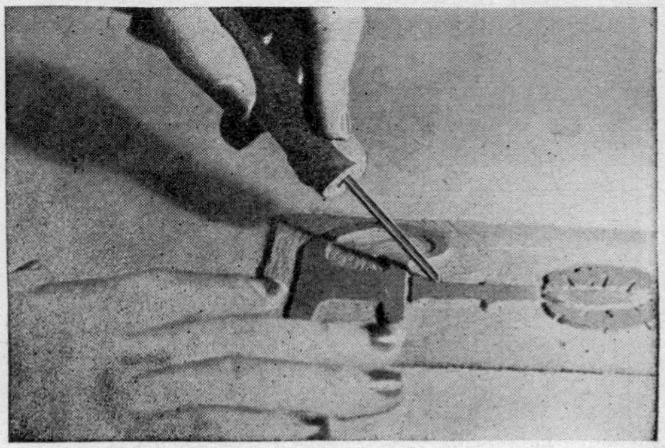

AN UMBRELLA rib, fitted into a handle, will serve as an efficient tool for carving linoleum blocks. Drive a rib about 4" long into a small hole in a handle shaped from a dowel. Spread or close the groove of the rib with pliers to form a V-shape for fine line work or a horseshoe shape for ordinary cutting. File the cutting end sharp; then harden by heating to a dull red and plunging in cold water. A curved cutting edge in the form of a crescent is best for scooping out large areas.—NATHAN A. GAINEN.

SMALL-DIAMETER CONDUIT WIRES [*ELECTRICAL*]

IN BUILDINGS originally wired with conduit or tubing, rewiring is sometimes necessary to take care of additions and alterations. In such cases, the conduits may not be large enough to accommodate the additional number of wires. To meet such conditions, the National Electrical Code permits the use of special small-diameter wires that can be installed in the conduits in greater numbers than conventional Type R wires. The following tables give the approved specifications.

Types RHT and RPT
(up to 600 volts)

Size of conductor	Number of conductors in one conduit or tubing — Size of conduit or tubing: 1	2	3	4	5	6	7	8	9
14	½"	½"	½"	½"	½"	½"	½"	¾"	¾"
12	½"	½"	½"	½"	½"	¾"	¾"	¾"	¾"
10	½"	½"	½"	½"	¾"	¾"	¾"	¾"	1"
8	½"	½"	¾"	¾"	1"	1"	1"	1"	1¼"

Types SN and RU
(up to 600 volts)

Size of conductor	Number of conductors in one conduit or tubing — Size of conduit or tubing: 1	2	3	4	5	6	7	8	9
14	½"	½"	½"	½"	½"	½"	½"	½"	½"
12	½"	½"	½"	½"	½"	½"	½"	½"	¾"
10	½"	½"	½"	½"	½"	½"	¾"	¾"	¾"
8	½"	½"	½"	¾"	¾"	¾"	1"	1"	1"
6	½"	¾"	¾"	1"	1"	1¼"	1¼"	1¼"	1¼"
5	½"	¾"	¾"	1"	1¼"	1¼"	1¼"	1¼"	1½"
4	½"	¾"	1"	1"	1¼"	1¼"	1¼"	1½"	1½"

POPULAR SCIENCE MONTHLY SHOP DATA

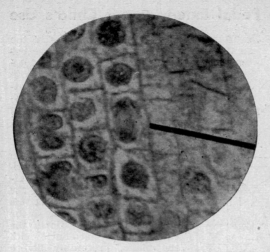

Abrasive Sleeve for Jig Saw Improvised from Old Blade

WHEN curved edges or cut-out work has to be sanded quickly, the job can be done on the jig saw, if no narrow-belt sander is available. Solder a piece of tin plate to an old jig-saw blade as shown below; then bend the piece over to form a half-round or oval section as indicated, making it small enough to pass through the saw-table opening freely. Apply adhesive tape over the metal as a soft backing, and stick on a folded strip of garnet paper with gasket cement or other adhesive. Despite the short stroke, garnet paper lasts a surprisingly long time, and when it is worn out at one end, the holder can be reversed in the saw chucks to bring the unused portion into play. Use the hold-down if the paper tends to lift the work off the jig-saw table during sanding.—H. W.

Microscope Eyepiece Pointer

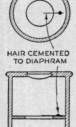

HAIR CEMENTED TO DIAPHRAM

OCULAR

AN EYEPIECE pointer that can be used for indicating a specific area on a specimen as above is easily attached. Cut a straight black hair slightly longer than half the diameter of the ocular. Next, apply a drop of Canada balsam to the upper surface of the diaphragm. Place the hair in the cement, making sure it lies flat and points to the center of the aperture. Trim the hair just short of the center.—H. WHITTAKER.

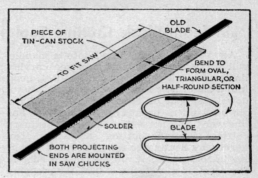

PIECE OF TIN-CAN STOCK

TO FIT SAW

OLD BLADE

BEND TO FORM OVAL, TRIANGULAR, OR HALF-ROUND SECTION

SOLDER

BLADE

BOTH PROJECTING ENDS ARE MOUNTED IN SAW CHUCKS

Drill-Press Milling Attachment Used in the Lathe

SMALL milling attachments of the type especially designed for use on a drill press can be adapted to light milling and precision drilling in the lathe by means of simple angle brackets like that shown.

This bracket was made from a piece of scrap steel obtained from a junk yard. It is of ⅜" stock, is 7" long, and measures 3" on one face and 5" on the other. The holes were already in it to receive the ⅝" stud on the bottom of the attachment and a ½" or ⅝" bolt to lock it to the tool-post slot. The braces shown were cut from 1½" by ⅜" bar steel and arc-welded in place. The faces of the bracket were machined flat and to a right angle with each other after welding.

This operation can be done on the lathe with the aid of an independent-jaw chuck. The sketch at left shows the angle piece bolted in place.

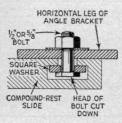

HORIZONTAL LEG OF ANGLE BRACKET

½" OR ⅝" BOLT

SQUARE WASHER

COMPOUND-REST SLIDE

HEAD OF BOLT CUT DOWN

HOME GARDENS FOR VICTORY

Irrigation before planting is important for dry soils. "Check up" your plot in 4' by 5' beds with borders 8" high. Fill each at least once from a sack-covered hose

How to Prepare the Soil and Seed Beds for a Bumper Harvest

By ROSS H. GAST

UNCLE SAM wants you to garden—for victory! To show that he means it, his Department of Agriculture in Washington has set a goal for this summer of 18,000,000 victory gardens—12,000,000 on city, town, and suburban plots, and 6,000,000 on farms. This is more than three times the number planted in World War I to yield what was then a record harvest. It is time now for you to prepare to do your share.

You won't need many tools, but buy good ones. The only indispensable items are a long-handled shovel or spade, a hoe, a rake, and about 50' of hose. A wheel hoe will save backache in large gardens. You'll find a man-size trowel, weeder, hatchet, and short-handled hoe valuable.

Have you ever turned a shovelful of soil? Irksome, isn't it? Well, here's a way to reduce strain and get more enjoyment from this necessary part of the job. Suppose you are single-trench spading. This means that you make a trench about 6" wide and 12" deep along one side of the plot, tossing the

Two pointed sticks nailed at proper intervals on a longer stick will help in making shallow parallel trenches in turned soil or on a raised bed. A good guide for keeping the trenches straight is a garden line strung down the center for the length of the rows

Water can be hosed quickly into furrows with no danger of breaking them down by using a 1-gal. can as shown above. Cut two holes in opposite sides of the can for the flow to go through, and hold the hose low in the can

Seedlings are transplanted in holes dug with a sharp stick or similar tool. Make the holes large enough for the roots to be dispersed without crowding to aid maximum early growth

Furrow beds 4" wide are best for planting peas, which should be scattered out. Hoe the dry soil on top to one side, the moist to the other, and replace the moist soil first in covering the seed

soil removed ahead of you. Force the spade or fork deep into the earth by stepping on the shoulder, working a 6" strip. Turn each load over, placing half in the trench, half on the shoulder. Thus you leave a new trench as you work across the garden. To ease the task, stand so you can use the right knee and upper leg as a lever. Press upward with the knee, down on the handle with the hands.

A certain amount of enrichment is usually necessary in preparing the soil, but do not use too much. For each 10′ by 10′ space, broadcast from 100 to 150 lbs. of barnyard manure, or else 10 lbs. of sheep manure, 10

lbs. of poultry droppings, or 5 lbs. of commercial fertilizer. Spread any one of these evenly over the entire plot, and spade in as deeply as possible. The natural fertilizers provide humus for the soil and also take care of the more important plant needs. They may be easier to get than artificial fertilizers.

Besides these, compost is a third food source. Keep it in a bin, about 8′ square and 4′ high, with either an earth or a concrete floor. Throw in plant refuse, kitchen waste, and wood ashes, and wet regularly with water. Slaked lime will hasten decay. If preferred, the refuse may be piled in a corner of the garden and covered with a thin layer of earth.

In most sections, the ground probably will have enough moisture in the spring to require little besides a thorough digging along with the fertilizing. Pulverize it well, casting the upper soil to the bottom of the trench. Do not work it too early because this tends to form a hard crust over the seed, holding back germination.

If you live in a dry area, such as some sections of California and the Southwest, irrigating before planting may be necessary. Be sure to examine the soil first with a spade to determine the amount of moisture beneath the surface, for early irrigation may also form a hard crust.

To flood dry plots before planting, "check up" the area in beds about 4' by 5', throwing up borders with the hoe 8" high. Fill each check at least once. For heavy soils use ditches 2' to 3' apart. When flooded soil is ready to work, break down the borders and, after a few days, spade or plow.

A pipe tee fitted on the hose coupling and wrapped loosely in heavy cloth at the joint will help in flooding, or simply wrap several layers of sacking around the hose outlet.

Tall-growing vegetables are planted in rows 30" apart, while the smaller root and leafy vegetables may be planted closer. If space is at a premium, the rows may be as close as 12", but this does not give much working space between them.

If you prefer to plant on raised beds, have them just far enough apart for working. Level the plot first; then stretch garden lines from the ends of two stakes placed horizontally at opposite ends of your plot. Short stakes driven at each end of the 30" ones will hold them. Now, walking backward, plunge the hoe into the soil with the cutting edge away from the guide line and draw the soil up sharply. Repeat the process along the other line, thus completing the first raised bed. For the second bed, complete the second furrow and start a third. Each bed must be smoothed level.

The seeds should be planted on the shoulders in parallel, shallow trenches. Two pointed sticks nailed at the proper intervals to a horizontal stick about 15" long may be drawn along the surface of the bed to make the trenches. A flat board, with a small stick projecting downward at one end, or a metal planter will also serve. The garden lines make a good guide.

Double-row crops include carrots, turnips, beets, parsnips, radishes, spinach, celery, mustard, onions, and Chinese cabbage. After planting, fill the furrows carefully but firmly and do not sprinkle. Sow plenty of seed; then thin to keep the stronger plants.

Peas are usually planted in single rows, especially for trellising. The furrow bed should be about 4" wide so the seed can be scattered out. With a hoe, scrape the drier top soil to one side and the moist to the

Short rows of peas may be trellised inexpensively on nets sold for the purpose at seed stores. Tied at the ends to two stakes, a net provides adequate support for the vines

Another method of forming seed furrows in turned soil is with a metal planter. The bed layout lines serve as guides

If you want early vegetables, cover the transplanted seedlings with "hot caps," little waxed-paper mounds that keep them warm at night and moist during the day

other. Plant ½" deep in spring, 2" during warmer months. Put the moist soil back first, the dry on top. Mulch and do not disturb again until the sprouts appear.

Tomato, pepper, cabbage, lettuce, and some other plants have small, fibrous roots, and are quick to make new growth when transplanted. Growing them in flats is comparatively simple. Use shallow boxes about 4" by 24" by 24". Sterilize the soil by drenching with boiling water, and immerse the flats and other equipment in boiling water for five minutes. Make up the soil from sterilized garden soil and a handful of screened sheep manure, leaf mold, or peat. Mix thoroughly and firm down in the flats until the surface is ¾" below the top. Plant seed from ⅛" to ¼" deep, according to the variety, and cover with screened light soil mixed with manure or leaf mold. Protect with burlap until the seedlings pop up.

When the plants are 1" high, transfer to a second flat, planting 1" apart. Never sprinkle, but "irrigate" by placing the flat in shallow water until it works up to moisten the surface. Transplant in the garden during a cool evening to avoid wilting. Use a sharp stick or other implement to make holes large enough for the roots to be inserted without crowding.

Once your garden is started, water becomes most essential. It is a good idea to cultivate four or five days after each rain or watering. The hose need be used only every 10 days or so in the spring, and every four to eight days in the summer.

Dusting young plants is essential when they are threatened by insects. The powder can be put on evenly by shaking from an ordinary sack

Ten Garden Tips

1 BEANS prefer heavy soil to loams. Plant seed 1" deep in clay, 3" in sandy soils

2 BEETS like mellow soil. Soak seed 24 hours before planting to hasten the germination

3 CABBAGES require strong, fertile soil, not sandy loam. Start them in a seed bed, and then transplant seven to eight weeks later

4 CARROTS need light, moist, warm soil. Mix sand with seed and do not sow over ½" deep

5 CORN dislikes frost. It does best in rich, sandy loam. Plant 4" apart, 1" to 3" deep

6 LETTUCE will grow in nearly any soil if kept moist. Shade from other plants helps in hot weather. Transplant or sow and thin

7 CUCUMBERS take to a rich soil. Plant after frost, and keep the three strongest plants of the five or six sprouting in each hill

8 TOMATOES are universal, growing well in any soil but light sand. Transplant after all danger of frost is past, spacing 3' apart

9 TURNIPS should never go in clayey soil or sand. Plant preferably in rich soil like other root vegetables and thin to 3". An early planting is better than one in summer

10 SQUASH should be irrigated from furrows, never by sprinkling. Pick before too large

Simply Built Utility Mantel

Packs a Lot of Real Living Convenience into Little Space

HAVE you ever wanted a fireplace in your house or in your one- or two-room apartment? Here is an artificial fireplace that will not only fulfill that wish, but also provide extra conveniences.

This mantel, built entirely of pine and plywood, has storage space for clothing and other articles, a mirror for shaving, and a drop front that can serve as a vanity table, desk, or breakfast bar. Some of the compartments are of just the size to take shirts folded at the laundry, an unusual feature.

The original design was the work of Miss Corinne Pascoe, of Brooklyn, N. Y., whose utility mantel is shown in photographs on the following pages. From her basic idea, the staff of POPULAR SCIENCE developed the modern mantel described here. Either mantel can be built with simple tools, but as in all such projects, power tools will speed the job.

Because of the large over-all dimensions, it is best to saw the pieces and make a trial assembly in the workshop, after which final assembling can be done in the room for which the mantel is intended. Cut the two endpieces, the two partitions, and the two bottoms to size. If the floor of the room is not level, the lower edges of the ends and partitions may be cut slightly out of true to allow for the variation. Next, attach the shelf cleats and bore holes for the shelf pegs. Fasten the ends and partitions to the bottoms with screws through the latter, and tack a board temporarily across the top of each unit to hold it rigid until the back and top shelf are attached later.

Cut the three moldings (section F-F) and miter the joints. Attach the 1″ by 1″ strips to the two side moldings and the other strip to the horizontal molding that goes across the top of the fireplace opening. Fit the ¼″ plywood panels to form the sides and top of the inside of the fireplace; then attach the three rear strips to the rear

Modern design and spaciousness feature this mantel. Some of the shelves are adjustable. Note the finger grips for opening the doors

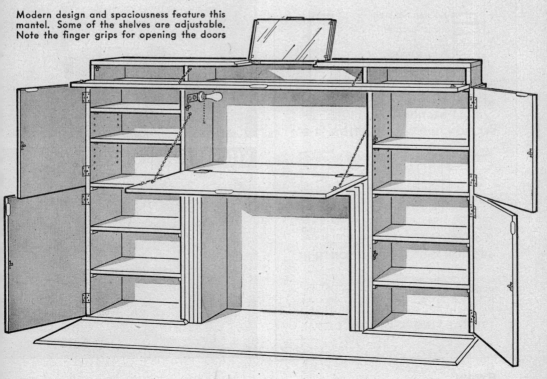

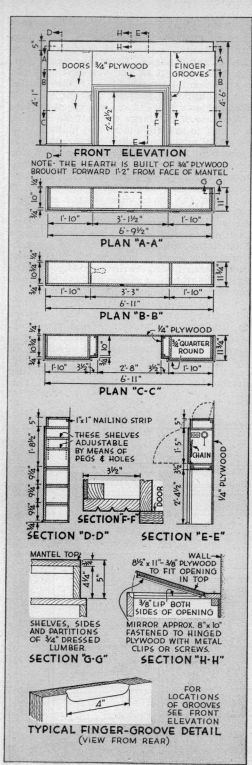

FRONT ELEVATION
DOORS ¾" PLYWOOD
FINGER GROOVES
NOTE- THE HEARTH IS BUILT OF ¾" PLYWOOD BROUGHT FORWARD 1'-2" FROM FACE OF MANTEL

PLAN "A-A"
1'-10" 3'-1½" 1'-10"
6'-9½"

PLAN "B-B"
1'-10" 3'-3" 1'-10"
6'-11"

PLAN "C-C"
¼" PLYWOOD
¾ QUARTER ROUND
1'-10" 3½" 2'-8" 3½" 1'-10"
6'-11"

SECTION "D-D"
1"x1" NAILING STRIP
THESE SHELVES ADJUSTABLE BY MEANS OF PEGS & HOLES

SECTION F-F
3½"
DOOR

SECTION "E-E"
CHAIN
¼" PLYWOOD

SECTION "G-G"
MANTEL TOP
SHELVES, SIDES AND PARTITIONS OF ¾" DRESSED LUMBER.

SECTION "H-H"
WALL
8½" x 11"-⅜" PLYWOOD TO FIT OPENING IN TOP
⅜" LIP BOTH SIDES OF OPENING
MIRROR APPROX. 8"x 10" FASTENED TO HINGED PLYWOOD WITH METAL CLIPS OR SCREWS.

TYPICAL FINGER-GROOVE DETAIL
(VIEW FROM REAR)
4"
FOR LOCATIONS OF GROOVES SEE FRONT ELEVATION

edges of these plywood pieces. This assembly is fastened to the ¼" plywood back of the whole piece.

After the shelves, back, ¾" plywood hearth, and top unit with ends and partitions are cut to dimensions, the mantel is ready to set up. Remove the temporary boards and attach the full-length top shelf. Next, fasten the top unit with ends and partitions to the top shelf. Then put the center shelf in position. After this, attach the fireplace assembly and back to the uprights, shelves, top, and bottoms of the mantel unit.

The fireplace moldings are fastened to the two partitions with screws through the partitions, and to the front edge of the center shelf with three fine finishing nails. Set the nails and putty the holes with white lead and whiting. Flathead screws, with the heads slightly countersunk, give a neat appearance and can be withdrawn if the mantel is to be taken apart for moving.

The doors and drop fronts should be fitted

How One Ingenious Woma

UTILITY CLOSETS

KITCHENETTE

after the mantel has been set up true and plumb on the hearth. Use four hinges on the long drop front, providing clearance for them by cutting a relief bevel on the upper doors and drop shelf. If the wall has a base-board and molding, it may be well to use a wider board for the mantel top and filler strips along the sides to close the gap between them and the wall. A flat or semigloss wall paint may be used for finishing.

LIST OF MATERIALS

No. Pc.	Description	T.	W.	L.	No. Pc.	Description	T.	W.	L.
2	Ends	¾	10¾	48¼	1	Top drop front	¾	5	81½
2	Partitions	¾	10¾	48¼	1	Center drop shelf (plywood)	¾	17	39
10	Shelves	¾	10¾	20½	2	Upper doors "	¾	20⅞	22
1	Shelf	¾	10¾	83	2	Lower " "	¾	22	27⅜
1	Top	¾	10¼	81½	1	Mirror back "	⅜	8½	11
2	" ends	¾	4¼	10	1	Hearth	¾	25¾	86
2	" partitions	¾	4¼	10	2	Moldings (quarter-round)	¾	¾	12¼
1	Center shelf	¾	10	39	2	" " "	¾	¾	23½
2	Bottoms	¾	11½	22	2	" " "	¾	¾	1½
1	Back (plywood)	¼	54	83	1	Nailing strip	1	1	81½
2	Moldings	¾	3½	32	4	" strips	1	1	28½
1	Molding	¾	3½	39	2	" "	1	1	39
2	Fireplace sides (plywood)	¼	10	28½	12	Shelf cleats	¾	¾	10¾
1	" top "	¼	10	32½	7	pair hinges, 8 friction catches, and 4 chains.			

Note: All dimensions are given in inches and are finished sizes.

Built a Mantel to Fill Many Needs in a Compact Home

THIS IS THE WAY Miss Corrinne Pascoe designed the original utility mantel for her home in Brooklyn, N. Y. The photographs show it fitted out as a pair of utility closets, a kitchenette, a bureau, and a vanity.

Miss Pascoe used the most elementary of tools—a small gimlet for starting nail and screw holes, a hammer, a saw, a screw driver, a pencil, and a tape measure. She drew her plans carefully, decided on the kind and thickness of wood for each part, took exact measurements, and had all the stock cut to size at a lumber yard. This method of construction will eliminate almost all sawing and make it possible for an apartment dweller to construct the piece with a minimum of noise that might disturb neighbors.

If this plan is followed, the dimensions should be set down on paper and checked against the drawings to be sure that each piece will fit when it is delivered. Once these dimensions are decided upon, no change should be made unless the builder is prepared to recheck the entire list, for different woods may vary slightly, especially in thickness, causing bad alignment.

Decorations used on Miss Pascoe's mantel are marble facings for the fireplace and half-round molding and ornamental wood trimmings for the doors. The electric fixtures and logs connect to a near-by outlet.

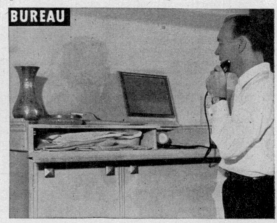

BUREAU

VANITY

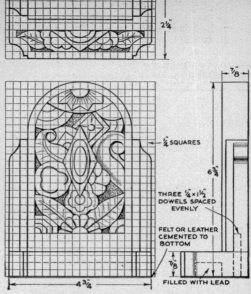

Their unusual carved motif makes these book ends an intriguing project for the craftsman

(Diagram labels:)
2¼
⅞
¼ SQUARES
6¾
THREE ¼ × 1½ DOWELS SPACED EVENLY
FELT OR LEATHER CEMENTED TO BOTTOM
⅞
4¾
FILLED WITH LEAD

Hand-Carved Book Ends Have Interesting Relief Design

THIS attractive pair of book ends, which was carved by a native Hawaiian, can be readily duplicated by the home craftsman. Any available wood having an interesting grain can be employed. Ordinary wood-carving tools, either manually or machine operated, may be used in carving the design, although an electric grinder or a drill press equipped with wood-cutting burrs will be found useful in routing out the background.

From the accompanying drawing of the design, draw a full-size pattern on ¼" squares. The upright is 5⅞" high by 4¾" wide and is attached to a ⅞" thick base by means of three evenly spaced dowels and casein glue. Before attaching the base, recess it on the underside to receive a block of lead or iron of suitable size to afford sufficient weight. Rough leather or felt is cemented along the bottom of the base to prevent slipping on polished surfaces and to protect furniture from being scratched.

The book ends should be nicely finished with shellac and wax, or with stain and shellac, depending upon the nature of the wood used.—HI SIBLEY.

LAYING OUT A LARGE ARC [WOODWORKING]

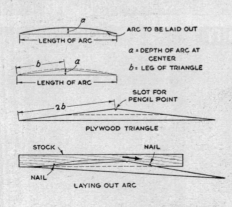

(Diagram labels:)
a
ARC TO BE LAID OUT
LENGTH OF ARC
a = DEPTH OF ARC AT CENTER
b = LEG OF TRIANGLE
b   a
LENGTH OF ARC
2b
SLOT FOR PENCIL POINT
PLYWOOD TRIANGLE
STOCK   NAIL
NAIL
LAYING OUT ARC

To DRAW an arc with a very small curvature on such work as the back rail of a chair, a curved drawer front, part of a garden arbor, and the like, proceed as follows:

Measure the length between the ends of the desired arc and also its center depth. Connect these points, making a triangle. Construct a similar triangle, with legs twice as long, from thin board, and at the apex cut a notch for a pencil. Drive two nails into the work at the end points of the arc to be laid out and place the wooden triangle in contact with both nails. Holding a pencil in the slot, move the triangle from side to side. A perfect arc of the correct size will be drawn.

POPULAR SCIENCE MONTHLY SHOP DATA

TANK BLOTTER

Also Holds Clips, Stamps, and Other Desk Accessories

By MYRON FLEISHMAN

THE LITTLE tank shown here doesn't pack a real gun, but it makes a novel desk blotter and container for stamps, clips, pen points, and the like.

Five sections of wood comprise the body of this realistic tank. The center section *A*, as shown in the drawing, contains the compartment recess and is cut from 1" stock. Sections *B* are of 5/16" stock and are glued or nailed to the sides of *A*. Make sections *B* slightly larger than *A*. After gluing or nailing, sand, plane, and file them down flush with *A*. The outside sections *C* are of ½" stock and are planed down to match sections *B* but are not glued on at once. After planing sections *C* to size, use a hacksaw blade to cut the grooves or "treads" of the tractor; then glue together.

The square block which is screwed and nailed to the underside of the turret should be made to fit the compartment beforehand. Turn the turret and gun on the lathe or whittle and sand to shape, fitting the gun in a slightly raised position to the turret. Headlights are fashioned from a piece of dowel ¼" in diameter and 5/16" in length. The two blotter holders are of ⅝" by 1⅝" sheet metal, with beveled corners. Cut the blotter 1⅝" in width and clamp it fast by the two ends.

Ready, aim . . . blot! This novel tank will add a military touch to a desk. The compartment under the gun turret holds stamps and clips

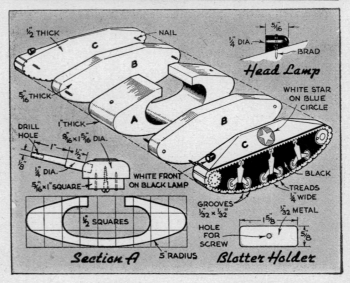

Cobbler's Bench Has

By FRANKLIN H. GOTTSHALL

THIS cobbler's bench, which has the authentic lines of an original, makes a quaint and charming coffee table for use in the living room. The traylike compartments will hold cigarettes, candies, nuts, cookies, and the like. Niches in the back of the bench form holders for pipes, drinking straws, paper napkins, spoons, and other small articles. The drawer may be pulled out from either side and is convenient for keeping chessmen, playing cards, dominoes, and similar game accessories.

To make the bench, first glue up or pro-

cure a plank for the top. Although the one shown was made of Georgia pine, any yellow or white pine will do if it is kiln dried to avoid warping, or maple may be used. Before rounding the corners for the seat, mark the place where the holes for the legs are to be bored.

A drawing shows the proper method to use in boring these holes. For each corner, draw lines parallel to the edges and bisect the angle thus formed with a third line. Using a protractor or a sliding T-bevel adjusted to the proper angle, line up the bit to bore the hole. In getting this angle, be sure that the bit is kept in the same plane as the bi-

Old-Time Charm

secting line while boring. Once the screw of the bit has penetrated the surface, finish boring from the other side to prevent splintering.

Scoop out the saddle seat with large wood-carving gouges. Clean up the saddle with a curved scraper blade, and sandpaper to a smooth finish. Finally, bandsaw the top to shape, notching the edge where the side containing compartments is to be fitted.

The legs should be made of extra strong wood such as maple, and they should be tapered and trimmed to an octagonal shape after the ends which go into the seat have been turned. Kerfs are cut in these ends on the band saw for wedges which help anchor them securely in the seat. Glue is used in addition to the wedges.

The three side compartments are gains and do not go clear across the stock. After boring holes for the screw heads, glue and screw the piece to the seat. Next, glue and screw on the side block and end, the former from the back as shown in the drawing.

When the drawer has been made and fitted, brad and glue the strips to the top to form the trays, and turn the drawer pulls. Finish the bench very carefully with stain and varnish.

List of Materials

No.	Description	T.	W.	L.
1	Top	1½"	16"	36¼"
1	Side	¾"	5½"	16½"
1	Side block	¾"	2"	8"
1	End	¾"	4"	15¼"
2	Drawer supports	1"	2"	15½"
2	Drawer strips	½"	½"	15"
2	Drawer ends	¾"	5½"	6"
2	Drawer sides	½"	5½"	14½"
1	Drawer bottom	¼"	5½"	14"
1	Strip	¼"	⅜"	13⅝"
1	Strip	¼"	⅜"	13¼"
1	Strip	¼"	⅜"	13½"
2	Strips	¼"	⅜"	4"
2	Strips	¼"	⅜"	4⅞"
4	Legs	1½"	1½"	14½"
2	Drawer pulls	1"	1"	2¼"

Great care must be taken to bore the leg holes at the proper angle, as shown below. The joints of the drawer are cut with a dado head on a power saw. If made with hand tools, they should be dovetailed

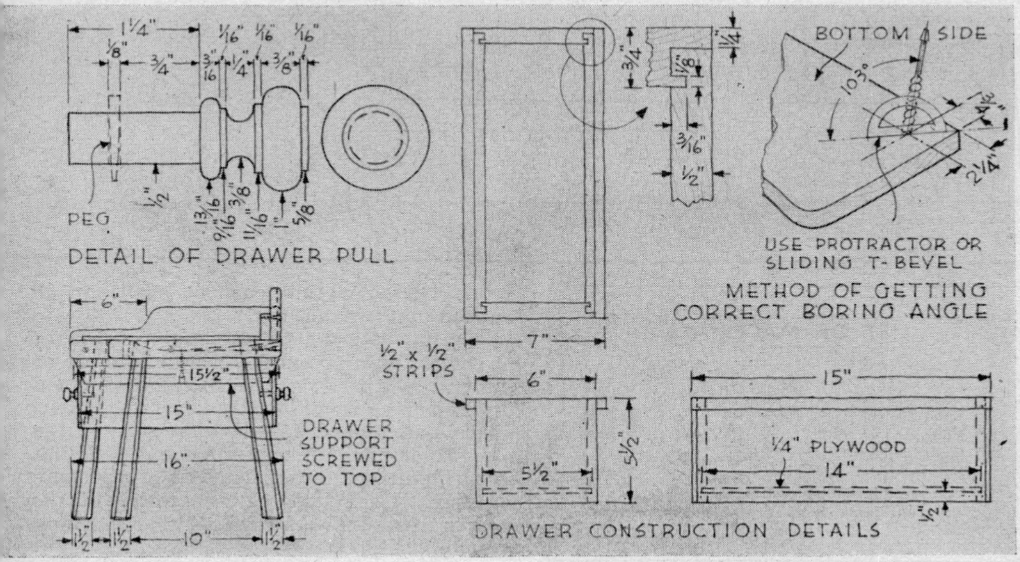

PEG
DETAIL OF DRAWER PULL
BOTTOM
SIDE
103°
USE PROTRACTOR OR SLIDING T-BEVEL
METHOD OF GETTING CORRECT BORING ANGLE
DRAWER SUPPORT SCREWED TO TOP
½" x ½" STRIPS
¼" PLYWOOD
DRAWER CONSTRUCTION DETAILS

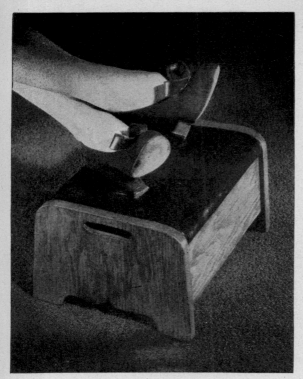

COTTAGE FOOTSTOOL
Has Compartment for Slippers

THE straightforward design of this useful footstool adapts it to any room with American furniture, and particularly for use with maple furniture. There is a provincial atmosphere about it that is enhanced by its upholstered top and slipper compartment. The parts and construction are comparatively simple.

Boards required to build this stool are all the same thickness, the cutting is along plain lines, and the end joints are merely doweled and glued. Further simplification can be made by the use of nails, screws, or exposed dowels.

Cut the endpieces to shape and form the handle slots by boring three ¾" holes and two ½" holes, then cutting away the excess wood with a keyhole saw. Cut the floor next, being careful to bevel the two long edges so the sides will have the proper slope. The sides may be made square, without beveled edges. The lid is cut ⅛" smaller all around so that it will lift freely, and the two long edges are rounded off generously.

After assembling, round all edges of the stool with sandpaper to give a slightly worn appearance. Finish to taste. The original model was made of soft pine, stained light

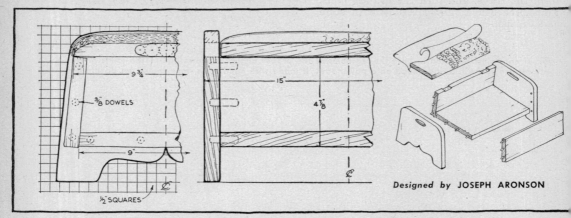

Designed by JOSEPH ARONSON

brown, given a thin coat of shellac, well rubbed and waxed.

The upholstery consists simply of a layer of cotton, hair, or excelsior, with a scrap of material—in this case leather from an old brief case—drawn neatly over the four edges and tacked to the underside of the top. Tapestry or upholstering material that is harmonious with other pieces of furniture in the room may also be used. Screw on the hinges after the upholstering and finishing are completed.

LIST OF MATERIALS

No. Pc.	Description	T.	W.	L.
2	Ends	¾	8¼	11¼
2	Sides	¾	4⅞	13½
1	Floor	¾	9	13½
1	Lid	¾	9¾	13¼
1	Pair small cabinet butts			

Note: All dimensions are given in inches

RUSTIC NAME POST

ATTRACTIVE name and house-number boards can be made of scrap lumber and a tree branch or sapling log. A crossbar and brace made from a branch support the name board, which is suspended with short lengths of rope run through heavy screw eyes. Remove the bark from the end of the post that goes into the ground. Paint this with creosote to prevent decay.

Use a smooth board with jagged ends and leave it unpainted. Carve the lettering with a V-shaped chisel, paint it dark brown, and apply two coats of outdoor spar varnish. A color effect is obtained by burning the board slightly, brushing with a wire brush, and painting the letters Chinese red.

abcdefghijklmnopqrstuvwxyz
ABCDEF GHIJKLMN
OPQRSTUVWXYZ

CUTTING WINDOW POCKETS   [SHIPSHAPE HOME]

Pocket openings for removing sash weights are omitted in many frames, but they can be cut out without much trouble when damaged sash cords must be replaced. Remove the stop, lower sash, and parting bead. Square pencil lines across the pulley stiles as guides, and bore a hole in the parting bead groove on each line. With a compass or keyhole saw inclined at 45 deg., cut along the upper line; then saw the lower end square across. Rip the stile down in the parting-bead groove. Pry out the piece. If a nail from the casing enters it, cut the nail off behind the casing, or pull it out with pliers.

Bore two shallow holes in the pulley stile to receive dowels set into the lower end of the cut-out. Incline the dowels slightly to fit. To replace the piece, slip the dowels into the holes and put a flathead screw into the upper miter cut. Adjust the fit by the length of the dowels. Replace the parting bead, sash, and stop.

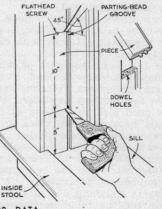

FLATHEAD SCREW — 45° — PARTING-BEAD GROOVE — PIECE — 10" — DOWEL HOLES — 5" — SILL — INSIDE STOOL

How to raise Rabbits
FOR QUICK MEAT PRODUCTION

By ANDREW R. BOONE

YOUR corner meat market is no longer as well stocked as it used to be, and the butcher now requires ration stamps as well as cash. Why not stretch your ration with home-raised meat? Experts agree that rabbit meat is a high-protein muscle and body builder, and that rabbits produce one of the best all-around meats in less time than any other domestic animal or fowl.

Four to six does and a buck, which can be housed in a small space, ought to provide the average family with one or more hearty meals every week.

Of the many varieties of white rabbits available, the New Zealand, Flemish Giant, American, Beveren, French Silver, and Chinchilla are the best producers. Although it is a good idea to get one of these white breeds because white pelts are generally more desirable than darker shades, the choice is entirely one of personal preference. Angora rabbits provide both good meat and useful wool, which can be clipped from the live animals at intervals.

Fryers weighing 3¾ to 4¼ lbs. will be ready for the table in two months, and they'll dress at better than two pounds.

Heavier rabbits will yield much more meat and are preferable for stews and fricassees.

Rabbits make little trouble and thrive on quiet and good treatment. They will happily munch garden waste such as vines and leaves, lawn clippings, and palatable weeds, as well as table scraps.

You may, advises George S. Templeton, Director of the United States Rabbit Experiment Station at Fontana, Calif., start your foundation stock either with young rabbits just weaned or with mature animals. To speed production, you should buy an older doe—one that has already been bred with a buck not related to her. Additional information about breeding and rabbit rearing can be had from the Fontana station, or from the Director, Fish and Wildlife Service, Merchandise Mart, Chicago, Ill.

There is no hocus-pocus about hutch building, either. Just be sure the hutch can be kept clean easily, thus simplifying the task of care and feeding. Wildlife Leaflet No. 218, "Domestic Rabbits in the Food for Freedom Program," published by the Fish and Wildlife Service, recommends an inexpensive hutch having two compartments as suitable for home rabbit raising. Copies of this leaflet, from which much of the other

These easily raised animals provide fryers in record time. New Zealand whites, such as are shown on the facing page, are a good breed. The buck, or male, is at left

Equipment for the back-yard rabbitry need not be costly. Materials for a self-cleaning hutch (above) are listed on the next page. Right, a nesting box made from a nail keg

METAL STRIPS   13"   6"   BORE FOUR 1"HOLES IN UPPER HALF OF END

material in this article was obtained, can be obtained from the Chicago office.

The hutch mentioned is of the self-cleaning type with a floor made of 1" by 1" slats spaced ⅝" apart. The hutch is 4' long, 2½' wide, and 2' high. The photo above shows the hutch, and the lumber required is listed in the bill of materials on the next page.

Other items you need include mangers large enough to hold a 24-hour supply of hay and so constructed that you can fill them from the front without opening the hutch doors, feed troughs of the drawer type to be placed under the mangers, guards over the mangers at 3" intervals to prevent young rabbits from contaminating the feed, water containers—preferably crocks—about 8" wide and 4" deep, and nest boxes. The last can be made from nail kegs or boxes as shown in the drawings above.

Rabbit breeding can be started at any time, regardless of season, for each doe should be bred to produce four litters a year. Does and bucks of small breeds may be mated when five to six months old, medium-weight animals at six to seven months, and giants at nine to twelve months. Mating should be undertaken when the doe is coming into maturity. At its completion, the

doe should be confined to her own hutch.

A doe will carry her young 31 to 32 days. During the third week after mating, place a nest box in her hutch, bedding it well with clean straw. She will usually arrange her own nesting material, lining it with hair pulled from her body.

The next day following kindling, place your hand quietly in the nest and remove any dead, deformed, or undersized young, leaving six to eight, depending upon the suckling ability of the doe. You can even transfer newly born rabbits from one doe to another to even up litters, but this must be done within the first two or three days after birth of the young.

Fryer rabbits are ready for consumption when they are weaned at 60 days of age, but they can be kept together in one hutch for two months longer. It's a good idea to rebreed the doe immediately. Any does and bucks you plan to keep for breeding purposes should be separated from the litter after weaning time.

Never lift a mature rabbit by the ears or legs. The proper way to carry a grown rabbit is to grasp a fold of skin over the shoulders with one hand, support the rump with the other hand, and hold the back of

Mature rabbits should be carried by grasping the skin above the shoulders and supporting the rump

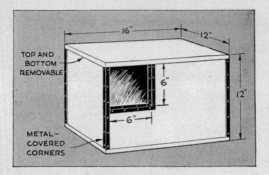

TOP AND BOTTOM REMOVABLE

16"

12"

6"

6"

12"

METAL-COVERED CORNERS

MATERIALS FOR CONSTRUCTING TWO-COMPARTMENT HUTCH

No. Pc.	Description	T.	W.	L.
4	Front corner posts	1	2	56
4	Rear corner posts	1	2	50
2	Top, front and rear	1	2	96
2	Bottom, front and rear	1	2	96
2	Bottom ends	1	2	30
2	Top ends	1	2	32
4	Front and rear braces	1	2	40
4	End braces	1	2	24
2	Door jambs	1	2	22
4	Horizontals of doors	1	2	24
4	Verticals for doors	1	2	22
2	Door latch pieces	1	1	4
2	Supports under slat floor	1	1	96
54	Floor	1	1	30
2	Sides of base under feed trough	1	2	28
1	Top of base under feed trough	1	8	28
1	Bottom of feed trough	1	8	29
1	Front end of feed trough	1	2	8
1	Manger front (V-shaped opening 9" by 14")	1	12	22
1	Manger back	1	12	16
1	Manger bottom	1	2	28
4	Manger strips for attaching wire netting	1	1	18
2	Manger top	½	8	28
13	Roof	½	8	36
12	Roof battens	½	2	36
2	Hutch boards for record cards	½	4	8
1	¾" Wire mesh, 16 gauge, 28" by 30" for hay manger			
1	1" Wire mesh, 18 gauge, 24" by 13' for front, doors, and ends			
1	1" Wire mesh, 18 gauge, 18" by 8' for back			
2	Tin, 2½" by 30", for feed-trough sides			
4	20d box nails for hinges			
18	20d nails, spaced 3" apart, for guards of feed trough			
	6d nails and wire-mesh staples			

Note: All lumber dimensions are given in inches.

the rabbit well cushioned against your body.

Rabbits require a minimum of attention except during severe hot and cold weather. Young rabbits can stand low temperatures once they are dry, providing they have a warm nest and a good covering of fur. To keep young litters and does ready to kindle from suffering in hot weather, place feed sacks on the hutch floor and wet them three or four times a day. Don't make the mistake of wetting the animals. This may bring on colds and pneumonia. If the very young become restless in hot weather, place them in a 6" by 6" by 15" wire basket hung inside the hutch, but return them to the nest box when the thermometer falls to normal.

There is no need to worry over the feeding problem. Rabbits will eat whole grain, provided it is free from mold or smuts. If the grain is mixed with fine meal, dampen it slightly to keep the meal from settling to the bottom of the feed trough. All table scraps may be fed excepting sour and greasy items. So may vegetables, lawn clippings, sweet potato and pea vines, green corn leaves, and the like.

Keep good-quality hay in the manger at all times. Cut the hay into 4" lengths. Legumes such as alfalfa, clover, vetch, and cowpea are more desirable than the carbonaceous hays like timothy, bluegrass, Bermuda, and similar grasses, although the latter are satisfactory if cut and fed when still green. Root crops, including carrots, turnips, and sweet potatoes, can be stored for winter feeding.

Regular feeding is important to keep the stock strong, so make sure that dry does, herd bucks, and developing breeding stock are fed daily the amount of grain or scraps that they will eat in a half hour or less. The young usually will start eating solid foods at three weeks, at which time both doe and young should get all the grain and scraps they can consume. When the litter is weaned, return the doe to the regular diet.

A diet for rapid growth of young rabbits, and for the doe until her young are weaned, should contain plant-protein supplements (soybean, peanut, or linseed) in meal, peasize cake, or pellet form. Mix the supplement one part by weight with two parts of one or more whole grains. Be sure the items are well mixed. All grains may be used interchangeably, as their food values are about the same.

To kill a rabbit humanely, stun it by striking it with a stick on top of the head back of the ears. Suspend it head down and remove the head immediately to permit thorough bleeding.

In dressing the carcass, first cut off the tail and front feet. Remove the left rear foot at the hock joint, cut the skin im-

Hay for feeding can be cut into 4" lengths on a table having a backboard and a slot for a saw

Above is a weaned litter busily feeding, while below are young rabbits in a hot-weather basket suspended to make the most of any cooling breeze

Below is an easy method of branding rabbits. An India-ink number inside ear identifies this Angora. Its valuable wool is plucked at regular intervals

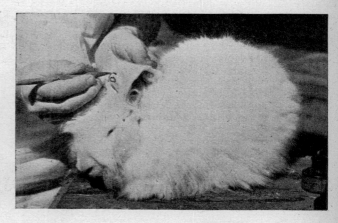

mediately below the hock of the suspended leg, and open the skin inside this leg to the root of the tail. Extend this incision to the hock joint of the left rear leg and, after separating the edges of the skin from the flesh, continue pulling the skin off, leaving the fat on the carcass. After the skin has been completely removed, slit the carcass open along the belly and remove the entrails, saving the liver, heart, and kidneys. Cut off the right hind leg at the hock joint, and the rabbit is correctly dressed.

The expense of raising rabbits can be materially reduced by selling the pelts. While the skin is yet warm, place it flesh side out over a shaper and remove all wrinkles. The fore part goes over the narrow end, with both front legs on one side. Don't stretch the skin unduly.

The day after placing a skin on a stretcher, make sure that the edges of the pelt are drying flat and that the skin on the front legs is straight. Remove surplus fat. Hang the skin in the shade beyond the reach of mice. Should you store dry skins for an extended period, sprinkle them with naphtha flakes and pack them in a tight box. Never use salt. Furriers will buy pelts that have been kept in good condition, thus helping you to keep the cost of fresh Victory meat for your family at a minimum.

Victory Shopping Bag Made of Fabric and Plywood

WITH some plywood, a piece of fabric, and the help of a brace and bit, anyone can make this victory shopping bag. It holds a surprising number of packages and is designed to keep them from falling out at the sides.

Two 9/16" holes centered 3½" apart are bored in each of two disks cut from ¼" plywood. Eleven ⅛" holes are bored 7/16" in from the edge of each disk and evenly spaced, as shown. After sanding and varnishing the disks, paint on the V's and varnish again.

About ½ yd. of 30" wide fabric such as drapery cloth is required for the bag. All edges are hemmed, and the rectangle of cloth is gathered and laced to the small holes with colored cord. Seamed handles 1" wide, cut from the same material, are slipped through the large holes and sewed.

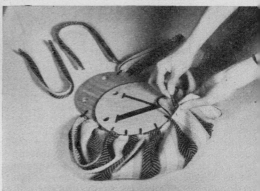

Above, the completed bag ready for marketing. Drawing at right gives layout of the holes in the disks. The photo at extreme right shows bag being attached to disks with colored cord

3½
9/16" HOLES
3 7/16 R.
⅛ HOLES 1¼ APART
¼ × 7" DIA
PLYWOOD DISK

Ice-Cream Containers Are Used for "Candle" Centerpieces

ICE-CREAM containers are easily transformed into make-believe candles which serve as attractive centerpieces for party tables and cost little or nothing to make. A patriotic motif can be added by making them red, white, and blue, but you can select any color combination you desire.

After removing the lids and inverting the containers, cover them with construction paper. Using the lid as a pattern, cut paper circles for the tops. Flames are fashioned from red cellulose film and glued to 1" lengths of pipe cleaner, which are inserted through holes punched in the tops. The pipe cleaner is secured by bending the inserted end. Leave a bit of it showing to represent a wick. Then tie a ribbon around each candle.

Small Drill Press Adapted to Bore Holes in End of Long Work

A SMALL bench-type drill press can easily be adapted to drill work longer than the maximum distance between chuck and table. Bolt the drill press at the extreme end of a sturdy bench that is itself bolted to the floor. The bench must not tip when pressure is put on the feed handle with the drill-press head turned to overhang the bench.

Raise the head to the top of the column and lock it there. Make a collar of two hardwood blocks rounded to fit the column and bolt them firmly around it just under the head. This will support the weight of the motor and head when the clamp is released to swing the head clear of the bench.

Construct a face of hardwood, to which the work can be clamped vertically for drilling, by fastening two arms of suitable length to a board by means of triangular braces. The arms are adjusted and fastened to the table by bolts.—BERTRAM BROWNOLD.

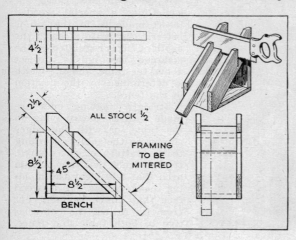

The work is clamped to a face held in a vertical position by two arms that are bolted fast to the drill-press table

At far right, the collar is shown bolted to the column

Wide Framing Mitered Accurately in Triangular Sawing Jig

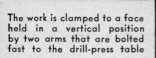

ALL STOCK ½"

FRAMING TO BE MITERED

45°

BENCH

CUTTING 45-deg. miters on wide boards can be done accurately with a narrow miter saw used in the triangular-shaped box shown at the left. It is designed to be attached to the edge of a bench so that the piece to be mitered can extend down below the bench.

The angle of the sloping bottom of the box, between the two sides of 2½" wide stock, is 45 deg. Both sides are notched to allow space for the thick back of the saw, and the slot in which the saw slides is vertical. The width of the box can be made to suit the length of the saw and the width of the piece to be mitered. A carpenter's steel square is helpful in getting true angles.—E. L. WESTDAL.

Shaping, Sanding, and Metal

By
EDWIN M. LOVE

In shaping the edge of an oval piece on the circular saw, keep the work pressed against a pencil mark above the arch in the fence. A molding head is mounted in place of the saw blade

Below, starting to cut a cove. The fence masks off the portion of the cutter not wanted. Be careful not to feed work too fast

A CIRCULAR saw is an invaluable piece of equipment for the home workshop because it not only makes sawing easy, but can also be used for shaping, jointing, sanding, and metal cutting. The accessories necessary for these additional tasks are comparatively inexpensive.

How can the saw be used as a shaper? A molding head fitted with interchangeable knives makes it a shaper. These heads are of several styles, some designed for the lighter uses to which home workshop equipment is generally put, and others for heavy-duty production work. The three cutters of a molding head are locked with screws in slots that are nearly at right angles to the radius, thus combining a shearing angle with safety. Solid two-winged cutters are available in a variety of patterns. They cost about the same as sets of cutters for a molding head and are very satisfactory.

Mount the head on the saw arbor in the same manner as a saw blade. The dado-head insert serves in most cases, but sometimes a special wooden insert made to fit the job is better. As with a saw, the depth of cut is regulated by the distance the knives project above the table, and the width is determined by the position of the fence.

Straight molding cuts are made with the board lying on the table, or with the edges sliding on the table, according to the pattern of cut desired. If the fence has no built-in arch that will clear the molding head, screw on a wood face that has a segment cut from it. Adjust the cut relative to both table and fence,

Cutting on the Circular Saw

and make a trial cut on a scrap of wood. When the setting is correct, pass the work over the cutters. Irregular motion may cause slight ridges, and feeding too fast leaves noticeable ribs. A better finish is usually obtained if a second pass is made without change of adjustments. If the molding extends around the piece, complete one end first, then one edge, next the second end, and finally the second edge. This enables the cutters to trim away the splintered corners left from cutting across the grain.

Can curved moldings be made on the circular saw? Outside curves are almost as easy to make as on a shaper. Feed the work against the molding head, keeping the edge against a center point marked on the fence above the arch. If irregularities appear due to shifting from the center line, a a second pass will smooth the work. When moldings require two or more settings, with or without a change of knives, be sure to

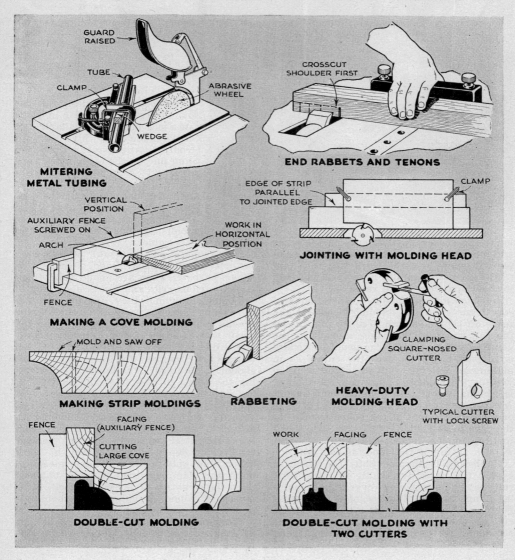

MITERING METAL TUBING

END RABBETS AND TENONS

JOINTING WITH MOLDING HEAD

MAKING A COVE MOLDING

MAKING STRIP MOLDINGS

RABBETING

HEAVY-DUTY MOLDING HEAD

TYPICAL CUTTER WITH LOCK SCREW

DOUBLE-CUT MOLDING

DOUBLE-CUT MOLDING WITH TWO CUTTERS

Metal can be cut by using an abrasive disk on the arbor instead of the saw blade. Be sure to wear goggles, use the special iron guard designed for this purpose, and stand to one side. Cutting wheels of this type can do much damage if they are shattered

A grit-faced disk replaces the saw blade when the circular saw is used as a sander. Such a disk may be purchased or made up of plywood and coarse and fine garnet paper

make the successive trial cuts on the same trial piece of work, so that the finished sample will show how the work will turn out.

Inside curves can also be shaped, but only if they have very large radii.

How can jointing be done? Insert squared-edged knives in the molding head, set the fence off center enough to allow for cutting the full width of the edge, and adjust the depth of cut to 1/16". The usual procedure is to pass the piece over the cutter as in making a molding, but since the edge in jointing is completely cut away, the support is gradually lost and gouging may result. A better method is to clamp a straight strip of wood to the side of the board parallel to the edge to be jointed. Slide this strip along the top of the fence or along a straight wooden facing if the fence is not true.

Rabbeting is simple. Shift the fence to expose the necessary width of cutter, and run the edge of the work over. The remaining flange carries the piece, thus preventing gouging. End rabbets and tenons can be cut as with a dado head. Crosscut the shoulders first to avoid splintering them.

Is the saw used for sanding? Special

grit-faced disks designed for mounting on the arbor in place of a saw blade are available, but disks made of ⅜" plywood with coarse garnet paper on one side and fine on the other work very well. If necessary, make a wooden insert for a plywood sanding disk. Most of the jobs that any small sanding disk can handle, such as dressing miter joints, shaping small blocks, and the like, are possible.

How is metal cutting done? Wheels used for cutting metal are made of emery or silicon carbide. They are about 3/32" thick and of various grits and bonds, according to the material which they are to cut. Before using such a wheel, examine it for cracks and chipped edges. Clamp it on the arbor with medium pressure, using a cardboard disk on each side to cushion it. An iron guard designed for the purpose also should be obtained. Stand aside when starting the wheel in case it should shatter.

The wheels cut steel amid a shower of sparks and leave precise, smooth surfaces, shearing through with ease. This method affords a simple way to cut sections from hardened steel without drawing temper to a great depth. The accuracy of work depends not only upon precision of measurement and clamping arrangements, but also upon the condition of the wheel itself. If it is out of round or chipped, it should be dressed true on the arbor to avoid wobble.

When mounted against a plywood disk for backing, cutting wheels can be used for surfacing, tool grinding, and similar operations.

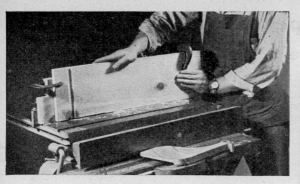

Moldings can be cut on outside curves almost as easily on a circular saw as on a shaper, and the operation is similar. A round piece is being molded in the photograph below, with the help of a notched fence used as a guide

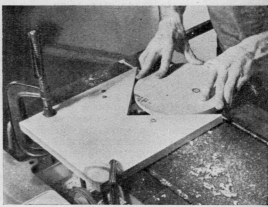

Shown above is a sure method of jointing. Clamped to the work, parallel to the edge to be jointed, is a straight piece of wood that slides along the top of the auxiliary fence. Square-edged knives are used in a molding head. The fence is set off center far enough to allow for cutting the full width of the edge, and the depth of the cut is adjusted to 1/16". Cut end rabbets and tenons as with dado heads

There's a Way to Sharpen Each Blade of Your Pocketknife

ROUGH down a dull pocketknife blade on a coarse oilstone and finish the whetting on a fine one. A razor hone is good for finishing. Rest the stone on a workbench or clamp it in a vise. Wet the surface with water, light oil, or kerosene. Incline the blade about 20 deg. and make long, oval strokes with even pressure, drawing the blade from heel to point. Change from one side to the other to equalize the bevels. The blade's wire edge can be taken off with light diagonal strokes toward the edge. Touch up the other side and finish on a finer stone.

To whet a blade of the saber type, sharpen the straight section and hone the point with rocking strokes that bring every part of the curve to bear on the stone. Keep the edge of a sheepfoot blade straight; otherwise the advantages of this shape are lost. The concave edge of a pruning knife is honed on an oval-shaped abrasive stick or slip stone. Sharpen a leather punch nearly at right angles to the stone, later removing the wire edge with a triangular slip stone. Keep the sides of a screw driver parallel.

Some mechanics prefer to sharpen a knife from one side only. This has certain advantages in difficult whittling projects. If a pocketknife has two or more blades, one may be whetted in this way. Whet the flat side lightly to remove the wire edge.

Grinding should be necessary only if the edge is very blunt, or to make the heel narrower. A sudden flush of blue means that the temper is lost at that place. Use a grindstone rather than an emery wheel if one is available.—E. M. L.

Moments spent in whetting the edge of a knife will pay dividends in time saved and better work

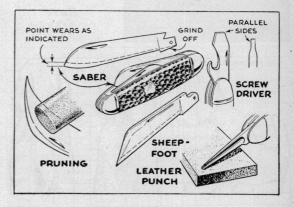

POINT WEARS AS INDICATED
GRIND OFF
PARALLEL SIDES
SABER
SCREW DRIVER
PRUNING
SHEEP-FOOT
LEATHER PUNCH

PAPER-WEIGHT PUP
Whittled with a Penknife
By ELMA WALTNER

PETEY, our jaunty pup paper weight, does a good job of keeping the papers on your desk from blowing off in each gust of wind. He'll be popular with visitors, too.

Petey is roughly carved, a fact that adds to his charm and to your ease in shaping him.

The drawings grouped around the photo below show him from three different angles. After some practice you may want to try a different pup, perhaps one with short ears and tail as shown at the right.

Make the pup from any soft wood—a scrap of redwood or soft pine works easily and takes a nice finish. Lay out the profile pattern on a block 1½" by 2½" by 3". The grain should run vertically to give strength to his front legs and head. Saw out the profile with a coping saw or on a jig saw. Drill several holes through the wood that is to be cut away between the front legs. This makes shorter work of the carving.

FASTEN TO BASE WITH DOWELS AND GLUE

WEIGHT   PLUG

Base
1½" × 2¾" DIA.

¼ SQUARES

A sharp jackknife is the only tool you need for shaping the pup. Turn the work often in carving, for this makes it easier to get the proportions correct.

The carving finished, sand down any rough spots. But don't be so enthusiastic in your sanding as to take off all the angles, for they add to Petey's individuality.

If you use redwood, a coat of shellac is all the finishing necessary. If pine is used, you'll probably want to apply a coat of mahogany stain. The eyes are white map tacks with black painted pupils; the nose is painted black, and the mouth red.

Turn the base 2¾" in diameter and 1½" thick. Make a shallow recess in the bottom to hold the weighting material. Lead shot or coarse sand may be used for this. Then turn out a thin disk of wood to fit the bottom of the recess. Glue this into place after the weighting material has been put in. Almost any wood will do for the base. In this case ordinary red cedar was used. Finish with two coats of shellac and wax.

Mount the pup on the base with glue and dowels, and he will be ready to do his small part in keeping your desk tidy.

Lay out on squares the profile at the extreme left or one of your own design. Transfer it to a wood block, saw to the outline, and carve

A rejected skin (one that has been poorly tanned) may be bought from a tanner. Goat, cow, calf, and deer hides are best

1 SAW HERE

2 NUMBER ALL STAVES IN ORDER

PICKLE OR NAIL KEG

3 DISCARD ONE STAVE

HOOP

4 ASSEMBLE OTHERS INSIDE HOOP AND GLUE EDGES

5 DRIVE BOTH HOOPS TOWARD MIDDLE LET GLUE DRY

6 REMOVE HOOPS

7 CUT HIDES 4" LARGER THAN DRUM

8 PUNCH HOLES AT EDGE WITH ICE PICK

9 SOAK SKINS OVER NIGHT IN WARM WATER; LACE OVER BARREL WITH BALING WIRE

10 TWIST WIRE TIGHT WITH SPIKE. PULL LEATHER 2" TOWARD CENTER

11 DRILL UNDERSIZED HOLES FOR ROOFING TACKS—ONE IN EACH STAVE

12 DIP TACKS IN GLUE AND DRIVE IN

13 TRIM 3/4" FROM TACKS

14 REMOVE TWISTED WIRE AND WASTE LEATHER

15 SCRAPE WOOD BODY WITH GLASS OR SCRAPER; THEN SAND SMOOTH

GILD TACKS

16 APPLY THREE COATS RED ENAMEL; THEN VARNISH

This unique method of using a barrel to make a tom-tom was worked out by Arthur M. Chase

Working

THREE CRAFTWORK

Designed by

Ernest R. Dewalt

DECORATIVE SCREEN. This is an interesting project in woven wood. Rip scraps for the two panels into ⅛" thicknesses and three widths as indicated in the drawing. Longitudinal strips are cut 59½" long and transverse ones 23" for the screen shown. Pine was used for all parts, but any wood will do.

Weave the panels square, using two lines at right angles on a piece of wrapping paper as a guide. Two wood strips based along the lines will be helpful. Spacers of wood or cardboard will save time.

Groove all frame members at the same saw setting; then saw the ends for splines as shown. Assemble the long members and the

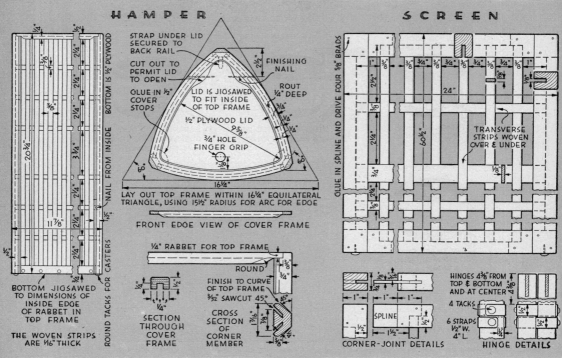

Time: Two Evenings

PROJECTS THAT MAKE THE MOST OF LITTLE MATERIAL

panels first, gluing in the splines and fastening with ⅝" brads at the splines and wider transverse strips. Apply two coats of white shellac or varnish. When the finish is dry, attach the leather hinge straps in pairs as shown. Working time: 5 hours.

WOVEN HAMPER. Scraps are also put to work in weaving the three panels of the triangular clothes hamper on the facing page. All of these strips are 1/16" by ⅜" and are woven as shown in the drawing.

Shape the corner rails from ¾" pine and cut grooves to receive the panels, which are curved to form a rounded triangle. Nail the panels in place from the inside. Lay out the top frame on ½" plywood; then rout out a ¼" groove for the top of the panels. After a trial fit, join the frame to the end rabbets of the corner rails with glue and nails.

To form the lid, simply shape the back end of the plywood cut from inside the top frame. A hole is bored for a finger grip, and the lid is drilled transversely with undersize holes for two clipped finishing nails that form the hinge. The bottom is sawed from plywood, the panels being nailed to it and overlaid with 1/16" by ¾" strips held by roundhead tacks. Finish like the screen. Working time: 5½ hours.

HUMIDOR AND PIPE RACK. Here is a dual-purpose project that will delight any pipe smoker. Obtain a glass jar that will hold ½ lb. of tobacco and supply the missing dimension in the drawing to fit it.

The upper section and bottom of the rack are turned from mahogany, as is a new top for the jar. Line up and bore the holes for the dowels, and drill pipe-stem holes in the upper section as shown. Finish with three separate rubbed coats of thin, clear shellac or varnish before gluing in the dowels; then insert a small humidor in the cover. Working time: 4½ hours.

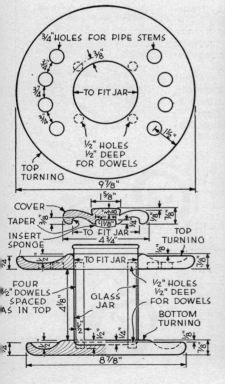

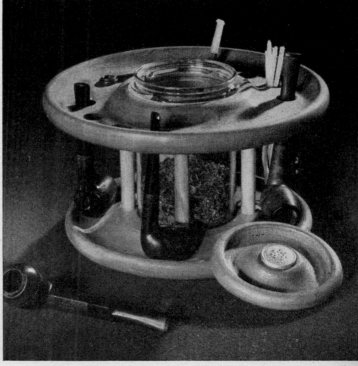

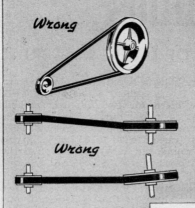

Wrong

Large pulleys provide greater driving pull with normal belt tension. The extra tension needed to prevent slippage on small pulleys overheats a belt

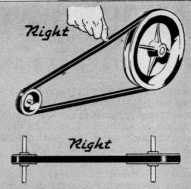

Right

Right

Wrong

Be sure that both shafts and pulleys are aligned. Improper alignment of either causes excessive side wear on a belt and will result in a rupture

Right

Never put too much load on a belt. Two machines driven simultaneously at full load always require an extra primary belt

Wrong

Longer Belt Life

ECONOMICAL use of belts in the shop means longer service from them and considerable saving in money and material. Always run belts at recommended speed. All belt-and-sheave combinations have a specific speed at which centrifugal force tends to throw the belt away from the groove, causing loss in transmitted horsepower.

It will pay also to use a sufficient number of belts on each drive to meet the power requirements of your machines. You will find it far better to overbelt than to underbelt. For example, using four belts on a drive requiring five reduces belt life about 60 percent. These drawings show other points to watch.—J. MODROCH.

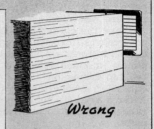

Wrong

Run belts cool and dry. An unventilated guard, excessive moisture, or heat makes the rubber in a belt hard and brittle

Right

Wrong

Prying a V-belt over a pulley rim may rupture it. If required tension does not permit the belt to be put on by hand, a slotted mount will allow the motor to be slid in for installing the belt

Right

Right

Lubricate bearings, but keep oil off belts, and don't use dressing on a V-belt — adjust tension instead. Dirt in grooves wears away belt rubber

Wm. Patrick

NEW
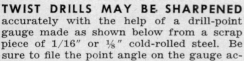
SHOP
IDEAS

SEPARATE STOPS can be set for multiple-tool operations in bench-lathe production work with the ingenious device shown on the lathe at the right. This carriage stop consists of a threaded cross bar having adjustable nuts to control the length of the cuts and appropriate connections for disengaging the carriage feed. It automatically stops the carriage without shutting off power as each tool in the tool-post turret finishes its work, thus releasing the operator for other jobs or for simultaneous drilling and similar tailstock operations.

The stop was invented by David I. Welt, owner of a New York City shop engaged in war work, when he was faced with turning out a large number of identical parts with all of his available machines. In addition to speeding the job, it reduced work spoilage, tool breakage, and danger to the operators.

TWIST DRILLS MAY BE SHARPENED accurately with the help of a drill-point gauge made as shown below from a scrap piece of 1/16" or ⅛" cold-rolled steel. Be sure to file the point angle on the gauge ac- curately to shape. This angle depends to a large extent on the material to be drilled, but 59 deg. has been found most satisfactory for average work. Both cutting edges of the drill should be ground to the same angle, since a difference will cause one lip to take a larger cut than the other and make the drill cut oversize to some extent.

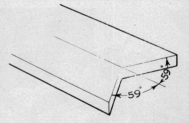

NONTOXIC HAND CREAM, used frequently by machinists to protect their hands against the action of soluble-oil cutting compounds, will also keep the fingers from leaving perspiration marks that might cause the rusting of precision parts or specially finished metals. The cream is spread on the hands before work is begun and can be washed off easily after it is finished. A companion product is a water-soluble rust-preventive liquid that may be applied to metal parts by dipping, spraying, or brushing. It is noninflammable and also nontoxic.

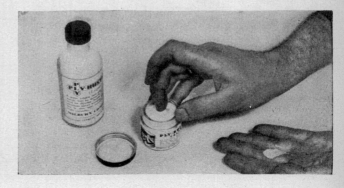

①

SHOP ACCESSORIES
You Can Turn Out from Scrap Stock

Odds and Ends of Steel Used to Make Lathe Carriage Stop and Depth Gauge

By C. W. WOODSON

②

③

④

TWO accessories any machinist will find useful are a lathe carriage stop and a depth gauge. Although these may not be available on the market today, it is possible to make both from scraps of steel such as can be found in any shop.

LATHE CARRIAGE STOP. A carriage stop is especially useful in production work or when duplicate parts are to be made. It is clamped to the front bedway of the lathe on either side of the carriage and may be set to limit tool travel at any point along the bed. An adjusting screw makes it possible to control the depth of boring or facing cuts, cut off work at a given point, or duplicate longitudinal cuts. Since the stop is not designed to shut off the power feed, the carriage should be fed in *by hand* for the last part of the cut.

The stop shown in use on a lathe in Fig. 1 was

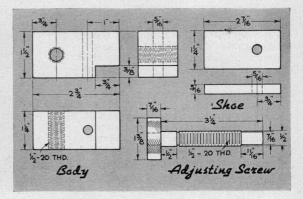

Shoe

Body

Adjusting Screw

made from short ends of cold-rolled steel. A block, which forms the body, was first drilled for the clamping and adjusting screws, the hole for the latter being tapped ½"-20. One end was stepped in the shaper (Fig. 2) to fit the flat top of the front lathe way. If the lathe on which the stop is to be used has V-ways, the block should be shaped accordingly to fit.

To prevent scratching or marring of the lathe way, the contacting surface of the block was carefully polished.

For clamping the carriage stop in place, a shoe was cut from bar stock to the dimensions in the drawings and drilled at one end to receive the clamping screw.

A disk hand wheel for the adjusting screw was drilled to fit a mandrel, on which it was turned to size and knurled as in Fig. 3. The screw was turned from a ½" bar, one end being shouldered to fit the disk, and then threaded in the lathe. Riveting the screw and disk together completed the job. All parts are shown in Fig. 4, along with a cap screw and nut, which are used for clamping the attachment to the lathe.

DEPTH GAUGE. Used in connection with a machinist's rule, this adjustable depth gauge (Fig. 8) is convenient for measuring recesses in dies, dimensions from plane surfaces to projections, the depths of holes, and so forth.

The body was sawed out of a ¼" by 1¾"

by 3" piece of cold-rolled steel (Fig. 5). It was draw-filed bright all over and the edges were filed smooth. Next, the ⅛" hole for the adjustable rod was laid out, center-punched at both ends of the piece, and drilled. This was done in the lathe by supporting one end of the work on the tailstock center, which aligned the work more accurately than could be done in a drill-press vise. The hole was drilled halfway through from each end with a No. 31 drill, then opened out to ⅛" by running the drill right through from one end to the other.

Another hole was drilled through the face of the work 1¼" from the wide end, as shown in Fig. 6, for the boss. The latter was turned with a shoulder to fit the hole, riveted in place (Fig. 7), drilled with a No. 25 drill, and tapped 10-24 as shown in the drawings. Then the ⅛" drill was run through once more to continue the lengthwise hole through the shoulder of the boss.

The thumbscrew was made by knurling the end of a short steel rod, which was then turned to size, threaded with a die, and cut off. With the piece reversed in the chuck, the threads being protected by heavy paper, the top was turned to shape and polished with emery cloth. A 7" length of drill rod, turned accurately square on the ends, formed the adjustable rod.

If etching or engraving facilities are at hand, the rod may be marked with any sort of scale desired.

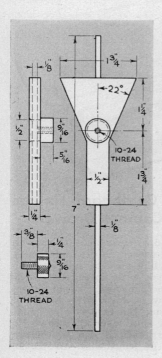

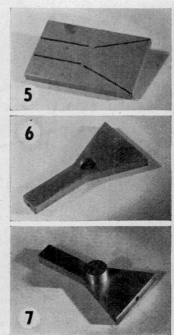

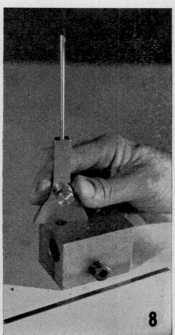

Lathe Spindle Trued with Lead Lap

ONE way to true a lathe spindle or other shaft worn out of round is to lap it with aluminum oxide grains or other abrasive and oil. The body of the lap is cut from wood stock. Although the lap shown in the photo below was about 1" thick, a thicker one may be used to advantage if the length of the bearing surface to be trued permits. Cast the lead around the spindle, set up as shown in the accompanying drawing. For lapping, mount the spindle to revolve on a brass rod held in a vise on the drill-press table. In the spindle taper, insert an arbor having a projection about ½" in diameter that can be gripped in the drill-press chuck. The press should be operated at a speed of about 300 r.p.m.—WALTER E. BURTON.

The lap is slotted and has an adjusting screw, as shown in the drawing below. Notch the hole to form anchoring lugs on the lead insert at the time it is cast

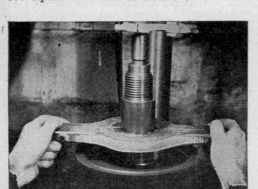

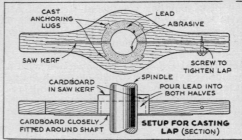

CAST ANCHORING LUGS — LEAD — ABRASIVE — SAW KERF — SCREW TO TIGHTEN LAP — CARDBOARD IN SAW KERF — SPINDLE — POUR LEAD INTO BOTH HALVES — CARDBOARD CLOSELY FITTED AROUND SHAFT — SETUP FOR CASTING LAP (SECTION)

Eyeglass Case Holds a Micrometer

A MICROMETER of the 1" size can be kept safely in an ordinary eyeglass case. The felt or plush lining usually found in these cases affords extra protection for this sensitive precision tool, and there is less danger that it will be mislaid or damaged in the shop. If the case happens to be slightly too small, it may easily be enlarged by prying open the lip against which the lid closes. This will widen the case a trifle without impairing its usefulness.—JACK J. SNYDER.

Corrugated Cardboard Linings Improve Cabinet Drawers

SHOP-CABINET drawers which are used to hold small articles such as drill bits, nails, screws, and the like may be improved by lining the bottoms with corrugated cardboard. These corrugations, placed uppermost in the drawers, form little hills and valleys that reduce the tendency of small objects to roll or shift when the drawer is moved. The corrugations can be placed either crosswise or lengthwise.—W. E. B.

Rifle Sighting Device Uses Mirror

AT THE University of Wisconsin, this sighting and aiming device is used to teach the alignment of gun sights by triangulation. A mirror on a swivel at the far end reflects a target held at the side of the rifle, thus doubling the effective range.

The rifle has an eyepiece in addition to peep and front sights and is mounted solidly at one end of the stand. On a board to its right is a sheet of plain paper facing the marksman. A forked stick fits over the board in such a manner that one leg holds a small target toward the mirror. The other leg has a hole in it directly behind the center of the bull's-eye.

By sighting through the eyepiece and adjusting the leaf, the front rifle sight is centered in the peep sight. The marksman then adjusts the target to obtain a bead on the bull's-eye reflected in the mirror. This he records on the paper with a pencil mark made through the hole in the rear leg. Three trials, before each of which the target is moved out of position for a fresh start, should result in marks close enough together to form a triangle no larger than a dime.

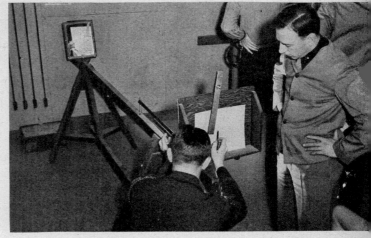

Sighting into the mirror, the marksman adjusts the target to get a bead, which he marks on paper. Below, another view of the device

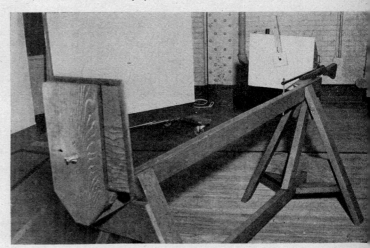

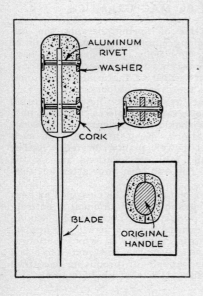

Cork Handle Keeps Fish Knife Afloat

A SIZABLE cork handle on a fish knife not only makes it unsinkable but provides a resilient and comfortable grip. The original handle can be covered with cork if it is not too large and heavy, or the handle can be removed and a cork handle substituted. Strips cut from scraps of cork flooring blocks or wall board are best to use if either material is available, but cork gaskets can be glued up in layers to serve, or large bottle stoppers can be halved lengthwise and glued end to end. Be sure to use waterproof glue, since the knife will often be soaked in water. For a practical grip, shape the handle slightly oval with a sharp knife and abrasive paper. Attach it to the tang with light rivets and washers, as shown at the left.

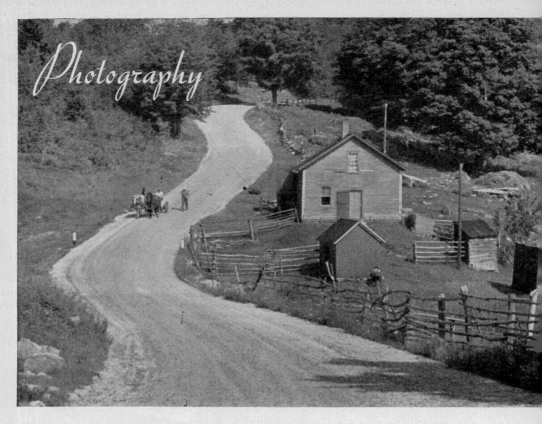

Photography

The shimmering beauty of these cherry blossoms was greatly enhanced by side lighting. A K2 filter was used to darken the sky. Taken at stop f/16, 1/10 second

How to Improve

By MAC GRAMLICH

THE end of spring heralds the approaching summer season, the time of year ambitious photographers have been anxiously awaiting. Alert picture takers find a wealth of material for summer photos in the great outdoors.

Wartime restrictions, however, forbid many photographic subjects, and the photographer should be very careful to observe all regulations. Keep in mind that such places as power plants, bridges, harbor scenes, and military locations are on the restricted list, and turn your attention elsewhere.

Summer pictures can be classified as general photography, and equipment is entirely a matter of taste and convenience. Elaborate and expensive cameras are not needed. With pictorial subjects in which action is not involved, even the least expensive box camera is capable of producing beautiful results. No matter what kind of camera you

A curving road adds much to the composition of this rural scene. Shot on pan film at f/8, 1/100 second, with yellow filter

Caught in the act! This thirsty kitty was snapped with a 4" by 5" Speed Graphic. Panchromatic film, f/8, 1/200 second

Your Summer Snapshots

use, however, be sure that it is in perfect working condition.

When planning to take several pictures in a nearby locality, study the lighting beforehand. This enables the subjects to be scheduled one after another in accordance with the position of the sun, thus saving valuable time. When taking pictures on a trip, make every shot count. Be discriminating in your choice of picture subjects, and do not shoot everything in sight.

For really brilliant outdoor negatives, sunlight is indispensable. The most favorable times for shooting pictorial scenes are in the early morning and late afternoon when the shadows are most pronounced, although it is true that a few types of pictures are best when taken during the middle of the day. In pictures shot at noonday, when there are no shadows to speak of and all objects are uniformly lighted, the major contrasts are in color variation. Under these conditions, take landscape pictures that have interesting foregrounds. Bring

the foreground into sharp focus; let it be the chief point of interest in the picture.

It is often advisable to shoot against the light—a technique called back lighting. An admirable example of this type of lighting is shown in the picture of the ship painters on the following page. Back lighting or side lighting is used to give greater detail and depth to summer pictures. For instance, wagon tracks on a country road will appear without detail of texture if taken with the sun directly overhead, but the same picture will have much more character if it is shot when the sun is at one side. Avoid straight, level shots whenever possible. Better effects are obtained by shooting either from a low angle or from a raised position.

Picture composition can be enhanced by framing the subject with overhanging tree branches or taking the shot through an archway. When open landscape pictures are taken, particular attention should be given to the foreground. A cottage, an old fence, or sometimes a group of animals can be in-

The lens was stopped down sharply for this pattern photo of window shutters. Pan film, ½ second at f/32

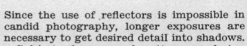

Ship painters against the setting sun form an interesting silhouette photograph

cluded to avoid emptiness in the foreground. On the other hand, don't crowd too many objects into one shot, as they tend to make the picture confusing. Subjects that have no particular relation to a scene are both distracting and annoying.

When landscapes are cropped horizontally, the effect is usually pleasing and relaxing. The choice of cropping, of course, depends on the subject. For example, a picture of very tall trees should be cropped vertically, whereas most pastoral scenes call for horizontal cropping.

It is usually best to take pictures of people, especially children, while they are engaged in some kind of activity. It is sometimes a difficult task to get your subject to concentrate on what he is doing, since the average person tends to become camera-shy and self-conscious. A good trick is to have your subjects rehearse their poses several times, and shoot the pictures while they are rehearsing. In this manner, posed pictures can be made to look very natural.

When taking character studies or close-ups of individuals outdoors, try to get the subject into a position so the sun will strike at about a 45-deg. angle. This will create interesting shadows and give the picture depth and roundness. Use a reflector when photographing people with dark or tanned faces, or those wearing hats that shade their faces.

Since the use of reflectors is impossible in candid photography, longer exposures are necessary to get desired detail into shadows.

Subjects for unusual pattern or design photography can be found in abundance in both city and country. Windows, pillars, cobbles, shingles, and fences are a few of the subjects that form interesting patterns.

Strive for a well-balanced composition in your pictures. Do not have too many dark or heavy objects on one side, for such a picture is badly weighted and is therefore unbalanced or "top-heavy." Focusing the picture on a ground glass helps to avoid bad composition.

When judging composition through a ground glass, beware of being misled by the visual values of coloring. In black-and-white photography it is the contrast between light and dark tones of objects which gives quality to the finished picture, and not the color seen on the ground glass.

Color filters are important when shooting outdoor pictures such as flower details, woodland scenes, or cloud formations. The most commonly used filter for general outdoor work is the K2 or yellow filter. Next in use is the light-green filter. Both of these are suitable for panchromatic and orthochromatic films. Red filters are usually used only to get dramatic sky effects, especially beautiful cloud formations, on panchromatic films. Filters should be used only when color corrections need to be made. For example, a picture of a yellow wheat field with a good sky effect above it should be taken with a yellow filter. This will darken the blue sky, bring out white clouds, and lighten the yellow wheat. To bring out heavy wooded scenes, use a light-green filter. Filter factors should always be taken into consideration, and film manufacturers' guides can be used for this purpose.

Guard against both underexposure and overexposure, for these can ruin a picture even when the lighting is good and the filter used is correct. Save your filters when shooting pictures on a gray or misty day, for under such conditions they are virtually useless. Photographs taken after rainstorms are usually brilliant because the air is free of dust.

For general outdoor photography where speed is not a factor, medium-slow films are preferable. They are less grainy and have greater latitude. Even with a film of medium speed, fast action shots can be made.

The use of a sturdy tripod whenever possible is recommended. A steady support will assure sharp negatives. Another accessory important to good photography is a properly fitted lens shade, but make sure it doesn't shade corners of the negative. A shade prevents unnoticed reflections from striking the lens. Last but not least, use a reliable exposure meter at all times. Light conditions are constantly changing, and the use of a meter is important in order to secure the best results from your photographic efforts.

With a camera in good working condition and a few accessories, the amateur photographer ought to be able to spend a busy and successful summer taking worth-while and interesting pictures. Even though you do not go away for a long vacation trip this year, the possibilities of picture material in your own vicinity are unlimited. The alert photographer recognizes good pictures no matter where they may be. Amusement resorts, swimming pools, zoos, city parks, all lend themselves to the photographic art of the wide-awake snapshooter.

Early spring . . . a running brook gracefully framed by a curving archway. Orthochromatic film, f/11, 1/10 second. A tripod was used

This hurtling equestrian was caught in mid-air at a speed of 1/550 second. Shot with a 4″ by 5″ Speed Graphic, without a filter

FOR CAMERA USERS

A FILM HOLDER that clamps to the post of the enlarger, or on the sliding sleeve, is shown in the photo at the right. It consists of part of a cut-film box attached to a spring clip fashioned from thin metal. This clip can be held to the back of the box by strips of adhesive tape or by a small bolt. Films placed in the box and attached to the enlarger are easily located, and are kept out of the way of developing and fixing solutions which may otherwise drop on negatives and ruin them. The holder is a convenient time saver.—HARRY RADZINSKY.

The film holder is shown attached to the enlarger in the photo at the left. Below, a spring clip of thin metal is taped to the back of the film box

UNIFORM LIGHT can be provided beneath the diffusing glass of a spotting easel by installing four 25-watt tubular lamps as shown. In comparison with the single brightly burning lamp usually employed, this unit operates with comparative coolness, for each pair of lamps is wired in series. This permits the lights to be mounted extremely close to the diffusing glass without causing discomfort to the hands. Tests show that the effectiveness of the light for ordinary spotting or tracing is the same whether the lamps are burned at full or at reduced intensity.—J. M.

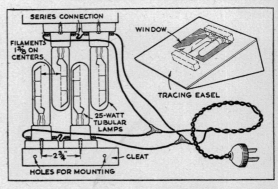

PHOTOGRAPHIC CHEMICALS in crystal form must usually be crushed in order to speed the mixing process. The frame of a discarded razor is an excellent tool for this purpose. Its curved surface permits it to be pressed down on the crystals with a rocking motion that does an effective crushing job quickly and efficiently. An old razor can usually be found in any home. Be sure that both the razor and crushing slab are clean before using.—WILLIAM SWALLOW.

SHORT LENGTHS OF FILM can be stapled together as in the photo at left, permitting two or more to be developed at one time as a single roll by either the tank or tray method. Sections of film pack can also be stapled and developed as roll film. This method is a great timesaver in the photo lab. Ordinary staples do not seem to be affected by the chemical solutions generally used.—ROBERT SCOTT.

Adjustable Finder Frame Simplifies Shooting Close-Ups

TAKING sharp close-ups of small objects such as flowers, insects, and tiny animals in their natural surroundings is simplified by using a finder frame like the one shown at the left. It is designed for use with double-extension cameras or single-extension cameras and supplementary lenses. By stretching rubber bands on the wire frame and setting the two sliding blocks as the focus may require, any field from negative size up to 5" by 7" can be framed off.

Cut blocks 1" by 2¾" and 1¾" by 2¾" from 1¼" stock. Bore two ⅜" holes through each, 1¾" apart and 7/16" from one face; then saw the blocks apart on the center line of the holes. The blocks are locked in place with wing nuts and ¼"–20 bolts on two straight ⅜" dowels. The wire frame is held upright in two notches filed in each end of the front block. A nut soldered to the upper part of the frame secures it in the folded position to the screw in the camera block when the device is not in use.

Adjust the camera to bring the desired field of view inside the limits of the ground glass, and focus accordingly. Any subject in the plane of the frame will then be sharp on the film. With cameras having no ground glass, tape a piece of tracing paper over the film rollers and focus visually on any convenient subject to determine by experiment the lens settings for various distances and the corresponding field areas.—FRANK HEGEMEYER.

Flowers and other nature subjects are easy to shoot with this focusing finder. Below, a nut soldered to the frame holds it to the camera block when the device isn't in use

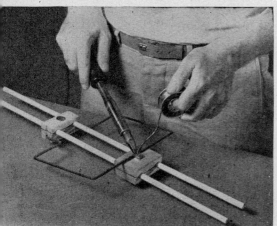

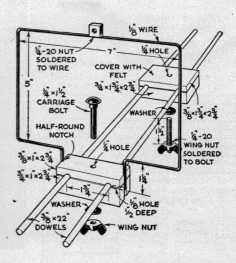

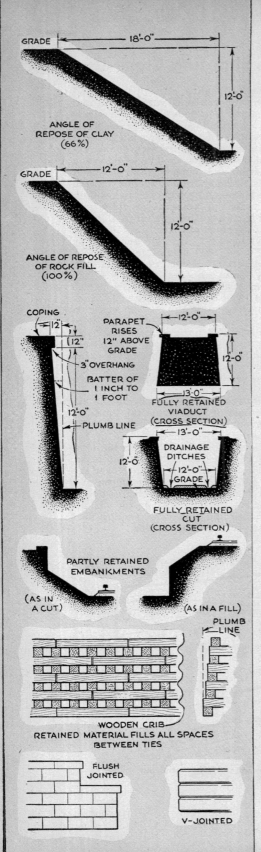

GRADE |←———— 18'-0" ————→|

12'-0"

ANGLE OF
REPOSE OF CLAY
(66%)

GRADE |←——— 12'-0" ———→|

12'-0"

ANGLE OF REPOSE
OF ROCK FILL
(100%)

COPING
|←12"
(12"
3" OVERHANG
BATTER OF
1 INCH TO
1 FOOT
12'-0"
PLUMB LINE

PARAPET
RISES
12" ABOVE
GRADE

|←— 12'-0" —→|

12'-0"

|← 13'-0" →|

FULLY RETAINED
VIADUCT
(CROSS SECTION)

|← 13'-0" →|

DRAINAGE
DITCHES

12'-0" |← 12'-0" →|
            GRADE

FULLY RETAINED
CUT
(CROSS SECTION)

PARTLY RETAINED
EMBANKMENTS

(AS IN
A CUT)   (AS IN A FILL)

PLUMB
←LINE

WOODEN CRIB
RETAINED MATERIAL FILLS ALL SPACES
BETWEEN TIES

FLUSH
JOINTED

V-JOINTED

Model-Railway

By DAVID MARSHALL

YOUR model railway is either made or marred by the accuracy with which the grade, at every point of line, balances cut against fill. The grade is the vertical profile of the track from terminal to terminal—a series of ups and downs and level stretches that follows the major contour yet also smooths out the minor inequalities of the land.

For us who are model railroaders, the grade is the batten or flooring on which we nail down our track, and our problem is to create the hills and valleys which will give us a well-balanced result. This necessity will in large part determine the character of the terrain that you will have to build around your model pike. Almost inevitably it will oblige you to construct retaining walls. These are extremely interesting to work with, yet you have no authority for building them unless you are by necessity driven to it.

ANGLE OF REPOSE. We can approach the subject of retaining walls precisely as if we were civil engineers at work on a grown-up railway. That is, we particularly notice the angle at which the earth is excavated to form a cut and the angle at which the sides of the embankment slope outward. This angle depends upon the character of the material excavated and dumped, and that material can range all the way from sand to granite. You can build an embankment of sand, but the sides of the embankment cannot be steep because sand settles at a low angle, or has a low angle of repose.

The model railway must be compact, and the railroader ought to represent compact substances such as clay and rock, for these are the two that make the

A model main-liner roars out of a realistic tunnel amid skillfully built hills. Note the flagged embankment beside the tracks

Retaining Walls

steepest banks. With due allowance for a margin of safety, heavy clay has an angle of repose of 66 percent, and broken rock rests well at a slope of 100 percent. In other words, a clay embankment should not slope upward at a rate of more than 8" to the foot, which is 30 deg., while a rock-fill job can slope 12" to the foot, which is a 45-deg. angle from the horizontal.

Use the rock fill among hard-rock hills, the clay embankment in rolling country.

SPLIT SLOPES. Cuts and fills need a great deal of lateral space. A clay embankment 4" high adds 12" to the width of your right-of-way, and a clay cut 4" deep is 12" wider at the top than at the bottom. You can't change these things, which are among the inflexible items of model railroading. However, when you lack space for these slopes, you have a right to use retaining walls, which may fully retain the embankments, as in the drawings of the viaduct and cut on the facing page, or you may use part wall and part slope with either above the other. In the sketches, this combination is shown as cut and fill embankments. In practice, of course, the two types are interchangeable.

A final word about embankments: a rock-fill job is always covered over with a layer of good soil. Then the embankments are planted with grass or shrubs so that the roots of these will form a binding element and prevent erosion. Thus only the greater angle of repose, plus the protruding shoulders of rock fragments, distinguishes a rock fill from a clay embankment.

MASONRY AND CONCRETE. Most of the retaining walls built in recent years are of concrete, though the older and more interesting types of masonry walls are still fairly common. Our retaining walls may be sturdily built of wood and painted on all sides to prevent warping. As a rule, retaining walls, whether of concrete, stone, or brick, are built with a batter so as to lean back several inches out of plumb.

The coping at the top usually overhangs the facade by 3". In some instances, however, the overhang is 4", or sometimes the coping is flush with the facade. In almost every instance the coping is 12" thick, which means you can make it—if you're an O-gauge railroader—out of wooden ties left over when all your track is laid. On the other hand, if the embankment is not more than 8' or so in scale height, it can be retained by cribbing. And here again you have use for excess ties.

Masonry walls, to a large extent, are built of rectangular stone of uniform size. The size is not standard, of course, but the blocks commonly used present a face 15" high by 48" long. Flush joints and V-joints are equally common, the ramps are stepped, and ends are formed simply by squaring off the stones.

Cuts and fills must have correct degree of slope depending upon the type of soil represented. Below are typical grass-covered embankments bordering the tracks in a cut on a real railroad

WOODEN TRACK
for Two-Rail Systems

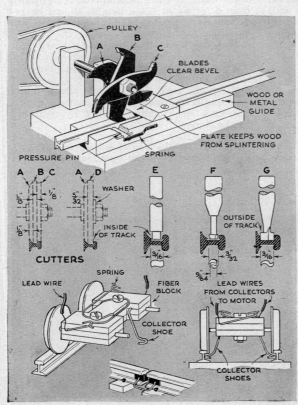

PULLEY

A B

C

BLADES
CLEAR BEVEL

WOOD OR
METAL
GUIDE

PLATE KEEPS WOOD
FROM SPLINTERING

PRESSURE PIN

SPRING

A B C   A D
1/8 1/8   5/32

WASHER

E   F   G

OUTSIDE
OF TRACK

INSIDE
OF TRACK

3/16   3/32   3/16

9/64

CUTTERS

SPRING

LEAD WIRE

FIBER
BLOCK

COLLECTOR
SHOE

LEAD WIRES
FROM COLLECTORS
TO MOTOR

COLLECTOR
SHOES

MODEL railroaders faced with a possible shortage of metal tracks for extending their systems may like to try making their own tracks out of wood. With 85′ of wooden trackage, including switches, in operation for more than two years on my O-gauge system, I find that wood has even some advantages over metal. Operation can be made almost noiseless, depending on the material on which the tracks are mounted. The cost is low—materials for 85′ of track might be kept to little more than $3. Furthermore, wooden tracks make two-rail operation possible without any need for insulating wheels.

Birch has proved satisfactory for the straight tracks, but pine serves better for curves, especially for those of small radius, since it is easier to bend. The tracks are made to scale, except for height, which is a little greater (3/8″) but looks "in proportion." Four special cutters ground from steel to the shapes shown in the drawings, as well as a spindle, two routers, and a countersink, are needed.

Cutters *A, B,* and *C* are

Router *E* is then chucked in the drill press, and the flange and tread on the inside are undercut for receiving a metal conductor strip. Tapered holes are drilled with countersink *F* for fishplate bolts, and the rail is turned over for routing spaces at the ends to receive fishplates. This is done with router *G*. Two bolts are used in each fishplate instead of the customary four.

Metal strips cut from tin cans run along the inside of the rails to deliver electricity to the locomotives. One strip is inserted at each end of a rail, and the two are joined at the center with solder applied through a hole in the rail at the halfway mark. This is easier than trying to solder from the inside. A simpler method of inserting the conductor strips is to run one the whole way through each rail. In this case, soldered wires join the ends, and fishplates and bolts are not needed.

In cutting the strips with tin snips, you will find that the metal curls and will have a decided curve when uncurled. The strips can be straightened by tapping the inside curve gently with a ball-peen hammer to expand the metal there. Be sure to lay the pieces on a steel plate, for otherwise tapping will dent them badly. A punch ground to an angle corresponding to the bolts will make countersunk holes in the strips if used over a countersunk hole in a steel plate.

Collector shoes used in third-rail systems are wedged out of the way, and a special fiber block carrying two contact shoes is mounted on the axles of each tender truck. The blocks should be free to slide sideways on the axles.—JOHN S. MEDCALF.

mounted on the spindle as in the drawings and used either in the drill press or in the special rig shown. The stock is first squared to size, then pushed up to the cutters through a guide that holds it in position.

When one side is finished, the piece is turned over and the other side is shaped. A thin strip may be used to shim up the rail for this second cut. Where stock runs undersize, it will be necessary to set a pressure pin in the jig to hold the work against the cutters.

The shaped stock is next cut off to size— 12″ lengths are used in my system—and the web on the inside is flattened with cutter *D*. This is best accomplished by substituting cutter *D* for *B* and a washer for *C*. Cutter *A* is left on the spindle as a spacer.

WIRE FOR HEATING ELEMENTS [ELECTRICAL]

The following table gives the length and size of nickel-chromium resistance wire of about an 80-20 alloy for repairing heating units or designing new ones to operate on 110 volts A.C. or D.C.

Watts	250	300	350	400	450	500	550	600	650	700	750	800	850	900	1000
Amps.	2.27	2.73	3.18	3.64	4.09	4.55	5.00	5.45	5.91	6.36	6.82	7.27	7.73	8.18	9.10
Ohms at 75 deg. F.	45.3	37.7	32.3	28.2	25.1	22.6	20.6	18.9	17.4	16.2	15.0	14.1	13.3	12.5	11.3
B. & S. Ga.	Length in Feet of Straight Wire														
16															45.2
17													41.5	39.0	35.2
18										39.9	37.0	34.7	32.8	30.8	27.8
19							41.0	37.7	34.7	32.3	29.9	28.1	26.5	24.9	22.5
20					39.6	35.6	32.5	29.8	27.4	25.5	23.6	22.2	20.9	19.7	17.8
21					31.3	28.2	25.7	23.6	21.7	20.2	18.7	17.6	16.6	15.6	
22				27.7	24.7	22.2	20.3	18.6	17.1	15.9	14.7	13.9			
23			25.4	22.1	19.7	17.7	16.2	14.8	13.7						
24	28.1	23.4	20.1	17.5	15.6	14.0									
25	22.3	18.6	15.9	13.9											
26	17.6	14.7	12.6	11.0											
27	14.0	11.7	10.0												
28	11.0	9.20													

For each volt above 110 (up to 120) increase wire length 1.9 percent. For each volt below 110 (down to 100) decrease wire length 1.9 percent.

POPULAR SCIENCE MONTHLY SHOP DATA

Blitzing

White dahlias are a late-season food for this most destructive of all garden pests. The earlier beetles are trapped, the less time they have in which to work damage

Japanese beetles attack leaves of hazel and linden trees about mid-June, leaving only veins. Set your traps early in the season in order to protect your garden

Photo courtesy of U. S. Department of Agriculture

Seven large commercial beetle traps like the one below can be set in the lid of a big ash can or similar receptacle to catch the insects wholesale

An extra strong attraction for these garden enemies consists of several traps set together and trimmed with partly eaten flowers dipped into bait solution

he Japanese Beetle

Ingenious Multiple Traps Can Be Made of Standard Units to Catch This Enemy of Our Gardens by the Bushel

SOAKING the Japs can be done profitably in more ways than one. Those who cannot go to the front can take a crack with bonds and war work and, in addition, can get some of the feel of the thing by taking an extra wallop at the Japanese beetle. There are many traps sold in infested areas for ridding trees, Victory gardens, and flower beds of the destructive Nipponese visitor, but L. J. Muller, of Westbury, N. Y., has devised a way of combining several commercial ones to catch the pest in a big way.

About seven of the biggest of the traps can be set up in holes punched in the top of a large ash can. This provides space for seven times the usual amount of the aromatic bait that attracts the beetles. The ash can, partially filled with kerosene or a similar insecticide, will be a death receptacle for bushels of the insects at a time.

Another good device may be made with an extra large funnel to which is soldered a bait holder like those shown in the photographs. The funnel may be inserted in a hole in the top of a large can or through wire netting soldered to the underside of an old dishpan from which most of the bottom has been cut. This dishpan can be set over a washtub or garbage pail to provide a top through which trapped beetles cannot crawl.

Also an effective killer is a mixture of 1 pt. molasses and 4 teaspoonfuls Paris green in 1 gal. water. *This is extremely poisonous* and should be kept well out of the reach of children and pets. A large pan of this mixture may be set up high in the garden and baited with flowers already partially destroyed by beetles. Such flowers may also be used on top of bait holders in the funnel traps. They will attract still more pests if soaked for a short while in some of the bait mixed with water.

Japanese beetles feed on almost anything in the garden, but they usually appear first on grape vines, raspberry bushes, roses, and linden and hazelnut trees about the middle of June. Later they choose white dahlias and marigolds as their favorite flowers. Repellents used freely on growing things will help to save them from the voracious appetite of the insects. One recommended repellent is arsenate of lead and lime for trees, while a mixture of 1 pt. liquid soap, 4 teaspoonfuls garden lime, and 2 teaspoonfuls arsenate of lead to 3 gals. water is excellent for flowers and vines. The spray should be repeated after each rain if attacks continue.

Arsenate of lead powder applied to a lawn in the fall kills many beetle grubs before they develop and keeps them from destroying grass roots.

In traps covered with open wire mesh, as this one is, some gardeners use only water, claiming that the smell of kerosene warns beetles away

To make traps blend with flowers and foliage and so render them less noticeable, they may be daubed with paint. This giant trap is mounted on a garbage pail

This huge capacitor is part of a 10,000-kilovolt impulse generator used for throwing a spark of high-voltage, man-made lightning across a 30' gap

charged negatively, and will drive out free electrons from the outer surface, since like charges repel. As the outer surface is connected to the positive terminal of the generator, the repelled electrons pass through the conducting wire to the positive terminal of the power source, which is deficient in electrons.

When the condenser is disconnected from the generator, the inner surface has an excess of electrons and the outer a deficiency, showing that electricity has been stored. This can be proved by shorting the two foil surfaces with a wire. If this wire is held by an insulated handle against one foil surface and near the other, a surge of electrons in the form of a spark will jump across the gap. The condenser is the only electrical device that can actually store electricity directly.

The measure of the ability of a condenser to store electrons is called its capacitance, and the unit measurement of capacitance is the farad. A capacitance of one farad means that a condenser is charged to an electrical pressure of one volt by a current of one ampere flowing for one second. This is such a huge unit that for practical purposes small

How Condensers Put the

FIRST STEPS IN ELECTRONICS

By CHARLES I. HELLMAN

THE giant air condenser used to set the frequency of a 50-kilowatt transmitter, the midget condenser in a portable military two-way radio, the capacitors in which bolts of artificial lightning are stored, all make use of the principle of the Leyden jar which was discovered almost 200 years ago by Prof. Pieter van Musschenbroek of the University of Leyden.

A Leyden jar is essentially a glass jar coated with tin foil inside and out for part of its height. The foil surfaces are entirely separated by the glass, which acts as an insulator, or dielectric, as it is called. The jar is charged by connecting the two foil surfaces to any source of high-voltage D.C. Excess electrons are stored on the negative terminal of the generator and overflow through a conducting wire to the inner tinfoil surface. This surface is therefore

subdivisions are used. A typical capacitor used in the power supply of a receiver may have a 16-microfarad capacitance. The microfarad is a millionth of a farad. Exceedingly small capacitance is sometimes stated in millionths of a millionth of a farad, or in micromicrofarads.

The capacitance of a condenser depends upon the area of the plates, the distance between them, and the material used as the dielectric. The Leyden jar, despite its bulk, has very little capacitance because the metal foil area is small and the glass dielectric rather thick. Benjamin Franklin devised the flat type in Fig. 1, page HW 236, which may be as large as convenient, or can be rolled up if necessary. Modern capacitors are usually of this type, although glass has been largely replaced by other dielectrics.

Most common of the dielectrics used today are mica, paper, and air. The air condenser generally has one set of movable plates made of aluminum or brass to permit variations in capacitance. Its movable plates are called the rotor and its fixed plates the stator, When the rotor is turned so that its plates lie entirely within those of the stator, the maximum capacitance results. As the rotor is turned out, the effective area of the condenser is reduced, and the capacitance is decreased.

Since the capacitance of an air condenser is easily varied, it is used for tuning the electrical circuits of a transmitter or receiver. In most receivers, several condensers must be tuned simultaneously. This is accomplished by mounting the rotors of the condensers on one shaft, a process called "ganging."

Since the spacing between the plates of receiving condensers is small, any conducting particles falling between them may short-circuit the condenser and destroy its usefulness. Variable condensers should occasionally be dusted by blowing air between the plates, and they should be handled with care.

Paper has a fairly high dielectric strength, hence very thin sheets can be used to insulate the foil surfaces, which results in a very high capacitance in a small space. Paper condensers are always constructed to have fixed capacitances.

The conducting plates of these condensers are of thin tin or aluminum foil, and the dielectric is made of several layers of thin paper rather than of one layer of heavy paper. Thus, even if there are imperfections, these are not likely to occur at exactly the same spot in all the layers. Long strips of foil and paper are rolled into a compact form (Fig. 2) and sealed into a container of cardboard or metal encased in wax or oil. The paper tubular condensers of a radio are an example.

Paper condensers are made in capacities from

Electron to Work

0.0001 to 8 mfd. Since paper suffers a considerable loss as a dielectric at high frequencies, this type is not used where the highest efficiency is required.

Mica is one of the best materials for use as a dielectric in a fixed condenser. It has a high dielectric constant; that is, it produces a capacitance five times that of an air condenser of similar construction, and its strength against breakdown is satisfactory for a great many applications. A typical mica condenser is shown in an accompanying photograph. Since mica condensers are comparatively expensive, they are used only when small capacitances at high efficiency or high-voltage ratings are needed, as for example in the radio-frequency sections of transmitters and receivers. In D.C. and low-frequency work, paper condensers meet ordinary requirements.

Today, paper condensers of capacitance above 2 mfd. have largely been supplanted by the electrolytic condenser, which has many times the capacitance of a paper condenser of the same volume and is less expensive to make, although its life is somewhat shorter.

The electrolytic condenser derives its name from the fact that the dielectric is a thin film of corroded

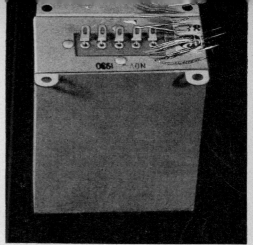
BLOCK OF SEVERAL CONDENSERS

DRY ELECTROLYTIC CONDENSER

PAPER TUBULAR CONDENSER

MICA CONDENSER

ELECTROLYTIC CONDENSER IN CAN

BY-PASS CONDENSER

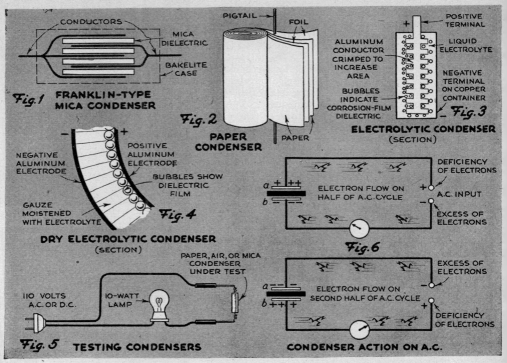

CONDUCTORS
MICA DIELECTRIC
BAKELITE CASE
Fig. 1 FRANKLIN-TYPE MICA CONDENSER

PIGTAIL
FOIL
PAPER
Fig. 2 PAPER CONDENSER

ALUMINUM CONDUCTOR CRIMPED TO INCREASE AREA
BUBBLES INDICATE CORROSION-FILM DIELECTRIC
POSITIVE TERMINAL
LIQUID ELECTROLYTE
NEGATIVE TERMINAL ON COPPER CONTAINER
Fig. 3 ELECTROLYTIC CONDENSER (SECTION)

NEGATIVE ALUMINUM ELECTRODE
POSITIVE ALUMINUM ELECTRODE
BUBBLES SHOW DIELECTRIC FILM
GAUZE MOISTENED WITH ELECTROLYTE
Fig. 4 DRY ELECTROLYTIC CONDENSER (SECTION)

DEFICIENCY OF ELECTRONS
ELECTRON FLOW ON HALF OF A.C. CYCLE
A.C. INPUT
EXCESS OF ELECTRONS
Fig. 6

PAPER, AIR, OR MICA CONDENSER UNDER TEST
110 VOLTS A.C. OR D.C.
10-WATT LAMP
Fig. 5 TESTING CONDENSERS

EXCESS OF ELECTRONS
ELECTRON FLOW ON SECOND HALF OF A.C. CYCLE
DEFICIENCY OF ELECTRONS
CONDENSER ACTION ON A.C.

aluminum formed by electrolytic action. The first electrolytic condensers were of the wet type shown in Fig. 3, but they have been largely replaced by the dry electrolytic condenser, the construction of which is shown in Fig. 4. The electrolyte is inserted in the form of a saturated gauze.

These condensers have polarity and must be connected as marked on the case. Electrolytic condensers pass some current, even when connected to a D.C. source, and are used where large capacitances are needed and where some losses can be tolerated, as in filtering the output of the rectifier in power supplies.

With parts from a disassembled radio set, and odds and ends of electrical equipment, you will probably find all the materials you need to conduct several interesting experiments that will help explain condensers.

Paper, air, and mica condensers may be tested by using the simple circuit shown in Fig. 5. Condensers of this type, of a capacitance of 0.1 mfd. or less, are in good condition if they do not pass enough current to light the 10-watt lamp in the circuit. An electrolytic condenser is tested by connecting it for an instant across D.C. of not more than 300 volts. If it is in good condition, it should produce an appreciable spark when removed from the power supply and shorted.

The following experiment will prove that the higher its capacitance, the more elec-

tricity a condenser will store at a given charging voltage. Charge a 1-mfd. paper condenser across any D.C. source (90 volts of a "B" battery or the output of a power supply). Now discharge the condenser across a 10-watt, 120-volt tungsten lamp. It will glow momentarily, proving that the condenser has stored electricity. If you repeat this experiment using a 4-mfd. condenser, the lamp will glow much more brightly.

A good condenser, with the exception of the electrolytic type, will not pass D.C., but will permit an appreciable amount of A.C. to pass through it, as shown in Fig. 6. Using the same apparatus as in Fig. 5, connect a 4-mfd. condenser across a test circuit and apply 110-volt D.C., then 110-volt A.C. Since the dielectric of a condenser is an excellent insulator, a steady voltage cannot pass through it. However, when the condenser is connected to A.C., it is charged on half the cycle of the alternating voltage and discharged on the other half, as shown in the drawing. This charging and discharging results in a current through the conductors although at no time does the current pass through the dielectric. This property of a condenser—the blocking of D.C. while A.C. is permitted to pass—is of considerable importance in electronic circuits, where it is frequently necessary to separate A.C. and D.C. or block the latter. Condensers used thus are called blocking or by-pass types.

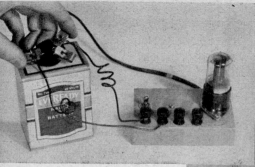

Charging a "B" battery from house current, left. "A" batteries are connected to the other two posts on the charger for similar rejuvenation. Only one battery should be recharged at a time

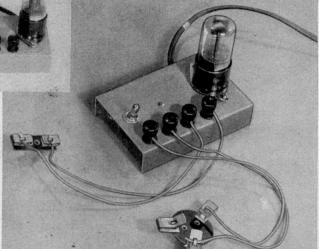

LIST OF PARTS

Metal chassis, 1¼" by 3½" by 4½".
Octal wafer socket.
Half-wave rectifier tube, 117Z6-GT.
Carbon resistor, 2 watts, 50 ohms.
Wire-wound resistors (3): 10 watts, 30 ohms; 10 watts, 7,000 ohms; 25 watts, 2,000 ohms.
Electrolytic condenser.
Toggle switch, S.P.S.T.
Binding posts (4).
Rubber line cord and plug.

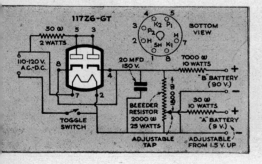

Four resistors and an electrolytic condenser are installed under the chassis, as shown above, with connections made as in the wiring diagram below

Radio Batteries Boosted on Homemade Charger

By ARTHUR C. MILLER

BATTERY life can be lengthened with this home-built charger consisting of a special resistor network and a 117-volt half-wave rectifier tube. Operation is on ordinary household current, A.C. or D.C., 110-120 volts. The circuit is arranged to provide a charging rate equal to about one third of the discharge rate of the average portable receiver having three to five tubes—a ratio found to give best results.

Batteries should be placed on charge immediately after each use, and the charging period should be at least twice the length of time they were operated. This may have to be extended even more as they age. Charging every few weeks, even when the receiver has not been used, is advisable. Be sure the battery terminals are connected to the proper posts to avoid damage.

Wiring connections are made as shown in the diagram at left, with the resistors and condenser placed under the small chassis. The carbon resistor in the plate circuit of the rectifier tube protects the tube and condenser from line surges, which may sometimes go as high as 300 volts if the unit happens to be turned off on a particular part of the cycle.

CARRIER-CURRENT TRANSMISSION has been developed to serve civilian defense in the sending of air-raid warnings and similar signals. On getting the proper impulse, the receiving device switches on a buzzer and a colored light. Signals for turning on sirens, controlling street lamps, and the like may be sent simultaneously, since a single power line can carry several different frequencies, including those for voice transmission. Apparatus resembles radio equipment, with energy generated as in broadcast transmitters and received as in home radios.

This device, connected in the light circuit, is used to signal defense wardens. At left, voice transmission

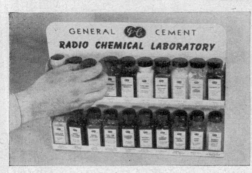

CHEMICALS AND CEMENTS needed by radio servicemen for the repair of speakers, coils, contacts, dials, controls, and other parts are included in a compact kit of 20 2-oz. bottles on a permanent stand. The bottles are provided with airtight stoppers equipped with glass-rod applicators and contain such universal repair liquids as dopes, contact and crystal cleaners, insulating and other varnishes, special oils, and dressings. Each is kept within sight and quickly accessible on the rack, which may be placed on the workbench or hung on the wall.

THIS CRYSTAL MICROPHONE is made from a metal sugar shaker and a single crystal headphone. Punch a hole in the bottom of the shaker for the phone cord (there are plenty of holes in the top for passage of voice vibrations) and hold the phone in place inside with cotton wadding. Make a stand of wood, or purchase one at a second-hand supply shop, and attach the shaker to it by the handle. Use at least a two-stage audio amplifier. In connecting the microphone to the amplifier, place a 1-megohm resistor load across the mike in series with a .05-mfd., 400-volt tubular condenser.

Servicing Your Radio

ANY OHMMETER MAY BE USED for testing a radio tube to determine whether its heater is burned out. Simply connect the two test prods of the ohmmeter to the heater or filament prongs on the tube base. If the ohmmeter needle is deflected or moves suddenly to the right of the scale, the heater is good; if there is no movement of the needle, the tube is defective. The No. 2 and No. 7 pins on octal tubes are usually the heater or filament connections, while the duplex-diode-triode detector tubes, such as the 12SQ7 type, have their heaters connected to the No. 7 and No. 8 prongs.

PANEL LAMPS may burn out prematurely on those small A.C.-D.C. receivers that use a 35Z5-GT half-wave rectifier but are not equipped with a shunting resistor across the lamp. For a few seconds after the set is turned on, a deteriorating, excessive load is often put on the panel lamp and that portion of the rectifier heater across which the lamp is connected. To avoid this, connect a wire-wound fixed resistor across the lamp or between the No. 2 and No. 3 prongs of the tube, as shown at right. Use an 80- to 100-ohm resistor rated at 5 to 10 watts.

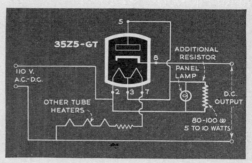

ORDINARY HEAVY THREAD, such as that used for sewing on buttons, can be requisitioned to make an excellent repair when a dial cord is broken. Take a piece of the thread about 1½" to 2" longer than the broken dial cord and pass it around the tuning-knob spindle twice, then about the large metal drum in front of the tuning condenser. Be sure to put it on in the same manner as the old cord. A dial so repaired should operate as well and continue in service as long as it would if the old cord had been replaced with a regular flexible wire made for the purpose.

NOISY WIRE-WOUND CONTROLS often found on old receivers, especially the large console models, can be repaired quickly and adequately with a new chemical lubricant when it is impractical to discard the old controls for new ones. The lubricant is applied with a brush directly to the contact surface of the resistance-wire element. This will eliminate the noise and cause the control to work smoothly even if it is one that has been in use on the receiver for a number of years. The new lubricant can also be used effectively on noisy wire-wound controls and wave switches of the newer models.

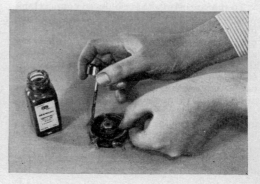

Heavy tip suitable for large connections

This size point is best for average jobs

Long point for fine work in tight spaces

Sizes and shapes of soldering tips have much to do with making good joints. The three above are the result of analyzing 65 different tips shaped by solderers at a radio plant. An expert rehammers tips to the three standard shapes as at left

JAWS SLIGHTLY OFF FLAT WHEN CLOSED

Insulation stripper for enameled wire

Pointers on Soldering Electrical

By W. R. SCHALL

Chief Inspector, Stromberg Carlson Telephone Manufacturing Co.

WHEN electrical equipment is being manufactured for war use, the soldering of terminal connections is of great importance, for each such connection forms a link in the communication system of our armed forces.

To make certain that soldered connections will not fail, the Stromberg Carlson Telephone Manufacturing Co., maker of communication equipment, gives its employees a course in soldering technique. Although this course was prepared with special reference to soldering joints in radio and telephone equipment, the principles it outlines apply to any type of electrical connection.

The first thing to consider in making a good soldered joint is the terminal. It must be clean. Solder won't stick to an oxidized or corroded surface. Cleaning a terminal with steel wool or sandpaper will insure its fitness to hold solder. Copper, brass, and even

steel can be soldered directly if patience and care are exercised, but if the terminal is coated with tin or cadmium, soldering is easier and faster. Nickel plating must be filed or sanded to make solder hold well.

No soldered joint is good unless the underlying mechanical joint between the wire and terminal is first solid. The function of solder is to seal the joint and to insure a permanent electrical connection. There should be no movement between terminal and wire while the solder is in a mushy state before it solidifies.

The condition of a soldering point is of great importance. For home use, a tip that has become pitted or blackened with burned flux or solder is best cleaned by filing the faces bright and smooth. If the iron is filed when cold, it should be tinned right after it is heated for the first time. If a tip is filed hot, it should be tinned immediately after filing to avoid oxidation. To tin an iron, have it hot enough to melt solder freely. Melt a puddle of solder and flux on a bit of

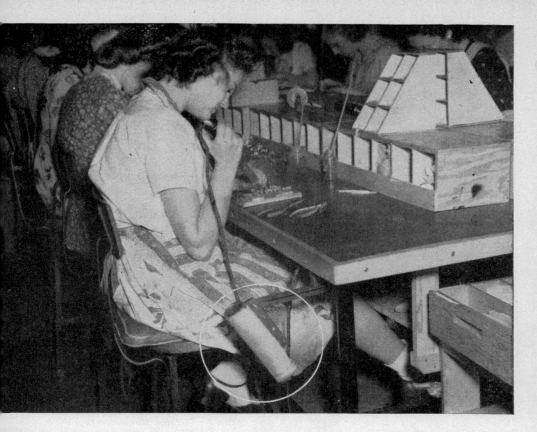

Connections

tin plate, and rub all surfaces of the tip in the solder until they are evenly coated.

Both the shank and threads of an electric soldering iron having a removable tip should be free of corrosion and black oxide, which retard transmission of heat.

Flux retards oxidation and promotes the fusion of heated metals. For electrical work, manufacturers use only rosin flux or rosin-core solder. Sal ammoniac or acid flux causes corrosion of the wire and joint, with subsequent failure of the connection. For soldering electric wires, rosin-core solder provides just enough flux at the time the solder is melted to form a good joint in one operation.

Hold a soldering iron flat against both the wire and the terminal. When all portions of the joint are sufficiently hot, touch the solder to the joint and the flat of the iron at the same time; then take the iron away as soon as the solder flows freely.

Never try to carry solder on the tip of the iron to the parts to be soldered, because the flux will burn out before the iron gets there.

If it is necessary to reheat the connection, use more rosin-core solder or rosin flux.

Sometimes a joint may seem firm yet in reality be held only by hardened rosin or by lumpy, improperly bonded solder. This is due to the terminal being heated insufficiently, or by dirt on the terminal or wires.

A good solderer uses only just enough solder for a job, but if some is splashed off, he will always remove it even though it seems to be stuck fast. Should the loose ends of wires need clipping after mechanical connections have been made, do the clipping before soldering and remove the clippings. Splashed solder or clippings may ruin a piece of equipment if they later get lodged in the wrong place.

When a connection goes through a hole in a terminal, be sure none of the insulation does, and that no end of wire beyond a terminal is long enough to reach to any adjacent terminal. Be careful not to nick wire in stripping off enamel insulation. The stripper on the facing page is safe to use.

HOME OWNERS

CRAB GRASS can be eliminated with a simple rake attachment that clamps on the lawn mower. The rake lifts the seed heads, which the mower then cuts. When not in use, the rake folds out of the way.

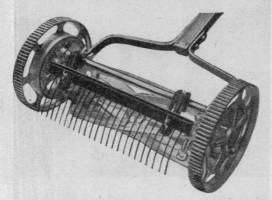

THE BARBECUE SET shown above contains 11 essential sauces and meat seasonings sure to contribute to the success of your barbecue parties. Featured is a 16-oz. bottle of old-fashioned barbecue sauce. Worcestershire and Swiss sauce are also included in this mouth-watering condiment set, which is attractively put up in a log-cabin type wooden tray that can also be used for serving.

EXCESS HUMIDITY and dampness inside cause a great deal of damage in many homes. The package at the left contains a harmless chemical that absorbs excess moisture from the air in confined places such as closets, pantries, basements, lockers, and the like. The chemical causes the moisture from the air to collect in the lower part of the container.

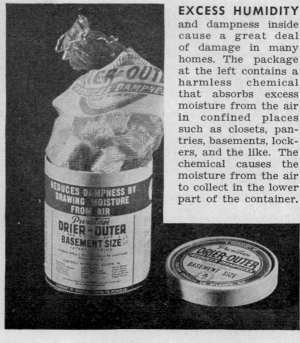

PLASTIC TANK FLOATS are said to be a definite improvement over former types made of copper or other critical materials. The tough, corrosionproof plastic will not dent or open at the seams, the latter being securely cemented. Because of the extreme lightness of the floats, shipping weight in quantities is greatly reduced.

A FLOOR CLEANER that also polishes and preserves floors is now on the market. An ounce of the chemical cleaner is dissolved in about a gallon of warm water. The solution is stirred, and a small area of the floor is gone over lightly, after which the mop is wrung out and used to dry the moistened area. This is continued until the floor has been completely covered. Afterward it can be polished to a warm glow. The cleaner is effective on wood and tile floors, and can also be used on any other surface which water does not harm.

PLASTER KNIFE OF PLASTIC. Molded entirely of one piece of a special plastic material, the plaster knife below is made without steel. Although the edge of the plastic blade is only 1/16" thick, it is said not to break or chip in use. The handle is designed to fit comfortably in the palm of the hand and, since it and the blade are molded in one piece, will not pull off or twist as sometimes happens with the former type. The over-all length is 7".

ASBESTOS SIDING SHINGLES requiring no face nails have been developed. They can be used for repairing as well as for new work. Felt backer strips to keep water and moisture from penetrating at the joints are supplied with these shingles. Extensive tests have revealed them to be satisfactory, and the absence of face nails is said to enhance the appearance of the finished job. The shingles are 12" by 24", and 66 are required to the square.

WOODEN DOOR HINGES may take the place of metal ones. Each set of hinges, such as the ones shown in the accompanying photograph, consists of four hardwood plates, one wax-impregnated dowel or pivot for the upper hinge, one 7/8" glass supporting ball for the lower hinge, and 12 flathead screws. The hinges

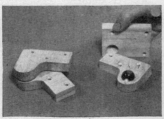

are easily attached with the help of a saw, a drill, and a screw driver. Simply saw notches to accommodate the plates in the top and bottom of the door, and use the screws to mount the various parts. The hinges, which are of hard maple or birch, come unpainted and may be enameled to match the door or simply finished with varnish and wax.

Rusted or corroded ribs are the real cause of a great deal of umbrella breakage, and the best preventive is careful oiling of the joints

A loose handle is annoying, but the stem can be reset by pouring in melted rosin

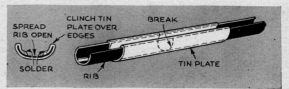

Umbrella Care

PAYS DIVIDENDS IN LONG USE

Should the flexible wire holding the ribs be in bad condition, new wire can be threaded in

Enameling the ribs with a fine brush will be helpful in prolonging the life of an umbrella

WAR production restrictions have limited the manufacture of umbrellas to such an extent that the care of those you now have becomes a matter of some importance. Not only have war-time restrictions cut manufacturing down to less than 10 percent of its normal volume, but they have also curtailed the variety of sizes and shapes.

A few precautions, however, will greatly stretch the life of an umbrella, and if one needs re-covering either because of wear or in order to match the color scheme of wearing apparel, even that job isn't too difficult. To re-cover an umbrella, carefully remove the old covering to use as a pattern.

When opening an umbrella, first hold it down and give it a twisting shake to loosen the covering and free the ribs from any binding. The umbrella will all but open itself, and any excess strain on the ribs will be avoided. A thorough occasional brushing of the fabric is a help in lengthening its life, as the action of rain tends to work dust and dirt into the fabric and hasten deterioration.

The joints in the umbrella frame are subject to rust and, if in this condition, they do not work freely and may cause a buckle. Prevent rust by applying a drop of light oil on each joint. To avoid staining the fabric of the cover, hold a piece of

A broken rib can be repaired with a piece of thin tin bent and clinched over the rib, neatly soldered, then enameled

SPREAD RIB OPEN

CLINCH TIN PLATE OVER EDGES

BREAK

SOLDER

RIB

TIN PLATE

cloth or paper under the joint to absorb excess oil that may drip from it.

If the wire at the sliding joint breaks or upon examination proves to be near breaking, a new wire can be threaded in. The twisted ends should be carefully bent inward to avoid tearing of the fabric when the umbrella is closed. Should a rib break, it can be replaced or repaired. To replace, cut it loose from the fabric; don't attempt to pull it out, for its rough ends may ruin the covering.

Repairing a broken rib is done by using a small piece of light tin plate bent as shown in the drawing. The edges are clinched over the rib and then soldered. Such repairs, as well as rusted spots, should be touched up with quick-drying enamel. Use a small brush to avoid staining the fabric. Repair parts may be difficult to buy, but in most cases they can be salvaged from an umbrella that has seen its best days.

Handle repairing is part of umbrella upkeep. To reset a loose handle, melt some rosin and pour it into the joint. Another good handle cement can be made by mixing glycerin and litharge, both of which can be purchased at a drug store.

A satisfactory way to hold the umbrella while doing many of the repairs is to put the tip in a small hole bored in the top of the workbench. This allows the umbrella to stay in a half-opened position, which makes it easy to work on.—BENJAMIN NIELSON.

Gay Butterfly Shelves for a Child's Room

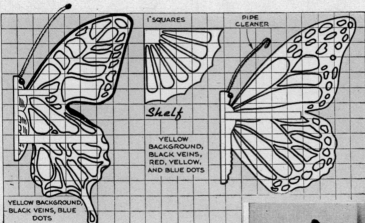

I" SQUARES

PIPE CLEANER

Shelf

YELLOW BACKGROUND, BLACK VEINS, RED, YELLOW, AND BLUE DOTS

YELLOW BACKGROUND, BLACK VEINS, BLUE DOTS

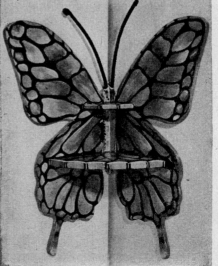

Vividly colored butterfly wings on this shelf brighten a room

CORNER shelves designed and colored to look like giant butterflies are especially appropriate for children's rooms. Two designs are given above. Lay out either on squares, or copy a suitable butterfly and its coloring from an encyclopedia or dictionary.

Two wings for each shelf are jigsawed from ¼" plywood. Miter the joining edges, or make one wing ¼" wider and assemble with a butt joint. Shelves are of ¼", ⅜", or ½" stock.

The wing parts and shelves are put together with small screws and glue.

Antennae, made of pipe cleaners with the ends bent or curved spiralwise and dipped in paint, are glued into small holes. A screw eye in the head serves as a hanger.

The butterfly is first painted with the predominant color, and the markings are applied afterwards.—J. RODGER DARLING.

KEEPING THE HOME

Flowers can be kept fresh longer if the stalks are trimmed, then quickly dipped into boiling water

To keep tie-backs of curtains together in laundering, thread them all on a large safety pin

Wall-paper cleaner applied on window shades will clean them and insure much longer service

If curtain rods are kept well waxed, they will be less likely to rust. The wax also permits the curtains to slide along them more easily

The letters on flour sacks can be easily removed if you rub them well with lard, let stand for several hours, then launder in hot sudsy water

SEAM TACKED ALONG BATTEN

BORE HOLE IN CENTER

CUT FOUR NOTCHES AROUND EDGE

CLEATS

7"

9"

Gay containers for flowerpots suitable for indoors or outdoors can be made from linoleum remnants as shown above. The containers can be built to fit pots of any size. Be sure to warm the linoleum before bending it

SHIPSHAPE

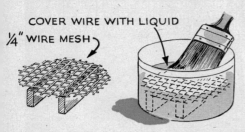

COVER WIRE WITH LIQUID

¼" WIRE MESH

Paintbrushes can be cleaned by placing a circle of wire mesh on two blocks in a can of cleaner and rubbing the brushes briskly across the mesh

PUTTY KNIFE

ASPHALT ROOFING PATCH

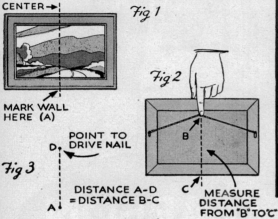

CENTER →

Fig 1

MARK WALL HERE (A)

Fig 2

POINT TO DRIVE NAIL

B

Fig 3

D

DISTANCE A-D = DISTANCE B-C

A

C

MEASURE DISTANCE FROM "B" TO "C"

If you follow the directions shown in these three diagrams, you will be able to hang pictures at exactly the desired height. This method is very good for hanging pictures side by side on the wall either in alignment or in a stepped arrangement

Wood-shingled roofs can be patched with slips cut from ordinary asphalt roofing. Using a putty knife, raise the shingle just far enough to allow the slip to be pushed into place. The sun will melt the asphaltum sufficiently to stick the patch in place. No nails are needed. The patches do not show, for the slip shingles cannot be seen after they are put in place

UNLOCKED

LOCKED BY TWISTING SCREW EYE A QUARTER TURN

PUNCH HOLES

CUT ON DOTTED LINES

TOBACCO

Outside window screens can be locked in place by twisting the screw eye a full quarter of a turn over the hump of the hook

Rubber heels can be salvaged from old shoes by clamping the shoes in a vise and cutting the nails through with a hack saw

A satisfactory pair of hinges for use on small boxes, cabinets, and the like can be cut from two old-style tobacco cans

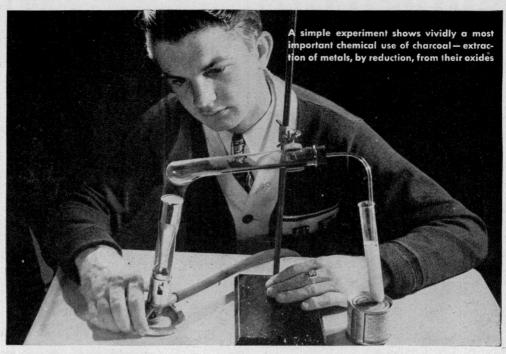

A simple experiment shows vividly a most important chemical use of charcoal — extraction of metals, by reduction, from their oxides

Directly above, cupric acid and powdered charcoal are ground together. The mixture is then put into the horizontal test tube shown in photo at top of page, where the reduction process is demonstrated

CARBON
FOUNDATION OF LIFE
Most Prolific of Elements, It Is Found in All Animal and All Vegetable Tissues

CARBON may well be called the central or pivotal element of the whole organic world. It enters into the formation of more compounds than any other element, and it is found in all animal and vegetable tissues, and in a great many minerals. Indeed, this prolific element might well be considered the foundation of life itself.

Carbon is found in the bodies of animals and plants in the form of sugars, starch, fats, oils, and cellulose. It is found in the form of hydrocarbons in petroleum and nat-ural gas. It is an important component of alcohols and ethers, and is even present in the air as carbon dioxide! As a carbonate, such as calcium carbonate, it is abundant in substances like limestone, marble, coral, and chalk. It exists in a free state in diamonds and graphite. It is not an exaggeration to say that carbon can be found everywhere in nature—in land, in air, and in water. The soot that collects on your clothing is a form of carbon. So are the smoky fumes that issue from the exhaust of your car!

From simply one form of carbon — the coal you use for fuel—comes an almost countless array of materials, including illuminating gas, fertilizers, explosives, photographic developers, medicines, and dyes. All of these products originate in the compounds that are distilled off and collected when coal is heated without air.

Although it would be difficult for the home chemist to produce most of these by-products in their final form, you can easily make illuminating gas and coal tar, and show the presence of ammonia and sulphur, by the destructive distillation of coal.

For these experiments it is best to use soft coal, as it contains more volatile matter than the hard or anthracite type. Break a lump into small pieces and put it into a heat-resisting test tube. Clamp this tube in an almost horizontal position as shown in the photo on the facing page. Through a one-hole stopper run a delivery tube nearly to the bottom of a vertical test tube, the latter serving as a condensing tube. From near the top of this condenser lead out a bent glass tube drawn to a jet at its upper end.

Heat the coal, first gently and then strongly, with a Bunsen burner, using a wing top to spread the flame. After a few minutes hold a strip of paper, moistened with lead nitrate solution, near the tip of the improvised gas jet. The dark spot which will appear on the paper indicates the presence of sulphur, in the form of hydrogen sulphide. Next, hold a strip of paper moistened with a solution of phenolphthalein and a drop of water over the jet. A pink spot appears on the paper, indicating that ammonia is present in the gas.

To prove that illuminating gas is issuing from the jet, apply a lighted match to it. Let the gas generate for several minutes before trying to light it, to drive out all air. Now look in the bottom of the condensing tube and you will see a dark, oily substance. This is coal tar, proud parent of hundreds of coal by-products. What remains in the glass tube after all the gas has been driven from it is coke, an almost pure form of carbon.

Millions of years ago, coal itself was living vegetable matter, and its relationship to present-day vegetable materials may easily be proved. Heat chips of wood or sawdust in your test tube, in place of coal, and you produce charcoal, which is chemically identical with coke. Heat samples of sugar, starch, and bread over your Bunsen burner, and in each case you again produce carbon. Thus white sugar and black coal turn out to be close relatives in a chemical sense.

The most important chemical use of charcoal and coke is in extracting metals from their oxides. Enormous quantities of iron, copper, and zinc are produced with the aid of these forms of carbon. The ores are generally mixed with coke, and the mixture is heated. Oxygen from the oxides combines with the carbon, and the free metal remains. This process is called *reduction*, and it may be vividly demonstrated by means of a simple experiment.

Grind together thoroughly in a mortar about 5 grams of cupric oxide and 1 gram of powdered wood charcoal. By means of a folded strip of paper, pour the mixture into a hard-glass test tube, which should be

Illuminating gas and coal tar are produced at left by heating lumps of soft coal in a test tube. At right below, lead nitrate paper shows the presence of hydrogen sulphide

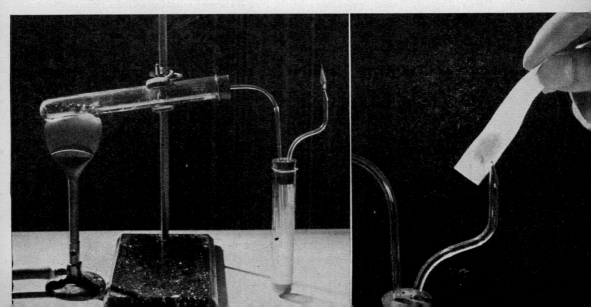

Because of the highly adsorptive power of charcoal, shown above, it is used in gas masks and in filtering liquids

reaction between the carbon and the oxygen stolen from the cupric oxide.

Continue heating for several minutes after the mixture begins to glow; then allow to cool. Pour out the contents on a piece of paper. Bright crystals of metallic copper will be found mixed with the carbon that was not consumed.

The charcoal form of carbon has still another important use in chemistry, a use which depends upon a physical rather than a chemical property. Finely divided, heated, and chemically treated bits of charcoal have an exceptional capacity for *adsorbing* gases and pigments on their surface. If you have made experiments in sugar chemistry, you probably found that charcoal or boneblack could remove most of the color from a brown sugar solution, the coloring matter of the sugar adhering to the surface of the charcoal.

Similarly, it can cause gases to condense on its surface, adsorbing them from the air, and because of this it is used extensively in gas masks. You can demonstrate this property by a simple stunt.

Pour a little concentrated ammonia water into a small flask and on top of it toss a piece of crumpled tissue paper. Sprinkle some powdered charcoal on the paper. Now close the bottle quickly with a stopper having a tube leading from it into a glass containing colored water. The charcoal will adsorb some of the ammonia gas liberated in the flask, as attested by the rise of colored water in the tube.—KENNETH SWEZEY.

mounted almost horizontally. This tube should be fitted with a one-hole stopper carrying a delivery tube which dips into another test tube containing limewater.

Heat the mixture in the horizontal tube, first gently and then strongly, as you did in the first experiment, for at least 10 minutes. Presently the mixture will become red-hot and glow like a miniature inferno. At the same time, gas is liberated. The gas bubbles up through the limewater in the second tube, turning it white. This whiteness is due to microscopic particles of calcium carbonate, precipitated by the reaction of the gas—carbon dioxide—with the calcium hydroxide of the limewater. Carbon dioxide is the product of the

Below, three distinctly unlike materials—sugar, starch, and a piece of bread—are placed over a Bunsen burner, where they are all gently heated

Now see what happens when these three substances are heated, as in photo below. Hydrogen and oxygen are given off and what remains is—carbon!

home EXPERIMENTS

THE FORCE OF INERTIA can be demonstrated by suspending a weight, as shown, with a piece of string only slightly stronger than is necessary to hold it. As a safety measure, tie a second, heavy cord with a little slack in it to the top of the weight. A string the same size as the first top string is tied to the bottom of the weight. You can, by pulling on the lower string, break either this or the top one at will. To break the bottom string, give it a quick, strong jerk. The inertia of the weight will prevent the impact of the jerk from reaching the top string. Pulling steadily on the lower string will break the top one, which is subject to your pull as well as to that of the suspended weight.

WHAT HAPPENS when you cut through an ice cube with a wire? Try this experiment and see for yourself. Mount an ice cube on top of an inverted dish and pass a thin wire through it, using considerable pressure. When the wire has gone completely through the cube, you will find the ice still frozen together as solidly as it was before. why? The pressure on the wire melts the ice beneath it, borrowing the necessary heat from the adjacent ice. This loss of heat from both sides of the ice cools it enough to enable it to refreeze the water remaining behind the wire.

BALANCING STUNT. Hold a carpenter's rule of the type shown over the edge of a table with the hinge side underneath, and the outer end of the rule will naturally drop down. But with a little care you may hang a hammer on the far end of the rule and so make that end stand out horizontally. Place the loop of thread as shown in the photo. The hammer acts as a lever exerting a *lifting* force against the end of the rule. The greatest weight of the hammer being in its head, the center of gravity comes under the table.

PRESSURE PARADOX. Construct three vessels of paraffined cardboard, all with bases of exactly the same diameter. The upper parts of them should vary in diameter as shown at the right. Tie and glue a piece of rubber from a balloon across the bottom of each. Now clamp the funnel-shaped vessel so that the rubber just touches the platform of a letter scale. Pour water into it to a height of 3″ and note the reading on the scale. Fill the other two vessels with the same amount of water in the same way, and you will find that the scale indicates the same reading in each case, for pressure depends only on the area of the bottom and the height of water above it.

MYSTERIOUS LIGHT BULB. When placed in *cold* water it floats, then sinks. When placed in *warm* water, it sinks, then floats. To perform this stunt, weight the base of a bulb with wire until it will just barely float when placed in cold water. When the weight is just right, you will find that the bulb will sink to the bottom after floating for a short time. Place the same bulb in warm water, and it will sink immediately, but after a few seconds will rise to the top. The explanation is simple. When you put the bulb in cold water, it floats until it contracts on cooling, whereupon it sinks to the bottom. The contracted bulb, placed in warm water, will stay at the bottom until it expands; then it rises to the top.

WHY WATER PIPES BREAK in the winter may be demonstrated with a test tube filled with water. Stopper it tightly. Now place the tube in a mixture of cracked ice and salt. As the water in the tube freezes, the stopper will be pushed out. If the stopper is wired down so that it cannot be pushed, the whole tube will break. Even bombs made of heavy cast iron may be exploded by water freezing inside them, so it is no wonder that pipes and auto radiators burst if ice is allowed to form in them. The reason is that water expands with terrific force as it freezes.

THE REASON ICE FORMS on airplane wings when the plane passes through cold, dry, winter clouds can be shown in a rather unusual experiment. Pour some water in a clean test tube, put a thermometer in the water, and pack a mixture of salt and ice around the tube. If the tube is left undisturbed and not jarred while the water is allowed to cool, a strange thing happens. The water reaches the freezing point, but does not freeze! However, if the tube is jarred a little, or if foreign matter is placed in it, the water will freeze almost instantly. This is what happens when a plane travels through a cold winter cloud. The moisture in the cloud is supercooled but not yet frozen. The plane, rushing through this supercooled moisture, turns it suddenly into ice, which forms on the fuselage and wings.

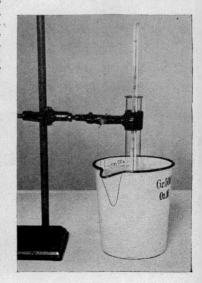

Unique Sweep Rake Attached to Tractor Saves Labor in Haying

FACED with a shortage of help, Earl Saum, of Fremont, Mich., devised a buck rake, or sweep rake, that cuts by one third the number of man-hours formerly required for haying on his farm.

The rake is 10' long and 10' wide. Its 10 tines are made of five 2" by 6" pieces of white pine ripped at a taper to be 2" wide at one end and 4" at the other. The crosspieces are 2" by 6" oak stock used full width. Two 3½" by 3½" angle irons are bolted to the frame of his homemade tractor so that they come out even with the rear tires, and the rake is attached by hinges to these angle irons. The tractor was put together from an old passenger-car frame and motor and a rear end and gears from a 3½-ton truck.

The outfit is backed into a windrow of hay until it is fully loaded. A crank raises the rear of the load, which is hauled to the barn without handling. The load is backed into the barn and slid off onto a 20' rope sling spread out on the barn floor. This sling is then wrapped over the hay, and the load is pulled up into the mow. A round trip for the outfit on a haul of 300 yds. takes about 15 minutes.—HARRY L. SPOONER.

Oiled Cigarette Paper Helps in Setting Mower Blades

A PIECE of cigarette tissue may be used to advantage for quick and accurate adjustment of the stationary blade of a lawn mower. Impregnate the paper with machine oil, place it on the stationary blade at one end, and turn the rotor until a blade is directly over the covered edge. Tighten down the rotor on this side with the adjusting screws. Turn the screws slowly, watching the paper closely, and when the descending blade presses down on the paper, you will see a thin line of oil oozing from between the blades. When this occurs, the adjustment at this end is just right. Move the paper to the other end of the blade and repeat the process.—W. C. WILHITE.

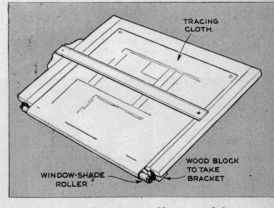

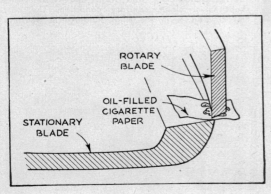

ROTARY BLADE

OIL-FILLED CIGARETTE PAPER

STATIONARY BLADE

Window-Shade Roller Holds Long Drawings on Board

DRAFTSMEN often find it hard to work with oversize drawings that are longer than the board itself. To overcome this difficulty, a window-shade roller of any length desired is fastened to the near edge of the drawing board by means of wooden blocks. One end of the tracing cloth or paper is tacked along the roller and rolled up until that portion not wanted on the board is out of the way. Another roller can be attached to the opposite edge of the board to receive the drawing as succeeding parts are finished.—SAMUEL DUKLER.

PAPER BLANKETS made of multilayers of cross-reinforced crepe paper have been developed to take the place of cotton and lightweight wool types. Laboratory tests have indicated that these blankets compare favorably in warmth-retention qualities to many kinds of textile covers. They are very light in weight and are snowy white in color with beige cotton-sateen bindings. Noninflammable and moth resistant, they come in the standard size 68" by 80". They are extremely low in cost, and can be used in the summer as a single covering and during the winter as an extra one

PLASTIC DRAIN STOPPERS to substitute for rubber ones are now on the market. They contain no metal or other critical materials and are available in seven standard sizes from 1" to 1¾" in diameter. Noncorroding, long lasting, and sanitary, these stoppers are said to have the same amount of elasticity and strength as the older types made of rubber. Even the rings on the stoppers are of plastic instead of metal

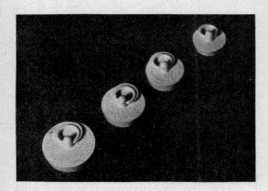

THE TRANSPARENT LUNCH BOX shown above is especially convenient for the war worker who has to submit his lunch equipment for a daily inspection. The box is made of a clear, sparkling, plastic material and opens from one end. It is designed to hold a 1-pt. vacuum bottle, sandwiches, and fruit, and it is easily kept in a clean, sanitary condition. The only metal used is in the rings holding the thermos

A CLEANING KIT containing materials for use on stainless steel, plastic, and enamel-ware utensils is shown in the photo at the right. The fluid cleaner contains no caustic abrasives, free alkali, or other injurious substances, and will not discolor, mar, or crack any utensils on which it is used. Besides the 12-oz. bottle of cleaning liquid, the kit contains two cellulose sponges, as well as a handy scouring pad. The cleaner is applied with one of the sponge pads, which is first dampened, and the utensil is then rubbed until all stains and marks are removed

PLASTIC JAR RINGS may be the much-needed substitute for rubber types, which are now proving hard to obtain. Tests conducted by the Department of Agriculture and by several food packers reveal that these new closures do as good a sealing job as the rubber rings. The necessary raw materials from which to make the rings are available, at least at the present time, in unlimited quantities, which is an added advantage. The rings are used in exactly the same manner as are the rubber ones, and come in widths and sizes to fit almost all jars and containers. They can be used by housewives and also by commercial packers

FLUTED PIE PLATES of heat-resistant glass are especially designed to prevent berry pies from losing their juices while baking. Pies are also automatically fluted when placed in these dishes, saving the housewife that tedious task. The plates are attractive enough to be used on the table. They may also be adapted for serving foods such as shortcakes, biscuits, and the like

BEAM LANTERN. Easily focused, this lantern throws a half-mile beam and uses only a 6-volt battery. An unusual feature is a droplight on an extension cord, powered by the same battery, that can be used to illuminate near-by objects when the strong light of the beam is not needed

WOOD AND FIBER CURTAIN RODS will save vital war materials, and are just as efficient as the metal types. The rods are finished in washable, baked-on, ivory enamel and are designed for windows up to 72" in width. They fit into brackets constructed of unfinished oak that can be painted to match surrounding trim or left natural and waxed. There are no sharp points or rough edges to snag the curtains. Should a very short rod be desired, simply get out the scissors and snip — the fiber is easily cut through, making the rods adjustable to almost any size window. Each package has full instructions for installing the rods

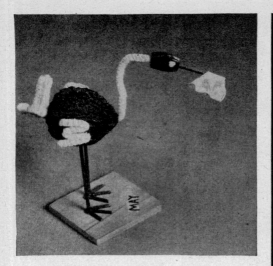

Amusing Stork Favor Is Made of Nuts and Pipe Cleaners

THIS amusing old bird is sure to make a hit at a stork party. A black walnut is used for the body. The tail, wings, and neck are made of pipe cleaners and attached with glue. Cut the tip and end from an almond meat and split the middle in half to form the head. Clamp a spring-type clothespin over the nut meat to hold it in place on the neck while the glue is drying. The beak is a reed or a toothpick, as are the legs and feet. Mount the bird on a square of cardboard or wood, shellac the head, paint in the eyes, and glue the "package" to his beak.

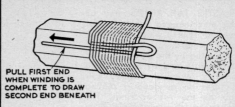

PULL FIRST END WHEN WINDING IS COMPLETE TO DRAW SECOND END BENEATH

Colorful Fish-Rod Winding

ATTRACTIVE windings on fishing rods, tennis rackets, and similar objects may be made with variegated crochet thread. The thread is wrapped in a single even layer, with the ends looped under, as shown in the drawing above, to conceal them. When winding is completed, apply lacquer, varnish, or some other sealer. For small objects such as fishing rods, No. 70 tatting cotton is good.—W. E. B.

Saving the Special Alloy Used to Solder Aluminum Work

ALUMINUM solder can be saved if, after the surface to be soldered is tinned with the special alloy, ordinary solder such as the rosin-core type is used over it for the rest of the work. The two solders will mix and a patch of different metal, such as tin, zinc, brass, copper, or the like can then be applied. The result is a patch as strong as one made entirely with aluminum solder.—R. S.

THE SQUARE KNOT   [KNOT WORK]

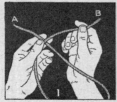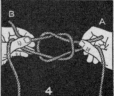

THE square knot, or reef knot as it is sometimes called, is one of the most important of all knots. It is used in first-aid work, in tying rope lengths together, and in all places where a strong knot, yet one that unties easily, is necessary. You can tie a square knot quickly and correctly every time by the following method:

Place the rope end held in the left hand *over* the other end, holding both where they cross with the left hand. With the right hand reach under and grasp end *B* as shown in Fig. 1. Pull rope *B* under and then up as shown in Fig. 2. Now guide rope *B* first over and then under end *A*, as shown in Fig. 3. Holding end *B* in the left hand and end *A* in the right hand, pull taut, completing the knot, as in Fig. 4.

POPULAR SCIENCE MONTHLY SHOP DATA

How to Dry Foods at Home to Boost Your Wartime Rations

ALONG with millions of other patriotic Americans, you probably have a Victory garden well under way and soon will begin gathering crops. Like them, too, you probably will have far more of some kinds than you need to supply your family table. Part of this surplus you will want to can, pickle, and make into preserves, jams, and jellies; some items you may wish to store in the cellar or in outdoor pits. This year it is a good idea to dehydrate some of the foods.

Dehydrated foods keep well and take little storage space, 1 lb. equaling 3 to 12 lb. of the fresh product. Their vitamin value is attested by the fact that the Army is purchasing many dried items. For home drying, the U. S. Department of Agriculture recommends both fruits and fresh vegetables. The fruits include apples, apricots, figs, peaches, pears, blackberries, dewberries, loganberries, raspberries, cherries, and plums; the vegetables, sweet corn, shelled mature beans and peas, beets, snap beans, peppers, pumpkins, squash, and leafy vegetables.

Home drying with artificial heat can be done in a cabinet having removable trays on which the foods are placed. Hot air rises through the cabinet from a heater underneath it and is baffled around and over the trays. These are 5" shorter than the depth of the cabinet and are placed alternately against the back and front.

To construct the cabinet, make two side frames of 2" by 2" stock as shown in the drawings. The upper 38" section of each frame is covered with ½" stock on the outside and with ½" insulation board in one piece on the inside. Slides for the trays are nailed across the inside of each face from the front edge to within ½" of the rear edge, leaving space for a sheet of ½" insulation board inside the back.

This sheet of insulation, measuring 15" by 38", is tacked to the ends of the tray slides to begin the assembly, after which the toppiece and cross brace are attached to the front posts, and boards are fastened on for the back. Attach the top next, putting a 3" board at the front end, leaving a 3" space behind it, and then adding the wider boards. Top insulation is put on in two sections nailed from the inside.

A removable plywood chimney fits into the vent, a 1" by 1" strip across front and back holding it in place. Nails driven partly through the strips help to keep it rigid. They can be withdrawn for removing the chimney when the cabinet is to be stored.

The seven trays are all alike, measuring 14½" by 23". They are made of ⅛" or ¼" galvanized wire mesh framed on both sides by ½" by 1" wood strips, but wooden slats will serve. The door is constructed of 1" by 2" stiles and rails, jointed as shown, then

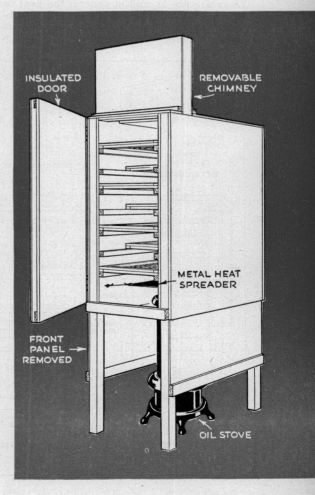

INSULATED DOOR

REMOVABLE CHIMNEY

METAL HEAT SPREADER

FRONT PANEL REMOVED

OIL STOVE

completely covered on the outside with ¼" plywood or other stock and on the inside with ½" insulation board.

Fireproof aprons of asbestos sheets or sheet metal are nailed permanently to the sides and temporarily to the front and back, to protect the stove from drafts and to direct the heat upward. A piece of sheet metal suspended by wires from the four corner posts spreads the heat. The distance between the top of the stove and the spreader should be at least 2".

A medium-size kerosene stove will supply sufficient heat, which should vary from 125 deg. F. to 160 deg. F. during the drying period of foods. Other types of controlled heat, including gas and electric heaters and even a battery of light bulbs, may be used instead. An electric fan may be included to circulate the heat more rapidly. A thermometer should be used to check temperatures.

The cabinet is heated before the filled trays are put in, and in general the heat is increased during the middle stages of drying. The drying foods should be moist to the touch and cooler than the air flowing over them. If they feel hot and dry, the drying is too rapid. The time required will vary according to the kind of food, the size of the pieces, the type of drier, and even the weather. Fruits may take from 6 to 24 hours, and vegetables from 3 to 15 hours.

The positions of the trays are changed every 30 minutes or so during the drying period. Remove the top tray and place it at the bottom, raising each tray up one place at each change. Be sure to alternate the trays against the back and front every time they are changed so the hot air will travel back and forth between them.

Fruits are ready to be removed from the drier when they are leathery and tough, and vegetables after they have been dried to brittleness. If in doubt, heat them a little longer at a reduced temperature. Some pieces may not be completely dried when the batch is removed. Cull these, as they may mold during storage. If there is a period of time between drying and storing, reheat the foods to 165 deg. just before storing. If during storage there is any sign of moisture upon occasional inspection, reheat the foods and repack them.

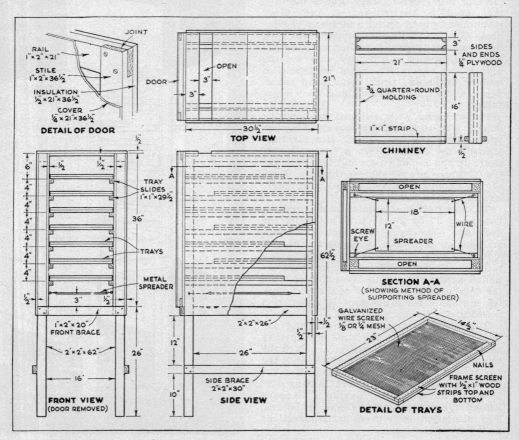

The various kinds of fruits and vegetables require different methods of preparation prior to being dried. Some are steamed, others boiled, and certain fruits are treated with sulphur. One level teaspoon of sulphur is used for each pound of prepared fruit. Wrap the sulphur in paper and place it in a shallow tin pan about 7" below the bottom tray. Light the paper, which will ignite the sulphur and release fumes to rise through the cabinet. *Be sure to do this outdoors* so that the fumes will escape harmlessly into the open air. While apples, peaches, and apricots are usually sulphurized before drying, they can also be dried after steaming.

Vegetables should be cooked in steam or boiling water before dehydrating. Steaming is said to preserve higher food values. If vegetables are boiled, only small amounts should be prepared at a time. To conserve vitamins and minerals, use the same water for several lots of the same kind of vegetables and cook as fast as possible to a point where they are almost tender.

Fruits should be mature, but not soft, and in prime condition. Apples are washed, pared, cored, and sliced. Peaches are peeled by dipping into boiling water, then halved or quartered, and dried with the pit side up. Apricots are dried with the skin on. Berries should be picked in early morning and dried quickly. They are spread two layers deep with a piece of cloth over the trays to keep them from sticking. Cherries are pitted and drained for about an hour; then they are spread in a single layer on the trays. Pears are sliced or cut into quarters or eighths. If the pieces are not dried immediately after preparing, keep them in a solution of four teaspoons of salt to a gallon of water.

Dehydrated foods should be packed in airtight containers, such as coffee cans with the tops sealed with tape, tightly sealed glass jars, or friction-top cans, and stored in a dry place.

The amount of elapsed time between picking fruits and vegetables and putting them into the dehydrator to dry is important. The shorter the time consumed the better, because the vitamin value, flavor, and cooking quality will be higher.

When preparing the foods for table use, soak them from ½ to 6 hours, adding as much water as necessary, and cook them in

Heat from an ordinary oil stove is sufficient to dehydrate fresh fruits and vegetables. A metal spreader will prevent scorching of the lower tray

Fairly constant temperatures must be maintained. Check them with a thermometer kept on the bottom tray. Staggering the trays aids the hot-air flow

Sulphurizing before drying is advisable for some fruits. The sulphur may be burned in a small tin

Peaches are halved or quartered for dehydrating; beans are sectioned and laid on a piece of cloth

the same water. Dried greens do not require any soaking. Cook these in salted water until they are tender.

Almost every fruit and vegetable calls for a different method of preparation as well as different drying time and temperature. The Department of Agriculture offers at a nominal cost (5 cents) Farmers' Bulletin No. 984, Farm and Home Drying of Fruits and Vegetables, giving comprehensive directions for home drying. With this bulletin and the dehydrator described, you can preserve the produce from your Victory garden, as well as fruits bought in season, for use when fresh foods are not available or are too expensive for the family budget.

Table-Model Drier Used in Kitchen

HERE is a table-model home dehydrator developed by the Tennessee Valley Authority and the University of Tennessee. It gets its heat from a battery of electric-light bulbs, and circulation is hastened with an ordinary electric fan. Both can be plugged into household wall sockets.

The unit will handle a half bushel of fresh fruits and vegetables at a time on trays approximately 18″ by 18″. Materials used in construction are inexpensive.

Longhorn Rack   Holds Many Ties

LONGHORN cattle are almost a thing of the past, but this wooden replica of a steer's head forms a unique tie rack. It should be made of straight-grained, dry softwood. The horns are bandsawed in one piece, from a 20½″ length of ½″ by 1″ stock. Round the edges and screw and glue the horns to the back of the head.

A piece of ¾″ by 2½″ by 3¾″ stock is used for the head. Bore the holes for the nostrils; then shape the piece as shown. Insert wood beads or glass marbles for eyes. Cut out a section of a curtain ring as wide as the nose between the nostrils, notch the outer edges of the nostrils to let the ring hang straight down, and glue it in.

A V-shaped block of wood screwed to the back of the head, with two holes drilled down through the top edge on a slant, will provide a suitable method of fastening the rack a little distance away from the wall. Paint the head brown, the forehead cream, and the eyes black. Finish the horns with orange shellac.—H. P. DONER.

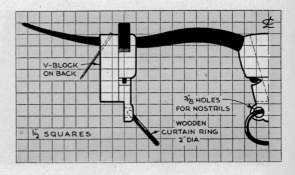

V-BLOCK ON BACK

3/8 HOLES FOR NOSTRILS

½ SQUARES

WOODEN CURTAIN RING 2″ DIA

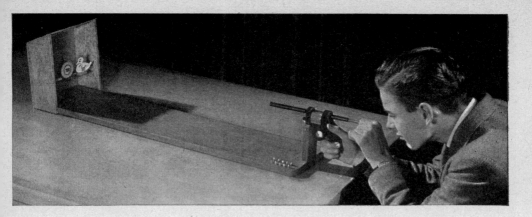

SAFE AND SANE SHOOTING GALLERY
IS A SURE-FIRE HIT

By Myron Fleishman

A ROOTIN', tootin', shootin' gallery that you can easily build at home will afford your family hours of enjoyment and be great fun at parties. The gun is mounted so that it cannot be aimed sideways or up in the air, thus restricting all shots to the gallery itself and making the game safe for children.

The base is a pine board ¾" by 7½" by 36". At one end is the gun mount and at the other is a backstop constructed of 7/16" stock. Both the targets are cut from heavy pressed board, and after being painted and labeled with the scoring number, they are nailed to wooden blocks and mounted so as to pivot on a wooden dowel in the gallery. They rest at the front on a second dowel or a piece of heavy wire placed as shown in the drawing. When hit, they fall over backward.

The gun is fashioned from ¾" stock, and the barrel formed of a cardboard tube or a thin tube of sheet metal. Two springs are used in the plunger which releases the shot —a strong firing spring and a weak recoil spring, the latter holding the plunger back so that bullets may be inserted. Any number of bullets can be made from short pieces of dowel. Point them at one end with a knife or in a pencil sharpener and fit them into holes drilled in the base.

Both the base and gallery should be stained and varnished. The gun and targets may be painted as shown in the drawing.

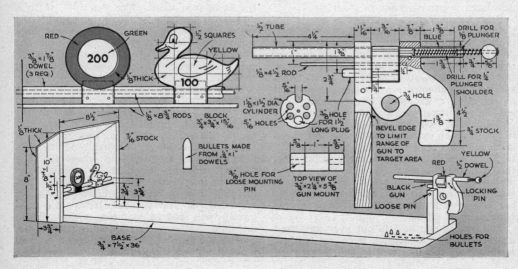

Bat raised, kangaroo in position, the player on the right aims for the "hole" while her opponent watches

KANGAROO GOLF

By PATTY DE ROULF

KANGAROO GOLF is a new and fascinating game the whole family can play out in the back yard, at the beach, or on a picnic. Although it has been patented by the inventor, Pietro A. Yon, the readers of POPULAR SCIENCE MONTHLY are invited to make their own equipment from the drawings accompanying this article.

The "kangaroos" are little wooden sticks that fly through the air when they are struck from a wooden tee with the narrow side of an oval-shaped bat. Mr. Yon, world-famous organist and composer, and musical director for St. Patrick's Cathedral in New York, received the inspiration for the game when he watched a group of boys playing "old cat" in a village near his home in the Alps.

Collapsible wooden enclosures are used in place of the usual golf holes. A kangaroo is placed on a tee so that it extends from 1" to 2½" over one edge. When it is hit with the bat, it will soar through the air for distances up to 50 yds. The game is scored similarly to golf, the smallest number of strokes around a nine-hole course winning the game.

The course can be laid out over any kind of terrain, and obstacles such as hedges, bushes, and the like add to the interest of the game. The enclosures, or holes, should be not less than 25 yds. nor more than 50 yds. apart. A good score for such a course is about 25 strokes. Each player has a set of four kangaroos, a tee block, and a bat, all of these being carried in a sack slung over the shoulder.

Direction of the kangaroos can be controlled by the tee as well as by the shape of the kangaroo itself. For example, if it is desired to have the kangaroo jump high, the tee should be placed with its highest edge facing the hole. If you want to hit the kangaroo level with the ground or downhill, place the tee with the low edge facing the hole.

Each one of the four kangaroos in the set is shaped differently. The Speeder is used for velocity and height, and end A for a low, fast flight, and end B for a high, fast flight. To attain distance, the Torpedo is used. If the player strikes end C, this kangaroo will usually stop where it lands without rolling. When it is necessary to go from low to high ground, use the Flash, striking it with end A pointed up; to get from high to low ground, strike this kangaroo with end A pointed down. Added distance can be gained by using Turtle, the fourth kangaroo, as it is designed to roll when it strikes the ground.

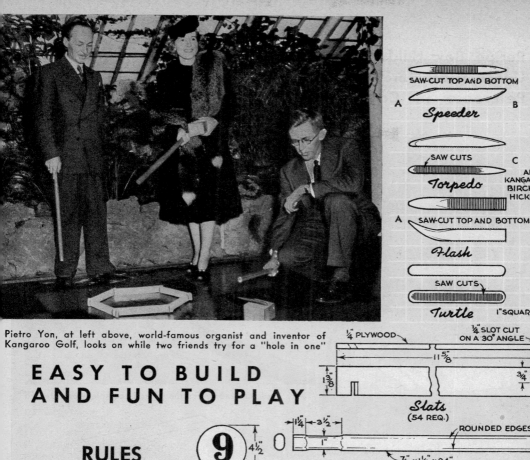

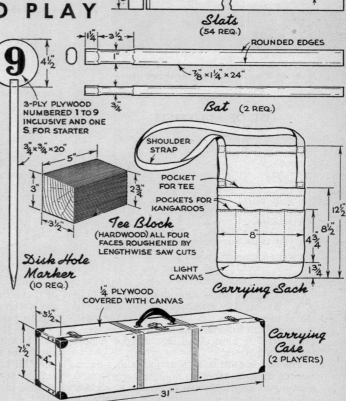

Pietro Yon, at left above, world-famous organist and inventor of Kangaroo Golf, looks on while two friends try for a "hole in one"

SAW-CUT TOP AND BOTTOM
A ——— B
Speeder

SAW CUTS
C
Torpedo

ALL
KANGAROOS
BIRCH OR
HICKORY

SAW-CUT TOP AND BOTTOM
A
Flash

SAW CUTS
Turtle

1" SQUARES

EASY TO BUILD
AND FUN TO PLAY

¼ PLYWOOD
¼ SLOT CUT ON A 30° ANGLE — ½
11 5/8
1 3/8"
¾"
Slats
(54 REQ.)

RULES

1¼ — 3½
4½"
1"
ROUNDED EDGES
¾"
⅞" × 1¼" × 24"
Bat (2 REQ.)

9

3-PLY PLYWOOD
NUMBERED 1 TO 9
INCLUSIVE AND ONE
S FOR STARTER

¾" × ¾" × 20"
5"
3"
2¾"
3½"

Disk Hole Marker
(10 REQ.)

Tee Block
(HARDWOOD) ALL FOUR
FACES ROUGHENED BY
LENGTHWISE SAW CUTS

SHOULDER STRAP
POCKET FOR TEE
POCKETS FOR KANGAROOS
8"
12½
8½
4¾
1¾
LIGHT CANVAS
Carrying Sack

1. One or more persons may play either for individual scores or as partners.
2. Each player has four kangaroos, any one of which may be used.
3. The starting point from each marker should not exceed the length of the bat.
4. Each player hits a first stroke. The second stroke is made by the player whose kangaroo is farthest from the hole. Others then play second strokes and continue in this manner until all have completed the hole.
5. After every stroke, the player places his tee block so as to touch the kangaroo wherever it has landed. In difficult positions, the tee may be placed at a distance of a hand span from the kangaroo, but not in the direction of the hole.
6. After striking the kangaroo, the player may strike it again while it is in flight without a penalty.
7. If the kangaroo breaks, or becomes damaged, the player may replay the hole.
8. The first stroke may be repeated if desired without a penalty.
9. If the kangaroo is lost, the hole must be replayed.
10. Penalties (one count): When a player misses the kangaroo in striking; when the kangaroo lands in a tree or other obstacle necessitating employment of other methods to recover it, or when it is lost; when the kangaroo is moved sideways, or backwards away from the hole, for a distance of not more than twice the length of the bat.
11. Additional rules may be made according to special conditions.

¼ PLYWOOD
COVERED WITH CANVAS
5½
7½
4"
31"
Carrying Case
(2 PLAYERS)

Recipe Box Holds Card Under Glass for Ready Reference in Cooking

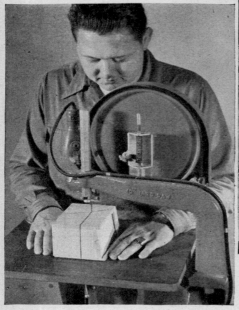

Any card inserted under the glass is completely protected

Build a closed box with a top and bottom; then cut it apart carefully as shown above

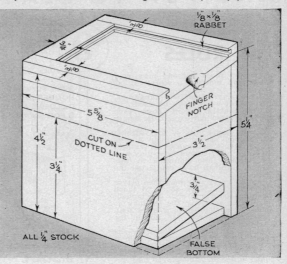

LIST OF MATERIALS			
No.			
Pc. Description	T.	W.	L.
1 Front	¼	4¼	5⅝
1 Back	¼	5	5⅝
2 Sides	¼	3	5
1 Top	¼	3 9/16	5⅝
1 Bottom	¼	3	5⅛
1 False bottom	¼	3 1/16	5⅛
2 Top slides	¼	⅜	5⅝
1 Top slide	¼	¾	3¼
1 Glass cut to fit slide			
1 Pair small box hinges			

Note: All dimensions are given in inches.

A NOVEL recipe box designed to hold about 250 standard 3" by 5" filing cards has a glass top under which the card to be used is inserted. In this way the written matter is kept clean and in good condition at all times.

The box is built with butt joints and has a sloping false bottom to hold the cards at a convenient angle. Strips to receive the glass are rabbeted on a circular saw or built up of three thin pieces of flat stock. File a finger notch on the right-hand edge of the box top to permit easy removal of the card.

Build the box as a unit; then saw it in two to form the lid and the bottom. Care should be taken when assembling the box to keep all nails clear of the section where the cut is to be made. After fastening the hinges, insert the false bottom. Finish with paint or enamel.—FRANK HEGEMEYER.

Dear Workshop Editor.
    Nowadays when health is so important,
summer bathing at the beach has become
so popular that it's sometimes hard to get
a bath house. Couldn't you publish plans
for making a light, portable, dressing room
to use right on the beach?
    Yours truly,
        A. R. M. San Diego, Calif.

You'll be all set for a day at the beach with this bathhouse that can be folded into two easily carried sections. Designed by Hi Sibley

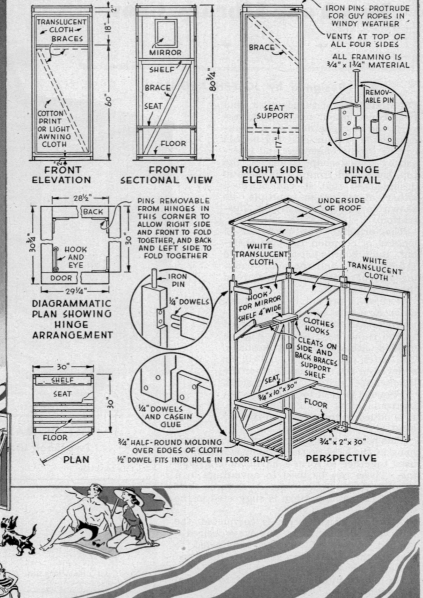

FRONT ELEVATION

TRANSLUCENT CLOTH
BRACES
18"
2"
60"
COTTON PRINT OR LIGHT AWNING CLOTH

FRONT SECTIONAL VIEW

MIRROR
SHELF
BRACE
SEAT
FLOOR
80¾"

RIGHT SIDE ELEVATION

BRACE
SEAT SUPPORT
17"

HINGE DETAIL

IRON PINS PROTRUDE FOR GUY ROPES IN WINDY WEATHER
VENTS AT TOP OF ALL FOUR SIDES
ALL FRAMING IS ¾" x 1¾" MATERIAL
REMOVABLE PIN

DIAGRAMMATIC PLAN SHOWING HINGE ARRANGEMENT

28½"
BACK
30¾"
30"
HOOK AND EYE
DOOR
29¼"

PINS REMOVABLE FROM HINGES IN THIS CORNER TO ALLOW RIGHT SIDE AND FRONT TO FOLD TOGETHER, AND BACK AND LEFT SIDE TO FOLD TOGETHER

IRON PIN
¼" DOWELS
¼" DOWELS AND CASEIN GLUE

PLAN

30"
SHELF
SEAT
FLOOR
30"

¾" HALF-ROUND MOLDING OVER EDGES OF CLOTH
½ DOWEL FITS INTO HOLE IN FLOOR SLAT

PERSPECTIVE

UNDERSIDE OF ROOF
WHITE TRANSLUCENT CLOTH
WHITE TRANSLUCENT CLOTH
HOOK FOR MIRROR
SHELF 4" WIDE
CLOTHES HOOKS
CLEATS ON SIDE AND BACK BRACES SUPPORT SHELF
SEAT ¾" x 10" x 30"
FLOOR
¾" x 2" x 30"

Add-a-Unit Bookcase

Lets Your Library Grow

✦ ✦ ✦ ✦

Designed by JOSEPH ARONSON

FURNITURE of the simplest kind of construction need not necessarily be of crude design. A bookcase made of plain shelving boards can be given refinement and interest by a few shaped lines at the top, sides, and front. This piece is designed so that it can be used either alone or in multiple, as shown in the accompanying illustration.

The original was made of 3' lengths of common 12" pine shelving. Such boards actually measure ¾" by 11⅝", and the accompanying bill of materials is based on these dimensions.

Both sides are cut to shape first, either on a band saw or with a compass saw. Next, the top is shaped in the same way, and its edge is molded with a plane or spokeshave. The sides are doweled, nailed, or screwed to the shelves. Both of the bracket feet are let into the sides.

Plywood is used for the back, being rounded off at all visible edges. It is nailed to the sides, and the ¾" cleat is glued to the top.

This bookcase is designed without an overhang at the sides so that two or more can be used together to form a harmonious grouping. These can be used to advantage in a room with much wall space. A three-shelf unit of the same pattern is suggested in the drawings.

After the construction is completed, the unit can be finished in any way desired—stained, varnished, or even enameled to match other home furnishings. If the wood has an interesting grain, it is a good idea to stain it only lightly in order not to conceal the grain.

LIST OF MATERIALS
Two-Shelf Bookcase

Pc.	Description	T.	W.	L.
1	Top	¾	11⅝	36
2	Shelves	¾	11⅝	34½
2	Sides	¾	11⅝	29¼
1	Back (plywood)	¼	26½	35
1	Back cleat	¾	¾	34½
2	Brackets (front feet)	¾	2¾	4½

Note: All dimensions are given in inches and are finished sizes.

BACK CLEAT
3/4" x 3/4"

3/4"

12"

30"

3/4"

13"

3/4"

2 3/4"

36" OVERALL

3/4" OVERHANG

11 3/8"

10 1/2"

11 5/8"

40"

3/4"

12"

3/4"

10 1/4"

3/4"

12"

3/4"

2 3/4"

36" OVERALL

10 1/2"

11 5/8"

11 5/8"

ABOVE, A TWO-SHELF
UNIT. AN ALTERNATIVE
THREE-SHELF DESIGN
IS SHOWN AT THE RIGHT

DESIGNED BY *Joseph Aronson*

For Your After-Hours

★ ★ ★ ★ ★ A WAR WORKER'S LUNCH BOX AND TWO OTHER

WAR WORKER'S LUNCH BOX. For saving time at war-plant gate inspections, this lunch box has clear-plastic window panes. It is made of waterproof plywood, ½" thick for the base and ¼" for all other parts. Saw the top and bottom of each end as one piece, separating them later with a band, jig, or scroll saw. The sides are alike, with openings jigsawed and rabbeted for the panes. Use waterproof glue in assembling. Clamp the sides and ends first; then glue on and clamp the base.

Have the grain of the facewood of the top run in the direction of the shorter dimension, and cut kerfs as shown in the drawing. Curve the piece gradually in a vise or with a belt jig, dampening with hot, wet rags. This section is glued into grooves in the top endpieces. Attach the panes with cement and glaziers' points; then hinge the top and bottom at the glued-in fillers. Finish with two coats of waterproof varnish. Working time: 5½ hours.

BAR STOOL. Here is an inexpensive way of making small, attractive stools for a breakfast or refreshment bar. Maple may be used throughout—1" dowels for legs and ⅞" stock for seats and spreaders. Glue the legs into the seats; then screw them to the spreaders, countersinking the screws ¼" and plugging the holes. Star-shaped thumbtacks over the plugs add a neat note. Finish with bright enamel; then stencil the star design on with a contrasting enamel. Two coats of varnish will preserve the finish. Working time: 5½ hours for one stool.

PAPER-WEIGHT BOX. Heavy walls and an angular design give this box a masculine touch. The stock may be cherry, walnut, or mahogany. Note that the ends of the longer walls are rabbeted and the others dadoed. Sand the inside of the pieces, assemble with glue, and chamfer the top and bottom edges. Make the base a snug fit and glue it in at the table line; then glue in the round-

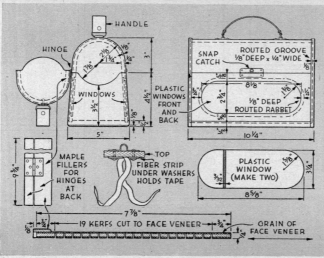

Craftwork
PROJECTS OF REAL UTILITY ★

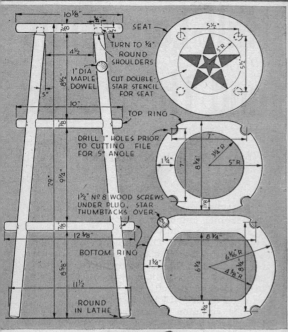

SEAT
TURN TO ¾" ROUND SHOULDERS
1" DIA MAPLE DOWEL
CUT DOUBLE-STAR STENCIL FOR SEAT
5½"
5" R
TOP RING
DRILL 1" HOLES PRIOR TO CUTTING FILE FOR 5° ANGLE
7"
7"
8¼"
1¼" R
5" R
1¾"
⅛"
1½" No 8 WOOD SCREWS UNDER PLUG, STAR THUMBTACKS OVER
BOTTOM RING
8¼"
6½₁₆ R
4⅝" R
8¼"
6½"
1¾"
1¼"
ROUND IN LATHE
10⅛"
⅜"
3½"
4½"
1" DIA
8½"
5"
29"
9½"
10"
⅞"
⅞"
⅞"
12⅜"
8⅝"
11½"

DESIGNED BY
ERNEST R. DEWALT

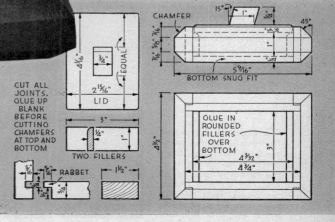

CHAMFER
15°
1"
45°
⅞"
⅝"
⅞"
1"
⅝₁₆
5⅝₁₆"
BOTTOM SNUG FIT
4⅟₁₆"
¾"
EQUAL
2¹⁵⁄₁₆"
LID
CUT ALL JOINTS. GLUE UP BLANK BEFORE CUTTING CHAMFERS AT TOP AND BOTTOM
3"
¼"
1"
TWO FILLERS
4½"
GLUE IN ROUNDED FILLERS OVER BOTTOM
3"
4³⁄₃₂"
4¾"
⁵⁄₁₆"
⁵⁄₁₆"
RABBET
1½"

ed fillers, which support the loosely fitted top and strengthen the base joints.

Sand the outside, rounding all edges. Spray or brush three coats of clear lacquer on the outside, rubbing with fine steel wool between coats. Wax several times for a sheen. Be careful to get no finish on the inside, which is left natural. Working time: 4 hours.

WHAT YOU SHOULD KNOW
about
Half-Lap Joints and Their Uses

By EDWIN M. LOVE

JOINTS made in building a mirror frame, cupboard door, and the like must be solid to give the piece rigidity and permanence. The half-lap joint proves satisfactory for this type of work and also for assemblies that must be taken apart occasionally. This joint consists of two members notched to half thickness and lapped on each other with the faces flush.

Most common of these joints is the end lap in which the ends of two pieces of wood are notched and cut to fit. In preparing the stock to be used, true it up and mark the working faces and edges with a sharp, hard pencil or a knife. Measure the width of the first member and mark it off on the second

Rip the cheek of a tenon by starting at the corner and sawing diagonally to the shoulder line. Then reverse the block in the vise and again saw from corner to line. The saw is steadied by the waste as these cuts are made

Two bench hooks support the member as the tenon shoulder is cut. Start making the saw cut at the farthest edge and, as the kerf extends across the wood, level off the saw. The block of waste wood will now fall out.

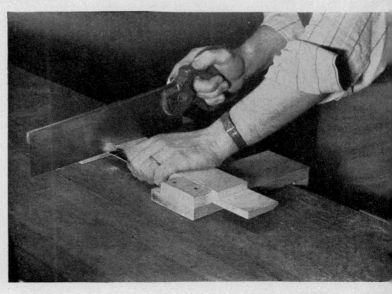

with a square, allowing a little extra length for the tenon. Repeat the procedure on the first piece, but mark it on the back. Using a marking gauge, scribe the depth of the joint on the edges and end of each piece. This measurement should be half the thickness of the joining members.

The notched surfaces of the tenon are known as the cheeks, and these should be ripped first. The reason for this is twofold: first, the waste stock supports the saw as it cuts to the bottom of the tenon, and second, there is less likelihood of cutting into the tenon thickness, as the waste block falls away when the shoulder of the joint is cut. Clamp the piece upright in a vise. Then saw down from the near corner diagonally to the line marking the shoulder of the joint, keeping the saw kerf in the waste. Complete the cut by reversing the piece and sawing in the opposite direction. If you have no vise, or if the stock is too long to be handled conveniently in this manner, rest it edgewise on a sawhorse and rip the cheek from one edge and then the other, handling it like an ordinary board.

In cutting the shoulder to remove the waste block, brace the wood on a pair of bench hooks. Start the cut at the far corner and level off when the kerf extends across the stock so that the tenon will not be partly sawed through before the block is detached.

Joints of this type can be glued, screwed, or nailed. In gluing, apply the binder on both joining cheeks and hold them together with a clamp. Tap the edges in order to close the shoulder joints. If the lap is to be screwed, bore and countersink holes in one tenon and, if the material is hardwood,

use this tenon as a template for locating pilot holes to be drilled in the other.

Such structural forms as X's make use of cross-lap joints, in which both pieces are notched between the ends. Extra saw cuts in the waste, made to the depth of the joint, make it easy to trim flat bottoms. Use a sharp, wide chisel with the bevel down, and make tapering cuts from both edges. This avoids splintering of the far edge that would occur if the cut were made full width. True the bottoms with the flat side of the chisel down.

Small joints can be trimmed with hand pressure and a side swing of the chisel handle, but larger work requires a mallet. If none is available, follow carpentering methods and strike with the side of a hammer head.

In order to avoid any chance of the edges of the boards not being parallel, hold one piece firmly in place on top of the other and run a knife along its edges when marking the shoulder. This will assure the correct angle at the intersection also.

The sharp corners of a snugly fitted joint tend to tear the edges when it is being assembled. To avoid this, chamfer the edges of the bottom of the cut. While it is most desirable to have tight joints, little force should be used in fitting the pieces together. When they are wedged too tightly, both members will bend back, throwing the work out of line, as one of the drawings shows.

A joint formed by a notch cut in the middle of a member and a tenon cut on the end of the other member, is known as a middle-lap joint. The methods of cutting the two pieces are the same as for the end

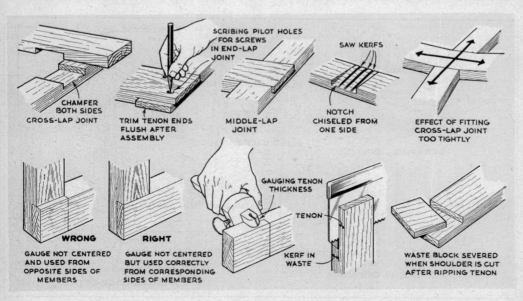

CHAMFER BOTH SIDES
CROSS-LAP JOINT

SCRIBING PILOT HOLES FOR SCREWS IN END-LAP JOINT

TRIM TENON ENDS FLUSH AFTER ASSEMBLY

MIDDLE-LAP JOINT

SAW KERFS

NOTCH CHISELED FROM ONE SIDE

EFFECT OF FITTING CROSS-LAP JOINT TOO TIGHTLY

WRONG
GAUGE NOT CENTERED AND USED FROM OPPOSITE SIDES OF MEMBERS

RIGHT
GAUGE NOT CENTERED BUT USED CORRECTLY FROM CORRESPONDING SIDES OF MEMBERS

GAUGING TENON THICKNESS

TENON

KERF IN WASTE

WASTE BLOCK SEVERED WHEN SHOULDER IS CUT AFTER RIPPING TENON

lap and cross lap that are described above.

A refinement of the half-lap joint is the mitered lap. In this, the end of one member is mitered and half the thickness of the mating piece is mitered, the remainder forming a tenon. The method of cutting is the same as for square joints. Miter angles need not be 45 deg.; for instance, the joint might be a union between a door stile and a wider lower rail, or it might join together parts of a hexagonal frame.

Blind half-lap joints, designed to hide end wood, can be made with little extra effort. The easy way is to cut one tenon short, and fill the remaining space with a dutchman cut extra thick and glued in. When the glue has dried, trim the filling flush. While this is adequate for paint finishes,

the workmanlike way to do the job is to chisel out the one cheek instead of sawing it so as to leave a continuous edge that will hide the other tenon end. Saw the shoulder to depth at the open edge; then trim to depth at the back with a chisel held vertically.

If the joints have been cut accurately, they should assemble with the faces flush. Usually, however, a little surfacing is needed although it may be only sandpapering. In rubbing with sandpaper, be sure to stroke along the grain, as cross sanding shows up in stain and varnish and even in enamel. If planing is necessary, use a smoothing plane set fine, and stroke diagonally in order to avoid tearing the wood. If the wood is hard, a scraper is excellent for this purpose.

When the tenons have been cut too deeply,

To remove wood in the notch, hold the chisel with the bevel down. Cut in and upward from each edge

This method of scribing a line insures accurate measurement even though the sides may not be true

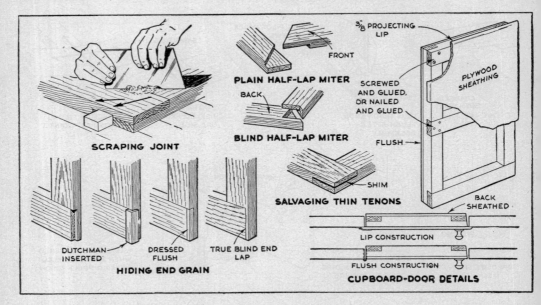

SCRAPING JOINT

PLAIN HALF-LAP MITER
FRONT
BACK

BLIND HALF-LAP MITER

SALVAGING THIN TENONS
SHIM

HIDING END GRAIN
DUTCHMAN INSERTED
DRESSED FLUSH
TRUE BLIND END LAP

3/8 PROJECTING LIP
SCREWED AND GLUED. OR NAILED AND GLUED
PLYWOOD SHEATHING
FLUSH
BACK SHEATHED

LIP CONSTRUCTION

FLUSH CONSTRUCTION

CUPBOARD-DOOR DETAILS

insert thin sheets of wood between the cheeks of the joint. If the joint is being glued, apply the glue to all contacting surfaces. In joints that are held with screws, use cardboard as a shim. If the joints are too tight, plane a shaving from the edges; if they are too loose, a skillfully made dutchman wedged in may hide the effect. Obviously, such salvaging should be done only as a last resort, as every effort should be made to cut joints that fit accurately.

Excellent flat-surfaced cupboard doors can be built cheaply by assembling frames with half-lap joints and sheathing them with ¼" or ⅜" plywood. These can be made in two different styles—lip doors and flush doors. In a lip door, the plywood projects at the edge and hides the joint between the frame and the cabinet opening, whereas the plywood on a flush door is trimmed to the frame so that the front is even with the front of the cabinet. In making the lip type, build the frame to fit the opening, allowing a clearance of as much as ⅛" all around. The flush door should be built nearly the same size, allowing for jointing the edges for a clearance of about 1/16" all around.

Before applying glue, make a trial fitting

When the surfaces of the joint are **not flush**, use a smoothing plane on them, but stroke diagonally so as not to rip the wood

of the joints by clamping them together to make sure that all edges fit firmly and that the faces are flush. When the glue has dried, remove any excess with fine sandpaper. Be especially careful to leave none under the lip, or on the edges of a flush door.

ELIMINATING DOOR FRICTION   [*SHIPSHAPE HOME*]

STRIKING JAMB WITH MALLET

TIGHTEN LOOSE SCREWS

TAMP STEELWOOL IN WORN HOLES OR DRIVE IN GLUED PLUG

Door drags on floor. Tighten the screws in the hinges, especially in the upper one. If screws have pulled loose, drive glue-coated wooden plugs into the holes, or tamp them full of steel wool, and turn the screws in. If composition wood is used, drive a wedge under the door until the screws are set.

If this treatment does not clear the binding, a cardboard shim may have been put behind the hinge. Remove this and tighten screws.

Door binds on lower end of lock jamb. If tightening the lower hinge is insufficient, hold a block against the jamb and strike with a heavy mallet or hammer, lightly at first, harder if necessary.

Door rubs side or head jamb. Try driving the jamb at these points. If the jamb was well blocked when installed, this driving will move it very little, but often a slight shift will clear the door.

Upper lock corner rubs. This is easily planed down, and the bare wood may be stained or painted.

Animated Scarecrow Frightens Birds from Your Vegetables

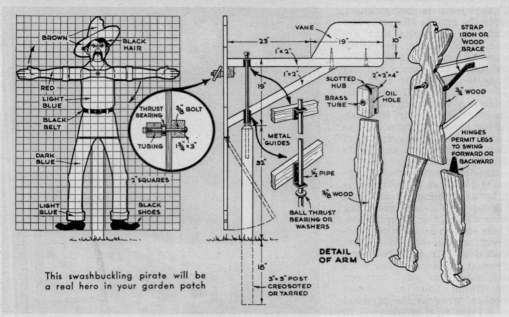

This swashbuckling pirate will be a real hero in your garden patch

A SCARECROW with spinning arms and dangling legs will help frighten birds from your Victory garden. Short lengths of board and odds and ends from the junk box are all the materials needed for building one.

The head and torso are cut from a piece of ¾" stock, and a heavy piece across the shoulders serves as both a cleat and a support for the bolt on which the windmill arms turn. These revolving arms are fastened into a slotted hub, with a short length of brass or copper tubing set in it for a bushing. Both legs are hinged to swing backward, and the vane is supported on wood members to which are screwed guides for the vertical axis made of ½" pipe.

Paint the scarecrow as shown in the drawing, or make up your own color scheme. A realistic flesh color can be made by mixing red, yellow, and white paint.

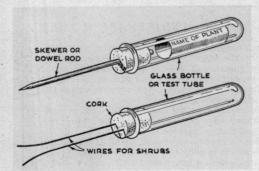

Markers for Flower Planting

GLASS tubes containing slips torn from paint color cards make good markers that show the hue of the bloom as well as the name of the plant. They can be stuck in the ground or tied to stems.—E. C. HANLEY.

Can Lids Protect Your Garden

COFFEE-CAN lids, paired 2" apart and suspended in a series, will effectively frighten away birds and other garden marauders. Pairing up lids of different sizes will result in different tones. The lids can be strung on wire or on heavy, waxed cord.—H. S.

IDEAS FOR MOTORISTS

MIRROR

SHEET-
METAL
CLIP

½"

1 PARKING IS SIMPLIFIED and damage to tire side walls prevented by a mirror on the right-hand car door. It is tilted to reflect the edge of the running board and curb line. A slight bend should be made in the mirror arm in order to place it below the rim of the door. Fit a setscrew to the ball socket so that the mirror may be locked in position after it is adjusted to the driver's line of vision.—C. L. B.

2 A WINDSHIELD WIPER that won't stay up can be held out of the way with a clip made of sheet metal or an annealed piece of clock spring. The clip should be bent as shown, and the flat end pushed or driven up between the glass and the windshield frame. Slip the arm of the blade under the clip when the wiper isn't needed.—A. H. W.

3 ADD TO YOUR TRAILER'S USEFULNESS by making a telescoping tongue of two pieces of pipe, one fitting into the other, as shown in the drawing at left below. Holes are bored into the pipes for a good-sized bolt, which serves as a locking pin. Such an arrangement will make your trailer more adaptable for hauling long objects.—A. H. W.

4 DIM-OUT DRIVING is a hazardous business. Here's a helpful hint that will be a boon to night drivers. Paint the rear edge of the driver's door solid white so that when the door is being opened the moving white strip will be seen by approaching cars.—D. H.

DRAWINGS BY STEWART ROUSE

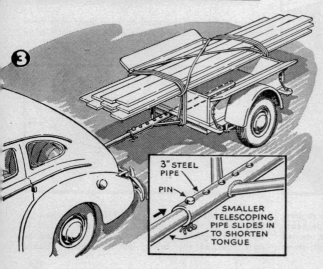

3" STEEL
PIPE

PIN

SMALLER
TELESCOPING
PIPE SLIDES IN
TO SHORTEN
TONGUE

KEEPING THE HOME

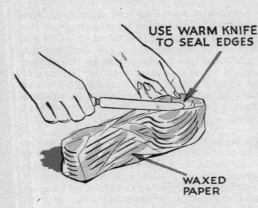

USE WARM KNIFE
TO SEAL EDGES

WAXED
PAPER

NAIL ROLISH REMOVER

Nail-polish remover dabbed on paint marks will serve as an efficient substitute for turpentine. It should be wiped off while it is still wet

Silverware is tarnished by sulphurous gases in the air. To protect it, wrap it in waxed paper and seal the edges of the paper by pressing a hot knife along them so that the wax melts together

UNCORKED
BOTTLE OF
MOTH SPRAY

Fumes evaporating from a bottle of moth spray will keep moths out of a closet. Just place an open bottle of the liquid on one of the shelves

Corset steels can be used to keep light rugs from curling at the corners. Baste one under each edge

FLOUR

Space can be conserved in the kitchen of a summer cottage if the bread box is mounted underneath one of the shelves. An auxiliary shelf nailed inside the box will accommodate smaller items

Powder puffs can be as useful in the kitchen as they are in the boudoir. A large one placed in the flour canister will come in handy if used to dust flour on the rolling pin and pastry board

IDEAS FOR MOTORISTS

MIRROR

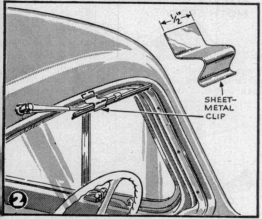

1/2"

SHEET-METAL CLIP

1 **PARKING IS SIMPLIFIED** and damage to tire side walls prevented by a mirror on the right-hand car door. It is tilted to reflect the edge of the running board and curb line. A slight bend should be made in the mirror arm in order to place it below the rim of the door. Fit a setscrew to the ball socket so that the mirror may be locked in position after it is adjusted to the driver's line of vision.—C. L. B.

2 **A WINDSHIELD WIPER** that won't stay up can be held out of the way with a clip made of sheet metal or an annealed piece of clock spring. The clip should be bent as shown, and the flat end pushed or driven up between the glass and the windshield frame. Slip the arm of the blade under the clip when the wiper isn't needed.—A. H. W.

3 **ADD TO YOUR TRAILER'S USEFULNESS** by making a telescoping tongue of two pieces of pipe, one fitting into the other, as shown in the drawing at left below. Holes are bored into the pipes for a good-sized bolt, which serves as a locking pin. Such an arrangement will make your trailer more adaptable for hauling long objects.—A. H. W.

4 **DIM-OUT DRIVING** is a hazardous business. Here's a helpful hint that will be a boon to night drivers. Paint the rear edge of the driver's door solid white so that when the door is being opened the moving white strip will be seen by approaching cars.—D. H.

DRAWINGS BY STEWART ROUSE

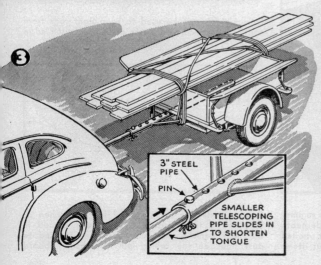

3" STEEL PIPE

PIN

SMALLER TELESCOPING PIPE SLIDES IN TO SHORTEN TONGUE

KEEPING THE HOME

USE WARM KNIFE
TO SEAL EDGES

WAXED
PAPER

Silverware is tarnished by sulphurous gases in the air. To protect it, wrap it in waxed paper and seal the edges of the paper by pressing a hot knife along them so that the wax melts together

Nail-polish remover dabbed on paint marks will serve as an efficient substitute for turpentine. It should be wiped off while it is still wet

UNCORKED
BOTTLE OF
MOTH SPRAY

Fumes evaporating from a bottle of moth spray will keep moths out of a closet. Just place an open bottle of the liquid on one of the shelves

Corset steels can be used to keep light rugs from curling at the corners. Baste one under each edge

FLOUR

Space can be conserved in the kitchen of a summer cottage if the bread box is mounted underneath one of the shelves. An auxiliary shelf nailed inside the box will accommodate smaller items

Powder puffs can be as useful in the kitchen as they are in the boudoir. A large one placed in the flour canister will come in handy if used to dust flour on the rolling pin and pastry board

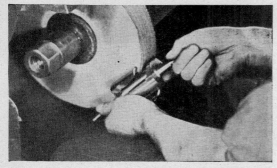

BUFFING OPERATIONS can be simplified if worn buffer disks are cut to half their original diameter and then used as spacers between the disks of new wheels, as shown in the accompanying photographs. The resulting air space between each layer of material causes the cutting compound to dry more quickly. Less compound is used, less pressure is required, and the cutting is much faster. With this method, sunken and intricate surfaces can be much more easily reached without forcing the wheel unduly.—VINCENT A. GUERIN.

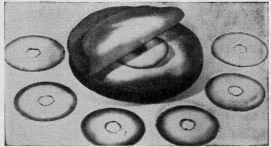

DRAFTSMEN often have trouble in drawing very small circles with an ordinary bow pen. I have found that bending the point toward the pen solves this problem. In drawing very small circles, first prick the center hole with another point; then apply the pen. Using this simple system, one can draw circles as small as 1/32" in diameter and they will still be perfectly accurate.—S. M. TILTON.

the work would be in a vertical position. The grinding wheel on an arbor in the drill chuck rotated in a horizontal plane.

Current from a 6-volt automobile storage battery flowed through a polarity-reversing switch to the magnet. The double-throw switch was wired as shown in the drawing, and although not absolutely necessary, is handy for releasing work instantly.

This improvised magnetic chuck had more than ample holding power for the disk-grinding job. It was found adaptable to various other kinds of grinding and machining on the drill press.

When the magnet was mounted in its final position, the work-holding surface was trued up by taking a light cut over it with the grinding wheel.—WALTER E. BURTON.

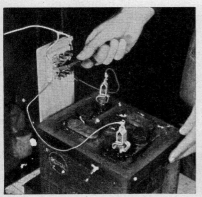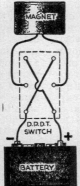

THE PORTABLE BLOWER shown above was made from junked parts by Bill Hesh of Santa Fe, N. M. He used an old ¼-hp. electric motor as the power unit, fitting to it a discarded auto fan. To make a base, he bolted an old axle housing to a brake drum. A large pipe or a portion of a drive shaft would do as well. The motor base was attached to the top of the housing in such a way that it could be tipped up or down. A sheet-metal drum was built around the blades and fitted with guards welded together of rods.

USING THE MODERN RADIAL DRILL
HOW HOLES ARE SPOTTED WITH PRECISION JIGS IN DUPLICATE WORK

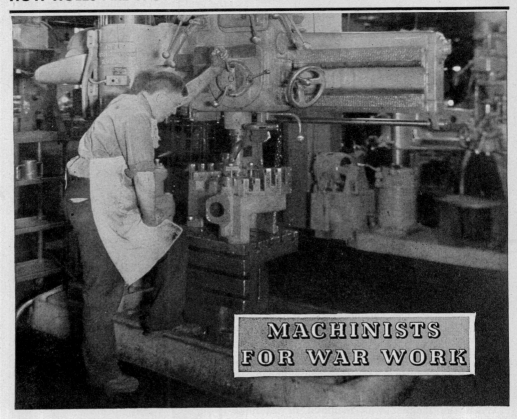

MACHINISTS
FOR WAR WORK

THOUSANDS of American men and women who had not even seen a machine tool a few years ago are today working on production lines with modern equipment that speeds the stocking of our arsenal of democracy. Among these machines for mass production of duplicate work is the radial drill, one type of which is shown in the photograph above. Used with a precision jig, it is capable of drilling and tapping a succession of holes in a metal casting with one clamping of the work. This is particularly valuable where work is too large for moving about and is to be duplicated in thousands of pieces.

One of the chief advantages of the radial drill over the drill press commonly found in home workshops is its horizontal arm, which can be swung radially about its upright standard and carries a spindle that can be slid back and forth on it. It is this move-ment of arm and spindle that permits drilling successive holes without shifting the work.

For precision, and to save the time required to lay out holes individually on each piece, the jig comes into play. This is usually made by an expert toolmaker, who locates, drills, and sometimes grinds the holes that guide the bit into the work. These holes are made to fit a hardened steel bushing, which in turn fits the bit to be used and keeps it from marring the jig. Either the same bushing may be used for all holes, or each hole may be provided with one.

Photographs on the three succeeding pages show the operations in drilling and tapping blind holes on two sides of a cast-steel valve body. They were selected from one of the 35 sound films prepared by the U. S. Office of Education and distributed by Castle Films to Government and industry-fostered schools for war machinists.

1 This is a typical radial-drill job. Several hundred valve bodies are to be drilled for 11 ⅝" tapped, blind holes, top and bottom. These are to be made ⅞" deep with a 17/32" tap drill

2 With the arm swung out of the way for safety, the operator cleans the table of dirt, chips, and burrs. This will keep the holes straight and will prevent breaking the bit during the drilling

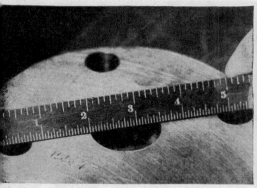

3 When he receives the drill jig, the operator checks the number to see that it corresponds to the one ordered for the job, and as an added precaution he also measures the holes in the jig

4 Next, the operator places the valve body on the table, being careful to avoid damage. He fits the jig to the work and clamps both securely to the table with two hold-down clamps and blocks

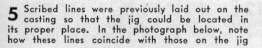
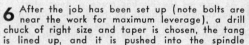

5 Scribed lines were previously laid out on the casting so that the jig could be located in its proper place. In the photograph below, note how these lines coincide with those on the jig

6 After the job has been set up (note bolts are near the work for maximum leverage), a drill chuck of right size and taper is chosen, the tang is lined up, and it is pushed into the spindle

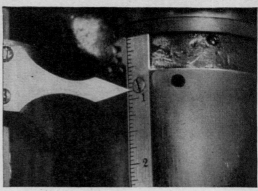

7 The correct size tap drill is next selected and set into a friction chuck, which puts a limited torque on the bit while it is running in the casting. This prevents breakage if it jams

8 Since the blind holes in the casting are to be drilled ⅞" deep, the spindle stop on the drill head is set at ⅞" on the scale in order to arrest the feed automatically at that depth

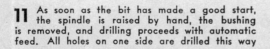

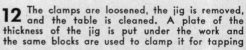

9 Reference to the handbook shows cast steel should be drilled at 350 r.p.m. when a 17/32" high-speed drill is used, and feed should be .007" per revolution. Gears are set for these rates

10 With a hardened bushing on the bit and resting on the jig, the drill head is moved about until the bushing drops into a hole. Arm and head are locked, and drilling is begun with hand feed

11 As soon as the bit has made a good start, the spindle is raised by hand, the bushing is removed, and drilling proceeds with automatic feed. All holes on one side are drilled this way

12 The clamps are loosened, the jig is removed, and the table is cleaned. A plate of the thickness of the jig is put under the work and the same blocks are used to clamp it for tapping

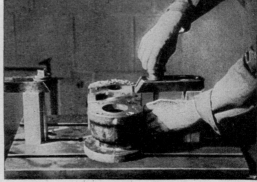

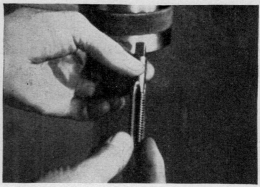

13 Burrs are filed, and each hole is carefully cleared of chips. This may be done with a piece of magnetized steel. It is dangerous to blow chips from the holes with shop air pressure

14 A tap of the size and shape required for the job is then selected. This is used with a friction chuck, which will slip if the hole loads with chips, and will keep the tap from breaking

15 With the drill arm and head loosened, they are shifted until the tap centers itself in the hole; then they are clamped. In tapping, the spindle is fed by hand, not by the automatic feed

16 Tapping in clear plastic shows the cutting action. Chips form in the flutes and drop down in the hole. The tap must be backed out for occasional removal of these in tapping blind holes

17 This view from the bottom of the plastic shows how chips curl in the flutes, slowing the tap and making rough threads. They may be broken loose by backing up the tap a half turn

18 When tapping on one side is completed, burrs are filed off, the table is cleaned, and the casting is turned over. All steps in drilling and tapping are then repeated for the second face

Watch Those Bearings

TO KEEP SHOP MACHINES ON THE JOB

By JOHN MODROCH

THE first requisite of efficient bearing maintenance is proper lubrication. Bearings are built to run in high-quality lubricants that are free from alkali or any other ingredients that might be injurious to the metal parts. Oil and grease are most commonly used.

Hand oiling should be done sparingly before the machinery is put in motion. Cold bearings do not absorb oil readily, and the excess is therefore thrown out for the first few revolutions. Thorough oiling by hand can be done after the machinery has been running for a while and the bearings are warm.

Belt guards should be made of wire netting or some similar material in order that the bearings under them may be seen and also to provide ventilation. Check the performance of newly installed bearings with and without a full driving load. Bearings should run only warm—never hot. Smoke, a burning smell, or a rattling noise is a danger signal. If you notice any one of these, stop the machine as quickly as possible and oil the bearings thoroughly while turning the shaft by hand. Wait until the bearings cool before starting the machine again. A slipping belt may also be a sign of a binding bearing.

Belts should be no tighter than is necessary for positive traction. As a rule, V-belts require less tension than flat belts to prevent slipping. Because canvas belts have a tendency to contract or stretch under certain weather conditions, they should be checked for proper tension frequently.

YOU CAN HELP KEEP PRODUCTION ROLLING BY FOLLOWING

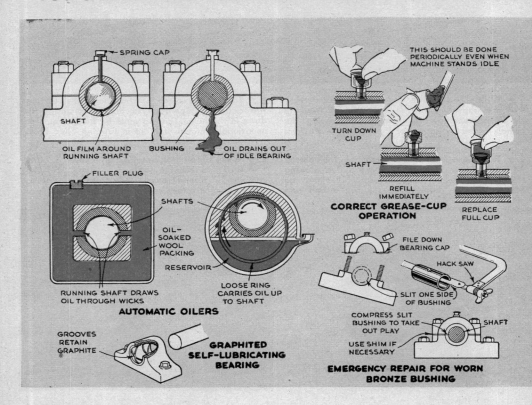

SPRING CAP

SHAFT

OIL FILM AROUND RUNNING SHAFT

BUSHING

OIL DRAINS OUT OF IDLE BEARING

FILLER PLUG

SHAFTS

OIL-SOAKED WOOL PACKING

RESERVOIR

RUNNING SHAFT DRAWS OIL THROUGH WICKS

LOOSE RING CARRIES OIL UP TO SHAFT

AUTOMATIC OILERS

GROOVES RETAIN GRAPHITE

GRAPHITED SELF-LUBRICATING BEARING

THIS SHOULD BE DONE PERIODICALLY EVEN WHEN MACHINE STANDS IDLE

TURN DOWN CUP

SHAFT

REFILL IMMEDIATELY

CORRECT GREASE-CUP OPERATION

REPLACE FULL CUP

FILE DOWN BEARING CAP

HACK SAW

SLIT ONE SIDE OF BUSHING

COMPRESS SLIT BUSHING TO TAKE OUT PLAY

SHAFT

USE SHIM IF NECESSARY

EMERGENCY REPAIR FOR WORN BRONZE BUSHING

THESE PRACTICAL POINTERS ON BEARING MAINTENANCE

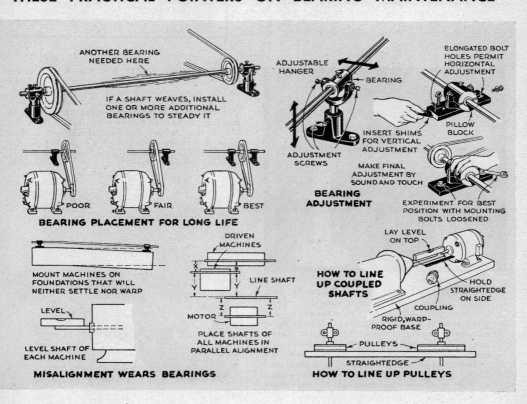

ANOTHER BEARING NEEDED HERE

IF A SHAFT WEAVES, INSTALL ONE OR MORE ADDITIONAL BEARINGS TO STEADY IT

POOR   FAIR   BEST

BEARING PLACEMENT FOR LONG LIFE

ADJUSTABLE HANGER   BEARING

ELONGATED BOLT HOLES PERMIT HORIZONTAL ADJUSTMENT

INSERT SHIMS FOR VERTICAL ADJUSTMENT

PILLOW BLOCK

ADJUSTMENT SCREWS

MAKE FINAL ADJUSTMENT BY SOUND AND TOUCH

BEARING ADJUSTMENT

EXPERIMENT FOR BEST POSITION WITH MOUNTING BOLTS LOOSENED

MOUNT MACHINES ON FOUNDATIONS THAT WILL NEITHER SETTLE NOR WARP

LEVEL

LEVEL SHAFT OF EACH MACHINE

DRIVEN MACHINES

LINE SHAFT

MOTOR

PLACE SHAFTS OF ALL MACHINES IN PARALLEL ALIGNMENT

MISALIGNMENT WEARS BEARINGS

LAY LEVEL ON TOP

HOW TO LINE UP COUPLED SHAFTS

HOLD STRAIGHTEDGE ON SIDE

COUPLING

RIGID, WARP-PROOF BASE

PULLEYS

STRAIGHTEDGE

HOW TO LINE UP PULLEYS

AIDS TO WARTIME
Housekeeping

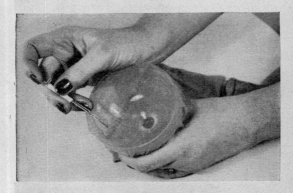

PAPER is now used as a substitute for some of the critical war materials. The clock case shown above is made of a cellulose fiber treated so that it is impervious to humidity. Below, burlap made of tightly twisted kraft paper is both flame and water resistant. It is being used in wrapping airplane parts

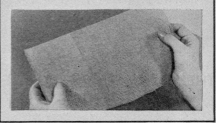

AUTOMATIC HOSE MENDER. This convenient gadget reknits runs in hosiery and lingerie with the same stitch as the original. It uses no thread and is said to be extremely simple to learn to operate. The stocking is placed over a small glass, and thus held firm and taut while it is being mended

SHOES CAN BE WATERPROOFED with a liquid that also lubricates the leather. It can be used on all shoes or boots that will take a polish, as well as on many other types of leather goods. One treatment is said to waterproof a pair of shoes permanently, but in order to lengthen the life of the leather, the fluid should be applied more than once. Shoes must be allowed to dry overnight, after they have been thoroughly coated with the liquid, before they are given a polish

THESE BATTERY LAMPS are convenient for children's rooms, tents, camps, porches, farm buildings, dim-outs, and for emergency use when electric power fails. They work on three standard flashlight cells. Both styles shown are 15" in height, with 9" shades. Bases and shades are enameled white and are available in both a plain and a handsome gilt-decorated finish. Both shades are mounted on swivels so that they can be adjusted to any angle

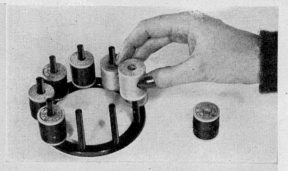

COMBINATION SPOOL AND TIE RACK. Made of plastic, this rack measures 4½" in diameter and will easily fit into a sewing basket or drawer. The nine prongs are 2" high, and each one will hold two spools of thread. Several holes drilled around the base of the rack permit it to be mounted in a convenient place on the wall, where it may be used for holding ties or belts. Color choice is red, green, or blue

HOUSEHOLD LABELS, 500 of them designed to meet virtually all household labeling needs, are contained in the handy book shown in the photo below. Included are labels for canning, mailing, marking photographs, storing boxes, and many special types. The book is 7" by 10". All the labels are gummed and perforated

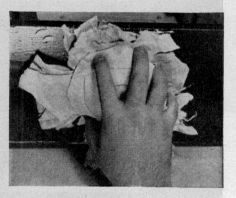

A CHAMOIS SPONGE has been developed that has many uses both as a chamois and as a sponge. It is ideal for washing windows, mirrors, furniture, painted walls, automobiles, carpets, and for all general household use. Small pieces of oil-tanned chamois are sewed together in a cluster to make this durable sponge, which is thoroughly washed and all ready for use. No breaking in is necessary. It is available in two convenient sizes

LIQUID METAL CLEANER. Especially made for cleaning kitchen utensils, this fluid is said to do the work of steel wool. It may be used on aluminum, brass, stainless-steel alloys, chromium, bronze, porcelain, and copper. A sponge or cloth is moistened with the cleaner and the metal is rubbed gently until thoroughly cleaned. Nonpoisonous, the fluid may be used safely on both the insides and outsides of pots and pans. It is put up in Victory cans and comes in two handy sizes for everyday household use

Photography

Silhouettes

ADD DRAMA TO YOUR PICTURES

By James Wong Howe, A.S.C.

Jimmy Howe, an American-born Chinese, for the past 20 years has been a first cameraman, filming among some 100 features such recent pictures as "Air Force" and "The Hard Way." "The North Star," a story of Russia, is now unfolding before his camera on the Samuel Goldwyn lot.

SILHOUETTES and shadows are a magic formula for putting punch into both home movies and still pictures. We use silhouettes and shadows in professional movies to introduce characters, obtain dramatic effects, and establish moods.

How do you go about making silhouettes, both outdoors and in? Unlike the usual shot in which you expose for the shadows and shoot away from or across the light, silhouettes demand that you catch your subject when it is in shadow. You expose for the brilliant background, deliberately underexposing the main subject. The result is a sharp black-and-white contrast and an effective picture.

Many outdoor silhouettes are made at dawn and sunset. When doing this, take a low camera position and pose your subject against the sky or on a slight rise to obtain the necessary elevation. Make sure the sun is beyond or behind the subject, but do not permit direct rays of the sun to reach the lens. Frequently, especially when the sun is low, you may have your subject directly between the camera and the sun, thus shading the lens.

For a silhouette, you will be photographing only the outline of your subject, which should be in full profile, either front, side, or rear. Elements of action may be added. The photograph on page HW 291 of a horse and rider etched against the ocean is an excellent example of a pictorial silhouette.

To illustrate how much the exposure must be cut down for silhouettes, a normal exposure for this scene would have been 1/25 second at f/8, but for the silhouette the shot was made at 1/100 second at f/22. Had the background been land, the proper stop would have been f/16 at 1/100 second. This picture is a good silhouette because it includes foreground reflection, which adds depth and draws attention to the center of interest. The swish of the tail and the raised foreleg add action. Back lighting gives form to the ripples on the water.

There are countless subjects which make good silhouettes. Have you ever noticed cattle standing on the crest of a hill, or a pretty girl leaning against a tree? Or trees alone, etched against the sky? All make excellent silhouettes. Sunrises are usually too brilliant to permit direct photography, but sub-

jects accompanied by a dusky rose sky and clouds aflame with yellow fire offer dramatic picture opportunities. Pose your subjects directly against the sky, or against a sparkling background of water such as a river or lake. Remember, too, that if you can look directly into the sun without glare, so can your camera. At such times, try shooting directly into the light.

Although you may be accustomed to thinking of silhouettes in terms of outdoor photography, you can take effective pictures of this type indoors against a sheet or a brilliantly lighted wall. Crisp black silhouettes against white backgrounds will

serve a variety of purposes in home movies and also make stills worthy of inclusion in your album.

For example, let's say your young son has acquired a new bat and ball. He will be eager to show them off. Stretch a white sheet smoothly across a hall archway and at a distance of 8' from the opposite side place twin reflector lamps facing the sheet. Pose the boy 2' in front of the sheet in a batting stance, hanging the ball from a thin white thread. Remember that he is to be on the camera side of the sheet.

Proper exposure for this picture depends upon the speed of the film you are using. If you wish, take a light-meter reading on the sheet, and expose for that bright area. With No. 1 photofloods or strong household lights in reflectors, the stop on a movie camera will vary from f/5.6 for comparatively slow films to f/8 for fast films.

A similar result can be achieved if you place two flood bulbs in cardboard reflectors and direct their light against a white wall. Be sure to keep the rest of the room as dark

as possible. Pose the subject in front of the bright spot on the wall as you would against the sun or sky outdoors. Snapshots of excellent quality may be made in this way at 1/25 second with the lens stopped to f/16.

All sorts of interesting compositions and poses may be arranged. Your small daughter can pour tea for a friend, or read to her doll from a book. Try pasting cardboard cut-outs of the moon and stars, or story-book characters and animals, on the sheet. As a party suggestion, why not photograph the guests against the sheet with cut-outs representing the season, such as popping champagne bottles and corks for New Year's Eve, or turkeys for Thanksgiving? Both you and your guests will get much pleasure from such pictures, made either as stills or home movies.

Silhouettes also present an effective means of introducing your characters in a home movie. Suppose you wish to present, "A Typical Day at the Jones Home." Who are the Joneses? Dad, in profile, pipe in mouth;

little sister, doll in arm; brother, full face to accentuate his big ears; and mother, hair fluffed, profile or full face.

As an interesting alternative to still silhouettes in home movies, try photographing the shadows of people against a wall. This offers the advantage of allowing your subjects to move around, thus giving action to the scenes.

Combinations of silhouettes and shadows will add zip to a movie, especially if you wish to develop a threatening, dramatic sequence. Place your subject at one edge of the lighted wall about 4' from the camera, and have a shadow from an assailant, or perhaps only a hand holding a gun, cast upon the wall from 10' away. By this means, your audience sees virtually two actors as your character reacts to a threat represented by the shadow.

Similarly, to introduce a comedy character such as a gossipy neighbor, open the movie scene with a profile silhouette through a window shade. Your audience sees it as a window profile framing two lips moving rapidly. Suddenly the shade flies up and the face appears, well lighted, chattering like a magpie. You'll need a little help doing this. As the shade moves up while you are taking the picture, have an assistant snap off the silhouetting light and turn on front lights. This must be done at just the right moment so that there will be no noticeable change in the lighting either before or after the face appears.

These suggestions will give you other ideas for interesting and dramatic effects that can be added to your pictures. Remember, however, that silhouettes may be overdone, especially in movies. Being underexposed, they produce effective photography, but shadows tend to become theatrical. In still photography each picture stands alone on its own merits; in movies, the use of silhouettes and shadows should be related to the picture as a whole. In both fields, silhouettes offer many interesting opportunities, and they are fun to make.

A RUBBER SUCTION CUP attached to a photographic thermometer by a rubber band will hold the thermometer upright in a tray so that it can be read easily. In mounting the thermometer this way, cut away a little of the shank of the suction cup so as to expose the thermometer bulb to the solution in the tray. This will make possible a true reading.—HARRY RADZINSKY.

DARKROOM SCALES should always be protected from dust and moisture, as these may cause friction or corrode the delicate mechanism. A simple safeguard is to place a cardboard box over the scales, as shown in the photo above. Be sure that the box is large enough so that it will not come in contact with the mechanism.—LOUIS HOCHMAN.

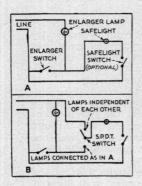

ENLARGER SWITCH CONTROLS SAFELIGHT AUTOMATICALLY

IN FOCUSING an enlarger, it is easier to obtain a bright image on the easel if the safelight is turned off. The wiring diagram *A* at the left shows how an enlarger lamp and safelight may be connected together so that the latter will go out automatically when the enlarger is switched on. A 100- or 150-watt enlarger bulb will pass enough current to energize the safelight without emitting light itself. When one switch is closed, the enlarger bulb lights and the safelight goes out. A second optional switch is for turning off the safelight at other times.

The diagram *B* at the left shows connections for both automatic and independent control. Two switches are connected as in *A*, but a double-throw switch allows the safelight to burn independently.

EXPOSURES WITH HOME LAMPS   [PHOTOGRAPHY]

BECAUSE the supply of flash and flood lamps for civilian uses is much curtailed, the following exposure table for taking indoor pictures with ordinary home-lighting bulbs will prove useful. Many photographic results are superior when less light and longer exposures are used.

This exposure table is based on the use of extra fast panchromatic films and white-lined cardboard reflectors. The next larger lens opening should be used for films of medium speed, and the second larger opening, or four times the exposure, for slow films. Box cameras should be considered as having a lens stop of f/16.

If the walls of the room are a dark color, use one lens opening larger. The smaller of the two lamps should be used as a camera light pointed directly at the subject, the larger lamp being used as a side light placed at 45 deg. to the camera axis, and 2' higher. Both lamps should be the same distance from the subject.

		Exposures in Seconds	
Distance of lamps to subject in feet	Lens Opening	One 60-watt One 100-watt	One 100-watt One 200-watt
3½	f/4.5	1/10	1/25
	f/6.3	1/5	1/25
	f/8	1/5	1/10
	f/11	1/2	1/5
	f/16	1	1/2
5	f/4.5	1/5	1/10
	f/6.3	1/5	1/10
	f/8	1/2	1/5
	f/11	1	1/2
	f/16	2	1
8	f/4.5	1/2	1/5
	f/6.3	1	1/5
	f/8	1	1/2
	f/11	2	1
	f/16	4	2

SIMPLIFIED UNIT MAKES IDENTIFICATION PHOTOS

THE wartime need for identification photos prompted the building of this simplified unit, which can readily be operated even by persons unfamiliar with photography.

A cabinet containing a fixed camera and brackets supporting two No. 1 flood lamps and reflectors is fastened to a wall. The height of the camera above the floor is the average height of a person's face.

Two brackets with ordinary half-round reflectors were cut down from regular drafting-table lamps. Although the reflectors are adjustable as to position and direction, they are set properly once and then merely swung into and out of the cabinet without changing the adjustment. To give better lighting, one lamp is above eye level and one below, the lower reflector being screened with

This photographic unit is so arranged and adjusted that any personnel employee can take good pictures

Film packs are used because exposed films can be removed separately for convenience

white tracing cloth. A buff roller shade is pulled down from the ceiling behind the subject.

The fixed camera is a wooden box built for a 10.5 cm., f/4.5 lens and shutter taken from an old 2¼" by 3¼" camera. Film packs are used so that any exposed negatives can be removed one at a time for developing and printing without wasting film. Small 1⅝" by 2½" packs are used, as the rather long and narrow shape compensates for the varying heights of subjects.

Before the lens board of the camera box was fastened in place, a ground glass was inserted where the film pack fits and the camera focused for the size of image desired. With the camera illustrated, the distance from lens to film is 5", and the distance from lens to subject is 53". The lens board was then fastened in the camera box, and the camera held in place on a shelf in the cabinet with short dowels. The lens is stopped at f/9, and the shutter set at 1/25 second.

Such a camera is inexpensive to build, and the use of a lens with a comparatively long focus eliminates the "fattening" effect so common in close-ups made with the average small camera. The back of the camera opens on hinges to release the film pack. All of the joints must fit tightly so as to prevent any light leaks, and the camera should be painted black inside. The dimensions of the camera box will be governed by the size of the film pack used and the thickness of the stock used in making the box. As shown in the accompanying photographs, the front of the top is cut away to accommodate the shutter-setting dial and cable release.—WILLARD ALLPHIN.

ELECTRONIC PHOTO TIMER

YOU'LL find in the radio-parts junk box most of the material you need to build this useful interval timer. It can be set to shut off a printing or enlarging lamp after exposures of from 2 to 56 seconds, and all subsequent exposures at the same setting will be uniform. For longer exposures, the original interval can be repeated by pushing the button again. The circuit will work with almost any two tubes, or with any one of a variety of twin-element tubes. Tubes no longer fit for radio use will do provided the filaments are good.

Much as a sand glass keeps track of time by allowing sand to trickle from a reservoir through a tiny opening, so this electronic timer allows electrons to trickle from a reservoir (a condenser) through a tiny opening (a high resistance). A 4-mfd. condenser is charged by the rectifier unit when the push button is pressed, and the charge leaks out slowly through a variable resistor across the condenser.

As long as the condenser is charged, it puts its full negative potential of about 150 volts on the grid of the amplifier. This heavy negative bias on the grid blocks the plate current in the tube completely, and the relay opens, closing the upper contact that turns on the enlarger or other device. As the charge on the condenser gradually drains off through the variable resistance, the volt-

By JOHN W. CAMPBELL, JR.

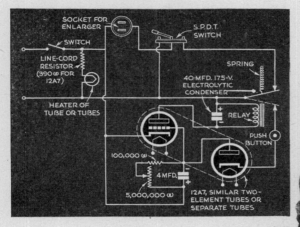

Above is a diagram of the wiring hookup. Be sure to use a suitable line-cord resistor. Below, an inside view of the timer is shown

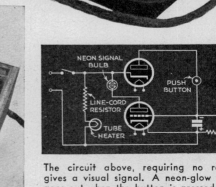

The circuit above, requiring no relay, gives a visual signal. A neon-glow bulb goes out when the button is pressed and lights again when the set time is up

Built from Old Radio Parts

age falls and eventually drops below the cut-off bias of the tube. The tube becomes conductive once more, and the relay is energized, opening the enlarger circuit.

The essential parts are a rectifier tube, any type of grid-controlled tube, a high-quality bank of paper condensers, a high variable resistor of the volume-control type, a push button, and a relay.

Paper condensers from the power pack of an old-type receiver are by far the best. Electrolytic condensers will not do, as they cannot hold a charge more than a few seconds. The condensers are the critical parts of the system.

The original timer shown used a 4-mfd. paper condenser, a 5-megohm variable resistance, and a 12A7 tube. A 100,000-ohm protective resistance in series with the variable resistance prevents it from short-circuiting the condensers and rectifier when set at zero, and makes the minimum time about 1¼ seconds.

The 12A7 tube is not the best for the purpose. It takes 13 volts grid bias to cut off the plate current in that tube; therefore, when the condensers fall to 13 volts, the relay closes. A tube that cuts off the plate current at 3 volts would give a time interval of about 80 seconds with the same resistance and condensers. A 6J7 or 6SJ7 tube would serve nicely as the grid-controlled element.

The 40-mfd. electrolytic condenser across the relay delays the opening of the latter long enough after the button is pressed to permit the paper condensers to reach full charge, and, in addition, prevents relay chatter.

If a pentode-type, grid-controlled tube is used, it is simply connected as a triode, with its screen grid connected to its plate. The rectifier tube can be any type—for example, a pentode with control grid tied to cathode and screen grid tied to plate will serve. A single twin-unit tube can be used *provided the two units in the tube have separate cathodes.*

An old audio transformer can be converted into an efficient, heavy-duty relay for use with this rig. Simply unbolt the core pieces and rearrange them to make an E-shaped, 3-pole electromagnet. This can be done with some cores merely by lifting off one section; those composed entirely of E-shaped laminations are converted by reversing half of these to match the other half.

Use only the primary winding of the transformer. The armature is fitted with contact points from an old buzzer, phone jack, or some similar device. A spring normally lifts it off the magnet. The double-throw switch shown enables one to turn on the enlarger as long as desired for focusing.

WINDING HEATING ELEMENTS [ELECTRICAL]

Electric heating elements are usually made from coiled nickel-chromium resistance wire. The following table gives the necessary data for winding the wire on arbors of various sizes.

	PER INCH OF CLOSE-WOUND COIL							
	3/32" arbor		⅛" arbor		3/16" arbor		¼" arbor	
B. & S. Ga.	Feet	Ohms	Feet	Ohms	Feet	Ohms	Feet	Ohms
16	.77	.19	.94	.23	1.29	.32	1.56	.39
17	.83	.26	1.02	.33	1.43	.46	1.76	.56
18	.90	.36	1.11	.45	1.56	.63	2.00	.81
19	.97	.47	1.21	.61	1.72	.86	2.22	1.11
20	1.06	.67	1.33	.84	1.91	1.21	2.50	1.59
21	1.15	.93	1.46	1.17	2.11	1.69	2.80	2.44
22	1.27	1.29	1.62	1.65	2.36	2.40	3.16	3.21
23	1.40	1.78	1.78	2 27	2.65	3.37	3.53	4.50
24	1.55	2.49	2.00	3.22	3.00	4.83	3.93	6.35
25	1.72	3.50	2.22	4.50	3.30	6.70	4.48	9.10
26	1.91	4.92	2.48	6.38	3.71	9.54	5.00	12.85
27	2.13	6.88	2.75	8.88	4.17	13.45	5.66	18.30
28	2.38	9.75	3.12	12.80	4.55	18.63	6.53	26.70

TO USE this table, measure the space available for the coiled wire and estimate the desired wattage. From a table that gives the length and size of resistance wire for the wattage desired, select the size best suited, using the middle size wherever possible. Coiled wire may be stretched from 1½ to 4 times closed coil length. If the space will take a longer coil than the middle size, try using the next size wire.

Example: a 750-watt element with space 37" long is to be wound on a ⅛" arbor. You will find that sizes from No. 18 to No. 22 could be used. The middle size is No. 20, which takes 23.6' of straight wire. Divide 23.6 by 1.33, which results in 17.7' of close-coiled wire. The element space is 37" long, so it would be stretched a little over twice its length, which is satisfactory.

POPULAR SCIENCE MONTHLY SHOP DATA

Giant transformers like these are used for stepping up voltage in long-distance transmission of power

HOW ELECTRONS WORK

FIRST STEPS IN ELECTRONICS

By CHARLES I. HELLMAN

WHEN it was once learned that magnetism could be produced with electricity, scientists strove to do the converse—that is, to produce electricity with magnetism. Michael Faraday successfully performed the first experiments that generated an induced current, which we today know as a flow of electrons. This Faraday experiment is shown in Fig. 1.

A coil of wire containing many turns is connected to a galvanometer. When a bar magnet is thrust into the coil, the galvanometer needle swings aside, indicating that an electric current has been produced in the coil. When the magnet is withdrawn, the needle swings to the opposite side, showing that a current of opposite direction has been produced, or that the current has been reversed. This process of producing an electric current—of setting electrons in motion—by

means of a varying magnetic field is called *electromagnetic induction.*

It is possible to increase induced voltage by using a coil with more turns, by strengthening the magnetic field, by moving the magnet faster, or by a combination of the three. In the huge dynamos that generate A.C. from the motive power supplied by water wheels or steam turbines, there are coils with many hundreds of turns, extremely powerful electromagnets, and a high relative speed between the two.

Another tremendously important application of the principles of induction is found in transformers, which are an integral part of power-supply systems. A transformer, shown in simplified form in Fig. 2 and in cross section in Fig. 3, consists of two separate coils—the primary and the secondary—wound on an iron core. When A.C. is sent through the primary, a magnetic field is set up. This magnetic field, varying in both intensity and direction, travels through the core and into the secondary coil, inducing a voltage in it. The process of inducing a voltage from one circuit to another is called *mutual induction*.

One of the greatest advantages of a transformer is its ability to step A.C. voltage up or down by the use of the proper ratio of turns on the primary and secondary coils. If the secondary has more turns than the primary, the induced voltage in the secondary will be greater than that applied to the primary, and vice versa.

A transformer is not limited to two windings. It may have, for instance, a primary and a number of secondaries. Such types are used in radios to furnish both high voltage for the operation of vacuum-tube plate circuits and low voltage to heat the tube filaments.

Electrical power is most efficiently transmitted over long distances if it is kept at high voltage and low current. The output of the dynamo at the generator station is stepped up by transformers to meet these transmission requirements and stepped down again for application at the receiving end.

Self-induction, occurring when a varying flow of electrons is sent through a coil, is defined as the cutting of a wire by the lines of force flowing through it. When the wire is cut by this expanding magnetic field, a momentary electromotive force (E.M.F.) opposed to the applied one is induced. If the flow through the wire is stopped, the mag-netic field collapses, again cutting the wire, but this time in the opposite direction. When a changing electronic flow in a coil causes changing magnetism in the core, this latter in turn induces a flow of electrons in the coil itself. As long as the flow in the coil increases, the lines of magnetic force increase, and electron movement set up in the coil will be in opposition to that producing the magnetism.

Since the counter electromotive force (C.E.M.F.) of self-induction opposes any change in the flow passing through a coil, inductance produces an effect that is the electrical equivalent of *inertia*. Just as the inertia of an automobile becomes most apparent when an attempt is made to start or stop, so electrical inertia shows its presence when an electronic flow is varied in intensity.

The reaction of a coil against the increase in the flow of electrons through it is known as *inductive reactance*. Coils that have as their main function reaction against these changes are called choke coils.

Self-inductance shows itself by the presence of an induced voltage due to a varying current, and the unit of self-inductance, known as the henry, has been defined as the value of inductance that produces an induced E.M.F. of 1 volt when the current through it varies uniformly at the rate of 1 amp. per second. Since some devices, espe-

WITHIN WIRE COILS

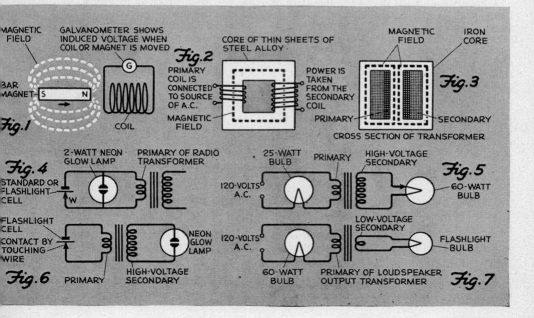

MAGNETIC FIELD
GALVANOMETER SHOWS INDUCED VOLTAGE WHEN COIL OR MAGNET IS MOVED
Fig.2
CORE OF THIN SHEETS OF STEEL ALLOY
MAGNETIC FIELD
IRON CORE

BAR MAGNET — S N
PRIMARY COIL IS CONNECTED TO SOURCE OF A.C.
POWER IS TAKEN FROM THE SECONDARY COIL
Fig.3

Fig.1
COIL
MAGNETIC FIELD
PRIMARY
SECONDARY

CROSS SECTION OF TRANSFORMER

Fig.4
2-WATT NEON GLOW LAMP
PRIMARY OF RADIO TRANSFORMER
25-WATT BULB
PRIMARY
HIGH-VOLTAGE SECONDARY
Fig.5

STANDARD OR FLASHLIGHT CELL
120-VOLTS A.C.
60-WATT BULB

FLASHLIGHT CELL
NEON GLOW LAMP
120-VOLTS A.C.
LOW-VOLTAGE SECONDARY
FLASHLIGHT BULB

CONTACT BY TOUCHING WIRE

Fig.6
PRIMARY
HIGH-VOLTAGE SECONDARY
60-WATT BULB
PRIMARY OF LOUDSPEAKER OUTPUT TRANSFORMER
Fig.7

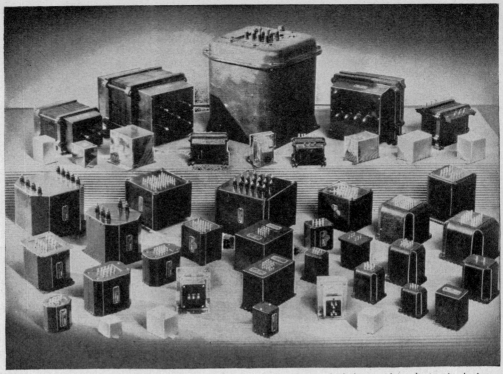

These are just some of the many forms of iron-core transformers and chokes used in electronic devices

cially in radio, have small inductance values, the millihenry, or 0.001 henry, and the microhenry, or 0.000001 henry, are frequently employed.

A 2-watt neon bulb shows the intensity of the E.M.F. of self-induction in an interesting experiment. Plug the bulb into a 120-volt lighting socket, and it will glow normally. Connect it across an ordinary dry cell, and it will not glow at all. This shows that the bulb requires a voltage considerably above the 1.5 volts delivered by the dry cell.

Now place the bulb in the circuit shown in Fig. 4. Connect the wire W to the dry cell; then remove it suddenly. One plate of the neon bulb will glow momentarily, indicating the application of a high voltage. This voltage is produced by the sudden drop of the electronic flow through the primary of the transformer. The resulting decrease of the magnetic field through the coil produces a high E.M.F. of self-induction.

That the transformer transfers power, but does not create it, is shown by the experiment in Fig. 5. A 25-watt lamp is used to indicate how much primary current flows. It glows dimly when no load is applied to the secondary. When a 60-watt bulb is placed across the secondary as a load, the bulb in the primary circuit glows brightly, indi-

cating that the primary is drawing more power in order to supply the output.

To show mutual induction, connect a neon bulb to the high-voltage secondary of a receiver transformer as in Fig. 6. If the connection of the primary to the dry cell is broken quickly, the neon bulb will flash, and it will do so whenever this primary circuit is broken. Electrical power is transferred by mutual induction from the primary to the secondary and is stepped up in the process.

An output transformer that may be obtained from an old receiver can be used as a step-down transformer. The primary leads are connected to the 120-volt A.C. leads through the 60-watt bulb (Fig. 7). The secondary output is about 2 volts and may be used when a low A.C. voltage is needed at approximately 1 amp. The exact voltage may be found by using an A.C. voltmeter, or by trying several flashlight bulbs of different voltages. Try all the bulbs, starting with the one of the highest voltage. If a 2.5-volt bulb, for example, glows brightly, the output voltage is about 2.5 volts.

This little transformer is useful for operating buzzers, lighting flashlight bulbs, and the like. The 60-watt bulb is a protective device in case the transformer is defective or improperly wired.

Servicing Your Radio

LEADS on replacement transformers, color-coded in much the way that condensers and resistors are coded, save about 50 percent of the soldering time required for parts furnished only with lugs. Below are some of the colors usually found on the leads of power, I.F., output, and audio transformers. All manufacturers do not adhere to a standard form of color code for their products, however, so it is advisable to check the part first with an ohmmeter to make sure that the color code has been used.

POWER TRANSFORMERS have at least 11 leads. On the standard 110-120 volt type, the primary winding has two black leads; the tapped secondary to the rectifier-tube plates, two red and one red-yellow; the tapped secondary to the rectifier-tube heater, two yellow, one yellow-blue; and to the amplifier-tube heaters, two green and one green-yellow. The two-tone leads are the taps.

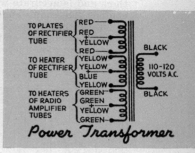

Power Transformer

I.F. TRANSFORMERS are simpler. The primary winding has a blue lead connecting to the tube plate and a red to the B+, while from the secondary a green lead connects to either the grid or diode of the following tube and the black to either the A.V.C. or ground. Where there is a tapped secondary winding, such as in a detector stage employing full-wave diodes, the lead is usually green-black.

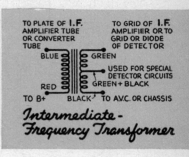

Intermediate-Frequency Transformer

OUTPUT TRANSFORMERS have a blue lead from the primary to the power-tube plate and a red to the B+ of the power-output tube, while for push-pull there is an extra blue lead to the plate of the other output tube used. The secondary to an electrodynamic-speaker voice coil has two or more leads, and the code varies, but the two leads from the speaker field are usually black-red and yellow-red.

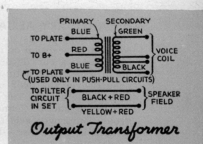

Output Transformer

AUDIO TRANSFORMERS are color-coded almost universally. A blue lead connects the primary to the plate of the preceding audio amplifier or detector tube and a red to the B+, while a green lead connects the secondary to the grid and a black to either the "C" bias or chassis. If there is a push-pull tube, a second blue lead connects to its plate and a yellow on the secondary connects to its grid.

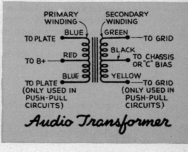

Audio Transformer

HW 299

radio ideas

THIS RADIO SLIDE RULE may be used to solve problems in reactance calculations and is accurate within 2 percent. It enables electronics engineers to calculate in one setting of the slide resonance frequency, capacitive and inductive resistance, dissipation factor, and coil "Q."

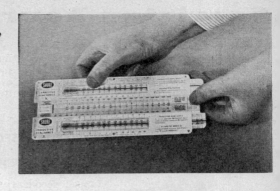

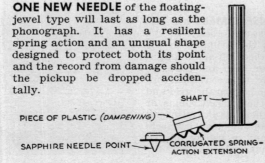

AN AUXILIARY AERIAL can be built with suction cups to fasten on an auto window for better reception on an ordinary portable used inside a car. Two frames are made of piano wire. One, acting as a condenser, is hooked over the door containing the built-in portable aerial. The other is attached to the car window. Connecting wire *A* to a ground improves selection when the radio is used in the house.—LARRY RUFFNER, JR.

ONE NEW NEEDLE of the floating-jewel type will last as long as the phonograph. It has a resilient spring action and an unusual shape designed to protect both its point and the record from damage should the pickup be dropped accidentally.

A HATCHET SOLDERING IRON is said to give better balance and to be less tiring for the operator on many soldering operations. Incorporating all the features of plug-tip irons, it has in addition a special device in the shaft which keeps the handle cool even when the iron is used for long periods at a time. These irons are available in sizes of 80, 100, 150, 175, and 200 watts. Each comes complete with a metal stand, and all elements are replaceable.

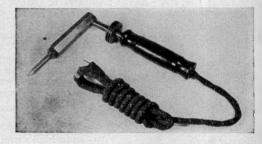

MINIATURE CERAMIC SOCKETS have been developed for use on ultrahigh frequencies with the 9000 series of miniature tubes and the 1S4 type. The sockets have contact points of heavily silver-plated phosphor bronze and are self-aligning so that they receive the tiny prongs without danger of fracturing the glass base of a tube when it is being inserted. The contacts can be oriented for minimum capacity effect.

. C. Motor Develops Full Torque at All Speeds

TEP pulleys and gear reductions may be largely eliminated from the machine op and factory of tomorrow, thanks to an justable-speed A.C. motor developed by rof. A. G. Conrad, S. D. Smith, and P. F. rdung, of Yale University. This revolunary motor, perfected after three years of search, affords a wide choice of speeds th practically constant torque—something therto possible only by combining an A.C. otor, a D.C. generator, a D.C. motor, and exciter in a complicated and costly okup unsuitable for general use.

With the new motor, which is powered om three-phase A.C. lines, a knob that can operated with one hand provides comete speed control from a standstill to the aximum speed for which the motor is deaned. The same control can be used to verse the motor or to obin a braking action to quickreduce the speed of the mainery driven. In the latter se the motor acts as a genator due to a reversal of the wer component of the armure current.

High starting torque makes possible to accelerate heavy loads readily, yet the armature currents at starting are at low voltage. The input currents are therefore small and do not occasion line-voltage disturbances as conventional motors do. Applied to the home of tomorrow, this means that lights will not dim momentarily when the refrigerator or oil burner starts up.

Operators of lathes, drill presses, and other machine tools powered by this type of motor will be able to obtain many speeds without shifting belts or gear-drive levers. As torque is constant, plenty of power will be available at all times for drilling and similar operations to be done at low speed.

The new control produces an unbalance of line currents that makes its application to very large motors undesirable, but this does not apply in the case of small motors.

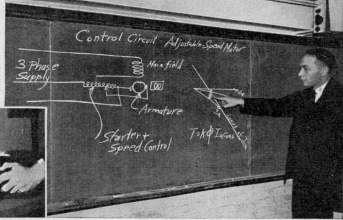

Left above, experimental motor and control unit. At the right above, Prof. Conrad explains vector diagram of the new motor. Note compensating winding set at 90 electrical degrees to field winding

The control unit can readily be mounted independently of the motor and within easy reach of the operator, as shown on the drill press at the left

In conjunction with step pulleys, a tremendous speed range is possible. The autotransformer control involves no energy loss such as resistors do

with thorough washing of the hand-wheel, bobbin winder, and mechanism in the left side; then brush gasoline on the treadle and large belt wheel. Remove any thread or lint that may have collected around the wheel shaft or pitman rod connecting the wheel and treadle.

Under the front shuttle slide there is usually a little well filled with wool waste. From this well a very small hole runs to the shuttle race in the

Coaxing New Life out of the *Old Sewing Machine*

By BENJAMIN NIELSEN

RESCUED from attic and basement, long unused and even obsolete sewing machines can be put back into service by thrifty wives and mothers who wish to make and repair family clothing to help along the budget or because of real and threatened scarcities. Grandmother's gilt-decorated relic, as well as machines of more nearly contemporary make, can be renovated so as to do excellent work. Cleaning and readjustment are all that many such old machines need.

The first step, regardless of the model, is to clean and oil the machine thoroughly. Remove the thread, bobbin, and shuttle. Take off the plate through which the feed points project and the large vertical plate above it after removing the screws that hold them. If there is a plate on the back near the handwheel, remove it also. Using an oil can, squirt a generous amount of gasoline in each oil hole and on all movable parts and joints.

Next, tilt the head back, arrange a drip pan such as a shallow baking pan underneath, and wash the machine thoroughly with a brush dipped in gasoline. *Be extremely careful, for gasoline is inflammable and explosive.* Never use gasoline near an open fire, nor in a room that does not have ample ventilation.

Follow the cleaning of the head

case of a vibrator (long-shuttle) machine. When this wool is saturated with oil, just enough works through to lubricate the shuttle. Take the wool out and clean the hole with a pin; then wash the wool in gasoline and replace it or use new wool.

Most oscillator-type machines have a split piece of felt that rubs on the shuttle race. This felt should be cleaned, oiled, and adjusted, if necessary, so that it rubs both sides of the shuttle. It is good practice to clean and oil it occasionally when the machine is in use. Many machines with ro-

Adjust tension of the lower thread by tightening or loosening the screw that holds the flat tension spring on the shuttle

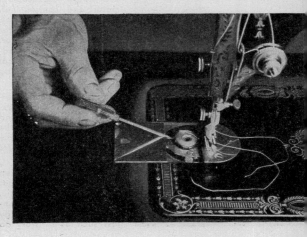

tary shuttles—the third common type manufactured—have an oil hole in the shuttle race. This should be oiled frequently.

Before doing any oiling, however, run the machine for a few minutes, wipe all the parts dry with a clean cloth, and wait an hour to allow all traces of gasoline to evaporate. If it is more convenient, kerosene may be used instead of gasoline, but in this event 24 hours should elapse between cleaning and oiling. Use only a good grade of sewing-machine oil and drop it in every oil hole and on every friction surface.

Unnecessary play can be taken up in most joints by turning an adjustment screw. Make only one adjustment at a time. If it does not correct the trouble, return it to the original position before trying another. Run the machine after each slight adjustment to avoid passing the proper setting.

Correct adjustment of both upper and lower tension, as shown in the photographs, is the determining factor of a proper stitch, one in which both threads are precisely at the same tension and produce a line of stitching exactly the same on both sides of the material.

In testing the stitch, double a piece of material and sew across it for a few inches with thread of the correct size. Remove the piece from the machine, hold the stitch with about 1" of it between thumbs and forefingers, and pull steadily until there is a snap. If both threads are broken, the tension is even. If only the upper thread is broken, the upper tension is greater; if only the lower is broken, it is the lower tension that is greater. Either tighten or loosen one of the tension screws, depending on whether the stitch is loose or tight.

After cleaning and oiling, if the machine still runs hard, the belt may be too tight or too loose, or the bobbin winder may be running on the belt or wheel. Missed stitches may be caused by a bent or broken needle, one too fine for the thread, or one not suited to the machine itself. The needle also may be set too high or too low. On modern makes, it should be pushed up as far as it will go, but on older models it must be set so that the eye is 1/16" to 1/8" below the point of the shuttle when that point is nearest the needle.

Stitches may be missed if the shuttle point is dull. It may be sharpened on a fine whetstone, but whet only the round side of the shuttle, not the flat side. A shuttle that has a broken point will have to be replaced. Dirt lodged under the tension spring or between the tension plates may cause looped stitches on one side of the material.

Breaking of the upper thread may indicate incorrect threading, or the needle may be turned wrong in the machine. If the lower thread breaks, the shuttle or bobbin case may be threaded improperly, or the thread may be wound unevenly on the bobbin. Bending the thread guide in the direction of least winding on the bobbin will correct the last. A rough needle hole in the throat plate may also cause thread to break. Smooth the hole with a small reamer.

If stitches "pile up" because the material is not advanced regularly, make sure the presser-foot pressure is great enough to hold the cloth against the feed teeth. These teeth may be too low, but on most machines they can be raised by turning an adjustment screw. They should rise about 1/32" above the plate. If the teeth are dull from wear, they may be sharpened with a stone or file.

The upper thread must have the same tension as the lower to insure proper stitching on all materials

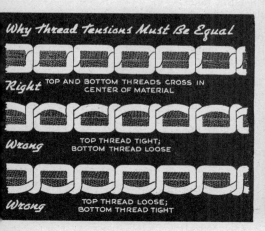

Why Thread Tensions Must Be Equal

Right TOP AND BOTTOM THREADS CROSS IN CENTER OF MATERIAL

Wrong TOP THREAD TIGHT; BOTTOM THREAD LOOSE

Wrong TOP THREAD LOOSE; BOTTOM THREAD TIGHT

HOME OWNERS

FRONT-DOOR MATS constructed of hardwood links fixed on wooden dowels have been developed to take the place of rubber ones. Beveled ends reduce the danger of tripping, and the mats can be folded or rolled into a compact package when they are to be stored. The wood is easily kept clean, for soap and water will not harm it. Mats are 1″ in thickness, but come in various lengths and widths from 18″ by 32″ to 30″ by 44″.

INSULATION RETAINERS made of gypsum, wood, or metal have been devised to hold insulation firmly in place. The strips are 24″ by 1¼″ and fit diagonally between studs spaced 16″ on centers, overlapping the horizontal joints of house insulation. In many cases the retainers may solve the problem of holding insulation permanently in place. They have notches in each end for nailing into studding.

PAPER SANDBAGS like that at the left, if dropped on a nonexplosive incendiary bomb from a height of 3′ or more, will burst and smother it under a layer of sand. The bags are sealed against moisture and will withstand ordinary handling without breaking.

PUTTY IN TAPE FORM comes in handy rolls for home repair jobs. It will not dry out, crack, or otherwise deteriorate in storage. To fix rattling windows, as at right, cut the strip to the required length, lay it over the old putty, and press down firmly. When it dries to a dark gray it may be painted.

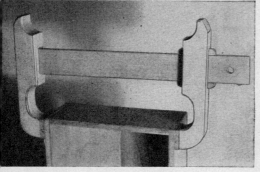

GLUE CLAMPS that have no threads or other turning parts are said to have a grip of almost 100 lbs., and will hold glued work up to 12" in size. They are made of smoothly finished hardwood, with cork pads to prevent work from being marred. The sliding member has a hole slightly larger than the bar and is fitted with two friction shoes which exert a wedging action when pressure is applied at the ends of the jaws.

PLASTIC SPRAY PUMPS which can be used for spraying small plants, flowers, and the like have been developed. The spray solution is contained in an ordinary Mason jar, and the pump part fits on the threads of the glass. It is easily manipulated and carried from place to place, and can be used to great advantage in all small spraying jobs where a great deal of coverage is not needed.

A WINDOW LUBRICANT that will not stain anything with which it comes in contact is shown at the right. It can be applied with a brush to either wood or metal surfaces. All rust should be removed from metal surfaces before the fluid is used.

PAPER CAULKING GUNS now take the place of metal types. The one shown at the left works on the principle of the old-time bellows. After the plug at the top is released, the bellows end is pressed and the caulking material dispensed in much the same way that toothpaste is squeezed from a tube. The gun comes already loaded.

WHEEL CULTIVATOR
for Your Victory Garden

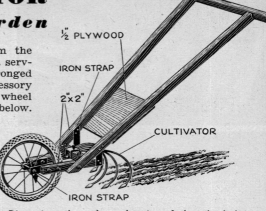

½" PLYWOOD

IRON STRAP

2"x2"

CULTIVATOR

IRON STRAP

WHEEL cultivators are disappearing from the market, but the Victory gardener can build a serviceable one from simple materials. The five-pronged tool can either be bought as a wheel-hoe accessory or taken from a hand cultivator. A bicycle wheel was used for the implement in the photos below. Panels of ½" plywood join the frame members and support the tool rigidly.

A smaller wheel, such as one from a discarded tricycle, should be used in the alternative design shown in the drawing. This has the advantage that force is applied in a direct line to the cultivator prongs. Assemble all parts with bolts and nuts. Strap-iron extensions support the axle. Two braces make a rigid unit of the handle members and the lower frame.

Dimensions depend on the size of the wheel, but the handle should come to about elbow height. Use bolts and nuts throughout in assembling the parts

Searchlight for Model Boat Is Made from Flashlight Bulb

TO MAKE this model searchlight, obtain a 2-cell, pen flashlight bulb and with a small soldering iron melt the two drops of solder on the side and bottom of the base. Wipe off the melted solder and free the two wires. Next, cut away the shell with a triangular file or a jeweler's saw (Fig. 1) and carefully chip away the cement underneath. Solder a 6" length of copper wire to each of the two wires protruding from the bulb as in Fig. 2. Insulate them with several coats of shellac; then bring them both to one side of the bulb as shown in Fig. 3. Coat the entire bulb, except for the magnifying tip, with aluminum paint. Mold plastic composition wood over it, let dry, and sand to shape.—N. P. GUIDRY.

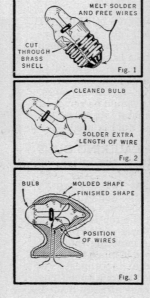

MELT SOLDER AND FREE WIRES

CUT THROUGH BRASS SHELL

Fig. 1

CLEANED BULB

SOLDER EXTRA LENGTH OF WIRE

Fig. 2

BULB

MOLDED SHAPE
FINISHED SHAPE

POSITION OF WIRES

Fig. 3

Above, the realistic searchlight is shown compared to a cigarette. The lead wires should be well inside so they will not be exposed when the molded shape is sanded down. Use one or two pen flashlight cells, depending upon the light desired

Professional Tricks
WILL BETTER YOUR
Lab Technique

Good equipment is essential in the home lab. One of the necessities is a wash bottle, which you can easily make

THERE is almost no limit to the number of experiments which may be performed in the home lab with simple equipment and only a limited number of operations. If you familiarize yourself thoroughly with the use of your equipment and master the best technique for carrying out various operations, your hobby becomes simpler, more enjoyable, and more scientifically valuable.

Once you learn how to handle chemicals properly, the results of experiments become more conclusive, and dangerous accidents are less likely to occur. The following hints are fundamental to *all* laboratory practice, and should be kept well in mind when working out any experiments in the home lab.

To begin with, the chemical laboratory must be kept scrupulously clean. A tiny speck of foreign chemical in a bottle of tested-purity reagent may spoil a test. A few grains of chemicals mixed in error may cause an explosion. For these reasons, never return excess chemicals to a reagent bottle. Either save the chemicals for another experiment or throw them away. Small quantities of dry reagent may be removed from a bottle with a clean spatula or a strip of paper folded to form a scoop. Never lay glass stoppers on a table where they might become contaminated, but place them in a clean glass or porcelain dish.

When weighing chemicals, never place them directly on the scale pans. Use a creased square of white paper, balancing this with a similar piece. Have a supply of these on hand and throw the papers away as they are used.

On precision scales, weights should always be handled with forceps to prevent possible contamination or corrosion of them by substances from the fingers.

Observe those caution signs on bottles of chemicals! Keep bottles containing acids or ammonia away from your face when opening them. Bottles marked *POISON* should be handled with special care, and should be kept away from the mouth and skin. Wash your hands repeatedly while using poisons, and carefully clean up any spilled chemicals with rags that can be thrown away. If these precautions are observed you need not fear to use poisons. As a further safeguard, keep a list of antidotes in a prominent place in the lab.

A few chemicals require extra special handling. Yellow phosphorus, for example, must be kept under water, as it catches fire spontaneously in the air. Never touch this chemical with your fingers. You may be seriously burned. To cut a piece for use, remove a stick of it from its bottle with tongs and place it immediately in a dish filled with water. While still holding it with the tongs, cut pieces off the other end with a sharp knife. Be sure all phosphorus used for an experiment is either burned or returned to the bottle. Pieces left lying about may cause a fire.   (CONTINUED)

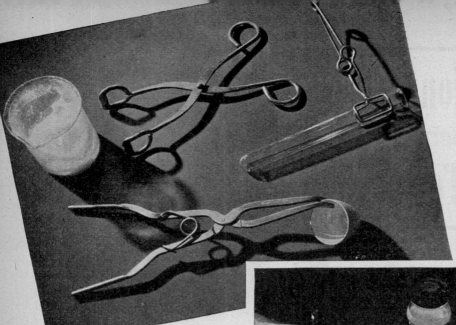

Beakers and flasks should be one third full if the contents are to be boiled to dryness. Keep them covered with a watch glass so as to avoid dangerous spattering ➡

Certain chemicals must be handled with great care. Yellow phosphorus is one. Never carry it except with tongs, and always cut it under water as shown below

Above are inexpensive devices for handling hot beakers, test tubes, crucibles, and the like. Ordinary hot-food tongs also are useful for these purposes

Sodium and potassium metals must be handled with similar care. However, these must be kept under kerosene, as water causes them to decompose violently and liberate hydrogen, which often catches fire from the heat of the reaction. Cut these in a dish under kerosene. Scrape off any coating of oxide and dip the pieces in some ether to remove the kerosene. Never throw waste sodium or potassium down a drain, as the reaction with water might cause a serious explosion. When reacting or cutting these metals, it is best to wear goggles to protect your eyes from possible spattering.

That *KEEP FROM FLAME* warning found on certain containers means you must keep them at least *twenty feet* from any exposed flame—especially when opening them. The vapors of some inflammable liquids travel far and fast. Even if they do not carry a flame back to the bottle, they may form an explosive mixture with the air.

Few experiments are performed in the home lab without the assistance of flasks, beakers, or test tubes. Be sure that all of these are sound and of good glass. For heating or reacting small quantities of chemicals, test tubes are ideal. They may be supported by a regular clamp on a ring stand, or by a wire holder in the hand. All test tubes should be heated gradually. For heating dry chemicals, or for the destructive distillation of coal, wood, and the like, use heat-resistant test tubes.

Beakers should be used for heating large quantities of chemicals. Always protect these from direct flame by means of a square of gauze with an asbestos center. When heating or boiling a liquid for a very short period, a beaker may be filled about three quarters full. For boiling a solution away to dryness, however, fill the beaker only one third full and cover it with a watch glass to prevent loss from spattering.

Florence flasks are the type generally used for boiling or distilling. Liquids are less likely to superheat or "bump" in the round-bottomed flasks than in the flat-bottomed type. A gauze square should be used under these also.

A pair of tongs such as used in the kitchen for lifting hot foods makes an excel-

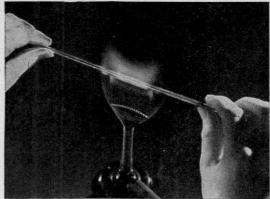

Strong, neat bends in glass tubing are easily made. Above, a wing top is used on the Bunsen burner in order to spread the flame, and the tube is twirled so that it will heat evenly all around. When the flame turns yellow, remove the tubing and, holding the two ends, gently shape to the proper curvature

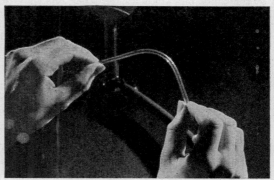

lent device for handling hot beakers. Crucibles can be handled safely with flat tongs having tips bent almost to a right angle.

Filtering is a laboratory operation which can be speeded and improved if proper attention is paid to details. Filter paper should be of a size which, when folded, does not reach quite to the top of the funnel. The long point at the end of the funnel should touch the receiving beaker near its top. This arrangement permits the continuous flow of the filtrate down the side of the beaker without splashing.

Before pouring in the solution to be filtered, wet the sides of the filter with a stream of water from the wash bottle; then press the paper to the sides of the funnel.

Hold a glass rod across the top of the pouring beaker and allow the liquid gently to strike the side of the filter paper about one fourth of the way down from the top. This glass-rod arrangement is useful whenever liquids are poured from beakers. If the

beaker has no lip, the edge should be lightly greased with petroleum jelly to prevent the liquid from running down the side.

Every home laboratory should have at least one wash bottle. Water from its nozzle can be used to wash down solid matter from the inside of beakers and test tubes, to moisten filters, to rinse the inside of glassware, and for many other chores.

A wash bottle may be easily made from a 500-ml. Florence flask, a two-hole stopper, and three pieces of bent glass tubing. The nozzle may be drawn from a piece of tubing.

To make perfectly round bends without kinks, a sufficient length of glass tubing is first heated as shown in the photo above. Use a wing tip on your Bunsen burner to spread the flame. Hold the tube loosely and rotate it slowly to heat it evenly on all sides. Remove the tube from the burner when the flame turns yellow. Then, holding the ends with your fingers, shape it gently to the proper curvature.

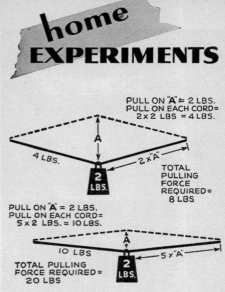

PULL ON "A" = 2 LBS.
PULL ON EACH CORD=
2 x 2 LBS = 4 LBS.

4 LBS.   2 x "A"

2 LBS.

TOTAL
PULLING
FORCE
REQUIRED=
8 LBS

PULL ON "A" = 2 LBS.
PULL ON EACH CORD=
5 x 2 LBS. = 10 LBS.

10 LBS   5 x "A"

TOTAL PULLING
FORCE REQUIRED=
20 LBS

2 LBS.

WEIGHT PUZZLER. Suspend a 2-lb. weight from the center of a stout cord about 2' long. Now pull on the ends of the rope and you will find that you cannot straighten the cord. The explanation is not as puzzling as one might think. The more nearly horizontal the cord becomes, the more the forces exerted by the hands pull against each other, and the harder it is to lift the weight. By constructing a parallelogram, as shown in the drawing, it is possible to measure directly the forces required to lift a weight to any position. To find the pull on each cord, divide the length of the cord by that of the diagonal A of the parallelogram; then multiply the weight of the quotient so obtained, as shown in the two examples above.

FOUR SIMPLE SCIENCE STUNTS

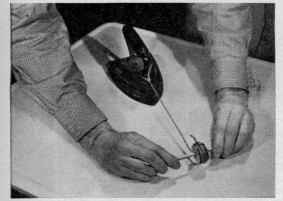

WHY ARE GEARS NECESSARY? Tie a piece of twine to a flatiron, or some similar weight, and fasten the other end to the edge of a disk of wood about 1" in diameter mounted tightly on a pencil. Now try to twist the pencil in order to wind up the twine and thus move the iron. You will find you cannot budge it. The disk corresponds to high gear. If you take the twine from the disk and wrap it around the pencil instead, you will find the iron will move easily. The pencil, with its smaller diameter, corresponds to low gear.

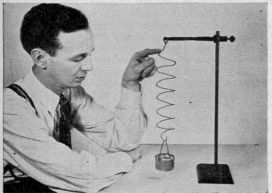

HEAVY CARS ride over uneven roads more comfortably than light cars because of inertia. The heavier the body, the greater is this inertia. A simple setup will demonstrate the effects of this. Suspend a little bucket from an improvised spring. The bucket represents the body of your car and the spring represents an ordinary auto spring. Tap the upper turn of the spring, and the bucket will respond quickly by vibrating greatly. If you weight the bucket and repeat the experiment, it will respond much more slowly, due to the added weight and the consequent increase in inertia. The vibration will not only be smoother, but the bucket will come to rest more quickly.

AN OPTICAL RANGE FINDER which illustrates the principle of elaborate military ones can be made from a stick and several mirrors arranged as shown. The fixed mirror on the left-hand side is placed at a 45-deg. angle. In the center of the base, two small viewing mirrors are mounted, one having its face parallel to the left-hand mirror and the other fixed at right angles directly below it. The mirror on the right-hand end of the base is mounted so it revolves on a calibrating scale below it. Placing one eye so that it can see part of the object in the upper viewing mirror and part in the lower one, rotate the right-hand mirror until the two images coincide. By measuring the angle of the movable mirror, a triangle may be constructed with its apex at the object itself. The scale on the mirror may then be calibrated to read the distance directly.

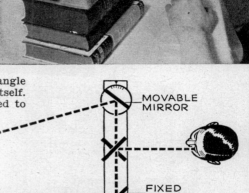

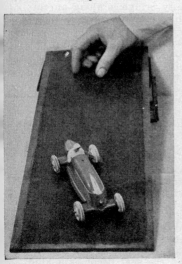

OBJECT

MOVABLE MIRROR

FIXED MIRROR

SHOW WHY YOUR AUTOMOBILE ACTS AS IT DOES

YOUR CAR MUFFLER is a metal cylinder through which sharp puffs of exploded gases are bent around circuitous paths in a stream so steady that it is almost silent. A model muffler can be built from a cardboard tube and five or six cardboard disks perforated and arranged as shown. Whistle through the tube before the disks are in place—the sounds go through clearly. Arrange the disks and try again. This time the sounds you make will be almost inaudible.

CAR BRAKES should be checked frequently. What happens when one brake responds more quickly or with greater force than the other may be demonstrated with a toy car. Wind some string around the axle of the left wheel so that it retards the turning of the wheel, and let the car roll down an incline. Because of the unequal speed of the wheels, the car will slide into a definite skid. On a real car the reaction would be just the same and much more dangerous.

ARRANGEMENT OF DISKS IN TUBE

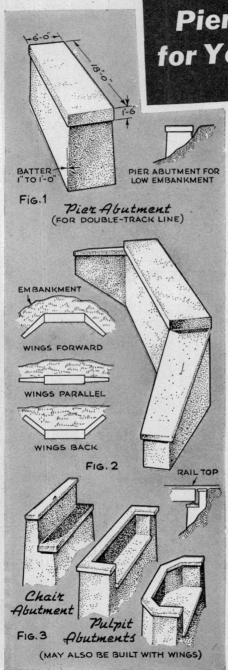

BATTER
1" TO 1'-0"

PIER ABUTMENT FOR
LOW EMBANKMENT

Fig. 1

Pier Abutment
(FOR DOUBLE-TRACK LINE)

EMBANKMENT

WINGS FORWARD

WINGS PARALLEL

WINGS BACK

FIG. 2

RAIL TOP

Chair
Abutment

Pulpit
Abutments

FIG. 3

(MAY ALSO BE BUILT WITH WINGS)

How to Design Piers and Abutments for Your Model Railroad

by David Marshall

WHEN we speak of a steel bridge, we don't really mean what we say, for only part of a bridge at most is ever made of steel. This is the upper portion, or superstructure. Below it is the substructure of masonry or concrete to which the steelwork is anchored and upon which it rides. This substructure consists of two abutments and usually one or more piers.

Piers and abutments, therefore, form the seats upon which the superstructure is erected. Steel slide or roller chairs are anchored to their broad upper surfaces, and upon these chairs the immense weight of the steel span rides with a certain freedom of movement.

To anyone who understands their function, such chairs are as interesting as the span itself. Indeed, if they are carefully modeled, they will enhance the effect of well-built piers and abutments beyond all proportion to their size.

ABUTMENTS AND PIERS. An abutment is a substructural unit that supports one end of a steel span or superstructure. It differs from a pier in that it is normally of somewhat heavier construction because it must serve not only as a pier but also as a retaining wall. Usually the approach to a railway bridge is along an embankment, or fill, which must be retained where it ends abruptly at the bridge abutment.

To a large extent this additional function of the abutment explains its many forms. Thus, if the embankment is low, or if the approach is along a trestle, we use a simple pier abutment (Fig. 1). If the embankment is high, we require a winged abutment (Fig. 2), which is structurally no more than a pier abutment with two retaining walls, or ramps. These always follow the slope of the embankment and may or may not lie in the same plane as the abutment.

Chair abutments and pulpit abutments are usually employed with deck-type bridges. The seats of these abutments must lie well below the grade level and, to prevent the embankment from encroaching upon the seat, the abutment is extended upward to grade level along the embankment side of the seat and occasionally also around the ends of the seat. The former type is a chair, the latter a pulpit abutment. In both cases, the seat becomes a kind of step in the abutment as shown in Fig. 3.

A pier is usually lighter than an abutment because it meets only one strain instead of two—the downward thrust of the superstructure and not both that and the lateral thrust of embanked earth. Piers are employed, however, only if the bridge is one of the type that is composed of more than one span.

RULES OF SPACING. In the field of railway bridge building, American practice is characterized by the types most easily erected. Plate girders are favored for spans up to 50′ and rivet trusses for those from 50′ to 75′. For viaducts, that is, for bridges of more than one span, girders are preferred. Pin trusses are indicated for all spans of more than 75′, but rivet-truss bridges, with certain exceptions, are the largest the average American model railroader can find space for building.

Any succession of piers must be built at center-to-center intervals of not more than 50 scale feet for girders and 75 scale feet for rivet trusses. Since experienced railroad engineers say that nothing is gained by shortening girder spans, but that everything is gained by keeping the trusses as short as possible, the rule for model builders is to keep trusses as short as possible and to space the piers for girders at as near a maximum of 50 scale feet (12½ inches in O gauge) as equal intervals will permit.

CONCRETE COLOR. Railway abutments and piers are made of brick, stone, or concrete, but we build them all of wood. The concrete specimens are weather-streaked plain surfaces and perhaps a little smudged. But clean or dirty, all concrete jobs are of a distinctive color, so if your model work is to be convincing, it must be painted accurately.

Use nothing but flat colors, never a glossy paint or an enamel. To find your concrete color, begin with a flat white and add a little yellow ocher and a little black. The proportions are difficult to prescribe, but you can't go wrong if you take your colors and a sample piece of wood outdoors on a day when the sun is not too bright. Set your sample against a piece of real concrete and continue mixing paint until an effective match has been achieved. You may have to mix the paint several times—but your patience will be rewarded if, at the end, the color is correct and realistic.

STONE AND BRICKWORK. For model stone masonry, there are several points to be observed. The blocks used in a stone retaining wall are 48″ long and 15″ high. The same size blocks are also used for the lower courses of stone abutments and piers, except where surfaces are curved. As the courses rise, the stones are shallower. For the upper courses, half stones of 10″ by 24″ are usual. Stones are often dressed for retaining walls at stations, but at other locations the faces that are exposed to view are rough.

Dressed stones in a single plane are easily imitated. Lay out the horizontal courses and staggered vertical joints on a piece of white pine, using a hard pencil; then scribe them into the wood. An excellent scribing tool can be made of a nut pick sharpened by filing. With a steel ruler as a guide, run the sharpened pick along each penciled line, cutting deeply into the wood. To produce the effect of V-joints, widen the cuts by forcing a blunt pick along them, being careful not to employ too much pressure.

Rough stones are made of ¼″ whitewood cut into strips to represent each course of stones. Bevel the strips along both edges to simulate horizontal joints. To make vertical joints, scratch the strips deeply with one corner of a file at regular intervals. Next scoop small bits out of the face of each stone with a pocket knife. Finally, glue and tack the strips in place on a surface of 1″ pine. All kinds of stones, from wedges and keystones to panels and buttresses, can be made in this way.

Paint stone masonry a dirty white, getting the paint well into every chink and crack. Then brush on a granite color lightly, covering all stone faces but missing most of the scribed lines. The effect of this will be the dirty white showing through as mortar. Granite color can be achieved by using gray paint as a base and adding raw umber and a touch of blue.

Successful brickwork is achieved by lightly scribing the horizontal lines on wood and painting a dull and soot-blackened brown. The staggered vertical lines are omitted.

Much of the success in building model-railway scenery depends upon details of piers and abutments

Cardboard, scraps of wood, and cement are all you need to make this realistic bridge

By

JOHN J.

GALLIVAN

Model Girder Bridge Can Be Built for a Few Cents

A MODEL through-girder bridge that will be realistic and surprisingly strong can be made of 1/16" thick glossy cardboard and thin wood such as can be bought at model-airplane supply houses. Full-size dimensions are given in the drawing, but these may easily be scaled down for an O-gauge, OO, or HO system.

Cut the web plates to shape first. These can be cut to any length up to about 75' scale size. Plates longer than 30' should have two or more splice plates instead of one. Glue on the splice plates and also the flat sides of the angle stiffeners all around the perimeter of the two web plates. Next, cut cardboard filler strips to go under the flat sides of the vertical angle stiffeners, and glue wooden faces to the sides after these are in place.

A strip of cardboard equal in width to the distance between the outstanding faces of the stiffeners on both sides is glued around the perimeter of the entire web. This strip forms the outstanding face of the perimeter angle stiffeners.

Rivet heads may be cleverly simulated with a typewriter. Set the machine for stenciling and, using stiff, glossy paper, strike the keys with enough pressure to make sharp impressions on the opposite side of the paper without cutting through it. Glue strips of the indented paper to the perimeter angle stiffeners, splice plates, and cover plates, all of which have a double row of alternately spaced rivet markings. The vertical angle stiffeners have one row of single-spaced rivets.

The entire bridge is next given a coat of diluted shellac, followed by black, green, or orange show-card paint.

A piece of plywood extended to rest on the abutments and supported on strips attached to the girders makes a satisfactory floor. Girder footings vary in type according to span lengths. For very long spans, use rocker shoes and set one of these on a roller shoe. The drawing shows two types of shoes supporting one span in order to illustrate both footings, but in practice the shoes would be of the same type.

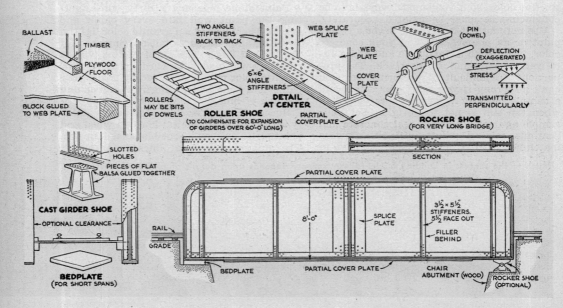

Longer Wear
from Metalware

By KENNETH M. SWEZEY

ONE way of contributing to the war effort is to take scrupulous care of home metalware that is still too useful to be turned in to the scrap drive. By learning the characteristics of different metals, and by applying this knowledge, you can prolong the life and preserve the beauty of objects made from them, thereby freeing men and materials that might otherwise be needed to make replacement goods.

Aluminum utensils should never be cleaned with alkaline solutions such as washing soda or trisodium phosphate, since these will darken and pit the metal. A bland soap is usually sufficient to keep aluminum ware gleaming, with the occasional use of very fine steel wool to remove stains.

You have probably noticed that when you cook certain foods in aluminum pots, the pots become darkened and discolored. This is because such foods contain soluble salts of metals, such as iron. The aluminum combines with these salts, freeing the metal they contain, which is deposited on the inside of the pot. Instead of trying to scour it off, simply cook some acid food, such as rhubarb, tomatoes, or the like, in the same pot—and behold—the mineral matter will be completely recovered in the form of valuable food elements, and your pot will be bright as a dollar again!

Tinware is really made of iron or steel,

coated very thinly with tin for protection. If this coating is subjected to careless treatment, it will break off, and the pan will rust. Such utensils should never be scoured. If you wish to remove burnt food, boil water containing baking soda or washing soda in the pan for a few minutes.

Enameled pots and pans should be treated as carefully as your choicest glassware, since the enamel coating is a close relative of glass. Sudden heating or cooling will cause the enamel to crack, and any sharp knocks will chip it.

Grease can be removed from iron pans by washing them in hot soapy water, or in a solution of washing soda and water. Since iron rusts easily, the pans should be dried carefully. If you wish to store an iron pot, coat it with a saltless oil or fat, wrap it in paper, and put it away in a dry place.

Chromium-plated and nickel-plated articles may look alike, but they should not be treated alike. Chromium plating is highly resistant to tarnish, but it can be scratched very easily. It should never be cleaned with any type of scouring powder or metal polish—a soft damp cloth is sufficient to keep it in its original bright condition. Nickel plating, on the other hand, tarnishes more easily than chromium plating, but it may be cleaned with any gritless metal cleaner.

Brass and copper pieces that have not been lacquered may be cleaned with a saturated solution of table salt in warm vinegar, or with lemon rind and salt, hot buttermilk, or hot tomato or rhubarb juice. Copper cooking utensils should always be kept scoured, since the brown oxide or green carbonate of copper that forms from tarnish reacts with the organic food acids to create undesirable salts.

To remove sticking food, soak a utensil in soapy water and scrape with a wooden spoon

Nickel-plated ware can be safely polished with a gritless cleaner or whiting paste

Unlacquered brassware or copperware is made clean with a solution of salt and vinegar

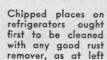

Chipped places on refrigerators ought first to be cleaned with any good rust remover, as at left

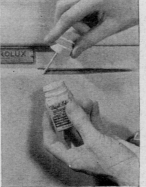

Right, the exposed metal is smoothed down with some emery paper, then coated with touch-up enamel

Boiling washing soda and water in tinware about five minutes will remove burnt foods

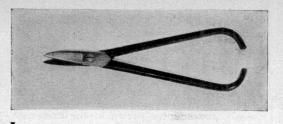

1 ....

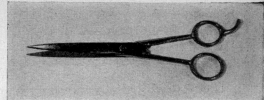

2 ....

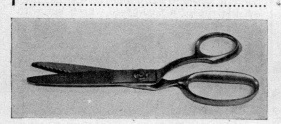

3 ....

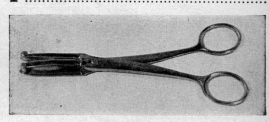

4 ....

Question Bee

SHEARS as we know them probably date back to the sixteenth century or earlier, for they were apparently used by the Venetians.

All shears fall into two classes: those whose blades are opened and closed by the pressure of one or more fingers and the thumb on the handle ends of the blades, and those which are closed by the hand, but opened by a coil spring between the blades or by spring action of the handle itself. Common scissors are an example of the former class; pruning and grass-trimming shears are examples of the latter. Can you name those shown here? Write down your answers; then turn the page upside down to see how correct you are.

ANSWERS

1. Jewelers' shears or snips
2. Barbers' shears
3. Pinking shears
4. Flower shears
5. Embroidery scissors
6. Straight trimmers (sewing shears)
7. Bent trimmers (dress-makers' shears)
8. Sheet-metal shears or snips

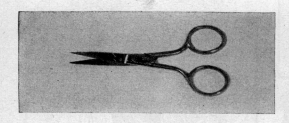

5 ....

6 ....

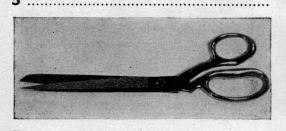

7 ....

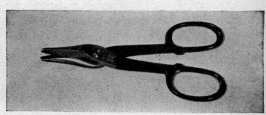

8 ....

USEFUL AUTO HINTS

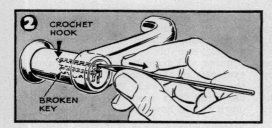

5.00 × 19 TIRE AND RIM

6.00 × 16 WHEEL

EXTENSION VALVE STEM

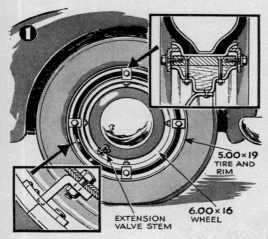

CROCHET HOOK

BROKEN KEY

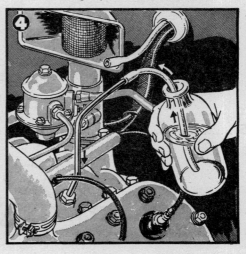

1 OLD-STYLE TIRES of large rim diameter can be made to serve on small wheels by the use of the adapter shown in the drawing. Here a 5.00-by-19 tire and rim are mounted on the rim of a 6.00-by-16 wheel, but with slight changes the method can be applied to other sizes. Bar stock, ⅝ by 1 inch, and as long as the rim is wide, is bolted with countersunk bolts to the small rim through hardwood filler blocks, as in the upper right inset. Drill and tap the ends for bolts holding angle-iron lugs. Channel-shaped shims may be needed to center the large rim on the bars and eliminate looseness. An angle lug (lower left inset) engages the existing lug on the small rim. A right-angle extension valve completes the setup.—A. A. L.

2 BROKEN-OFF KEYS are easily removed from car-door or other locks with the help of a fine crochet needle. Push the needle in above the key until the hook is past the end, and pull out carefully.—A. H. W.

3 BOTTLE-FEEDING A MOTOR may save a tow if the feed pump fails. Puncture the cap of a bottle and feed gasoline through it directly into the carburetor.—J. R.

4 ZERO-WEATHER PRIMING can be done when necessary through the windshield-wiper vacuum line. Pull the hose off near where it enters the intake manifold, attach another hose and insert it in a bottle of gasoline. Turn the engine over a few times, remove bottle, and start as usual.—H. D. DE W.

Drawings by STEWART ROUSE

O AID THE MOTORIST

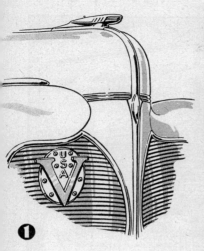

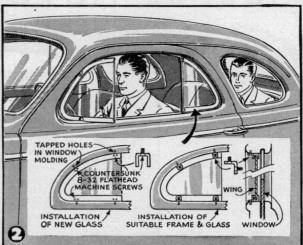

TAPPED HOLES IN WINDOW MOLDING

COUNTERSUNK 8-32 FLATHEAD MACHINE SCREWS

WING

INSTALLATION OF NEW GLASS

INSTALLATION OF SUITABLE FRAME & GLASS

WINDOW

BREAKS IN GRILLS can be concealed by mounting radiator emblems over them. To do this, drill suitably spaced holes in a piece of flat stock such as heavy sheet metal and place this behind the bars of the grill, running the mounting screws through it.—J. B.

AUXILIARY WIND WING. Drafts coming from the wide front door of a club coupe or two-door sedan can be eliminated by the addition of a wind wing. Cut a template from a piece of stout cardboard and buy a matching wind wing at a wrecking yard. If you cannot procure a wing of the correct shape, obtain a windshield-wing frame and bend it to conform to the inside molding of the car door; then have a piece of safety glass cut to fit the frame. When fastening the frame to the door, leave about ½" clearance so the wing will not interfere with the operation of the door glass.—A. S. L.

TIRE THIEVERY can be prevented by running a 3/16" wire rope through the wheels and the knee-action assembly, or else over the axle. Insert a lock through loops on the ends, which are secured by a soldered wire binding as shown.—M. S.

A CRACKED CYLINDER HEAD can sometimes be repaired by placing a steel plate over the crack, as shown. Two rows of holes are drilled alongside the crack, and one hole at each end to prevent further cracking. All holes are tapped, and a gasket placed between the head and the plate.—J. B.

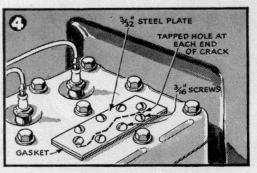

SOLDERED

WIRE BINDING

3/16" WIRE ROPE

DRAWINGS BY STEWART ROUSE

3/32" STEEL PLATE

TAPPED HOLE AT EACH END OF CRACK

3/16" SCREWS

GASKET

USEFUL AUTO HINTS

DROPS OF SOLDER
FOR IDENTIFICATION
OF KEYS IN DARK

WHERE HOOD OBSCURES DRIVER'S VIEW IS THE BEST PLACE FOR WINDSHIELD STICKERS

DRAWINGS BY STEWART ROUSE

1 **CAR KEYS** can be easily identified by drops of solder. For instance, the gas key might have one drop of solder, the ignition key two drops, the door key three drops, and so on. Tin the surface first to make the drops adhere. With this system, keys are easy to distinguish from one another even in the dark.—W. K. K.

2 **AUTOMOBILE STICKERS**, inspection tags, stamps, and the like should be placed on the windshield in such a position that they will not conceal other cars or pedestrians. If they are placed near the center at the very bottom of the windshield, in line with the hood of the car, they will in no way obstruct the driver's view, and may still be seen clearly from outside.—G. J. K.

3 **AN INGENIOUS HOLDER** for hanging clothes in a car can be improvised on short notice. Take a piece of rope about 6″ long, double it, and tie the two ends together. Place the knotted end outside the window. When the window is closed on the rope, the part hanging on the inside forms an adequate loop for a hanger.—T. D.

4 **SCUFF PADS** placed as shown in the drawing will protect your car's upholstery. The pads are made of artificial leather or other durable material. Cut them to fit the door, bind the edges with tape, and fasten with ordinary upholstery pins. The material used for this may be matched with the upholstery fabric on the door panels of the car.—J. B.

How to Keep Your Home Cool for Hot-Weather Comfort

By J. HAROLD HAWKINS
Author of *Your House*

RELAXATION comes with bodily comfort, and your bodily comfort depends upon relief from oppressive heat and humidity. Any comfortable indoor temperature in summer is relative. That is, if it is 90 deg. outdoors in the shade, 75 deg. in the house will give you that desired relief. Less than 75 deg. would be too great a variation in temperatures under normal conditions, especially when you are likely to be going outdoors several times during the day.

Cooling your house to create a 15-deg. variation between outdoor and indoor temperatures, without benefit of mechanical air-cooling gadgets such as air-conditioning systems, depends to a large extent upon ventilation. Other important factors are awnings, window shades or shutters, and insulation between the joists of the attic floor, in the order mentioned.

Ventilation divides itself into natural and artificial methods. Natural ventilation consists of opening all inside doors of the house from cellar to attic, which allows warm air to rise gradually to the attic and drift out through one or the other of two opened windows or louvers located at opposite sides or ends of the attic. As the warm air escapes from the attic, it is replaced by warm air from the rooms below, and as this air moves upward, it in turn is replaced by cooler air coming up from the basement.

Outside air must be taken into the basement, normally through a cellar window near the ground level and on the shady side of the house. Any natural movement of air in your house depends upon a ready supply of fresh, cooler air to take its place as it rises. Warm air cannot force its way outside through the attic if it has to leave a partial vacuum in order to do so, and the comparatively cool air cannot rise from the basement unless there is more incoming cool air to replace it. Nor will the cooler air rise from the basement if there is any way for other air to get into the house through windows or outside doors. The house must be shut tight on all intervening floors to create a draft from the cellar to the attic.

Direct sunshine on the outside walls of the house, and especially on windows, heats the air inside the house to a marked degree. Much of this rise in temperature can be avoided if both awnings and window shades are used to keep the direct rays of the sun off the windows. Awnings should be of the open-side variety, not the type that enclose a window on three sides, to allow currents of air to pass by rather than to collect under the hot canvas and form heating zones. On the inside, two shades with an air space between them form a surprisingly effective insulating blanket before each window.

At night, when the heat of the day has cooled down to the inside temperature of your house, windows and doors may be opened for a complete change of air. Upstairs windows left open all night, if the temperature outside is cooler, will tend to cool not only the indoor air but also walls and furnishings that have absorbed heat during the day. In the morning, however, just as soon as the sun begins its warming-up process, close the house tight, lower all awnings, and pull all the shades down on the sunny side.

Inside doorways, as a rule, do not reach to the ceiling level by a foot or two, and even though all the doors are kept open, a thick blanket of warm air will be trapped against the ceiling and be pretty well stymied for an opportunity to move and rise to a higher level. The remedy consists of either grills or transoms between the tops of inside doorways and the ceiling, or registers through the ceilings to rooms above or to the attic. These aids for air to circulate of its own free will are very important, not only for summer cooling but for warm-air heating in winter as well. Shutter doors can be used in place of solid doors for any rooms where daytime privacy is required.

Artificial methods of air circulation give more rapid results and, of course, will do a thorough job of ventilation against odds. There are two general ways of forcing air through a house. One is to use a fan in the warm-air furnace to force cool air up through the regular heating ducts to the various rooms in the house. Such a circulating fan is regular equipment on many modern warm-air furnaces and can be installed in the top of the jacket of many types of old furnaces. The other means of air circulation is an attic fan which draws warm air out of the attic and delivers it outdoors through a louver, preferably one located as near the ridge of the roof as possible. Either or both fans can be operated at the same time to boost the volume of air being moved up through the house and out through the attic.

To furnish a supply of comparatively cool air for the furnace fan to handle, an intake can be built, with a little effort, by digging a trench from a shady spot in the yard to the basement. Lay a continuous line of sewer pipe in the trench and seal the joints with cement mortar to keep water from leaking into the line. This air, taken from ground level and passing underground to the basement, will be still further cooled because of its travel. It will provide a positive feed that will relieve any tendency toward forming a vacuum in the basement because of the action of the fan in taking the air out.

Cool air forced up through furnace ducts will tend to create a pressure in upstairs rooms which, in turn, will help force warm air up to the attic. The regular cold-air returns to the furnace from upstairs must definitely be cut off or the grills covered with rugs. Remember that the use of a furnace for cooling is the reverse of

One method of getting cool, fresh air into a basement is through an underground pipe with an intake at a shady spot in the yard. This helps to replace air drawn from the basement to circulate through a hot-air system

An exhaust fan over a grille set in the attic floor draws warm air up. Return ducts in a hot-air furnace system must be closed to keep cool air in the house

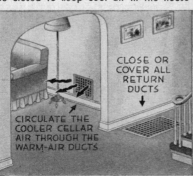

CLOSE OR COVER ALL RETURN DUCTS

CIRCULATE THE COOLER CELLAR AIR THROUGH THE WARM-AIR DUCTS

Open doors in all rooms inside your home allow cool air to circulate freely. If they do not reach to the ceiling, a vent or transom will keep a stagnant blanket from forming. Shutter doors may be used where privacy is desired. Two shades on the inside of a closed window will afford additional insulation against outdoor heat

using it for heating, and to draw the cool air off the floors down to the basement through return ducts would only defeat the whole cooling effort.

An attic exhaust fan, used with or without a furnace fan, is a most important part of artificial ventilation for home cooling. Such a fan, used in an attic that has no opening other than the one between it and downstairs, has a positive effect in that it constantly draws air up into the attic to replace that which it exhausts outdoors. If the exhaust fan has an intake box, it will function to better advantage than if it is merely mounted on a shelf in front of a louver. An ordinary electric fan will be of some help, but it will not be nearly as efficient as one designed for the job.

Insulation, we all know, is a barrier against heat as well as cold, so insulation in the walls of a house, between the joists of the attic floor, or between roof rafters adds its effect in the matter of house cooling. If, for instance, you have attic-floor insulation in your house, it will be a help in ventilating for coolness. Although the air under the roof will be heated as usual, the temperature of the air downstairs will be lessened because of the layer of insulation between it and the hot attic. The forced circulation of air from downstairs to the attic and out through a louver will not only further cool the downstairs rooms, but will keep up the continuous flow of new air that counts so much in summer cooling. This continuously moving air will prevent the forming of a hot-air blanket in the attic and avert a partial reduction of the efficiency of the insulation.

Humidity coupled with high temperature is particularly exasperating when you are trying to relax in hot weather. Circulating cool air not only reduces the relative humidity—because the cooler the air the less its ability to hold moisture—but moving air also assists your body in its normal function of dissipating its own heat which, summer or winter, remains at 98.6 degrees. It is surprising what a difference a positive flow of air will make. Of course an electric fan will give temporary relief, but when you shut the fan off the reaction is that of being more uncomfortable than before.

Dear Workshop Editor:

I am interested in building a simple air-conditioning unit for my home. Could you publish plans for one that would not be too difficult or too expensive to make?

J. A. – Flushing, N. Y.

A hose connected to an overhead manifold supplies water to the filters. Where running water is not available, a tank may be used

WILLIAM J. BURTON answers this query with a description of such a cooler. It consists of an old 20″ automobile fan, a 1/10-hp. motor, six homemade air filters, a drip pan, and a water supply system, all enclosed in a wooden cabinet 2′ by 2′ by 4′.

Warm, humid air is drawn into the cabinet by the fan and forced past the filters, which are kept moist by cold water dripping on them from a pipe above. They not only absorb moisture from the warm, humid air, but cool the air as it passes. The water collects in a drip pan, and any excess is drained off through a ¼″ copper tube located 2″ above the bottom.

Wire screening protects the fingers from contact with the fan, while several coats of hot, boiled linseed oil seal the plywood interior against the moisture in the air. Where running water is not available, the cabinet should be built higher so that a tank may be placed in the upper part.

The 2″ by 28″ filters are suspended from the top of the cabinet at an angle so as to partially obstruct the passage of air. A baffle between the pan and the front of the cabinet guides the moving air to the louvered opening. Water is fed to the filters by ⅛″ copper tubes soldered into a ¼″ manifold. A valve of the type found on gas heaters passes just enough water to maintain a continuous, slow drip from the filters into the pan.

Filters (left) are made of burlap sewed on galvanized-wire frames. Solder together two oil cans as shown below for the drip pan, and paint them inside with asphaltum. Mount the fan bearing on a crosspiece as in the photo at right, which shows the cabinet before the filters are set in. Fan and motor pulleys are same size

Toy Birds Enliven This Nursery Plaque

QUAINT, pink-spotted birds in flight across a rose-tinted cloud form this decorative plaque, which will intrigue children and provoke a chuckle or two from grownups.

The bodies and heads of the birds are small turnings fastened together with short lengths of dowel. Round-headed brass tacks serve for eyes. Short bits of dowel are notched at one end to form the bills. Wings and tails are of bright tin cut from a tin can. The birds are mounted about 1⅛" in front of the plaque by ⅛" dowels glued into holes drilled ⅜" deep.

Both the wings and the tails fit into saw cuts. The V-cuts in wings A and B face toward the tail. All wings and tails should be fitted into the slots before they are bent.

The birds shown have pink backs, spots, and bills, and white bodies. Two tones or two colors may be applied to the plaque—for example, the top half may be pink and the lower part white. Leave the parts made of tin plate unpainted.—JUAN OLIVER.

A gay note for the nursery is this colorful wall plaque. Any number of similar birds might be grouped on a large panel in various ways

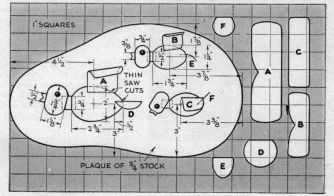

AUGUST CHECK LIST   [SHIPSHAPE HOME]

1. Replace frayed sash cords and tighten rattling windows.
2. Make permanent roof repairs, or completely reroof if necessary.
3. Check gutters and leaders; make any necessary repairs or replacements.
4. Inspect all flashings; apply roofing compound.
5. Repair rotted porch columns, railings, and steps.
6. Waterproof basement walls during dry weather.
7. Replace or repair deteriorated siding or siding shingles.
8. Paint flat porch roofs, patching first if necessary.
9. Clean chimney flues from top to bottom.
10. Overhaul fireplace damper and clean out smoke shelf.

POPULAR SCIENCE MONTHLY SHOP DATA

GARMENT-BAG CLOSERS made out of wood, like that shown below, take the place of zippers and other types of metal fasteners now scarce. The chief parts of the closure are two well-rounded edges on the cloth and a grooved rod to slide over them. The bag is open 30" from the top to permit access, and is sealed from dust and moths when the rod is moved into place. When it is necessary to launder the bag, it is an easy matter to remove the sliding member entirely

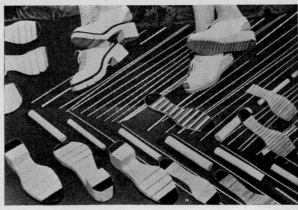

WOODEN SHOE SOLES that have the flexibility of leather and rubber, and are said to outwear both, are now available through development of a new binding material that joins the sole with the upper. The soles are made in sections or of wooden dowels. They are bonded to a waterproof fabric made of cotton on carpet looms and impregnated with a plastic. It is "vulcanized" to the sole and then to the upper

THIS PLASTIC TIE RACK with pegs for twenty ties is made entirely of noncritical materials. A hook at one end holds two leather belts, and a shallow plastic cup at the other keeps cuff links and tie clasps from rolling under the bed. Hung inside a closet door, the rack can be swung back so that it is flush with the door when not in use

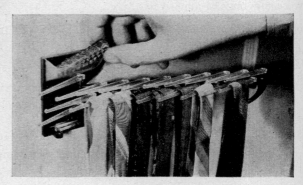

AN ODORLESS DEODORANT (not shown) has been placed on the market that does away with odors by chemical action, which neutralizes them at the source instead of covering them up with another odor. It comes as a powder that is applied to the offending area either by sprinkling it from the package or by using a spray gun. Because it is non-poisonous, it can be used to kill odors in animal cages and in barns without danger to the animals. The powder can easily be removed after it serves its purpose, either by sweeping or by washing it away

SHOE POLISH and dauber are kept together in this glass container. A large compartment at one end holds the shoe-cleaning paste, while at the other end there is a smaller compartment for keeping a special applicator. Each end has its own cover. The applicator is made to take the place of a brush for the purpose of rubbing the polish on the shoe, and it is said that it will last as long as the supply of paste will, or for about six months of average use by one person. The shoe polish is available in all of the popular shades, including black, light tan, and dark tan. The compactness of the outfit makes it especially handy for those who travel

AN ELECTRIC BRUSH, shown above, picks up animal hairs and lint as it removes dust from clothing, rugs, felt hats, furniture, draperies, and the like. Static electricity generated when the brush is used causes it to attract all such loose particles. The brush handle is made of a plastic and is of a size that can be conveniently gripped for use

TARNISHPROOFING SILVER for vacation storage is now a simple matter with a new chemically treated tissue paper. Family heirlooms, jewelry, or table service will be protected against the sulphurous fumes in the atmosphere just as long as they are snugly wrapped in the paper, which is made in various sizes to accommodate most needs

HERE IS A CUP AND SAUCER that is really "in the groove." A groove in the saucer locks the cup firmly so that it will not tip over. These pieces are made of crackproof plastic and weigh three quarters as much as crockery cup sets. They were designed for the Navy for use on patrol bombers and similar small vessels

LETTERS AND PHOTOGRAPHS that a man in the service sends home can be safely treasured in this handsome record book. The leatherette-finished cover is die engraved with a full-color reproduction of the service flag. Plastic rings used as binding permit the book to be opened perfectly flat without bending the pages. Large enough to hold many letters, photos, clippings and the like, it should prove a welcome gift to any service man's family

EXACTLY TWO CUPS is what this economical little drip coffee pot holds. It was especially designed for these days of coffee rationing when every single drop counts. With this pot it is easy to make fresh cups of coffee for members of families who eat their breakfast at different hours, and at the same time waste is prevented. Because it is glass, it is easily kept immaculate

HW 327

Mirror of American Colonial Design

IS FRAMED WITH HALF TURNINGS

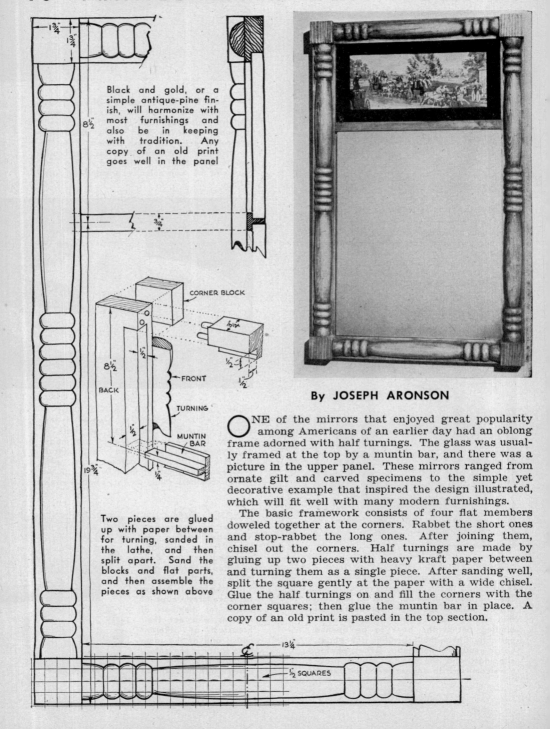

Black and gold, or a simple antique-pine finish, will harmonize with most furnishings and also be in keeping with tradition. Any copy of an old print goes well in the panel

CORNER BLOCK

FRONT

BACK

TURNING

MUNTIN BAR

Two pieces are glued up with paper between for turning, sanded in the lathe, and then split apart. Sand the blocks and flat parts, and then assemble the pieces as shown above

By JOSEPH ARONSON

ONE of the mirrors that enjoyed great popularity among Americans of an earlier day had an oblong frame adorned with half turnings. The glass was usually framed at the top by a muntin bar, and there was a picture in the upper panel. These mirrors ranged from ornate gilt and carved specimens to the simple yet decorative example that inspired the design illustrated, which will fit well with many modern furnishings.

The basic framework consists of four flat members doweled together at the corners. Rabbet the short ones and stop-rabbet the long ones. After joining them, chisel out the corners. Half turnings are made by gluing up two pieces with heavy kraft paper between and turning them as a single piece. After sanding well, split the square gently at the paper with a wide chisel. Glue the half turnings on and fill the corners with the corner squares; then glue the muntin bar in place. A copy of an old print is pasted in the top section.

½ SQUARES

YOUR VICTORY GARDEN TOOLS
and How to Use Them

TWICE the pleasure can be had from a garden, and half the drudgery can be eliminated, if you spend just a little time keeping your tools in good condition and always select the right tool for each job. Every garden tool is designed for some special purpose, and although it may substitute occasionally for some other, it does its own work best, as the accompanying illustrations show.

Twigs and stiff refuse may break the flexible prongs of a bamboo rake. Use a rigid steel rake for cleaning up this type of trash even if it is mixed with leaves

Don't use a digging tool as a crowbar for prying stones or as a sledge for driving stakes. The strain may break it

TOO BIG A BITE

SMALLER BITE

ALL STAYS IN SPADE

Take moderate bites with a spade. Just enough to pry loose and lift easily will be right. Oversize bites may break the spade handle

Never try to break shale or stony soil with a spade or hoe. To do so will dull the cutting edge or may even damage it. Use a pick mattock for this kind of job

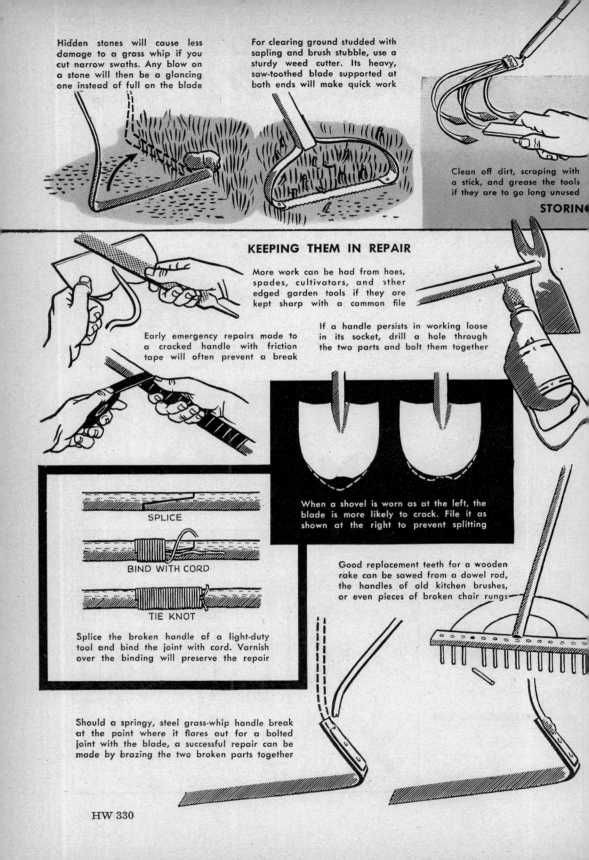

Hidden stones will cause less damage to a grass whip if you cut narrow swaths. Any blow on a stone will then be a glancing one instead of full on the blade

For clearing ground studded with sapling and brush stubble, use a sturdy weed cutter. Its heavy, saw-toothed blade supported at both ends will make quick work

Clean off dirt, scraping with a stick, and grease the tools if they are to go long unused

STORING

KEEPING THEM IN REPAIR

More work can be had from hoes, spades, cultivators, and other edged garden tools if they are kept sharp with a common file

Early emergency repairs made to a cracked handle with friction tape will often prevent a break

If a handle persists in working loose in its socket, drill a hole through the two parts and bolt them together

SPLICE

BIND WITH CORD

TIE KNOT

Splice the broken handle of a light-duty tool and bind the joint with cord. Varnish over the binding will preserve the repair

When a shovel is worn as at the left, the blade is more likely to crack. File it as shown at the right to prevent splitting

Good replacement teeth for a wooden rake can be sawed from a dowel rod, the handles of old kitchen brushes, or even pieces of broken chair rungs

Should a springy, steel grass-whip handle break at the point where it flares out for a bolted joint with the blade, a successful repair can be made by brazing the two broken parts together

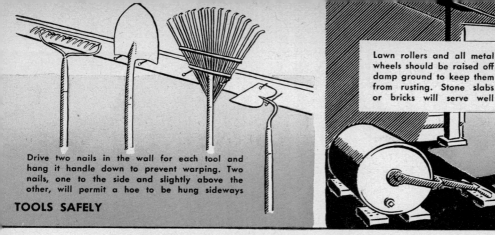

Lawn rollers and all metal wheels should be raised off damp ground to keep them from rusting. Stone slabs or bricks will serve well

Drive two nails in the wall for each tool and hang it handle down to prevent warping. Two nails, one to the side and slightly above the other, will permit a hoe to be hung sideways

TOOLS SAFELY

When hose must be left out-of-doors, it should be shaded from the warm rays of the sun, but it is still better to hang it on a rack. Always drain excess water

If an open-socket shovel or similar tool is used on wet jobs, seal the exposed end of the handle with two or three coats of waterproof paint and wax the remainder of the handle

PROTECTING THEM FROM EXPOSURE

Soaking rain and baking sun will shorten the life of any tool by encouraging rust and rot. When a lengthy pause is taken in a gardening job, tools should be put back in the tool shed until needed again

Bamboo lawn rakes should always be kept dry—not left out in rain, especially where their tips are likely to get a prolonged soaking. Such exposure as this may cause the bent tips to straighten out

HOMEMADE OUTDOOR GAMES

Provide Fun in Your Own Back Yard

BY JOE THERIAULT

After cutting holes for the midget golf course, set in small flowerpots

YOU don't have to have a priority number to enjoy the sunshine. And it isn't necessary to travel hundreds of miles to have a good time. Around the outside walls of your home, on the sundeck or roof, in the back yard, and along the driveway you can try your ingenuity at games that will provide hours of amusement for every member of your family as well as your guests. With a little bit of this and a little bit of that you can make a variety of games that will give you fun and exercise all summer long!

The following games, although improvised and by no means orthodox, have been thoroughly enjoyed by my friends and myself. If they are not quite suited to your needs, it is likely that you can make some variations that will be equally pleasing.

MIDGET GOLF. Without disfiguring your lawn, you can convert it into a nine-hole golf course in about 15 minutes. The simplest layout is to place the holes around the base of a shade tree. Dig out the holes with a small tin can or a transplanting tool, carefully removing the grass and earth, which can be returned at the end of the game. Then force a small can or flowerpot into each one of the holes.

To make the game more interesting, scatter hazards around the approaches to the holes. Shingles leaned against small rocks make good bunkers; other shingles driven endwise into the earth add difficulty to the approaches. Plant a numbered flag at each hole by tacking a small triangle of cardboard to a 9" stick and tapping the stick into the ground. Putter, niblick, and ball are the only other items needed for this amusing game. You can play it with partners or singly—each man for himself—adapting the ordinary rules of golf to your space or making up your own set of rules.

DART BOWLING. From a 3" bass plug or an oblong wood float you can quickly make a dart for playing a good muscle-bending game. First, remove any metal attach-

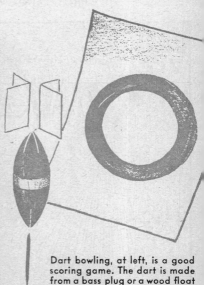

Dart bowling, at left, is a good scoring game. The dart is made from a bass plug or a wood float

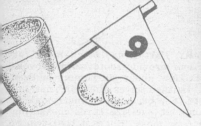

Place a numbered flag at each golf hole. Small hazards will also add to the fun

Fore! The player at the left aims for a hole on this pint-sized golf course that can be laid out under a shade tree

ments such as guides and hooks. Drill a hole in one end ½" deep and cut two ½" deep slots in the other end in the form of an X. Cut the head from a small nail, drive the nail into the hole, and file to a sharp point. Bend two pieces of cardboard into the X to make a tail, the dimensions of the latter depending upon the size and weight of the dart.

Draw the target on a piece of cardboard tacked to a wooden board and nail the board to the side of a tree or building. You ask where does *dart bowling* come in? If you place the target at a low elevation, squat on your toes, and toss the dart underhand, you will not only stretch unused muscles, but you'll afford yourself and your friends considerable amusement, especially if you use as the target some comical caricature or picture. If you prefer ordinary targets, they are easily made as shown below.

Just draw concentric circles on a piece of cardboard and you'll have a target for the dart game

BRICKBALL. This is a combination of bowling, underhand dart throwing, and miniature golf—believe it or not! Place four concrete blocks on the pavement in echelon but with the ends touching, as shown in the photo on page HW 334. Prop shingles or even cardboard so the ball will roll up the little incline into the holes. Take a squatting position about 12' from the target and try your luck, using a hand ball or other wooden or rubber ball small enough to enter the holes in the blocks. Assign target values to each pair of holes. Ordinary bricks will serve equally well if they are spaced far enough apart to receive the ball.

SHUFFLEBOARD. The only equipment needed for this game is a worn-out broom, a short lathlike stick, one nail, a few short boards ¾" thick, and a small amount of rosin. Cut off the broom handle and nail a 12" length of lath across the end. Whittle as many 6" disks as you wish from the boards. Coat your driveway with a thin layer of rosin and you are ready to play, using the same technique as in regular shuffleboard. It's a good idea to mark your target with chalk or paint if you want to keep score and really test your skill.

BOUNCE TENNIS. All you need for this stroke-improving game is space equal to about one half of a standard court, and a wall. Chalk or paint the bare outline of a net on the wall; then mark lines representing half a court on the pavement or yard. This requires space approximately 27' by 39'. You

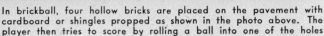

In brickball, four hollow bricks are placed on the pavement with cardboard or shingles propped as shown in the photo above. The player then tries to score by rolling a ball into one of the holes

can fudge a little on length, but not too much, if you are really serious about your game. Wood and Goddard in their *Complete Book of Games* suggest that you serve from behind the back line from the right, the first ball striking the wall on the left and bouncing back into the service court so your opponent can play it. Play the ball on the bounce or on the fly, changing sides after each serve. If you're practicing alone, let your conscience be your guide in scoring.

BASKETBALL. This game is particularly fun for children. Circle an old wood or metal barrel hoop with some netting. Fasten the hoop to a backstop board measuring 2' by 3' and nail the board at a convenient height above the garage door. All your children need now is a ball to be all set for an afternoon of sport, exercise, and fun.

JUMBO RUMMY. Parties are much more fun when you can provide some laugh-provoking games. How about gin rummy or even solitaire? In themselves they are not humorous, but they become real merrymakers if you hand out oversize cards measuring 8½" by 11" or more. Suggest that two of your guests play an exhibition game; then bring out the cards as a laugh surprise. Large cards may be purchased, but you can easily mark cardboard of the desired size.

GIANT CHECKERS. A large square of black-and-white checked linoleum will serve as a board, and large checkers can be easily whittled out of wood, or grocery-container lids may be painted. You can have a chess game for the more intellectual of your friends. Cut the chessmen from heavy cardboard and mount them on wooden blocks.

Card games played with giant cards will raise a good crop of laughs at parties, especially if you put on exhibition games

BOAT HINTS

Dolly Helps in Transporting Boats from Beach to Water

A DOLLY built as shown in the drawing at the right is an invaluable aid in transporting small craft down the beach and into the water. The wide roller that carries the load is especially designed not to sink into the sand as ordinary wheels would.

Any 2" thick scrap lumber will do for the frame, the two ends of which are shaped to conform to the bottom of the boat. Notches receive the keel. The four surfaces on which the boat rests are padded with carpeting or burlap to prevent damage to the hull.

The roller is built of 1" by 1¼" slats

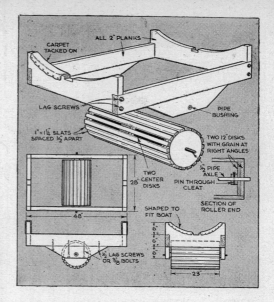

nailed about ½" apart to ends built up of two 12" disks each. Place these so that the grain of one is at right angles to that of the other. A piece of ½" pipe pinned to the ends turns in pipe bushings set into wooden bearing supports. These latter are bolted to the frame after the axle has been inserted in the bearings.—H. S.

Keeping Canvas Taut When Replacing Decks

IN REPLACING canvas decks, remove the cockpit coaming, coat the deck with white-lead paint, and while the paint is still wet lay on the canvas. Draw it as taut as possible and carefully tack it along the gunwale. Next, place sandbags as shown in the drawing over the cockpit opening to stretch the canvas even further. This is an easy way to assure tight-fitting canvas decks. After the canvas has been thoroughly stretched, apply two extra coats of paint.

Oil Cans Give Boat Additional Buoyancy

AN EXTRA margin of buoyancy can be given a boat by fastening empty 1-gal. tin cans beneath all the seats. The tall rectangular ones oil is sold in are best for the purpose. Dip the cans into melted paraffin or paint them to prevent rusting. Make certain that all the covers are screwed on tightly.

Fasten each can under a seat board with two straps of thin band or hoop iron. Be sure that the straps are so bent that the cans will not rattle around loosely. In small boats, it may be sufficient to affix cans under the center seat only.—J. A. EMMETT.

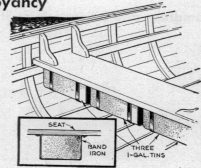

Glass Table Lamp

LIGHT SOCKET

SHORT NIPPLE FOR 8" SHADE (USE 1¼" STEM FOR 10" SHADE)

LOCK NUTS

COVER

GLASS JAR

DETAIL OF SOCKET ASSEMBLY

By ARTHUR C. MILLER

YOU probably have discovered that prune juice has vitamins. But did you know that the bottle itself has glamour? Glance at the photo above if you don't believe it—then go ahead and make this charming lamp yourself.

Ordinary flat paint is used in applying the design, which can be of any color and style desired. Paint only one side of the bottle, however, since paint on the back will show through the glass.

Let the paint dry for two or three days before attaching the socket and light cord. The original jar cap forms a base for the socket. Two ½" holes are drilled in this cap, one in the center for the socket, the other slightly to one side for the cord. Slip a plastic or rubber grommet into the latter hole to prevent the cord from fraying against the sharp edge of the metal.

Choose a white electric cord about 8' in length or longer, according to your needs. Enamel the metal cap apple green to blend with the color of the bottle. A white silk shade 8" in diameter was chosen for the lamp shown, but the size of the shade should be determined by the use to which the lamp is to be put. If a larger shade is desired, the socket must be raised by means of a stem attached to the base. This stem may be a ⅛" pipe nipple about 2" long.

A pair of these lamps placed on end tables on each side of a divan will serve ideally for reading. It is advisable to use 10" shades.

Gumdrops and a Peppermint Stick Form This Amusing Cannon Favor

THIS realistic candy cannon makes a novel party favor. Two large gumdrops serve as wheels, a long slender gumdrop forms the axle, and two baby gumdrops are the wheel caps. A toothpick holds everything together. The body of the cannon, a long candy stick, is held in place with a ribbon.—B. N.

Decorations are jigsawed, rounded off at the edges, and glued to the sidepieces

Two C-clamps and a wooden jig provide pressure for gluing the ends and floor

Used on the top of a writing table, the bookstand makes a handsome, useful piece for holding books, pens, and paper

TABLE-TOP BOOKSHELF HAS HANDY DRAWERS

By Charles and Bertram Brownold

THIS decorative bookshelf with two small drawers is particularly useful on a flat-top writing table. It should be made of a wood harmonizing with that of the table and given an appropriate finish.

The base is jigsawed from half-round molding that has been ripped on both sides. Screw a temporary holding block to one side of the moldings to facilitate handling them on the jig saw. After the curves are cut, miter the ends. Fasten the three pieces to a ½" board with screws driven at an angle through the edges of the board into the moldings.

Cut the sidepieces to shape after you have dadoed them to take the back and the floor.

Jigsaw the decorations from ¼" stock, round all edges off neatly, and glue the pieces to the sides. When gluing the floor and back into the dado grooves, small C-clamps used in conjunction with a wooden jig will provide the necessary pressure if a vise or clamp large enough to take the whole piece is not available.

Secure the base to the upper part by means of screws through the molding into the sides and back. The fronts and backs of the drawers are rabbeted to take the sides. A center piece ½" by 1½" by 6¾" separates the two drawers.

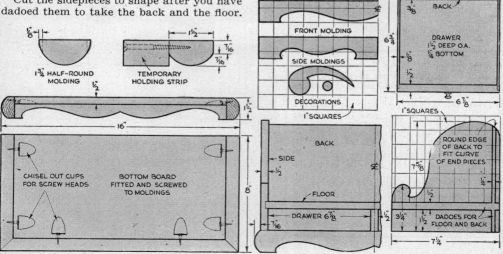

Ingenious

DEVICE THAT CAN BE

A NEW accessory, which the craftsman can make at home for his local Red Cross chapter, folds surgical dressings three to five times faster than by hand. Invented by Philip W. Burnham, an engineer with E. I. du Pont de Nemours and Company, it is already in use by the Delaware chapter for folding dressings. All the rights, plans, and specifications have been turned over to the American Red Cross. In Delaware alone the folder will, it is said, increase production by 150,000 worker-hours.

The device consists of a composition-board base with six hinged flaps that are folded over with the gauze in the order in which they are numbered in the drawing, thus creasing the material precisely to measurement. After each operation, the flap is returned to its original position. The accompanying photographs show the steps taken by a worker as she folds a dressing. Gauze must be cut to Army and Navy specifications so that with accurate folding the completed dressings can be packed to exact requirements. The folder is so easy to operate, however, that

1. The narrow flap, No. 1, is folded over first of all. The corner of the gauze is mitered to conform to specifications

2. Flap No. 2 is turned over on its hinge for a second correct fold in the series

3. Under the left hand of the worker is a finished third fold, while step No. 4, the next sequence, is being completed. The mitered corners may be seen here

4. With the folding over of flap No. 5, work on the dressing is nearing the end

5. It is finished with the sixth fold, which brings the dressing to regulation size

Red Cross Dressing Folder

MADE BY HOME CRAFTSMAN SPEEDS OUTPUT OF SURGICAL AIDS

even children have no difficulty using it.

Although construction of the folder is equally simple, all parts must be accurate to within 1/16". Materials needed are ⅛" composition board, adhesive tape having a tough, washable coating, and a few staples. The board should be the impregnated or tempered variety that will not shed particles that might become enmeshed in the dressings. The only tools necessary are an ordinary office stapler, shears or a paper cutter, a hammer, a sharp knife, and a chisel.

Staple the strips to the baseboard, using the flaps as spacing guides together with strips of thin cardboard temporarily inserted to provide clearance. Then butt the flaps against the hinge strips and tape them securely in place, leaving the clearance at the other end.

Dimensions given in the drawing are for a folder that will make standard 4" by 4" surgical dressings. Similar folders have been designed for making standard 2" by 2" and 4½" by 8" dressings. Construction plans for them may be obtained from the Red Cross.

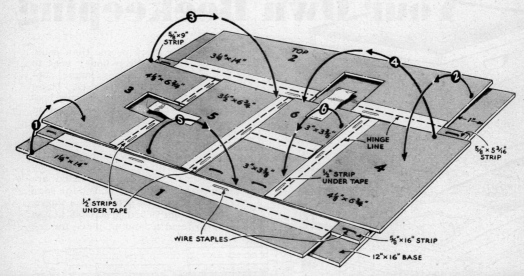

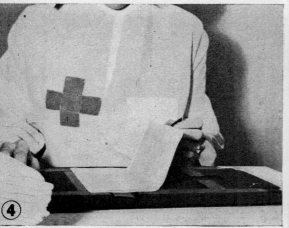

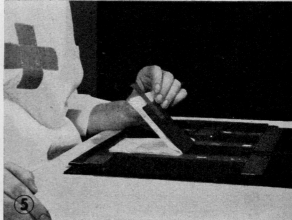

Locked corner joints may be made on a circular saw if one is available

Right, cutting a finger hold in one side. Grind the edge of an ordinary chisel round for this job

How to Build
Your Own Beekeeping

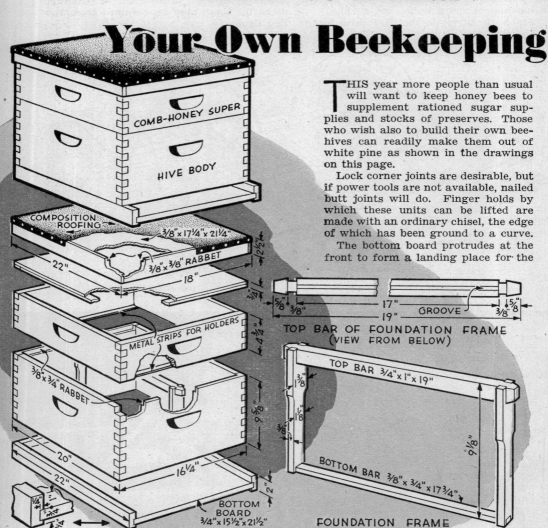

COMB-HONEY SUPER

HIVE BODY

COMPOSITION ROOFING

3/8" x 17¼" x 21¼"

22"

3/8" x 3/8" RABBET

18"

2½"

METAL STRIPS FOR HOLDERS

4½"

3/8" x 3/4" RABBET

9⅝"

20"

16¼"

22"

¼"

2"

BOTTOM BOARD
3/4" x 15½" x 21½"

TOP BAR OF FOUNDATION FRAME
(VIEW FROM BELOW)

5/8" 3/8"

17"

GROOVE

5/8" 3/8"

19"

TOP BAR 3/4" x 1" x 19"

3/8"

1/8"

3/8"

9⅛"

BOTTOM BAR 3/8" x 3/4" x 17¾"

FOUNDATION FRAME

THIS year more people than usual will want to keep honey bees to supplement rationed sugar supplies and stocks of preserves. Those who wish also to build their own beehives can readily make them out of white pine as shown in the drawings on this page.

Lock corner joints are desirable, but if power tools are not available, nailed butt joints will do. Finger holds by which these units can be lifted are made with an ordinary chisel, the edge of which has been ground to a curve.

The bottom board protrudes at the front to form a landing place for the

Material from an apple box is just right for the inner cover, which is shown being assembled in the photo above

How the bottom board is assembled. Make this longer than the hive so as to provide a landing place for the bees. Rabbeting of the strips is not necessary if power tools are not available

Equipment

The inner lining is placed inside the cover. This provides adequate protection against summer heat

bees. An entrance stick is used in cold weather to reduce the opening to the hive. The double lid, consisting of an inner and an outer cover, affords maximum protection against summer heat. Apple-box stock is just the right thickness for the inside cover, and ordinary lightweight asphalt roofing makes a good outside sheathing. It should be quite warm when it is bent over the edges, so that it will not crack.

Hives and supers should be painted on the outside only. Give them two or three coats of white outdoor paint before installing your bee colony. If ready-made frames are not available, you can make them as shown in the drawing.—BENJAMIN NIELSEN.

As a further protection, a layer of asphalt roofing is tacked securely over the assembled cover

---

WIRING CONVENIENCE OUTLETS   [ELECTRICITY]

In conformity with the recommendations of the National Electrical Code (1940 edition), convenience outlets which supply current in a kitchen, laundry, pantry, dining room, or breakfast room for other purposes than lighting should be wired on separate circuits and with wire not smaller than No. 12. This allows for the use of flatirons, refrigerators, waffle irons, washing machines, and other accessories that draw considerable current.

One outlet is suggested for every 20 linear feet, or fraction thereof, in the total distance around the room. As far as possible, the outlets should be spaced equal distances apart. Nonmetallic overhead receptacles should be installed in laundries and similar damp locations. These requirements are obviously intended to eliminate the dangers arising from the use of flexible-cord wiring in homes, and from overloading of branch circuits.

POPULAR SCIENCE MONTHLY SHOP DATA

TWO-EVENING

THREE USEFUL ITEMS FROM BITS

HOURGLASS WITH PLASTIC FRAME. *Average time: 4 hours.* This piece, having a scale graduated between one and 15 minutes, will be useful in the kitchen as well as in the darkroom. A 15-minute sand glass can be purchased at an optical store. Small pieces of scrap plastic are used for the disks, feet, and posts. Scribe the circles with dividers and cut the disks full; then finish by sanding to the line. Drill holes part way through the centers and countersink them to receive the ends of the hourglass. Spot three holes for the screws, as shown in the sketch.

The six feet are turned in a lathe and can be cut from the same stock used for the posts. Drill 1/8" holes through the feet and countersink one end to receive the round head of a brass machine screw. Round the edges of the countersunk ends. Now cut the three posts, being sure they are flat and true at both ends. Drill both ends to a depth of 7/16" with a No. 44 drill and thread with a 4-36 tap. When using the tap be careful to avoid binding by removing chips. This prevents stripping of the threads. When assembling, have the glass slightly loose to avoid breakage. Mark a scale on one post in time intervals to suit. Drill small holes at the marks and rub black paint into them for ease in reading.

BACHELOR'S CATCHALL. *Average time: 4 hours.* A wife, too, will appreciate this transparent case of clear plastic and walnut for keeping her spouse's cuff links, shirt studs, tie clasps, and collar buttons all safely in one place. Before turning the walnut base, cut a 3/8" deep slot in the stock for the partition. Trim the stock on the band saw and mount it on a screw center after inserting a tight spline in the groove to prevent the shoulders from breaking. Turn it to the dimensions shown on the drawing; then finish it with two coats of white shellac and wax. Fit the round plastic wall, which is cut from tubular stock, to the base and cement in place.

Use a screw center when turning the walnut cover, first cutting the inside ring to fit the plastic wall, then reversing and cutting the rounded rim and the inside rabbet for the plastic top to fit in. In turning the knob, follow the dimensions on the drawing and finish the piece in the lathe. Center an undersized hole in the bottom of the knob for the screw. Finish both pieces with white shellac and wax.

The plastic portion of the top is cut slightly oversize from flat stock and trial-fitted to a tight fit in the rabbet of the wooden rim with the aid of fine sandpaper on a disk sander. Drill a hole in the center for the screw that fastens it to the knob.

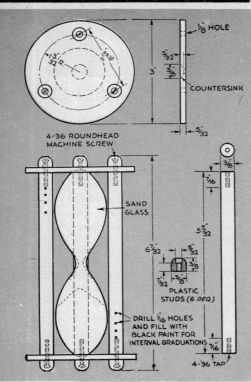

PROJECTS

OF PLASTIC AND WOOD

Average time: 5 hours.

TIDBIT TRAY. This handsome server, suitable for holding tasty snacks and canapés, is made of mahogany except for the partitions, which are of contrasting walnut. Before turning the top tray, cut the grooves for the single partition in the stock and fill the slots with tight-fitting splines. Bandsaw into shape and turn on a faceplate, rounding the rim as shown. Before removing the piece from the lathe, drill a ½" hole for the dowel in the end of the post. Finish on the lathe with two coats of clear lacquer. Repeat the procedure for the bottom tray, cutting an extra groove for the second partition.

Roughly shape the knob on the band saw; then mount it in a chuck and turn the shank and lower half of the ball. Drill the hole for the post joint and insert a snug-fitting dowel to hold the wood in the chuck while the other half of the ball is being turned. Finish this also with two coats of lacquer. In cutting slots for partitions in the post and the ball, use the jig illustrated for steadying against the saw fence.

Partitions, shaped on the band saw and sanded to the contours of the rims, are fitted into the saw cuts. Glue all parts. Use four brads at the bottom.

ALL PROJECTS DESIGNED BY ERNEST R. DEWALT

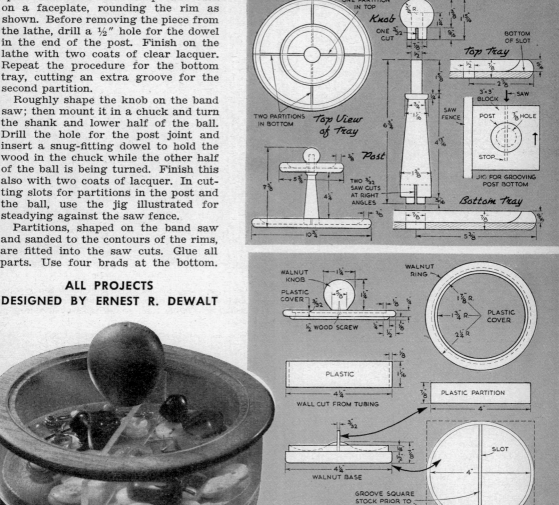

Corner Joints Are Speedily

By EDWIN M. LOVE

ANYONE owning a circular saw is equipped to make reinforced corner joints that would be extremely difficult to execute by hand. Splined miters across the face of stock, much used for frames, are easy to make on such a machine. Similar miters in the edges of material to be used for box sides are also quickly cut. The more elaborate mitered rabbets and lock joints are not much more difficult.

There are certain hazards normally present in grooving the end of a piece of wood, because it must be slid against the ripping fence in an awkward vertical position, and may catch in the saw opening of the inset. Consequently a jig should be built to hold stock firmly upright while end cuts are being made.

What type of jig is used? An end-sawing jig for the home shop that can be adapted to a variety of work and will prove a useful, permanent accessory for the circular saw is shown in the drawings and in the photographs on this page. Built of scrap wood, such a jig has three simple parts: a wooden auxiliary fence to be screwed fast to the ripping fence, an inverted U-section built to slide without play on the auxiliary fence, and two 45-deg. wooden guides fastened to the face of the sliding section. Dimensions may vary from those shown in the drawing so long as the section clears lock nuts or other obstructions on the ripping fence and holds the work securely. When assembling a jig, insert a piece of heavy paper between the back guide and the spacer to provide sliding clearance on the auxiliary fence.

How is the jig used? To groove a face-mitered piece for a spline, mount a dado head of the required width on the saw arbor and adjust for the depth of the cut. Place the jig on the auxiliary fence and lock the latter with the face of the jig at the proper distance from the

saw. Screw one 45-deg. guide in place and clamp the stock to the jig against this guide. Cut the groove in the miter by pushing the jig along the fence. When one end of each piece has been grooved, remove the guide and attach the other one. This will insure flush fitting of the joints because all face sides can be kept against the jig. If a

A jig is used in grooving a face miter joint for a slip tongue, as above. Edge miters are grooved for splines either with the same jig (below) or with the miter gauge as shown in a drawing

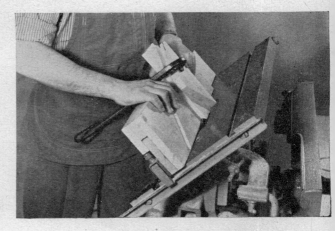

Made on the Circular Saw

molding is to be splined, regard the flat back of the molding as the face side.

Should the rip fence on your circular saw allow the auxiliary fence to be transferred to the other side, all the grooves can be cut with the pieces inclined forward. This also facilitates the making of a blind groove in which the spline is hidden from the outer edge. In a face-mitered joint, a spline with grain running crosswise projects at both ends and is trimmed flush after assembly. In a hidden-spline joint, the outer end is rounded to fit the arc of the saw cut.

How is a mitered rabbet joint cut? Tilt the arbor or table of the machine at 45 deg. If the under corner of the insert opening rubs, file it clear or make a wooden insert. Set the face of the jig lightly touching the dado head, adjust the saw for depth, and screw on a guide in a vertical position. Clamp a piece of waste to the jig and make trial cuts until a sharp, 45-deg. lip is left on the face side; then proceed with the ends to be joined. Finally, level the table and rabbet the ends by

After the miter for a mitered rabbet joint has been cut on a tilted saw table, the rabbet can be cut with the miter gauge

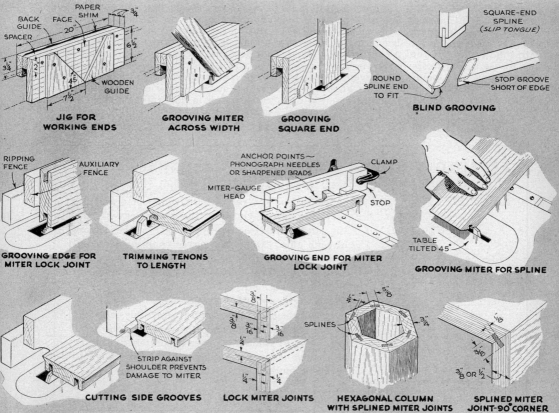

JIG FOR WORKING ENDS

GROOVING MITER ACROSS WIDTH

GROOVING SQUARE END

BLIND GROOVING

SQUARE-END SPLINE (SLIP TONGUE)

ROUND SPLINE END TO FIT

STOP GROOVE SHORT OF EDGE

BACK GUIDE — FACE — PAPER SHIM — SPACER — WOODEN GUIDE

GROOVING EDGE FOR MITER LOCK JOINT

TRIMMING TENONS TO LENGTH

GROOVING END FOR MITER LOCK JOINT

GROOVING MITER FOR SPLINE

RIPPING FENCE — AUXILIARY FENCE

ANCHOR POINTS — PHONOGRAPH NEEDLES OR SHARPENED BRADS — MITER-GAUGE HEAD — CLAMP — STOP

TABLE TILTED 45°

CUTTING SIDE GROOVES

STRIP AGAINST SHOULDER PREVENTS DAMAGE TO MITER

LOCK MITER JOINTS

SPLINES

HEXAGONAL COLUMN WITH SPLINED MITER JOINTS

SPLINED MITER JOINT-90° CORNER

using a miter gauge in the usual manner.

Can mitered lock joints be cut? Yes. On ¾" stock use a ¼" wide dado head, making miter cuts as for a miter rabbet joint. Then level the table and, supporting the material in a vertical position, cut a groove ¾" deep in one end ¼" from the face. Use the miter gauge to cut the square-end tenon to length and also to cut a mating miter, groove, and tenon in the joining piece. The cross-grained edges of the joint can be strengthened against splitting off in assembly by reducing the thickness of the tenons. A 3/16" groove can be cut with two passes of a ⅛" outer dado blade. A tenon ⅛" thick will fit a one-pass groove. Lock joints mitered longitudinally use the same cuts, but the work is slid lengthwise along the ripping fence.

How are splined miter joints cut? Such joints are made in the ends of boards with the table or saw arbor tilted 45 deg. for mitering the ends. The fence is then used as a length stop in connection with the miter gauge while the groove is cut at right angles to the face of a miter. A still better method is to use a board screwed to the gauge head and fitted with points to prevent creeping, as shown in the drawing. This accessory is also useful when cutting cross grooves for lock miter joints. A notched stop block bears

To groove a corner for a reinforcing spline, use two 45-deg. guides on the jig. Clamp and saw both frame members together

against the rabbet shoulder so as to avoid damaging the sharp edge of the miter.

When grooves for a spline are cut in miters along the long edge of two boards, tilt the table or arbor 45 deg., mount a dado head, adjust the fence, and slide each mitered edge against the fence while cutting its groove. For thin stock, use an ordinary saw blade, shaving a hardwood spline to fit. Aside from affording more gluing surface, splined miter joints help in clamping because there is no slipping of the ends past each other when pressure is applied.

FREEING BINDING DOORS   [SHIPSHAPE HOME]

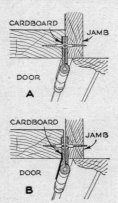

IN OBSTINATE cases that other means have failed to remedy, remove the hinge pins and lift the door down. Unscrew the hinge leaves from the jamb. Chisel a thin shaving from the bottom of each gain. Screw the leaves back in place and replace the door in its opening. If the lock edge still binds, loosen the door hinge leaves and slip thin cardboard strips behind the outer edges as at *A*. Tighten the screws again.

If the door is hinge-bound after this, slip the cardboard under the hinge leaves from the joint side as at *B*. Should it prove absolutely necessary to remove some wood, plane the binding edge to give not more than 1/16" clearance.

POPULAR SCIENCE MONTHLY SHOP DATA

Attractive Glove Box Built with Splined Corner Joints

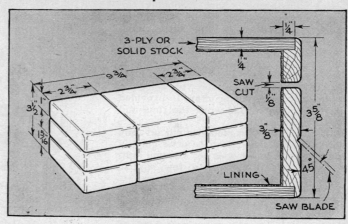

START this box by cutting a strip 3' long for the sides and ends. Rabbet its long edges to receive the top and bottom pieces, which may be cut from either plywood or solid stock. Saw the sides and ends roughly to length by mitering one end of each; then bring them to exact dimensions by mitering the other ends. Bevel the edges of the top slightly so as to secure a wedging action. Now cut the grooves for the splines and make the splines, following the directions given in the preceding article. Cover all joints with a thin coat of glue, allow it to dry for a few minutes, and assemble the box. Clamp it together, forcing in the top and bottom pieces; then true it up. Wipe off surplus glue with a damp cloth.

Score the surface lines on the circular saw, having the table tilted at an angle of

Shallow saw cuts make the surface lines on the sides, ends, and top

45 deg. Round and smooth all corners and edges by hand. Cut the box into two pieces at the point indicated in the drawing. It can then be given a natural finish or a coat of enamel. Line the interior with leather or velvet to add a neat and professional touch.—E. M. L.

Hinge Used on Handle to Grip Blade of Tiny Keyhole Saw

A DIMINUTIVE keyhole saw for use in model-making and other delicate tasks can be made from workshop odds and ends. The handle is shaped from ⅜" plywood, and a rectangular section is rabbeted to receive one leaf of a ½" by 1" brass hinge. Two

3/16" holes are drilled in the recessed area to match those in the hinge. Then a section of a coping-saw blade is laid in the hinge and both leaves are bolted to the handle with machine screws so as to clamp the blade securely. If a hole about 3/16" in diameter is drilled in the opposite end, a handy receptacle will be formed in which additional blades can be kept at hand.—A. ALBANESE.

Hack-Saw Blade Serves as Cutter in Simple Hand Molder

THE home craftsman who has no power shaper may still make moldings by using an old hack-saw blade for the job. Grind the blade to the desired shape and carefully sharpen the edges. In a stepped handle bore a set of holes and saw across them to provide a slot for holding the blade. Insert the shaped cutter and tighten it in place with small bolts and nuts. By using the inside shoulder of the handle as a guide, the cutter can be drawn across the surface of the molding for forming the corresponding contours. A number of cutters of different shapes can be ground as need arises, and as many may be inserted in the holder at a time as are required.—R. E. DAVIS.

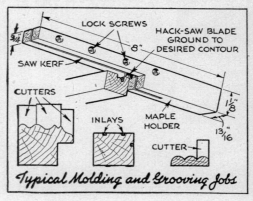

Typical Molding and Grooving Jobs

QUALITY of finish is the reward of painstaking effort, probably no more so on any job tackled by the home craftsman than that of painting or staining unfinished furniture. Yet there is no mystery attached to getting results worthy of a professional cabinetmaker, and even the rankest amateur need not hesitate to take advantage of the wide selection of unfinished pieces being offered—provided he is willing to give his work the time and care it requires.

Finishing unpainted pieces is not an easy job in the sense that it can be done quickly or haphazardly, but it does not demand difficult techniques. Following a few simple, fundamental rules is all that is necessary. And it means creating a piece you will like to have in your home instead of doing just a so-so job.

First, decide on the color and kind of finish you want. The former should harmonize with the existing decorative scheme of the room; the latter should be suitable for the type of piece—a living-room bookcase and a lawn chair call for different treatments. There is also the matter of wearing quality. A much-used piece, for example, needs a hard, impervious finish such as enamel or varnish.

Be sure to buy furniture made of a wood suitable for the finish you have chosen. If this is to be mahogany, walnut, oak, or a similar finish through which the grain shows, select a piece made of a wood that has an open and pleasing grain. If the finish is to be paint or enamel, the kind of wood makes little difference. For the newer soft finishes sometimes called blond, platinum, or driftwood, the smooth, soft texture of Western pine is desirable.

It is important to use the exact kind of painting materials needed if the finish is to turn out exactly as desired. There is no such

IT'S EASY TO FINISH UNPAINTED FURNITURE

Simple Methods Used with the Proper Materials Will Enable You to Put a Lasting Coat of Beauty on New Pieces

By Fay Turpin

thing as an "all-purpose" paint. Manufacturers make complete lines of paints, enamels, varnishes, dyes, and stains, and each maker's printed directions for his product should be strictly followed.

Don't mix old and new paints, nor paints of one manufacturer with paints of another, because the ingredients may be chemically unsuited. The make-up of finishing materials is changing because of new discoveries and shortages of such items as tung oil from China and lac from India. This doesn't mean that excellent finishes cannot now be had, but it does mean that there is grave danger in mixing old and new materials.

Four grades of sandpaper on a piece of wood. Left to right, they are Nos. 4, 2, 0, and 0000, No. 4 being the coarsest

Unpainted pieces seldom come sanded well at joints and the ends of rungs

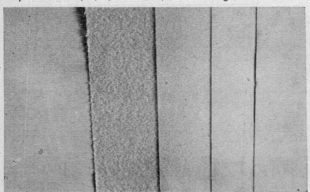

Oak and other dyes are followed by a clear finish, rubbed with pumice and oil, and then waxed to a sheen

For furniture, use a soft varnish or enamel brush. To some extent these are also being made with substitutes. New Chinese hog bristles are scarce, yet fair brushes are available made partly of Chinese bristles, and others contain horsehair and Mexican istle, a vegetable fiber. A medium-quality brush will do a good job, but it will not last a long time. A cheap brush is a hazard at any time. Removing trailing hairs from a shedding brush can completely ruin a coat of quick-drying finish. Brushes should be preserved by thorough cleaning after use. They may be washed with warm water and soap, or a commercial brush cleaner may be used. Never stand a brush on its bristles when putting it away.

The proper conditioning of a piece to be finished is easily half the work of doing a good job. Any finish is only as good as the surface to which it is applied. Bare wood absorbs moisture, dirt, oil, and grease, and all these must be removed. The piece must be thoroughly dry all the way through. Moisture must not be painted in.

When clean and dry, the surface should be sanded to a pleasing smoothness with sandpaper wrapped around a block of wood having rounded edges. The final sanding should be done with the finest grit available, and if the sandpaper has been used before, so much the better. Keep your fingers off the surface so oil from the skin will not get into the pores of the wood. After sanding, dust the piece thoroughly with a clean brush or cloth.

Dust and dampness in the air are a hazard. Ventilate the room and put papers on the floor as a precaution against both raising dust and spilling paint. The time a coat of paint takes to dry varies with the weather, the type of paint, and even the ingredients in paints of the same type. As a general rule—and it is a safe one—double

A few light strokes of coarse and then fine sandpaper remove the rough edges

Smooth finishes depend upon smooth sanding. Use sandpaper on a block of wood, with even strokes following the grain

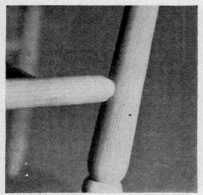

It is a safe plan to try colors on bare wood before they are applied to the piece to be finished. This allows changes if the shade is not just that desired

In general, the best method of painting stools, chairs, tables, and the like is to start with the piece turned upside down; then right it to finish the top surfaces

the time the directions give. Each coat must be dry all the way through, not just dry to the touch. Most first coats, and some intermediate coats, need sanding, so be sure each is thoroughly dry.

For pieces upon which brilliant, colorful coats are desired, such as outdoor furniture or small interior articles, there are quick-drying enamels that give satisfactory results in one or two coats. The larger indoor pieces, however, usually call for softer finishes that more or less show the grain of the wood. The general method of using these soft finishes is to treat the bare wood with a coat of white lead tinted with the color and rub it off before it dries; then follow with a coat of clear enamel and later with one or two coats of wax or varnish.

Enamels and paints are similar except for the final coat or two. An undercoat of flat or primer paint should precede the coats of enamel or paint. Enamel is flowed on with no more than one or two strokes of the brush. Paint, on the other hand, takes several strokes to spread properly. Enamels have hard surfaces and are best for pieces that get hard wear and washing.

Varnish is a transparent finish and may be clear or a varnish-stain, that is, varnish with a stain mixed directly with it. It is similar to enamel in that the latter is like an opaquely colored varnish, and, like enamel, varnish is applied with a soft brush and flowed on. Handsome finishes are obtained by rubbing between coats with fine wet-or-dry abrasive paper. Rubbing with rotten-stone and oil at the very end will impart a high polish.

Oil stains have a wide appeal because both hard and soft woods take them and

finish beautifully. Stir the oil stain well before and during use. Apply a medium coat thinned with turpentine, and let dry. One coat is usually enough, and a second should be applied only if necessary to deepen the shade. If the first coat appears too dark as it goes on, it can be rubbed off with burlap, excelsior, or crumpled newspapers. Varnish is applied as a finishing coat, or the piece can be waxed. A wood filler of

DO'S AND DONT'S FOR BETTER FINISHING

★

DO select the kind of wood for the kind of finish wanted.

DO prepare the surface of the piece thoroughly.

DO follow painting directions on the container through the entire procedure.

DO use paint made for the particular results desired.

DO sand between coats for a professionally smooth surface.

DO clean, wash, and store brushes properly for future use.

★

DON'T paint damp wood or paint in a damp atmosphere.

DON'T use the wrong kind of brush for the job.

DON'T buy cheap paint and expect good results.

DON'T paint over a coat that hasn't dried through thoroughly.

DON'T paint in a dusty atmosphere.

Hold the paintbrush lightly but firmly with the handle extending between the thumb and forefinger; then, regardless of the direction of the stroke, the brush will always be under complete control

the proper shade is used before this final varnishing or waxing if the grain of the wood is extremely open.

Dye coats offer a wide choice of finishes ranging all the way from platinum through sandalwood to walnut and mahogany. Both close-grained and open-grained woods are suitable for dye finishes. First, apply a dye coat sparingly with a brush and let it dry 24 hours. Then apply a clear finish made by the same dye manufacturer and, after another 24 hours of drying, sand lightly. Finish with another coat of clear, and buff with wax after it is dry. Varnish or clear shellac may be used for this third coat.

Antiquing furniture surfaces of light color takes off the effect of newness, yet at the same time preserves the protective coating. The process is simple. Squeeze a little oil color, preferably burnt umber, raw sienna, or Vandyke brown, in a cup and thin it with ⅔ turpentine and ⅓ linseed oil. Rub this mixture on the piece and off again, using a wad of cheesecloth. Leave darkened places in the corners and little or no color on the flat surfaces.

A pumpkin-brown finish is obtained by rubbing on and off a coat of boiled linseed oil colored with burnt sienna and a bit of ultramarine blue. After drying, sand lightly, apply a clear coat, and follow with wax. These colors are transparent pigments and allow the wood to show through.

Driftwood-finished effects are made by first applying a thin base coat of dye of this particular color. Use a fine brush. Follow this with a thin coat of clear finish and sand it lightly when dry. A second coat of clear finish completes the job.

Light walnut can be put on fine-grain woods by mixing burnt umber, lampblack, and rose lake, which has a slightly reddish cast, or rose pink, which is a little browner, in boiled linseed oil thinned with a little turpentine. Try the mixture on a piece of wood first to make sure the color is right. After drying, finish with a clear coat and wax.

Blond finishes are obtained with a white undercoater paint tinted with raw sienna and raw umber and thinned with turpentine and boiled linseed oil. Rub this across the grain and let it set until it gets sticky; then rub it off. When the surface is thoroughly dry, apply a coat of clear finish, white shellac, or varnish, and then wax.

This cream corner cupboard is a trifle lighter than the wall. Its blue interior was softened by rubbing with thinned white and a trace of pumice

KEEPING

SECTIONS OF GARDEN HOSE

Crepe-paper rolls that are to be cut into strips often are too bulky to be easily cut with scissors. A bread knife with a serrated cutting edge will do the job more quickly and leave as neat an edge

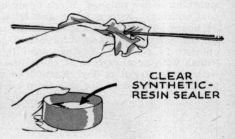

CLEAR SYNTHETIC-RESIN SEALER

Perhaps the extra strain from trying to keep your Victory garden well watered this summer has put your old hose on the scrap pile. Before turning it over to the salvage collector, you might cut off three or four 3" sections. These will make handy holders for brooms, mops, and the like in your hall closet. Split them lengthwise and nail to the closet wall. Just a moderate downward pressure on the handles is sufficient to make the holders grip firmly

Wire clotheslines can be protected against rust with a sealer such as is used for new woodwork. Remove any excess before it hardens, leaving a thin film. This will also make lines easier to clean and keep clean

SANDPAPER

The rough bottom of a vase can be smoothed by rubbing it over fine sandpaper. In severe cases, wet the bottom with turpentine first

Dress up a drab-looking flowerpot by covering it with a lamp shade. Shades that fit are easily found, since they are made in many sizes

To remove the lid from a jelly glass without damaging the top, place half a spring clothespin between it and the can opener

THE HOME SHIPSHAPE

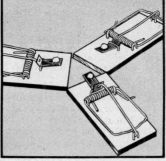

MOLESKIN PAD

Mucilage kept in a small oil can will spread more evenly and more neatly on the backs of clippings you are pasting in your scrapbook. Apply along the four edges only

Mice or rats who eat the bait left for them in the trap, and then go off instead of being caught, will back themselves into trouble if you set three traps in this manner

When swinging drawer handles mar furniture, pad the underside with the adhesive moleskin that is sold for padding shoes. Use it also on lamp bases to prevent scratching

NAIL TO WALL

Here's how to keep the kinks out of your garden hose so that it won't wind up as rubber salvage. Simply nail an old water pail to the side of the house or garage and wrap the hose around the pail as shown

WAXED PAPER

ADHESIVE TAPE

GRAPE RASPBERRY STRAWBERRY BLUEBERRY

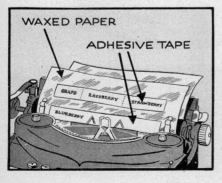

EXTRA SHELF

BRACKETS

Adhesive tape can be used for durable typed labels if it is stuck on wax paper before insertion in the machine. It readily sticks to other surfaces after it is pulled off

You can make an extra closet shelf by using a piece of board long enough to stretch between the existing shelf and a cleat on the opposite wall. Two Z-shaped strap-iron brackets fastened to the board rest atop the old shelf

This useful cup center punch saves time in the small shop

Chuck a piece of steel, center-drill, and turn to dimensions

Reverse the piece, counterbore for stock size, and knurl grip

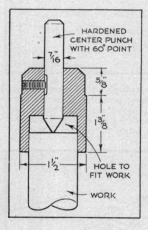

HARDENED CENTER PUNCH WITH 60° POINT

7/16"

5/8"

1 3/8"

1 1/2"

HOLE TO FIT WORK

WORK

A CUP CENTER PUNCH, shown in the photo at left above, is a timesaver in locating center holes, especially in the small shop with a quantity of round bar stock to center. It differs from the bell-type center punch in that it is made for one size stock only and, when it is slipped over the end of the work, is held rigidly in line with the bar. When the punch is tapped with a hammer, the center is located quickly and accurately.

In making up the body of the punch, a piece of steel is chucked, centerdrilled for tailstock support, turned to the dimensions given on the drawing, knurled for a good finger grip, and cut off. With the piece reversed in the chuck, the center-punch hole is drilled and the end counterbored to fit the stock. A hole is drilled and tapped in the body for a set-screw, which projects into a flat filed on the punch and keeps it from falling out but allows it a limited movement. The punch is turned to a blunt point at one end and slightly beveled at the other. It is then hardened, tempered, and ground to a 60-deg. point.—C. W. WOODSON.

LARGE WOODEN PULLEYS for V-belts can be made of ¾" thick wood as shown in the drawing at the right. The pieces are cut to shape and fastened together with glue and corrugated fasteners. A large square piece is then screwed to one side for additional strength and to prevent warping. The groove can be made quickly and smoothly on a shaper, or it may be cut with a chisel. When finished, the wooden pulley is attached to the side of the flywheel or crown pulley by means of U-bolts or heavy wire.

A single big pulley such as this will give the necessary speed reduction for operating a concrete mixer, corn sheller, cream separator, fanning mill, or other such equipment from a ¼-hp. electric motor.—R. E.

SHAPER CUTTER

V-FENCE

ADJUSTABLE PINS in the edges of factory trucks at the General Electric plant in Schenectady, N. Y., replace blocks once used to keep such articles as studs, pipes, and boxes from sliding off. Six ¾" steel pins set in holes drilled in the platform of the truck, two on each side and two at the open end, can be adjusted with cotter pins from a position flush with the deck of the truck to one 3" above it. In the raised position, the pins not only keep the load on the platform but facilitate tying it with rope when this is necessary.

USING THE MODERN SHAPER

How a Steel V-Block Is Machined on This Versatile Power Tool

MACHINING a rectangular slot or a V-groove in a short piece of metal is a job that might well be done on a shaper, which is a small planing machine with a short, forward cutting stroke. The piece is fastened to a table that holds it stationary as the tool takes its cut. This table can be adjusted to any convenient height, and it has a cross feed, operated both by hand and power, for use when a finished cut is to be wider than the tool. Depth of cut is regulated by vertical movement of the tool head.

A crank mechanism changes circular motion to reciprocating motion, and is so designed that the return stroke is faster than that for cutting, thus reducing the time on a job. The tool head has a clapper action on the return stroke, making withdrawal of feed between cuts unnecessary.

Work may be clamped to the table, held in a vise, clamped to an angle plate, or held between index centers. Often the piece is rested on cast-iron or steel parallels.

Tools, though smaller, have the same shapes and clearance angles as those for planers, and are described in any good machinist's handbook. They may be made to cut at an angle by swinging the post and head on a swivel and setting to a scale marked in degrees. Special tool holders are available for mounting interchangeable bits ground for other cutting operations.

Be sure any tool is tight in the tool post and that the work is neither loose nor too high—otherwise you run a risk of damaging or wrecking the machine. Always wear goggles and keep your hands away from the work while the machine is in operation.

One of the motion pictures produced by the U. S. Office of Education for training machine-tool operators, and distributed for the Government by Castle Films, deals with shaper operations for machining two rectangular slots and two V-slots in a piece of tool steel 6⅞" long and 3" square. Operations from the film are shown in the photos on the following pages.

1 Two rectangular slots and two V-grooves are to be cut in this block of tool steel. The ends are painted with Prussian blue, and the layout is made according to the plan as a guide for cutting

2 After the shaper is carefully brushed, papers are laid at each end of the parallel to serve as indicators that the work is down tight. If it is, the papers can't be pulled out after clamping

3 When the vise has been tightened snugly, the block is driven down on the parallel with a soft hammer; then the vise is tightened further. If a paper pulls out, the work must be reclamped

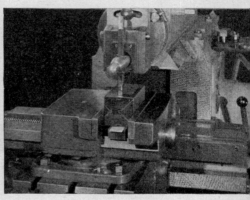

4 To avoid clamping difficulty when the block is turned, the rectangular slots are machined first. A square-face tool is ground to the width the slots are to be and is clamped in the tool post

5 After the tool is leveled on the block, the length of the ram stroke is set. For a block 6⅞" long, an 8" stroke will allow 1⅛" at the end for tool clearance and downward feeding

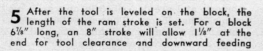

6 On some shapers, the stroke is controlled by an adjustment screw, as in the photo at left. Others have a scale on the ram, as below. Both principles are the same. Readings are in inches

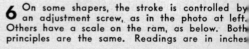

7 Once the ram stroke is set, the speed of the ram and tool must be determined. Reference to a handbook shows tool steel can be cut at 11" per minute, so the gears are set for that speed

8 Now the cutting action begins. With the tool placed over the layout, it is fed down .002" on each stroke. A tool as wide as the slot is used, since extreme accuracy is not required here

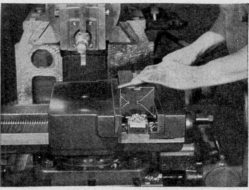

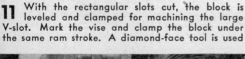

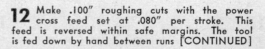

9 At the end of each return stroke, the tool head is fed down by hand. This can be done by tapping the feed screw handle with the heel of the hand. Practice soon makes feeding uniform

10 When the slot has been cut to the proper depth, burrs are removed by filing. The work is then turned over, and the opposite side is machined by following just the same procedure

11 With the rectangular slots cut, the block is leveled and clamped for machining the large V-slot. Mark the vise and clamp the block under the same ram stroke. A diamond-face tool is used

12 Make .100" roughing cuts with the power cross feed set at .080" per stroke. This feed is reversed within safe margins. The tool is fed down by hand between runs [CONTINUED]

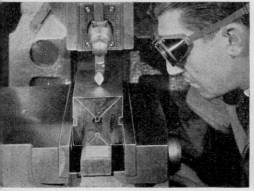

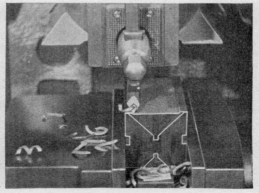

13 Near the bottom of the V, the power drive is shut off, and cross-feeding is finished by hand. The rectangular slot is next cut in the bottom with a square tool ground to full width

14 For finishing the sides, the tool head is set at 45 deg., and a roughing tool is set vertically in the tool post. Hand feeding will move the tool down the 45-deg. slope of the slot

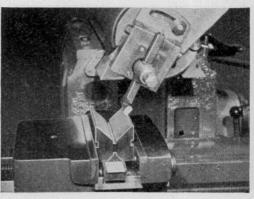

15 This preliminary finishing cut should leave .010" for a final cut. The tool and head both remain in position, the vise is marked, and the work is turned for machining the second face

16 The final finishing tool has a long cutting edge that is set parallel to the machined surface and is fed by hand at 1/8" per stroke. One face is finished, and the work is again turned

17 Instead of the work being turned, the head could have been set at the opposite 45-deg. angle. A square shows both surfaces to be true

18 Following the machining of the small V and its rectangular slot in the same manner, all dimensions are checked against the blueprint

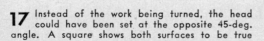

NEW
SHOP
IDEAS

A MAGNIFYING GLASS cemented to a cardboard ring and mounted over the safety window of a bench grinder is a great help in grinding tool bits and other precision work. The focal length of the lens should be such that the work is in sharp focus as it is held at the normal position against the wheel. For a typical bench grinder, a lens of about 10" focal length will be suitable, or a low-power reading glass can be pressed into service.—W. B.

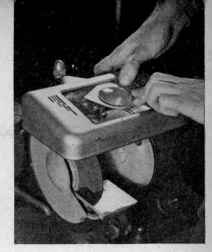

SHOP DATA in the form of charts and tables can be kept handy by pasting it on large shipping tags. If the tags are then riveted loosely together, any one of the charts or tables can be fanned out for reference. Machinists, toolmakers, and mechanics can prolong the life of their expensive handbooks by cutting tables and charts out of magazines and manufacturers' catalogues and using them on the tags.—RONALD EYRICH.

SPLICED ROPE will serve in place of a long ⅜" or ½" V-belt. When cutting the rope, allow two to three feet for splicing. A transmission splice is preferable, but a long splice is also satisfactory if carefully made. The splice should be pounded with a mallet and rolled on the floor under one's foot in order to make it smooth and flexible. Coat the rope with belt dressing to make it wear longer and to prevent it from slipping. The motor should be hinged at one side so that only its weight tightens the belt.

THE LONG SPLICE
[KNOTS]

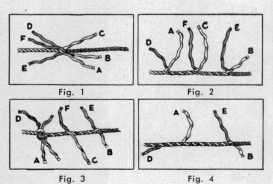

Fig. 1

Fig. 2

Fig. 3

Fig. 4

Unlay the end of each rope about 15 turns and place the ropes together, alternating the strands from each end, as shown in Fig. 1. Start with any opposite pair, unlay one strand, and replace it with the strand from the other part. Repeat this operation with another pair of strands in the opposite direction, as shown in Fig. 2. Now tie each pair of opposing strands (Fig. 3) with an overhand knot like *B* and *E*, tuck each strand twice, then twice more.

Still another method of making a long splice is to halve each strand and tie it with an overhand knot before tucking. This method results in a smaller splice, but one with less strength. Roll and pound the splice well before cutting the strands off close to the rope (Fig. 4).

Pictures in Natural Light

ONE good day of brilliant sunshine will warm the heart of any camera enthusiast, but few of us realize that the sun can help us to produce just as excellent pictures even when it is hidden by clouds in the dullest kind of weather. Just so long as it gives enough light to register on your film, it will make a picture. What kind of picture depends on you—and especially on your ingenuity.

You have a choice of natural light as far as direction is concerned. If you decide that a certain building will photograph better with the sun shining on its western gable, you have but to wait until a certain time in

the afternoon when that condition occurs. Most good pictures are planned, not made at a moment's notice. After you have chosen your subject, decide upon the quality of light you want when photographing it.

As the direction of the sun changes from east to west, the quality of its light also changes. The low-angle light of early morning and late afternoon is a form-revealing light that enables you to experiment with shadows and patterns to your heart's content. But remember that the light at sunrise and sunset is much redder than at other times of day, and that proper allowances must be

SUNFLOWERS at 2 P. M. with the light angle high in relation to the petals. This reveals form. A gray day in a railroad yard produced the dramatic shot below

**BY
KONRAD CRAMER**

Bright sunlight at about 10 A. M. helped with this shot of lamb's-tongue. A low angle of light puts half the area in shade for an all-over pattern

made for this in calculating exposures.

For good results in photographing against the source of light, a lens shade is essential. A good type is the rectangular kind that is accurately designed for the viewing angle of the lens so that it does not block any part of the film area. A sun shield that permits shooting almost directly into the sun can be made easily from cardboard and soft wire. It is described in a short article on page HW 362 and shown in a drawing. Be sure to adjust it carefully.

The best and quickest way to become familiar with the many effects produced by varying light conditions is to make the following experiment. Select an outdoor scene, which need not be photographically ideal but should be conveniently near your home. It may be a view from a window, a corner of your back yard, or the tree in front of your house. Shoot the same scene at intervals during the day —several times from dawn to dusk, including one exposure in the brilliant light of the noonday sun. You will be astonished to find how many different pictures the same subject will yield.

Illustrating this article are photographs of birch trees taken back of my house. These represent only two of many pictures of this same scene taken under different light conditions. When we consider light first and subject matter second, the quality of our pictures is sure to improve.

All light will become good light for picture taking, if we have a mind to make it so. Don't despise the soft and diffused light of a gray day, but do select the right subject to fit that kind of light. The picture at the left is an example.

The direction of natural light can be partially controlled by means of reflecting surfaces, such as a

DIFFERENCE IN LIGHTING the same scene is clearly shown in the winter sunrise at the left above and the sun and fog at right. Shooting into the sun is effective but difficult. In the sunrise photo, the only protection the camera lens had was afforded by the birch tree. Here is a commonplace subject transformed by proper illumination into excellent picture material, and many good views are possible

white cloth or a white wall. White sand or snow also will modify the original direction of light on your subject. A sheet of corrugated cardboard covered with pieces of tin foil that have been crumpled and then straightened makes an ideal reflector to control and modify light in outdoor portraiture. If made of two pieces hinged in the center, it will be portable and the tin foil will be protected when it is being carried.

Give the cardboard backing two coats of shellac. When the second coat is tacky, mount the tin foil. Then finish the piece by binding the edges with cellulose tape. Surfaces that are too smooth, like mirrors and

pieces of bright tin, are not suitable for reflectors because they tend to produce harsh "spots" of light. In using a reflector, remember that light is reflected at the same angle at which it reaches the reflecting surface, just as a billiard ball rebounds from a cushion.

Intensity of light can also be controlled to a certain extent, especially in making outdoor portraits. For small areas, a child's wooden hoop or one made of a piece of wire can be covered with thin muslin or cheesecloth to temper the sun's rays where they fall on your subject.

Natural light, however, is not confined to

Cardboard Disk Protects Lens from Direct Sunlight

GOOD shots can be made almost directly into the sun with a lens shade designed as shown in this drawing. It is made by fastening a small disk of black cardboard to one end of a piece of soft wire. The other end of the wire is attached to the camera, permitting adjustment of the disk to keep the sun's rays from striking the lens.—K. C.

WISTERIA shot against the light is but one example of the large number of photographs of this class. Shooting against light requires two or three times the normal exposure; otherwise only a silhouetted figure will show

READING by a window with the natural light from outside as illumination presents this fine picture possibility. Too often the introduction of additional artificial light sources simply destroys both the character and the personality of the interior

...tdoor photography. Some ...autiful pictures are made ...doors with natural light. ...n't forget this just because ...ch indoor light fails to reg-...er strongly on your meter ...it may nevertheless yield ...od photos. If you have ...ver made pictures either ...doors or outdoors with ex-...sures of many seconds, you ...ve missed much of the real ...n of photography.

Many picture fans are apt ...confine their activities to ...od-weather shooting. This ...as limiting as though a ...usician confined himself to ...ajor scales only. The time ...s passed when photography ...uld be practiced only in ...rong light. Get a new thrill ...t of your camera by dis-...vering its possibilities under ...-called bad lighting.

Whatever light you work ...th, always remember that ...m does not record it as you ...rmally see it. Your eyes ...e sensitive to a much great-...range of brightness than ...ur film is. To teach your ...es to see light photographi-...lly, I suggest you make ex-...nsive use of a good view-...g filter. Hang one around ...ur neck and use it freely to ...k at scenes about you. The filter elim-...ates most of the color and helps you see ...ings as your film does. One can be made from several layers of blue cellulose wrapping material sandwiched between two pieces of glass.

THE CLOSE-UP VIEW FINDER shown below can be adapted to fit any camera. It consists of a finder from an old camera fitted with a wire spider which clips on the sunshade. The view finder is held by the spider in front of and in line with the lens, so that there is no parallax. In order to make it possible to center the spider quickly and accurately, it is advisable to paint four spots on the sunshade at the places where the spider legs grip it. Compare the field of the view finder to that of the lens by checking it against a piece of ground glass held over the film track. With black paint, mask off the field of view of the finder so that it corresponds to that of the lens.—ROBERT F. BENENATI.

A CAMERA SHIFTER for taking still stereographs with a single camera is shown below Two pairs of hinges are soldered together with the distance between the center of the hinge pins measuring exactly 1 9/32". This distance is one half of the average spacing between the two shots taken of one subject in making a stereograph. The free leaves of the hinges are screwed to two plywood boards in such a way that when the hinges are folded together in one direction the ends of the boards will coincide. When the hinges are folded in the other direction, the top board to which the camera is fastened will shift 2 9/16". This device holds the camera rigid and makes the shift in camera viewpoint accurately.—WILLARD ALLPHIN.

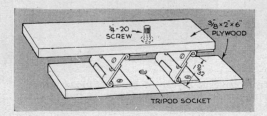

¼-20 SCREW
⅜×2"×6" PLYWOOD
TRIPOD SOCKET

EXPOSURE RECORDS are usually kept by the amateur, especially if he is working with a new type of cut film. It is sometimes difficult to remember in which order the exposures were made. For a foolproof system of numbering the negatives, just include the number in the composition where it will register on the film, yet be readily cropped out. In the photo above, a desk-calendar number was shot in the picture.—L. H.

PAPER DEVELOPER can be stored economically if it is removed from its large container and poured into small bottles. The ½-gal. package made into solution will fill eight 8-oz. bottles which, if tightly capped, may be stored indefinitely. As the majority of such solutions are diluted two to one, 8 oz. of stock solution make up 24 oz. of working solution, which is usually sufficient for the amateur's use.—HARRY F. LEEPER.

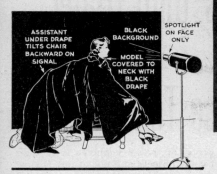

This "heavenly" picture was shot in a very earthly studio. The assistant, kneeling behind the chair as at the left, tilted it backward at the instant the shutter was opened

HUMAN SHOOTING STAR.

In snapping this unusual photograph, advantage was taken of the fact that a moving light object before an open shutter will register its trail on the film.

The model, covered up to the neck with a black drape, was seated on a chair before a black background. A spotlight set before her illuminated only her features, thus making it impossible for the black materials to register on the film. An assistant hidden under the drape behind the chair gripped its back. The shutter was set for "time."

At the instant the shutter was opened, the assistant was given a signal and immediately proceeded to tilt the chair backward on its legs. This left a light trail on the film that was terminated by closing the shutter when the model's head passed a certain point. Her features registered at the start of the trail because there was a slight delay in the reaction of the assistant to the signal so that the model remained posed for a fraction of a second before moving backward. The stars were retouched later on the negative.—LOUIS HOCHMAN.

AN OLD FILM-PACK ADAPTER

can be readily converted into a serviceable retouching stand at very little cost. A piece of cardboard inserted in the frame contains a window the size of the negative for the admission of light and serves as a backing for holding the negative against the glass. The glass plate should be the same size as the adapter frame and is held in position with two small nails at the bottom of the frame. Two wooden supports 3/16" by ½" by 6" are

held against the frame with a rubber band over the slide clasp and two catch points. A small bulb illuminates the negative. If daylight is needed in addition to the light from the bulb, a small mirror may be attached to the frame.

This method of conversion does not damage the film-pack adapter in any way for future use. However, if there is no further use for the adapter, the stand can be built on a more rigid base.—JOHN K. KARLCVIC.

A mirror placed in the bottom of the stand as shown below acts as a daylight reflector

Retouching becomes an easy job if you build one of these stands from your old film-pack adapter

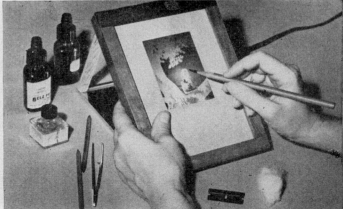

Experiments with Water *show* How Surface Tension Acts

WHY are drops of water round? Why does water wet some objects and not others? How is it possible to float an object heavier than water? The answer is *surface tension*—the tendency of a liquid surface to act like a stretched elastic membrane.

When water is in contact with air, the molecules at the surface are attracted more strongly to the water beneath than to the air above. As a result, a thin membrane of molecules stretches itself over the surface. A needle or razor blade placed on carefully will not sink; it will merely dent the surface and float.

When water or other liquids are freed from the action of gravity and other outside forces, the

PUT SOME STRING on the surface of clean water as shown in the photo at the top of this page. The string will float, and the water will hardly wet it. However, add a few drops of some soapless shampoo to the water, and the string instantly sinks to the bottom. The shampoo acts as a "wetting agent," lowering the surface tension of the water until it is less than the attractive force of the string. This causes the fibers of the string to become soaked, and it sinks.

DROP OLIVE OIL on a mixture of water and a little alcohol. The oil will sink just beneath the surface, as at the far left. Add more alcohol slowly, and the oil will sink further, as in the next photo. Still more alcohol will finally cause the oil to float beneath the surface. It then assumes a spherical form because of surface tension. At the right, the globe seems flattened, but this is an illusion caused by the water.

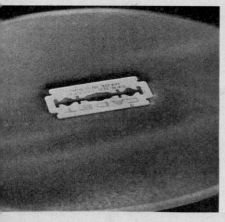

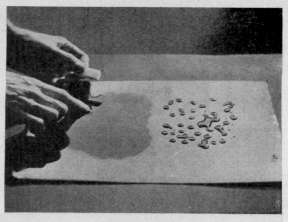

PLACE A RAZOR BLADE on the surface of some clean water, and the blade will float. If you look closely, you will notice that the blade is a trifle lower than the surface, and that the water bends down as if a film were stretched tightly over its surface. This occurs because the molecules of water have a stronger attraction for each other than they have for the razor blade, hence the blade floats on a surface film of water.

ENAMELED FERROTYPE TIN of the type used in photography will cause water poured on it to draw into little globules, as at the right in the photo above. The cohesive force between the water molecules is stronger than the attraction between the water and tin, so they arrange themselves to present the smallest possible surface. Soap added to the drops will allow them to be spread over the plate as at the left in the picture. The surface tension of the water is lowered by the action of the soap, and the plate becomes thoroughly wet.

cohesive force of the molecules pulls the surface into a sphere—the form possessing the smallest possible area.

Such materials as cotton or wool attract the molecules of water strongly. Oily or waxed surfaces are harder to wet, having

less attraction, but some agents will aid by reducing the surface tension of water. One of these is ordinary soap.

The accompanying striking examples of surface tension are easily duplicated, and the results are interesting to watch.

SURFACE TENSION may be easily measured with the simple apparatus shown. A clean glass disk is supported from a light spring made from a dozen turns of fine wire. Before touching the disk to the water surface, the extension of the spring is noted. Lower the disk squarely on the surface. If you now attempt to lift the disk, you find that the water holds it down, stretching the spring far below its original position. You can test the surface tension of other liquids with this same method.

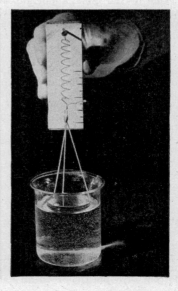

SILICON..
THE SOCIABLE ELEMENT

Though Its Compounds Just About Cover the Earth, It Cannot Be Found Alone

By KENNETH M. SWEZEY

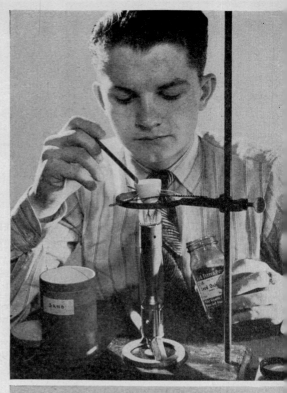

You can demonstrate how glass is made by mixing equal parts of sand, sodium carbonate, and lead oxide. These are melted in a porcelain crucible

ALTHOUGH silicon can never be found alone, its compounds make up more than a quarter of the earth's crust. Common sand is silicon dioxide, or silica, as are the minerals quartz, agate, amethyst, and opal. Almost all rocks, except limestone, contain this vital element. Sandstone is merely silica bonded with clay or lime. Feldspar and clay are both compounds of silicon and aluminum. Silicon carbide, used as an abrasive, is an artificial compound produced by heating silicon dioxide and carbon in an electric furnace.

One of the most important and familiar artificial compounds of silicon is glass. Ordinary window and bottle glass is a mixture of silicates produced when white sand (which is almost pure silica) is melted with sodium carbonate and lime. When potassium oxide and lead oxide are substituted for sodium and lime, glass with a low melting point and high index of refraction is formed, which is especially suitable for lenses. Different types of glass may be made by other slight alterations in the composition.

With a small porcelain crucible and a Fisher or Meker burner, you can easily make and color bits of glass in your home laboratory just as it is done in industry.

Because of its lower melting point, it is better to experiment in making lead glass, rather than glass containing lime. Mix about 3 grams of clean white sand with equal weights of dry sodium carbonate and yellow lead oxide. Put this mixture in a crucible and heat it strongly until it melts into a fluid mass. Pour the contents on the bottom of a pie tin or on an asbestos mat,

and the drops that form will become, upon cooling, sparkling bits of real glass.

You may color your glass by adding to it a trace of some metallic oxide while it is still in its molten form. Cobalt oxide produces blue glass—chromium oxide colors it green. Used in minute quantities, manganese dioxide produces amethyst glass, while larger quantities color it black. Colloidal gold turns glass a beautiful ruby red. The bright red of traffic lights and automobile taillights is generally produced by the addition of selenium.

Compounds of silicon owe much of their usefulness to the fact that chemically they are extremely stable. They resist all common acids, except hydrofluoric, and they are also little affected by bases, except hot sodium or potassium hydroxide. This inactivity explains why most chemical containers and laboratory apparatus are made of glass, and why buildings of glass, brick, and stone have been able to weather centuries.

The resistance of silica to acids and bases makes it of special value to the carpenter

A fairylike chemical garden is produced if you drop the salts of heavy metals such as copper sulphate, zinc sulphate, nickel sulphate, cobalt chloride, and the like into a solution of water glass in water. The compounds form insoluble silicates which literally grow before your eyes, taking on fantastic colors and shapes as they rise to the surface

The melted mixture is poured on a tin plate or asbestos pad, where it forms globules of glass

and home craftsman. In the form of silex, an extremely fine sand made from quartz rock, it serves as a base for wood fillers that is totally unaffected by vapors in the atmosphere or chemicals in paint.

Because hydrofluoric acid dissolves, or "eats," silica and glass, it is used extensively for glass etching. Commercial acid is supplied in wax bottles. If you have none, you can make a crude form by mixing sodium fluoride, which is sold as a common insecticide, with concentrated sulphuric acid.

If you want to etch an initial on the side of a plain glass tumbler, first warm the glass; then apply a coating of paraffin a little larger in area than the initial desired. Build up a frame of wax completely around your wax panel, high enough to hold the etching mixture. Then scratch away part of the wax to form the initial. Cover the panel with a layer of sodium fluoride. (Be careful not to breathe this powder or get it into cuts or in your mouth, as it is very poisonous.) Drop sulphuric acid on this until a creamy paste is formed. Let this stand for about ten minutes; then carefully wash off the etching material, remove the wax, and there is a perfect initial.

Of all the silicates, only potassium and sodium silicates are soluble in water. Sodium silicate solution is the well-known water glass, used extensively for making cements, for fireproofing, and for preserving eggs. With the sirupy variety, you can make cement for glass and china. Dilute it, and you can produce a gel and a chemical garden.

You can use thick water glass alone as a good transparent cement for glass or china. First heat the edges to be cemented; then apply the water glass. Clamp the parts tightly together until the water glass is dry. A cement that will stand acids and high heat may be made by mixing two parts of the thick water glass with one part of fine sand and one part of ground asbestos.

To make a gel, two solutions must be prepared. The first is made by diluting 15 ml. of thick water glass with an equal amount of water. The second consists of

If you pour together into a small glass or beaker a solution of dilute hydrochloric acid and a solution of sodium silicate, almost immediately a solid white mass will form that will support the stirring rod as at right. This is silica gel, which, in its dry form, is used as a dehydrating agent

2 ml. of concentrated hydrochloric acid diluted with 20 ml. of water. Pour these two solutions simultaneously into a small glass or beaker, and immediately stand a stirring rod in the center of the beaker. Within a few seconds, the clear solutions will have united to form a solid whitish gel that will support the rod and will not fall out if the beaker is inverted. When dried, this silica gel contains millions of microscopic pores that will take up quantities of water. It is widely used as a drying agent.

A chemical garden affords a beautiful experiment which no home chemist should miss. Obtain a small fish bowl or a low jar that will hold about 1 qt. and sprinkle a layer of coarse sand about ¼" deep on the bottom. Fill the remainder of the bowl or jar almost to the top with water glass diluted with an equal amount of water.

"Seeds" for your garden consist of salts of the heavy metals, such as copper sulphate, nickel sulphate, cobalt chloride, ferrous sulphate, zinc sulphate, and manganese chloride, which are dropped to the bottom of the globe. In an hour or two the garden should be completely grown—a forest of intricate and varicolored growths.

After a day, the sodium silicate solution may be carefully siphoned off and replaced with clean, fresh water. As the "plants" all consist of metallic silicates, they are insoluble. They should last until they are broken down by jarring.

Scratch an initial on the waxed surface of a tumbler, cover with sodium fluoride, add sulphuric acid, and let stand about 10 minutes. Remove the chemicals, and a perfect initial will be formed on the glass

FIRST STEPS IN ELECTRONICS

By JOHN W. CAMPBELL, JR.

THE storage of electro-static energy in a condenser and electromagnetic energy in an inductance coil give rise to one of the most useful tricks of the whole science of electronics —the phenomenon of electrical *resonance*.

An electric current, whether it is in a copper wire or a vacuum tube, consists of a movement of electrons, and in either case obeys the same basic laws. As a matter of fact, as far as an electron is concerned, a copper wire is a sort of vacuum tube filled with a coarse, rigid grating of immobile copper atoms. Trillions of planetary electrons wander at random among the fixed nucleuses of the copper atoms, restrained only from leaving the surface of the wire. However, if an electric current flows through the wire, this horde of electrons drifts slowly in

Goliath of the radio world is this giant inductance coil used in the transmitter of station WEAF to smooth the power output

RESONANCE EXPLAINS
The Mystery of Tuned Circuits

one direction, like a crowd leaving a football field through a tunnel. The apparent speed of electricity is due to the fact that the instant an extra electron is pushed in at one end of the wire, a corresponding one is pushed out at the other.

Resonance, however, can stir those electrons up so that, instead of wandering gently along, they surge back and forth in the wire and spill over like waves in a bathtub. This movement now becomes a dangerous thing—so dangerous that resonance is to be avoided in any application where there is a considerable current.

Resonance can turn tiny voltages and minute currents into readily detectable

surges of energy, which is why the radio engineer employs it. The electrical engineer, on the other hand, must make sure that his power lines don't accidentally get into resonance and turn 110 volts at 50 amp. into 10,000 volts at 5,000 amp.

If you have a charged condenser and connect an inductance coil across its terminals, the excess electrons on the negative plate of the condenser will enter the wire and push enough electrons out of the far end to satisfy the lack on the other condenser plate. But that flow of electrons builds up a magnetic field in the inductance. With the condenser now discharged, the current tends to stop flowing; but then the

Above left, compare the inductance of many turns and the big variable condenser found in standard radio receivers with the six-turn coil and single-plate condenser employed in short-wave and FM sets. In the photo at right, a resonant circuit that can be tuned as a wave trap for 60-cycle current

magnetic field it has established must collapse, and in collapsing it cuts the coil, driving the electrons onward again. They are crowded onto one plate of the condenser, and presto! the condenser is charged again—this time in reverse.

Immediately the cycle repeats itself. Round and round it goes, and it comes out as heat that develops in the resistance of the wiring and as radiated electromagnetic energy, or radio waves. If it were not for the gradual dissipation of energy in these forms, the electrons would continue to surge back and forth forever, for the system is an electrical equivalent of a pendulum.

A heavy pendulum can be started swinging if it is tapped lightly with a pencil in time with its natural rhythm. Likewise, trillions of electrons in a copper wire can be made to surge back and forth with tremendous violence. It takes a certain amount of time for the discharging condenser to force its excess electrons through the magnetic reaction of the inductance; it takes time also for the inductance to force electrons back into the condenser again. With every combination of inductance coil and condenser there is a certain natural rhythm. Find that rhythm and give the electronic pendulum little electric pushes at just the right time, and the whole horde of electrons in the copper wire will take on an oscillating motion. The separate spurts of energy pushed in on each swing add up, the electrons surge more and more violently, the current through the inductance becomes greater, and voltages pile higher on the condenser.

A radio signal captured by an aerial, so minute as to be measured in millionths of an ampere, when fed into a perfect resonant circuit will start the electrons in the wire swinging until quite detectable currents charge back and forth through the inductance coil.

However, you can't drain off heavy currents or high voltages continuously. A resonant circuit is only a reservoir of energy, just as a condenser or inductance is. But where these and all other electrical storage devices store D.C. energy, with positive and negative neatly separated, a resonant circuit stores A.C. energy. The result is a condition hard to understand at first glance, because the electric current is present but not working. As long as energy is merely transferred from one storage tank to another and back again, it is in reality doing no work.

This is possible because, in alternating current, the current and voltage can be going in different directions at the same time—they can be "out of phase" with each other, as shown in Fig. 1. In a perfect parallel resonant circuit (Fig. 2) the current in the condenser and the current in the inductance are, at any given moment, going in exactly opposite directions, and the voltage in the inductance is going in exactly the opposite direction from the current in the

A CONDENSER ⊣⊢ LOOKS TO DIRECT CURRENT LIKE A BROKEN CIRCUIT ⌐_⌐ BUT TO ALTERNATING CURRENT IT IS A RESISTANCE ⟋⟍⟋⟍⟋⌐ WHOSE MAGNITUDE VARIES WITH THE FREQUENCY OF THE ALTERNATING CURRENT. WITH HIGH FREQUENCIES, IT ACTS AS THOUGH IT WEREN'T THERE, OR AS THOUGH A HEAVY SHUNT ⊏⊣⊢⊐ PASSED AROUND IT.

AN INDUCTANCE ⟿ LOOKS TO DIRECT CURRENT LIKE A LOW RESISTANCE ⟋⟍⟋ BUT TO ALTERNATING CURRENT IT IS A HIGH RESISTANCE ⟋⟍⟋⟍⟋⟍ AND TO HIGH FREQUENCIES IT MAY EVEN BE AN IMPASSABLE RESISTANCE EQUIVALENT TO A BROKEN CIRCUIT ⌐_⌐

inductance, while an A.C. line feeding the resonant circuit. if it is "in tune," is 90 deg. out of phase with both the condenser and the inductance. This condition gives the resonant circuit an infinite impedance—no current can flow into it.

This phenomenon is easily demonstrated. Filter condensers and an inductance coil or audio-frequency transformer from one of the old "all electric" radio models will serve. A 7½-watt, 110-volt light bulb will act as your "ammeter."

If we were to put our electric-bulb "ammeter" in the resonant circuit itself, it would consume energy. Since a resonant circuit is an energy-storage system, a constant drain of energy to operate the lamp would prevent it from operating as a resonant circuit. But if we put a resonant circuit in series with the lamp, it will have a high impedance when it is tuned to match the frequency of the 60-cycle power line, and the lamp will go out. At any other tuning, the 60-cycle current will pass, and the lamp will glow.

In the circuit of Fig. 2, using a filter condenser of about 2 mfd. and an inductance of 3.5 henries, resonance is at 60 cycles. The relationship of inductance, capacitance, and frequency in a circuit is such that if either the inductance or the capacitance is increased, the natural frequency of the circuit is lowered. Radio practice tunes the resonant circuit of the set by varying the capacity of the condenser; in the early days fixed condensers and variable inductance coils were frequently used. Since a 2-mfd. variable condenser would be too huge, we shall use this latter system.

The setup in Fig. 2 consists of two 1-mfd.

filter condensers in parallel across the primary windings of an old audio-frequency transformer, the resonant circuit so formed being in series with a small lamp and the 110-volt, 60-cycle power line. The secondary of the transformer is not used. This transformer had a core consisting of an E-shaped section and a separate leg clamped together. By cutting the sheet-metal strap away, the leg was freed. The effective inductance of the winding could then be altered by adjusting this loose leg to coincide more or less with the other section. At some point in changing the position of the armature, the circuit is in tune with the 60-cycle current. No current passes, and the lamp is dark. In any other position, the circuit is tuned to higher or lower frequencies, and the lamp lights, showing that 60-cycle current can pass.

The frequency to which a circuit is tuned is determined by the product of the inductance multiplied by capacitance; for 60 cycles the value is approximately 7 mfd. henries. If the product of capacitance and inductance in the circuit of Fig 2 were made 0.07039 mfd. microhenries, 100,000,-000 times smaller, the circuit would be tuned to 600 kc. in the broadcast radio band and would serve to block the passage of a 600 kc. radio signal. That is the principle of the wave trap used in series with a radio aerial to cut down the strength of a powerful signal from a near-by transmitter while letting other stations in unhindered.

Since your old radio contained tuning condensers and inductance designed for broadcast-band use, you can substitute them as in the circuit of Fig. 3 and have a wave trap for use with any receiver.

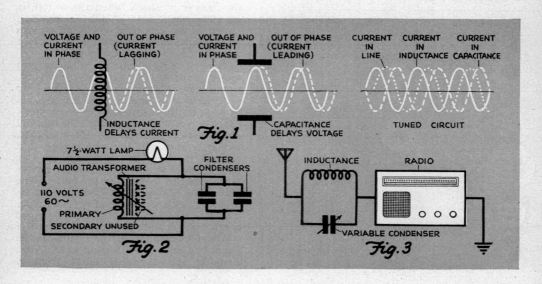

VOLTAGE AND CURRENT IN PHASE — OUT OF PHASE (CURRENT LAGGING) — VOLTAGE AND CURRENT IN PHASE — OUT OF PHASE (CURRENT LEADING) — CURRENT IN LINE — CURRENT IN INDUCTANCE — CURRENT IN CAPACITANCE

INDUCTANCE DELAYS CURRENT — *Fig.1* — CAPACITANCE DELAYS VOLTAGE — TUNED CIRCUIT

7½-WATT LAMP — AUDIO TRANSFORMER — FILTER CONDENSERS — INDUCTANCE — RADIO

110 VOLTS 60~ — PRIMARY — SECONDARY UNUSED — *Fig.2* — VARIABLE CONDENSER — *Fig.3*

Everything from a toaster to a battery can be tested on this panel. The wiring diagram is shown below

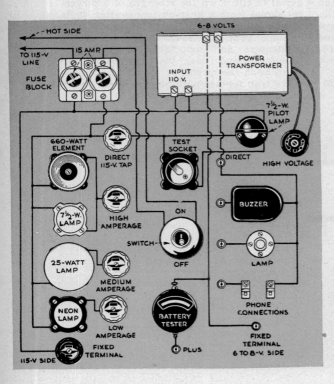

Electrical Test Panel

BUILT OF

JUNK-BOX PARTS

By Walter E. Burton

WITH this electrical test panel you can check lamps, motor windings, coils, and the like without having to rummage through boxes and drawers for the necessary equipment.

A piece of ¼" plywood 12" by 17" with strips of wood ¾" square nailed to the back and around the edges to form a frame will serve for the panel proper. At the left side of the layout is the 115-volt testing circuit, and at the top is a fuse block through which current reaches all circuits on the board. A switch, seen near the center of the panel, controls the input current. This should preferably be a double-pole, single-throw switch inserted in both line leads so as to open them when the switch is off. However, a single-pole switch may be used as shown in the wiring diagrams. It is connected to the "hot" or ungrounded side of the 115-volt line, which minimizes the danger of shock when the switch is off. The "hot" side of a house-lighting circuit is the one that will light a lamp when the leads are touched to it and to a "ground" such as a water pipe.

The test-wire terminals or "jacks" are made from small, surface-mounting, single convenience outlets. These are secured to the panel by one screw each. In hooking them into the circuit, connect the wire to *both* terminals. On the end of each test wire of the 115-volt pair, mount a standard two-prong plug, but connect the wire to *one* prong. In this way, the wire will be connected no matter how it may be inserted in the outlet. The other end of each test wire should be provided with a spring clip or with an insulating handle having a pin-shaped contact about ¼" long at the tip.

Above the switch in the center of the panel is a socket for testing light bulbs. Remove the threaded shell from a surface-mounting socket, place it over a round rod or the tip of a small anvil, and hammer out all the threads. When the socket has been reassembled, a light bulb can be pushed in and removed in an instant. A small night lamp connected in parallel serves as a pilot light and panel illuminator.

A radio power transformer, the secondary taps of which provide a low-voltage circuit, is mounted in the upper right-hand corner of the panel. You can probably obtain up to 20 volts, but 6 volts will suffice for most low-voltage testing. Insert a variable resistance in the secondary leads if the taps give too high a voltage. If you have occasion to use extremely high voltage, you will find that most radio transformers provide anywhere from 400 to 1,200 volts. A multipronged radio connector is used to plug in high-voltage wires. A small toggle switch connected in series with one of the input wires will permit the transformer to be turned off when only the 115-volt side of the panel is being used.

The low-voltage circuit is wired in much the same manner as the 115-volt side in that there are four testing outlets and a fixed or common outlet. Uninsulated phone-cord tip or banana jacks may be used, and the test wires should be equipped with plugs to match. A pair of headphones may be connected for testing radio parts and circuits, photographic flash bulbs, and similar low-amperage devices.

Directly below the main panel switch is a small battery tester of the type used to check the charge of a 6-volt storage battery. The low-voltage test wires are used with this meter, with the main panel switch at the "off" position. Besides serving to check the charge in a battery, this tester also acts as a polarity indicator for checking flashlight cells, auto and radio batteries, and the like.

To illustrate how to use the test panel, let us assume that you have a field coil from an old radio loudspeaker and want to determine whether you can use it on 115 volts as an electromagnet. Plug a test wire into the fixed outlet and clip the other end to one of the coil leads. Clip the other test wire to the remaining coil lead and plug it into the lowest test outlet. The glowing of the neon lamp in the adjacent socket indicates that there is no break in the coil. Now move the test plug to the next outlet. The 25-watt lamp lights, but not to full brilliancy, indicating that the coil offers resistance to the current. Try the next outlet, which is in series with a 660-watt or similar heater element and a small 7½-watt pilot lamp. The heater element gets warm—not hot—indicating that the coil will carry the full 115-volt current without the use of an intermediate resistance. Next, shift the plug to the outlet giving a direct connection to the line. If a small A.C. ammeter is in series with this outlet, you can determine the exact current drain.

If you desire to test some equipment on a very low current, use the glow lamp. Higher currents can be tested with a 25-watt or 100-watt lamp and the 660-watt heater element. When testing for all the amperage the apparatus will draw, use the direct tap.

Flexible lamp cord or No. 14 wire is satisfactory for wiring the test panel, unless the low-voltage side of the transformer has a high amperage, in which case No. 10 or No. 12 wire should be used. The fuse block and exposed transformer terminals should be shielded to prevent accidental contact with live parts, and all portions of the 115-volt circuit and the high-voltage transformer line should be properly insulated.

Left below, the high-voltage connection is made through a multipronged speaker connector. In the same photo, the buzzer and lamp of the low-voltage circuit are shown, as well as the threadless lamp-testing socket. The drawings at right show how to mount the battery tester and make various small fittings

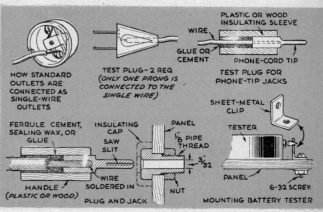

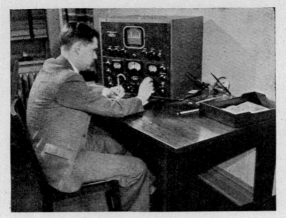

radio ideas

A CATHODE-RAY TUBE has been incorporated into the multitube communicating receiver at the left to give a visual checkup on the characteristics of incoming signals. Placed above the receiver proper, the cathode-ray tube can be switched on any time the operator desires. The image obtained is dependent on the kilocycle width of the intermediate-frequency stages. It enables the operator to adjust the receiver for the best possible reception at all times.

LOCKING CLAMPS for radio tubes, shown below, are in use all around the globe in United Nations aircraft transmitters and receivers. Made of stainless steel, the clamp permits a tube to be removed or replaced instantly, yet prevents it from working loose of itself. Such clamps can be attached to all wafer-type tube sockets and are available in sizes to fit all standard tubes.

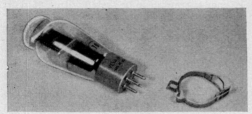

TERMINAL INSULATORS that serve also as wire markers are shown above. They consist of short lengths of extruded plastic tubing marked with appropriate letters and numerals. The material has high dielectric strength, and the markings resist water, chemicals, and oils.

SIMPLE LAMP-BULB RESISTOR LENGTHENS LIFE OF RADIO TUBES

TUBE life can be much prolonged with a simple device consisting of an ordinary lamp bulb connected in series with the line cord of the set. The bulb acts as an auxiliary resistor and decreases the current flowing through the tube heaters. The size of the bulb must be determined by experiment. Select one that allows the set to operate at a little under normal volume. A 100-watt bulb works well with most small A.C.-D.C. sets.

Such a tube saver may be used with either A.C. or A.C.-D.C. receivers containing not more than nine vacuum tubes, but not with radios having 82 or 83 mercury-vapor rectifiers, the operating voltage of which should not be tampered with.—H. B. SMITH.

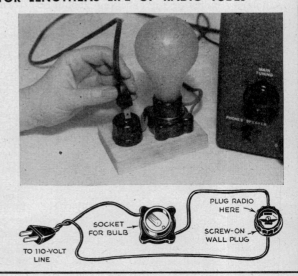

Servicing Your Radio

IT IS possible to realign trimmer condensers on old superheterodynes and T.R.F. sets without the use of a signal generator. A screw driver is the only tool needed.

The only difference in aligning a superheterodyne receiver as compared with a tuned-frequency type is that the former has two intermediate-frequency transformers that have to be adjusted, in addition to the ganged condensers.

Remove the chassis from the cabinet. The photographs show that of a small A.C.-D.C. superheterodyne that will serve as an example. Notice that one of the ganged tuning condensers is smaller than the other (Fig. 1). This is the oscillator tuning condenser and is the harder to adjust. Before touching the trimmers on these condensers, turn the dial to a known station at the high-frequency end (1,500 kc.) and check whether the dial pointer is opposite the correct frequency on the dial. If it is not, adjust the trimmer condenser on top of the oscillator tuning condenser 1/16" at a time by loosening the setscrew as in Fig. 2, thus decreasing the capacity of the trimmer condenser. For example, if the station has been coming in at 1,600 kc. instead of 1,550 kc., by decreasing the capacity of the trimmer the station will be "moved" back to the proper setting. Then readjust the trimmer on the other condenser for the loudest reception. This second condenser tunes the antenna circuit of the superheterodyne.

After the two-gang tuning condenser is aligned, the trimmers on top of the intermediate transformers, which are sunk into the top of the shielding can (Fig. 3), are adjusted either way until the maximum signal reception is obtained. Be careful not to move the setscrews more than 1/16" at a time. Some superheterodynes have padder condensers in the oscillator circuits that have to be adjusted, but in most cases this condenser is fixed.

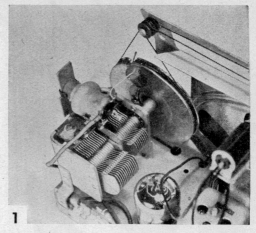

1

Use the same procedure to realign a tuned-frequency receiver. In this case, of course, there is only the two- or three-gang tuning condenser to adjust. The one tuning the R.F. stage is most critical. Turn the setscrew on the trimmer condenser 1/16" at a time and keep the other trimmers in step in the same manner described for the superhet.

It is important to remember that the high-frequency end of the dial (1,500 kc.) must be correctly aligned. Once the stations between 1,250 kc. and 1,600 kc. come in at the proper dial setting, the stations at the lower end will also be correctly aligned on the dial.

With many older receivers it is not always possible to receive stations around 1,500 kc. However, by gradually loosening the setscrew on the trimmer condenser of either the oscillator or radio-frequency tuning condenser, as the case may be, and by keeping the trimmer on the other condenser in line, it is possible to bring in those stations at the high-frequency end of the dial.

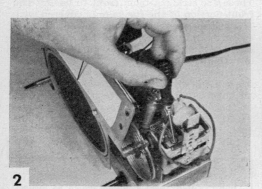

2

3

Towline Glider

THAT YOU CAN BUILD OF PINE

ALTHOUGH the making of model airplanes has been greatly curtailed because of rubber, metal, and balsa shortages, model makers need not despair. A glider is easily built from available supplies, and will afford plenty of excitement.

This towline glider is simple in design and easy to construct. Pine was used throughout in building the model shown, but if balsa is available the same sizes given for pine may be used for ribs, covering, bulkheads, and trailing edges. For other parts, balsa members should be of about double the cross section specified for pine.

Templates for the wing and stabilizer ribs are made first. Do not cut out the spar slot on the template. Instead, prick both the spar outline and the slot through the template on the rib stock. After the rib is cut, the pin marks will serve as guides for cutting the slot.

Before cutting the outline for the front portion of the fuselage, cement the pieces together. Cut the triangular bulkheads individually to the dimensions given. Notice that all are ¼" wide at the top and 1/16" wide at the bottom except No. 1 and No. 2. On a 1/16" by ¼" by 15½" strip, mark bulkhead locations 1⅜" apart. Fix the bulkheads at these points with model cement, making sure that they are all perpendicular.

The assembly should now be pinned to a board so that it will keep its shape while the bottom longeron is cemented to the bulkheads from No. 3 back. Attach the front portion as shown in the drawing. When the cement has set, attach the side longerons. These are straight from front to back. The front portion of the fuselage is covered with 1/32" sheet pine. Leave one lower side (between bulkheads No. 1 and No. 2) open so that the balancing weight can be cemented into this space.

In constructing the wing and stabilizer, draw a full-size view over which to assemble them. It is a good idea to cut the roots of the spars to the correct dihedral angle before assembly. The joint between the center spars is reinforced by two 1/16" by ¼" by 1½" strips as shown. This joint is fur-

SHORTAGES OF MATERIALS NEED NOT STOP YOU FROM BUILDING THIS ALL-PINE MODEL FOR NEW THRILLS IN MOTORLESS GLIDING

By Frank Zaic

Dimensions are based on pine construction. If balsa is used, some members should be larger

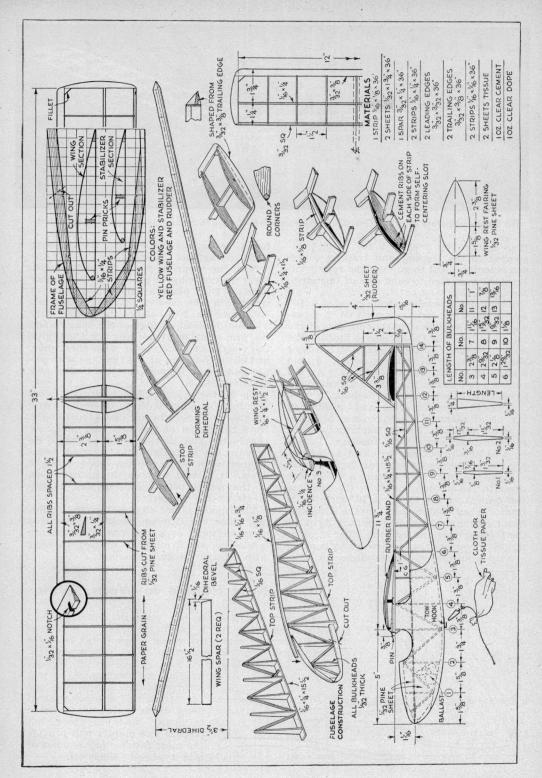

MATERIALS

1 STRIP 1/16 x 1/8 x 36
2 SHEETS 1/32 x 1 3/4 x 36
1 SPAR 3/32 x 1/4 x 36
2 STRIPS 1/16 x 1/4 x 36
2 LEADING EDGES 3/32 x 3/32 x 36
2 TRAILING EDGES 3/32 x 3/8 x 36
2 STRIPS 1/16 x 1/16 x 36
2 SHEETS TISSUE
1 OZ. CLEAR CEMENT
1 OZ. CLEAR DOPE

COLORS:
YELLOW WING AND STABILIZER
RED FUSELAGE AND RUDDER

LENGTH OF BULKHEADS

No.		No.		No.	
3	2 3/8	7	1 1/2	11	1"
4	2 9/32	8	1 3/8	12	15/16
5	2 1/8	9	1 9/32	13	7/8
6	1 29/32	10	1 1/8		

HW 379

The framework before covering. One side of the nose is left open so that balancing weight may be added

ther secured by a strip 1/16″ by 1/8″ cemented to the leading and trailing edges and smoothly bent to go over the spar joint. Ribs are cemented to each side of this strip, forming a slot.

The upper fuselage member has a 1/16″ by 1/4″ by 1½″ strip mounted on it crosswise, with a similar strip running forward to form the base for the incidence block. The wing is fastened on the fuselage by a rubber band looped from bulkhead No. 6 and hooked under the incidence block. As the rubber band lies in the slot, it automatically centers the wing on the fuselage.

Cover the fuselage, wing, and stabilizer in the usual manner. Use cement-thickened dope for adhesive. Fasten paper only to the spars and longerons of the fuselage. Dampen it to smooth out any wrinkles. Later, apply one or two coats of clear dope over it.

Make the rudder by cutting a 1/32″ pine sheet to the outline shown in the drawing and cementing a 1/16″ by 1/16″ strip to its front. Then fasten both to the fuselage. Form a triangle by adding another strip for the leading edge and add the other straight strips. Complete the framework by bending a strip over the center stabilizer rib. Be-

fore covering the rudder, trim the tissue to fit snugly against the stabilizer.

Now the model is ready to be balanced. First fix the wing in place with the rubber band. Then place a sufficient amount of weight in the space between bulkheads No. 1 and No. 2 to balance the model about 1″ from the trailing edge of the wing. When the proper balance has been achieved, glue the weight in place, cover with sheet pine, and cover the front of the fuselage with paper and dope. Cement the tow hook under bulkhead No. 3.

To fly the model, glide it into the wind and note whether it dives or stalls. Add weight in the form of clay accordingly. Note the shape of the tow ring and how closely the pull-off tissue is tied to it. Be sure the tow is straight into the wind, as indicated when the sag of the line is straight down. It is best to note the natural turn of the model before making any adjustments on the rudder.

This model is not eligible for contest flying, since the fuselage lacks the required cross-sectional area and the wing loading is too low, but it might, if desired, be built with a larger, heavier fuselage.

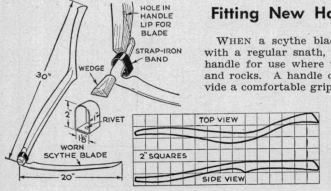

Fitting New Handle to Worn Scythe

WHEN a scythe blade has worn too short for use with a regular snath, it can be attached to a shorter handle for use where the swing is restricted by trees and rocks. A handle cut to the shape shown will provide a comfortable grip. A healthy tree branch approximating the desired shape will form a stronger handle than one cut from a straight-grained piece. Such limbs can be found on many kinds of trees, but birches and maples will provide the most satisfactory handles of this type.—J. MODROCH.

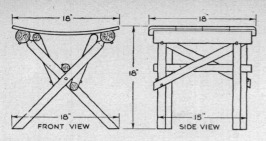

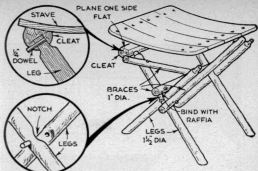

OUTDOOR FURNITURE constructed of rough materials always harmonizes well with the natural setting of a garden or lawn. This stool made of saplings has a curved seat of old barrel staves. Trim, fit, and dress the staves as shown in the drawing, being sure to smooth any splintery edges. Countersunk screws hold the seat to two cleats made of saplings planed smooth on their top sides. The cleats are bored to take the shaped ends of the legs, and ¼" dowels through the cleats into the ends of the legs secure the joints.

All bracing joints are also doweled, with one end of the dowels protruding as pegs. Where braces and legs cross, they are slightly notched to make for sturdiness. Binding the end joints of the straight brace with raffia will add strength and a touch of rustic craftsmanship.

The stool has no finishing of any kind, in keeping with its character. If desired, a set of these can be made for barbecue parties or back-yard picnics.—HI SIBLEY.

A HOT-WATER SYSTEM for farm kitchens without running water can be made of standard parts as shown at the right.

The force pump should be the type having an extra discharge outlet in addition to the spout. When the faucet on the spout is turned on, cold water can be pumped directly from the cistern. When this faucet is turned off, however, and the pump is worked, water goes up through pipe A and into the bottom portion of the hot-water tank. In so doing, it displaces hot water from the top of the tank. This water is forced through pipe B until it comes out directly over the sink. A hot-water jacket in the kitchen range is connected to the boiler in the usual way.

It must be remembered that no hot water is obtained unless the faucet is closed and the pump worked. The range boiler is in no danger of running dry if the pump is not used, for no hot water leaves it unless the pump is worked. The

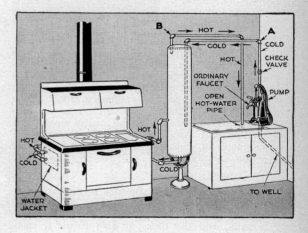

only other outlet from which water can be drawn is the drain at the bottom of the tank, which is used only when it is necessary to clean it out.—JOSEPH W. REIS.

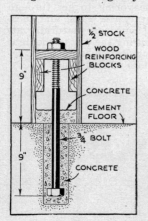

SECURING A HOLLOW POST to a cement floor presented a problem which my carpenter solved ingeniously.

He first chiseled a hole about 10" deep in the cement, and inserted a ¾" bolt around which he poured concrete. Next, he constructed three sides of the post, leaving the front open. A square of ¾" stock with a hole in the middle for the bolt was butted on top of two reinforcing blocks and nailed to them and to the side boards of the post. After the cement had hardened around the lower part of the bolt, the nut was drawn up tight. Cement was poured around the bolt at floor level, and the front board of the post was then nailed in place. The result was a newel at the **foot** of the stairs strong enough to stand all stresses.—PAUL B. MANN.

NEW MAIL BOXES made of plastic with a wood-fiber base, which is a noncritical material, are now available for house or R.F.D. use. The boxes are finished with a paint durable enough to withstand the most severe exposure out of doors. Both the porch and R.F.D. types are shown in the photograph below.

OUTSIDE WINDOW FRAMES with interchangeable glass panes and screen panels can be permanently installed outside of ordinary sash. Glazed upper and lower sashes are provided with each unit, along with a screen to be used in summer in place of the lower sash. Both glass and screen sections are attached to the frame on the inside with clips that can be fastened or released in a matter of seconds. All parts are removable for cleaning.

VERSATILE WAX. Besides serving all ordinary household purposes, this wax can be used to waterproof rope, awnings, tents, sails, and the like. It also forms a rust-preventive coating on machinery, firearms, tools, fishing tackle, and other metal articles. It is said to prevent cracking and drying out of leather articles, and can be used as a dressing on luggage, boots and shoes, belts, harness, handbags, wallets, and leather upholstery.

THIS INSECTICIDE is applied to screens and kills moths, gnats, mosquitoes, and flies. The solution comes complete with applicator. It is brushed on the inside surface of the screens and is said to last four to seven days. Insects endeavoring to get through the screen are paralyzed. Flies and mosquitoes inside the house are naturally attracted sometime during the day to the light coming through window openings and receive their lethal dose at that time.

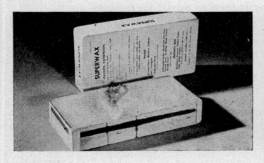

FIBER RECEPTACLES like that shown at the left may replace metal garbage and trash cans, the manufacture of which has been curtailed by the war. According to the maker, these new lightweight containers made of asphalt-impregnated fiber have a bursting strength of 500 lb. per square inch. They are water resistant and vermin-proof and have a capacity of 20 gal. Sturdily made, these receptacles are suitable for either outdoor or indoor use.

"PACKAGES" FOR PAINT. Since the new glass paint containers do not have wire handles, a special paper container with paper handles has been devised for carrying them on the job. These bags are made of extremely tough paper and are of convenient size for carrying glass paint jars that hold up to 1 gal.

SCREEN PAINTING has been simplified by a new applicator (not shown) which is used by rubbing it on the screen like a blackboard eraser. A special paint-retaining fabric on the applicator covers the wire mesh yet does not clog the spaces as so often occurs when an ordinary brush is used.

PREPASTED WALLPAPER can be applied without the professional help that is usually necessary for ordinary paper hanging. Created primarily to enable the home owner to redecorate his own walls, it is sold in packages with matching borders. No special tools are needed to apply the paper, which comes in attractive designs and colors. Each package contains an 81' roll of wallpaper and 16½' of border.

Put the rolled strip in water and reroll it so that the adhesive will become thoroughly wet. Cold or at least cool water should be used

Unroll about a foot of paper and smooth it out with the flat of a hand to work out air bubbles as you continue down to the baseboard. Trim the end with a razor blade

Wooden Initial Book Ends Are Adjustable and Nontipping

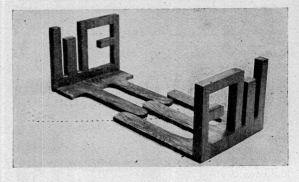

BY USING a wood for the initial ends that will take an attractive finish, and thin plywood for the fingered bases, very satisfactory book ends can be made similar to the pair shown in use above. They are adjustable as to length, and the base prevents them from toppling over.

Lay out two initials on a 4" by 5" sheet of paper, or three initials on a piece 4" by 7½". Paste the paper to the endpieces and cut out the initials on a jig saw. Rabbet the bottom edge of each end to receive the plywood bases. Secure these with flathead screws countersunk in the plywood.—ELMA WALTNER.

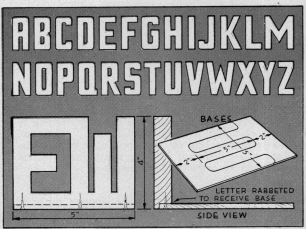

Adapter for Photomicrographs

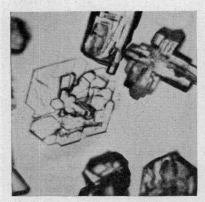

Boric acid crystals photographed with an ordinary camera and a microscope

Sheet metal, plastic, or composition board with one ¾" hole drilled or reamed in it forms the adapter plate

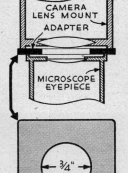

MICROSCOPE specimens can be easily photographed with a small camera by the use of an adapter that supports it on the microscope eyepiece.

Cut a 1¼" square piece of 3/64" thick sheet metal, plastic, or hard composition board and drill or ream a ¾" hole in it. Roughen the surface of the adapter with emery cloth to prevent the camera from slipping. With proper lighting on the subject, care being taken to avoid reflections that might reach the lens, good pictures are possible without the elaborate equipment usually necessary. To check the focus, lay ground glass over the film track.—ROBERT GOLBY.

FROM
Peacetime Freighter
TO Fighting Carrier

TWIN MINIATURE MODELS SHOW HOW AMERICAN INGENUITY ALTERS CARGO VESSELS TO ASSIST NAVY IN GUARDING VITAL WAR CONVOYS

By Theodore Gommi

TWO ship models in miniature—particularly fascinating projects for the home craftsman to tackle at this time—show how the U.S. Merchant Marine has come to the help of the Navy in furnishing craft for guarding other cargo vessels that carry arms and supplies to the A.E.F. and our Allies. Several motor freighters have been converted into efficient aircraft carriers—too slow for regular combat duty with swift-moving warships, but well fitted to accompany convoys and to provide an effective umbrella of fighter planes able to spot and destroy surface and undersea raiders even in the middle of the Atlantic.

The two models shown here are the

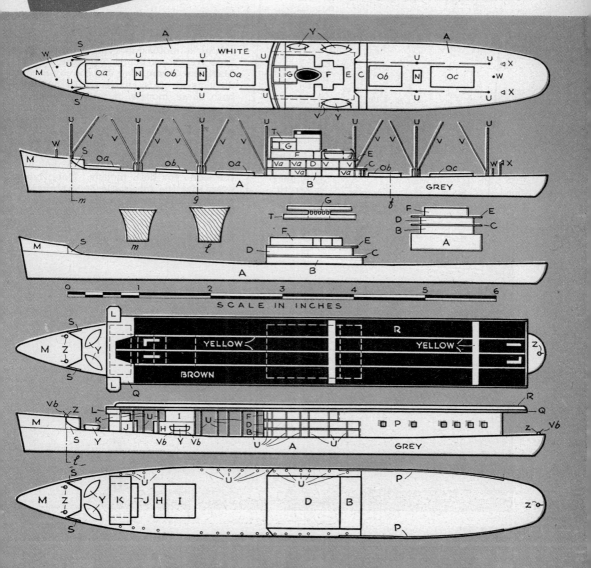

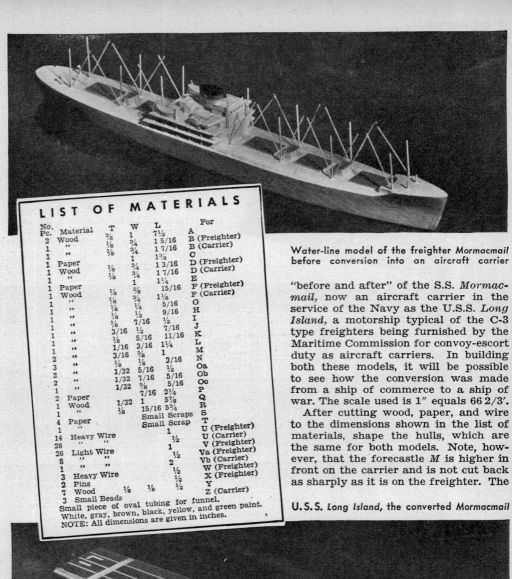

Water-line model of the freighter *Mormacmail* before conversion into an aircraft carrier

LIST OF MATERIALS

No. Pc.	Material	T	W	L	For
2	Wood	3/8	1	7½	A
1	"	1/8	3/4	1 5/16	B (Freighter)
1	"	1/8	3/4	1 7/16	B (Carrier)
1			1	1 3/8	C
1	Paper		3/4	1 3/16	D (Freighter)
1	Wood	1/8	3/4	1 7/16	D (Carrier)
1	"		1	1¼	E
1	Paper			15/16	F (Freighter)
1	Wood	1/8	5/8	1⅛	F (Carrier)
1	"	1/8	3/4	5/16	G
1	"	1/8	1/4	9/16	H
1	"	1/8	1/2		I
1	"	1/8	7/16	1/2	J
1	"	3/16	1/2	7/16	K
1	"	1/8	5/16	11/16	L
1	"	1/16	3/16	1¼	M
1	"	3/16	5/8	1	N
2	"	1/8	1/8	3/16	Oa
3	"	1/32	5/16	1/2	Ob
2	"	1/32	7/16	5/16	Oc
2	"	1/32	5/8	5/16	P
1			7/16	2¼	Q
2	Paper	1/32	1	5 7/8	R
1	Wood	1/8	15/16	5¾	S
1	"			Small Scraps	T
4	Paper			Small Scrap	
1				1	U (Freighter)
14	Heavy Wire			½	U (Carrier)
28	" "			1	V (Freighter)
26	Light Wire			½	Va (Freighter)
8	" "			2	Vb (Carrier)
1	" "				W (Freighter)
3	Heavy Wire			½	X (Freighter)
2	Pins			½	Y
7	Wood	1/8	1/8	½	Z (Carrier)
3	Small Beads				

Small piece of oval tubing for funnel.
White, gray, brown, black, yellow, and green paint.
NOTE: All dimensions are given in inches.

"before and after" of the S.S. *Mormacmail*, now an aircraft carrier in the service of the Navy as the U.S.S. *Long Island*, a motorship typical of the C-3 type freighters being furnished by the Maritime Commission for convoy-escort duty as aircraft carriers. In building both these models, it will be possible to see how the conversion was made from a ship of commerce to a ship of war. The scale used is 1″ equals 66 2/3′.

After cutting wood, paper, and wire to the dimensions shown in the list of materials, shape the hulls, which are the same for both models. Note, however, that the forecastle *M* is higher in front on the carrier and is not cut back as sharply as it is on the freighter. The

U.S.S. *Long Island*, the converted *Mormacmail*

funnel on the freighter is for looks only since it is a motorship, and it is simply re moved on the carrier to make room for the flight deck.

The carrier requires more work, especially in arranging the supports U for the flight deck. These must be inserted close to the edge of A in an absolutely vertical position. The bridge, J, K, and L, and the elevator housing, H and I, must reach the same level as the top of F. The deck, Q and R, is then glued to F, I, and L, and the supports U are trimmed to touch the underside of Q. The sides of the rear hangar P are cut from heavy paper or thin cardboard. The edges are glued to the extreme edges of A and to

the underside of the flight-deck piece Q.

Boats and davits are attached in the positions shown. The AA guns are short bits of wire inserted through small beads.

In finishing the freighter, paint the sides of A and M gray and the rest white with the exception of the hatch covers, which are brown, and the funnel, which is yellow with green and black stripes.

The carrier is painted battleship gray except for the flight deck. This is medium brown with dark yellow guiding stripes and identification letters. If you prefer, you may glue on brown paper on which the stripes and letters are ruled with thin tempera paint and a ruling pen.

Salt and Pepper Shakers Reminiscent of Crinoline Days

AN EVENING'S work at the lathe will produce these quaint little shakers, which can be made any size desired by drawing the pattern on larger or smaller squares.

Mount a piece of stock for each shaker in the chuck or on a screw center and bore out the inside with a small turning chisel, keeping the sides of the recess straight and square. Turn the bottom slightly concave.

Next, turn a piece of scrap stock to a tight fit in the bored portions. Mount each piece on this mandrel to turn the outer contour and the top. If the stock is long enough, the peglike upper body may be turned from the same piece; otherwise, turn the upper part from dowel with a shoulder to insure its being glued squarely into a hole in the skirt.

Dowel will also serve for the bonnets.

Demure is the word for these salt and pepper shakers. The same design can be altered to make up into powder boxes

Turn a short piece to the bell-like contour shown, with the wider diameter toward the tailstock. Run a 5/16″ drill in from this end, flare the mouth, and cut off the piece. Saw off a narrow segment to form the bonnet, which is glued to the turned stem.

A French polish may be applied in the lathe, or the bodies may simply be stained and waxed. The bonnets may be painted white for salt and black for pepper. These condiments are sprinkled through holes drilled through the top of the skirts. Use a 1/16″ drill for the salt shaker and a 3/64″ drill for the other.—BRUCE MACINTOSH.

A pocket made from cardboard, heavy paper, or even fabric, and attached with tape or stitched with thread to the outside of your shopping bag, will hold marketing lists and save you the annoyance of having to dig through your purse for buried memos

SHOPPING LISTS

ATTACH POCKET WITH CELLULOSE TAPE

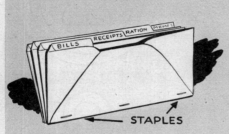

BILLS   RECEIPTS   RATION   MEMOS

STAPLES

An inexpensive household file can be made by stapling together the bottoms of several large-size envelopes. Index tabs are formed by cutting the flaps and gluing them down

A short length of flat curtain rod tacked to the inside of a drawer will form a safe holder for your sewing or household scissors. The sides of the rod can be bent to hold shears of any size

PERFORATED TOP OF CONTAINER

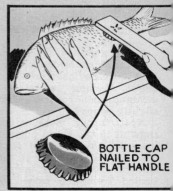

BOTTLE CAP NAILED TO FLAT HANDLE

The top of a scouring-powder can placed over a glass makes an ideal holder for starting small plants such as African violets

A note left in the milk bottle can be protected from rain and kept from being blown away by a glass inverted over the neck

An ordinary bottle cap nailed t[a short wooden handle makes good fish scaler. If desired more than one cap may be use[

SHIPSHAPE

PAINT HANDLES OF ALL TOOLS A BRIGHT COLOR

You can easily distinguish your own garden tools from borrowed ones, and also identify any tools that your neighbors may have borrowed, by painting all the handles of yours the same bright color

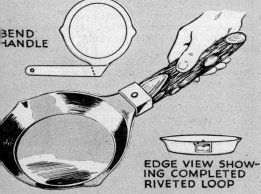

BEND HANDLE

EDGE VIEW SHOWING COMPLETED RIVETED LOOP

To make an easily packed camper's frying pan, bend the handle as shown above, then down, and continue to form socket. Cut off any excess and rivet the joint. A branch whittled to fit the socket serves as a handle

Keeping the family's umbrellas conveniently in one place is easy if you build shelves inside a closet door as shown above. Holes are bored in the top shelf and the umbrellas inserted in these so that the tips rest in blind holes in the lower shelf. Before rolling umbrellas for storage, be sure they are thoroughly dry

The sharpened tips of a worn-out ruling pen will cut two parallel slits in paper, useful for holding stamps and like enclosures

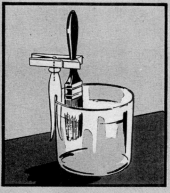

One spring-type clothespin and one ordinary clothespin nailed together as above will form an adjustable paintbrush holder

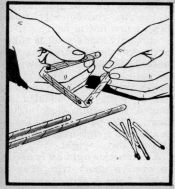

Matches can be kept dry on fishing or camping trips if they are inserted in cellulose straws, folded, and made into packages

Wise Planning Helps You to Enjoy the Unrationed Outdoors

By JACK HAZZARD

MANY pleasures, especially long vacation trips, have been curtailed by war, but the great outdoors remains unrationed, and the enjoyment that can be derived from hikes and outings is unlimited, provided such ventures are carefully prepared for and equipment is judiciously selected. The following suggestions, which will help greatly in making life in the outdoors as pleasant as it is healthy, were culled from the writer's own experience and from a pamphlet published by the New York State College of Agriculture, Cornell University, Ithaca, N. Y.

Hiking clothes should be comfortable and sturdy. Wear thick-soled shoes with soft uppers, and be sure they are large enough since you may have to wear an extra pair of woolen socks. Always equip yourself for rainy weather. A waterproof poncho is the best for this purpose, for it can be conveniently folded away when not in use.

An easily made pack is shown in one of the illustrations. The material is 10-oz. duck sewed or riveted together. Web trunk straps make the best carrying straps, with the buckles arranged to permit easy adjustment. The pack when loaded should not weigh over one third of your own weight.

A hatchet or light ax is needed on even a short trip. The ax should have a sturdy handle— one as long as you can carry. Grind the edge to a long cutting bevel and keep it sharp, but never carry it in your belt without having a leather sheath over the cutting edge to protect yourself against serious injury in case of a fall. An ordinary jackknife will also be needed.

The tarpaulin shown in an accompanying drawing is made of unbleached cotton. The material should be shrunk before being made up, and then waterproofed. It makes a serviceable tent with a front flap that may be left open for sleeping in fine weather or tightly closed to keep out wind and rain.

To waterproof the tent, use two tubs or wash boilers. In one dissolve alum in hot, soft water in the proportion of ¼ lb. to the gallon. In the other, using the same amount of hot, soft water, dissolve sugar of lead (lead acetate—a *POISON*) in the same pro-

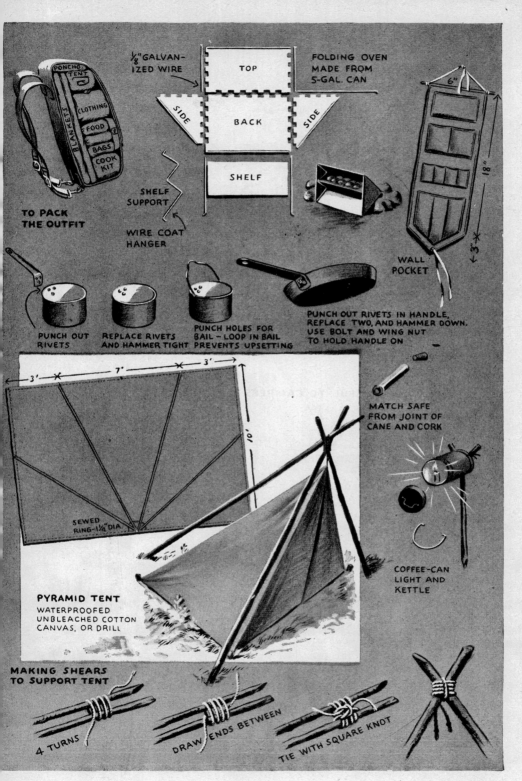

TO PACK THE OUTFIT

PONCHO TENT
BLANKETS
CLOTHING
FOOD
BAGS
COOK KIT

⅛" GALVANIZED WIRE

FOLDING OVEN MADE FROM 5-GAL. CAN

TOP
SIDE
BACK
SIDE
SHELF

SHELF SUPPORT
WIRE COAT HANGER

6"
18"
3"

WALL POCKET

PUNCH OUT RIVETS

REPLACE RIVETS AND HAMMER TIGHT

PUNCH HOLES FOR BAIL — LOOP IN BAIL PREVENTS UPSETTING

PUNCH OUT RIVETS IN HANDLE, REPLACE TWO, AND HAMMER DOWN. USE BOLT AND WING NUT TO HOLD HANDLE ON

MATCH SAFE FROM JOINT OF CANE AND CORK

3'   7'   3'
10'

SEWED RING—1¼" DIA.

COFFEE-CAN LIGHT AND KETTLE

PYRAMID TENT
WATERPROOFED UNBLEACHED COTTON CANVAS, OR DRILL

MAKING SHEARS TO SUPPORT TENT

4 TURNS

DRAW ENDS BETWEEN

TIE WITH SQUARE KNOT

CAMP CRANE
LIFT HERE
AND SWING

BACK LOGS
FOR BAKING

COCOA
POTATOES

BISCUITS IN OVEN

CHOPS

WOODSMAN'S RANGE
CHOP PLACE LOGS
FLAT ON THREE SIDES

12"
36"
4" LOGS

STONE REFLECTOR
(LOGS ARE GOOD)

PLACE LOGS 3'
FROM FRONT
OF TENT

HARDWOOD MAGAZINE FIRE
WILL BURN ALL NIGHT AND
KEEP TENT WARM

TREES MOST USEFUL TO CAMPERS

WHITE OAK (A)(C)(E)

RED OAK (A)(C)(E)

RED BIRCH (A)(D)(E)

MOCK HICKORY (A)(C)

SILVER MAPLE (D)(B)

TULIP (D)

SHAGBARK HICKORY (A)(C)

RED ASH (A)(D)(E) (B)

KEY
(A) FIREWOOD
(B) KINDLING
(C) COOK'S FITTINGS
(D) TENT POLES
(E) STAKES

HARD MAPLE (A)(C)(D)(E)

RED MAPLE (D)(B)

YELLOW LOCUST (C)(E)

portion. Let the solutions stand until clear; then add the sugar-of-lead solution to the alum. After four hours, pour off the clear liquid and work the tent in it with the hands until every part is thoroughly penetrated. Let the tent soak overnight, and in the morning rinse well, stretch, and hang it up to dry.

Comfortable brush beds can be made of twigs and boughs. Make the first layer of heavy boughs 2' and 3' in length. These are the "springs" of the bed. Smaller pieces are laid on next in overlapping shinglelike layers. The bed when complete should be approximately 2' by 2' by 6'. A lightweight, waterproofed canvas bag will also serve as a good bed. This may be stuffed with any soft material such as leaves, straw, rushes, evergreen twigs, and the like. A rough flooring of dead branches placed under the bag will make sleeping warmer and also provide a store of dry wood for the morning fire. The bag should measure about 2½' by 6½' when finished.

A piece of mosquito netting, hemmed and fitted with tie strings, is a seasonal requirement. It can be folded up in the tarpaulin for safe carrying.

Cooking utensils should be cut to a minimum, for they are too heavy and bulky to carry for great distances. Most important of all your cooking equipment is the frying pan. Be sure to choose one that has plenty of depth, for it can also be used to make stew or soup. Pans with detachable handles are good since they are easy to pack.

The folding oven shown in a drawing can be used to make biscuits or pastry, to heat canned goods, and to keep pancakes and the like warm. It was made from a 5-gal. square kerosene can, and when folded takes up no more room than a schoolboy's tablet. The size can be worked out according to the dimensions of the pack used and the material that is available.

Kettles for camp use should have broad bottoms rather than high sides. Two or three should suffice. Pack them with bags of supplies such as flour, corn meal, baking soda, coffee, powdered or canned milk, sugar, and other cooking needs. These, plus the oven and frying pan, are all the cooking utensils needed—but be sure to carry matches. Many a camping trip has been ruined because they were forgotten. The large kitchen matches are best, and they should be carried in a tin or waterproof container along with a piece of sandpaper that can be kept dry for use in wet weather.

One of the banes of camping is sunburn. Great care should be taken to avoid being burned unless your skin is accustomed to it. If you are mildly burned, treat the affected areas with a solution of cold tea, lemon juice, or vinegar before exposing yourself to the sun again.

Poison ivy and sumac are also sworn enemies of the camper. Learn to recognize both, and never make camp near them. A good preventive measure is washing the hands and other parts of the body that might become exposed to the poison with a strong alkali such as yellow laundry soap. A 5-percent solution of potassium permanganate painted on the skin will cure mild cases.

Nettles, though annoying, are seldom serious, for the sting passes quickly. If the camper moves through a clump of nettles very slowly he will seldom be stung at all.

Take along some simple remedies such as ammonia for insect bites, aspirin, and toothache wax. Sulphur tablets are good in chigger country.

Do not eat roots that have an "edible look"—some of them may be poisonous. And beware of toadstools! The really efficient camper should familiarize himself with various types of roots, herbs, and so on before he makes his trip.

Hiking just for the fun of it is good fun and healthy exercise, but for the best enjoyment of a hike, no matter how long you intend to walk, have an objective in mind, plot out your course beforehand, then "go to it," a modern trail blazer—prepared for the worst—and the best.

All the above paraphernalia will actually fit into the bicycle pack. Included are a pup tent, raincoat, shaving kit, camera, blanket, and change of linen. Left, the completed pack in place on the carrier

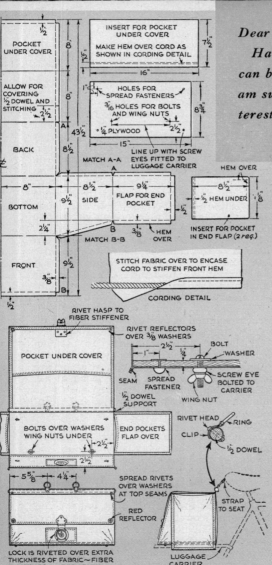

POCKET UNDER COVER

INSERT FOR POCKET UNDER COVER

MAKE HEM OVER CORD AS SHOWN IN CORDING DETAIL

ALLOW FOR COVERING ½ DOWEL AND STITCHING

HOLES FOR SPREAD FASTENERS
3⁄16 HOLES FOR BOLTS AND WING NUTS
¼ PLYWOOD

BACK

MATCH A-A

LINE UP WITH SCREW EYES FITTED TO LUGGAGE CARRIER

BOTTOM

SIDE

FLAP FOR END POCKET

HEM OVER

HEM UNDER

INSERT FOR POCKET IN END FLAP (2 req.)

MATCH B-B

HEM OVER

FRONT

STITCH FABRIC OVER TO ENCASE CORD TO STIFFEN FRONT HEM

CORDING DETAIL

RIVET HASP TO FIBER STIFFENER

RIVET REFLECTORS OVER 3⁄8 WASHERS

BOLT
WASHER

POCKET UNDER COVER

SEAM
SPREAD FASTENER

½ DOWEL SUPPORT

SCREW EYE BOLTED TO CARRIER

WING NUT

RIVET HEAD
RING

BOLTS OVER WASHERS WING NUTS UNDER

END POCKETS FLAP OVER

CLIP

½ DOWEL

SPREAD RIVETS OVER WASHERS AT TOP SEAMS

STRAP TO SEAT

RED REFLECTOR

LOCK IS RIVETED OVER EXTRA THICKNESS OF FABRIC~FIBER STIFFENER UNDERNEATH

LUGGAGE CARRIER

Dear Workshop Editor:

Have you plans for a bicycle pack that can be attached to the luggage carrier? I am sure many other readers would be interested in such a pack now.

B. W., Salt Lake City, Utah

LIGHTWEIGHT, compact, and waterproof, this pack holds all the essentials for a bicycle trip and can be securely fastened to the seat and luggage carrier of any wheel.

Waterproof artificial leather was used for the pack shown, but canvas, which you can waterproof yourself, may be substituted. A piece of fabric 43½" by 51½" is necessary. Lay out the full pattern from the half pattern shown in the drawing. Inserts for pockets should be cut from the waste material after the pattern has been formed. Before shaping the bag, the top front edge is seamed and a cord stiffener is pulled through the seam. The inserts for all the pockets are corded in like manner and stitched into the flaps on the flat material. After the pockets are stitched, the bag is French seamed with strong thread.

A plywood floor ¼" by 8¾" by 15" is fitted into the bottom of the bag and fastened with four roundheaded upholsterer's spread fasteners. The latter serve as casters when the bag is off the bicycle.

Two 3/16" holes are drilled through the plywood floor and fabric for the bolts, which rest on ¾" washers and are lined up with the screw eyes bolted to the luggage carrier. Wing nuts are used to adjust the bag and prevent side sway. The seat straps hold some weight, but the bag rests mainly on the carrier.—ERNEST R. DEWALT.

Enhancing the charms of the smiling miss above is the attractive frame made from show-card stock

Modernly Styled Picture Frame Made from Show-Card Stock

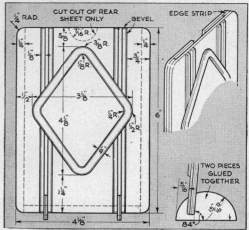

LIGHTWEIGHT yet rigid is this picture frame that is made from 14-ply show-card stock. A metal-edged ruler, a compass, and a penknife are the only tools needed to make it.

Using the ruler and compass, lay out the diamond-shaped center on a piece of cardboard and cut. Place this in position on the panel, as shown; then mark the inner lines of the center design and cut out the inside. Next, mark off the trimming strips from cardboard and glue in place. Be sure to bevel the edges of the strips and the cutout with fine sandpaper before gluing.

Strips of cardboard ¼" wide are glued at the sides and bottom between the front and back panels. The removable, semicircular bases are slipped on between the strips on the front panel. Smooth all the edges with fine sandpaper. If the picture or snapshot is too small to fit into this frame, it may be attached to thin cardboard.—FRANK SHORE.

Button Place Cards

BUTTONS and a few scraps of colored paper make amusing place cards. Features may be drawn on the buttons with India ink, as below, or the buttons may be sewn on with black thread that will form features. Cut petals from contrasting paper and draw on the stem.—B. N.

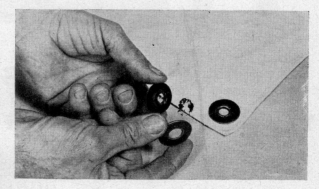

Film-Spool Ends Form Useful Grommets

GROMMETS for use on tents, auto covers, and the like may be made from the metal end of wooden film spools and ordinary ½" washers. Insert the spool end in a hole in the fabric, put on the washer from the other side, and clinch over the collar of the spool end from the washer side. To do this, place the round head of a carriage bolt on it and hammer the bolt, being careful to hold it steady. Such grommets, if carefully made, will hold securely.—B. N.

Willie Wobble-Tail

Gray V-Mouth

Silver V-Mouth

(SHORT)
Open-Mouth
Wiggle Minnow
(LONG)

Pete Popper

FISHING PLUGS

YOU CAN WHITTLE WITH A POCKETKNIFE

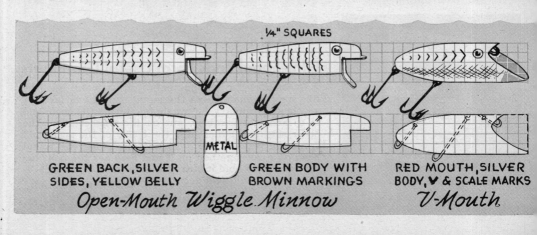

¼" SQUARES

METAL

GREEN BACK, SILVER
SIDES, YELLOW BELLY

Open-Mouth Wiggle Minnow

GREEN BODY WITH
BROWN MARKINGS

RED MOUTH, SILVER
BODY, ♥ & SCALE MARKS

V-Mouth

By ELMA WALTNER

LURES that will attract a fisherman as well as a large-mouth bass or a Northern pike can be made—if you know how to wield a pocketknife—in hardly more time than it takes to buy a new assortment for your kit. And even if you aren't a fishing enthusiast, making plugs can become an interesting and profitable hobby, for commercial lures command a good price.

While some of the newer ones in the sporting-goods shops are of plastic, most are of cedar—a lightweight, buoyant material when properly finished. A common white-cedar post—picked with an eye to as few cracks as possible—will furnish you with material for many lures. Cut 6" lengths and split them into pieces about 1½" thick. Whittle the body—or turn it if you prefer to use a lathe—to the size of the plug you plan to make. In whittling, keep the body as symmetrical as possible by turning the stock often as you work. But don't throw away your first crude efforts. They may prove to be the very plugs to arouse the fighting blood of the big ones when they land with an inviting "plop" beside the lily pads.

Double or triple hooks are the only parts you need to buy, and even these may be salvaged from old plugs. Hook loops and line loops are fashioned from nails. The nickel housing of an old alarm clock, or even a tin can, will furnish metal plates.

Finishing is important, but it need not be artistic. Give the plugs two coats of paint followed by two coats of spar varnish, sanding carefully after each coat has dried. If you wish to try your hand at a scale finish, dip a piece of veiling in dark paint and allow the surplus to drip off. Then, holding the veiling taut, lay it on the plug and immediately lift it off.

Perhaps the easiest plug to make is "Pete Popper," shown in an accompanying drawing. He floats on the surface when at rest, but "pops" and dives obligingly when retrieved with short, quick jerks. The hook and line loops on "Pete" are used on most of the plugs. Bore a hole of nail diameter on a slant from the top of the body to the tail and counterbore the upper part to take the nail head. Push the nail through as far as it will go, slip a hook over the point, bend the point upward with a pair of pliers until it touches the body, and then drive the nail into the wood. If the counterbore has been deep enough, the head will be perfectly countersunk and can be filled over with plastic composition wood.

The line and the hook on the bottom of the lure are held by loops made with the same nail. Select a longer nail than the one used in the tail and push it through a hole bored from the mouth. This hole need not be counterbored, and the nail head should project for about 1". Slip the hook over the point, bend the nail over, and drive the point deep into the wood; then cut the head off the nail, bend that end over, and drive it a short distance into the wood to form the line loop. Rustproof both nails with a coat of spar varnish.

The V-mouth plug is a versatile fellow. He works equally well for trolling or casting. Two finishes are shown. It is hard to say which the fish prefer.

"Open-Mouth Wiggle Minnow" matches his name. He is streamlined and has a metal plate fastened to his head with four small nails. The two that pass through the top of the head are clinched for safety. A small hole in the horizontal projection of the plate is for fastening the leader snap.

"Willie Wobble-Tail" is perhaps the most complicated of the group. His hook fasteners were bent from heavy wire and fastened with small screws. However, the other type of hook fastener would be equally satisfactory. The line loop is bent from heavy leader wire. It passes under the metal plate and is fastened with the same screw that holds the forward hook loop.

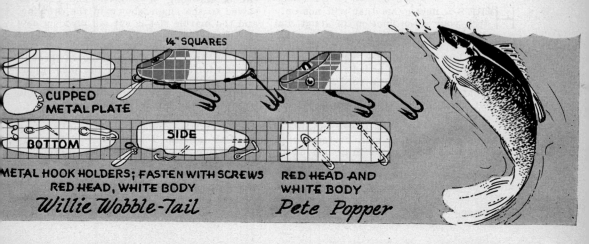

¼" SQUARES

CUPPED METAL PLATE

BOTTOM   SIDE

METAL HOOK HOLDERS; FASTEN WITH SCREWS
RED HEAD, WHITE BODY
Willie Wobble-Tail

RED HEAD AND WHITE BODY
Pete Popper

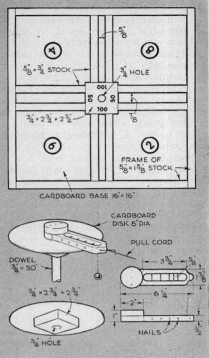

In the Groove...

CAN YOU SCORE FIVE PERFECT HITS IN THIS MARBLE GAME THAT CALLS FOR A KEEN EYE AND A STEADY HAND?

By MYRON FLEISHMAN

HERE'S a new game that will not only test your co-ordination of hand and eye, but will also provide good fun for everyone. Made of cardboard and wood, it is played with five marbles. The latter are dropped to the scoring board from a small tablelike disk by pulling a cord attached to a marble holder. This is pulled over the edge of the disk just far enough to release one marble at a time.

The base is cut from heavy cardboard and enclosed with four sides fastened with butt joints. A block bored to a snug fit for a ¾" dowel is glued or nailed to the center, and from each of its sides extends a slot made of two pieces of ⅝" by ¾" stock.

Two opposite slots are ⅝" wide and are scored for 100 points, while the other two are ⅞" wide and score 50 points. These are the widths necessary when marbles 9/16" in diameter are used. Short dowel feet raise the base off the floor and keep the marbles from bouncing too high.

A heavy cardboard disk 8" in diameter has a block fastened to it to take the other end of the long ¾" dowel. The guide is sawed to the shape shown in the drawing, and the marble slot is cut out on a jig saw or with a scroll saw. Four nails through the slot form divisions for holding the five marbles, and a small hole is bored through the end for the cord. A circular piece glued to the round end of the guide adds enough weight to keep it on the disk when the end overhangs the edge.

The player stands 3' from the disk and maneuvers the guide in an attempt to drop marbles into the four narrow slots. Only one marble should be dropped into each slot unless the first four all reach their mark, in which case the fifth may be aimed for any slot except the one last scored.

Handle on Wooden Salad Bowl
Makes It a Muffin Server

handle will be attached with wooden pegs.

To make a peg, drill a ¼" hole in the end of a piece of ½" dowel and glue a short piece of ¼" dowel in the hole. Saw the ½" dowel off ⅜" long and the other so it projects ¼". Round the end of the larger dowel to form a head.

The handle can be made from orange-crate stock, a fruit-basket hoop, or maple or elm ripped 3/32" thick and ⅞" wide. Cut it a little longer than half the circumference of the bowl, round both ends, and bore ¼" holes about 1¼" from the ends. Soak the strip in tap water for 24 hours, following in boiling water for 30 minutes; then bend it wet on the rounded end of a board, and fasten. When dry, sand and shellac it before removing. It is attached to the flattened sides of the bowl by gluing in the pegs. Clean off surface oil if the bowl is to be decorated, and then shellac.—BERTRAM BROWNOLD.

A QUAINT muffin server can be made of scrap materials and a small salad bowl from a five-and-ten-cent store. Select a slightly oval bowl about 8¾" by 9" and with a pleasing grain. Draw the outline of the top of the bowl on paper; then fold the paper in half to locate the spots where the

In shaping the handle, soak it thoroughly and bend it over a rounded board until it dries. The sides of the bowl are flattened and bored to receive handle pegs made from ½" and ¼" dowels, as at the right

ADJUSTING LATCH PLATES [SHIPSHAPE HOME]

LATCH PLATE
STRIKE
STOP

Door does not latch freely. Inspect the joint between the lock stile and jamb. If the door is greatly shrunk, the latch may not enter the plate far enough to catch. This can be remedied by placing cardboard shims behind the hinges.

Should rub streaks show that the latch catches the edge of the plate opening, drive the plate toward the streak with a hammer and the point of a screw driver bearing in the corner of the opening. If the plate cannot be driven sufficiently, remove it and file the opening. In extreme cases chisel out the plate gain and screw it back in a new position. Mortises that are too small should be enlarged with a chisel.

Pressure of one corner of a warped door against the stop may prevent entrance of the latch. Adjust the latch plate or drive the stop over with a hammer and block. Too much play will allow the door to rattle.

If the door rebounds when slammed, hammer back the projecting strike to provide better wedging action with the latch.

POPULAR SCIENCE MONTHLY SHOP DATA

Three

The two smaller tables slide on guides fastened under the tops to the side aprons. This makes it possible to pick up all three tables at one time

When nested, the tables make a neat appearance and occupy only a 16" by 20" floor area

NESTING TABLES STYLED FOR TODAY ARE PRACTICAL ACCESSORIES FOR ENTERTAINING IN THE SMALL HOME

FOR the moderate-size living room where tables are needed for multiple purposes on occasion, a practical and economical solution is a nest of tables. Three tables ordinarily take little more room than one end table, yet when the need arises they may be brought into the open for the use of guests.

As handsome as it is unobtrusive, the set shown here can be made in the home workshop from available materials. Success in building it demands chiefly the ability to glue up perfectly square frameworks.

These frameworks are the side-leg structures, which should be assembled first by doweling together the legs, side aprons, and bottom stretchers. Be sure they are held perfectly square while the glue is drying. Then join the pairs of frames with the back and front aprons. The back aprons are placed with their faces vertical, while the front aprons are placed with their faces in a horizontal plane. This permits the smaller tables to nest, as shown in the drawing.

The middle table is supported by its overhanging top ends upon two guides screwed to the insides of the aprons of the top table. The smallest table likewise hangs from the middle table. The overhang of all three tops is ½" on the sides and ⅛" on the front and back. When nested, the two smaller tables do not touch the floor. Fasten the tops on, as shown in the sketch, with screws extending upward through holes bored through the aprons. Round off all sharp corners and edges which might impair easy movement of the tables when they are being nested.

The set of tables shown in the photographs was made of scraps of walnut, the tops being glued up of several boards. Almost any wood, however, is suitable for tables of this design. Plywood, either ½" or ⅝" thick, can be used for the tops. Such nests of tables are also attractive in smooth paint finishes.

Tables in One

DESIGNED BY Joseph Aronson

List of Materials

PIECES	DESCRIPTION	THICKNESS	WIDTH	LENGTH	PIECES	DESCRIPTION	THICKNESS	WIDTH	LENGTH
1	TOP	1/2	16	20	1	BACK APRON	3/4	1 3/4	14 7/8
1	"	1/2	14 7/8	17 3/8	1	FRONT "	5/8	2	14 7/8
1	"	1/2	13 5/8	14 5/8	2	SIDE APRONS	3/4	1	11 1/8
4	LEGS	3/4	1 1/8	20 1/2	2	FRONT AND BACK APRONS	3/4	1	12 1/8
4	"	3/4	1 1/8	19	2	STRETCHERS	5/8	3/4	13 1/2
4	"	3/4	1 1/8	17 5/8	2		5/8	3/4	12 3/8
2	SIDE APRONS	3/4	2 1/4	13 1/2	2		5/8	3/4	11 1/8
1	BACK APRON	3/4	2 1/4	17 1/2	2	GUIDES	1/2	1	14 3/4
1	FRONT "	5/8	2	17 1/2	2	"	1/2	1/2	13 5/8
2	SIDE APRONS	3/4	1 3/4	12 3/8					

NOTE: ALL DIMENSIONS ARE GIVEN IN INCHES.

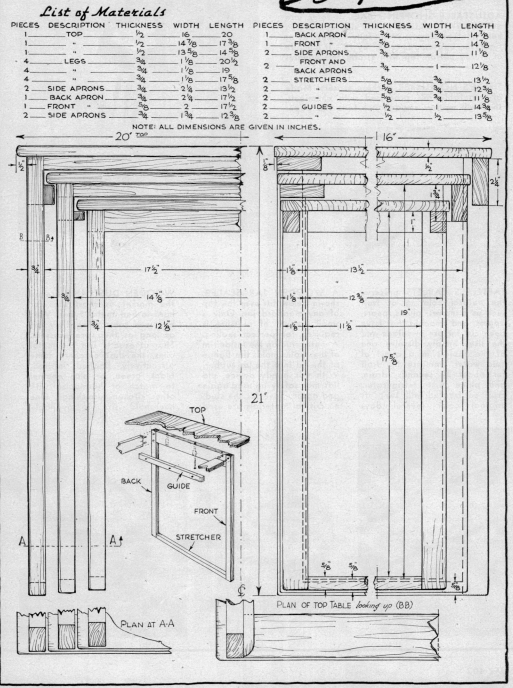

PLAN OF TOP TABLE *looking up* (B.B)

PLAN AT A-A

AIDS TO WARTIME
Housekeeping

ADJUSTABLE SHOPPING BAG. It folds into a 7" by 7½" handbag with a side opening to hold small packages. When fully opened, as at right, the bag measures 18" by 18". It is made of sturdy cotton rep with strong felt handles

THERE'S NO RUBBER in these erasers! Made of vegetable oils processed with chemicals, they will neither smudge nor tear the paper

TASTELESS TABLETS preserve the natural coloring of fruit such as bananas, plums, pears, apples, and peaches that have been cut for use in salads and the like. Simply dissolve one of the tablets in a quart of cold water, immerse the fruit for about 30 seconds, drain, and place in a refrigerator. Fruit so treated will keep its original color several days

A WOODEN JAR SEALER, shown below, fits over the top of any standard jar. Only a small amount of pressure is required for perfect sealing. A metal stud on the inside rim of the sealer molds the flange of the lid into the jar rubber. With this handy device, old lids may safely be used again and again. Save for the stud, no critical materials are used

WOODEN DUSTPANS are on the market as substitutes for hard-to-find metal types. Well built and nonwarping, they last as long as their predecessors. Shaped exactly like the metal ones, the dust catchers come attractively finished in red, black, green, or blue enamel to match or harmonize with other kitchen furnishings. One household size is available

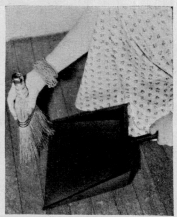

PLASTIC SALT AND PEPPER SHAKERS. Besides adding a decorative touch to a table, these unique shakers are moistureproof and nonbreakable. The opening rests on the table, thus preventing the entrance of air into the salt or pepper chamber. They contain no metal parts for salt to corrode

LIQUID CEDAR. You can cedar-line a closet or a chest with this liquid that is painted, sprayed, or brushed on wood or paper surfaces. It retains its fragrance and does not evaporate, thus repelling moths and other harmful insects. A pint bottle of the liquid will cover approximately 200 sq. ft.

WITH THIS HOME DEHYDRATOR, you can prepare foods for storage even if you live in a small home or apartment. A table lamp with a 300-watt bulb in it provides adequate heat for dehydration. The fiber-and-hardwood cabinet contains five trays that hold the prepared fruits and vegetables. In it, 25 lb. of tomatoes can be dried to 1½ lb., or 25 lb. of apples to about 4 lb., and stored in a proportionately small space. Such dehydrated food is prepared for use by soaking it in water

SHOE TREES made of a noncritical cellulose material fit into the toe of the shoe, as shown above, without stretching the sides or straining the stitching. They are scientifically designed to allow free circulation of air inside the shoes

SOAP FOR WOOLENS in the form of a faintly scented, jellylike preparation has appeared on the market. It is added to lukewarm water, and wool washed in it and dried properly, according to the makers, retains its original softness and fluffiness

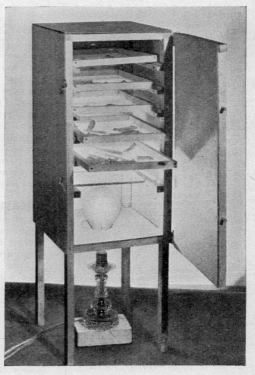

DON'T LEAVE A FURLED SAIL UNCOVERED. IT MAY MILDEW.

USE A WATERPROOF COVER LACED TIGHT AROUND THE MAST.

DON'T WHIP ROPE TOO CLOSE TO END. SWELLING ROPE MAY FORCE WHIPPING OFF.

STOP WHIPPING SHORT OF END.

DON'T USE SMALL BLOCKS THAT BIND ROPES.

USE BLOCKS BIG ENOUGH TO ALLOW FOR SWELLING WHEN WET.

DON'T LET MOORING LINE WEAR AGAINST CHOCK.

PROTECT IT WITH A PIECE OF RUBBER HOSE.

DON'T LEAVE CLEW LASHING TIGHT. IT WILL SHRINK WHEN WET.

LEAVE CLEW LASHING LOOSE TO AVOID STRETCHING SAIL OUT OF SHAPE.

DON'T RUN BARE ROPE THROUGH EYE.

INSERT METAL THIMBLE TO PREVENT WEAR

BOAT HINTS

by J. A. Emmett

ATTENTION TO THE SAILS and running gear of your sailboat will yield dividends in longer life. Turn halyards and sheets end for end to keep them from wearing at the same spots. Mutton tallow applied to ropes where they rub against block sheaves will reduce wear there. If your sail slides aren't swiveled, leave some play in the marlin servings to avoid strain.

Mildewproof your sails with a waterproofing compound made for the purpose. Ease off the main halyard so that shrinkage in wet weather won't stretch the luff of your sail. When using reef points, tie them in such a way as to distribute the strain of the filled sail evenly along its foot. Such precautions, together with those shown in the sketches, will delay replacements and may prevent failures in use.

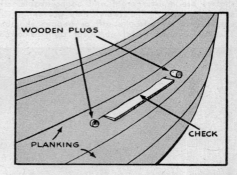

WOODEN PLUGS

PLANKING

CHECK

CHECKS IN PLANKING AND DECKS never get better of their own accord, and filling or caulking forces the opening to widen and extend at both ends. Instead, drill a hole at or just beyond each end of a check, its size in proportion to the thickness of the plank—3/16" for the average ⅝" or ¾" material. Make cedar or pine plugs a snug fit for the holes, dip them in waterproof resin glue, and tap them in, but not too hard. After 24 hours saw them off and tackle the check itself. If this is small, fill it with thin resin glue, working it well down, but if it is wide, shave off a strip of cedar or soft pine the length of the check, coat this with glue, and press it in. Dress off any excess the next day.

GREASE CUPS in inaccessible places on an outboard or inboard engine will be easier to service if extended by the use of pipe fittings. Screw a short or long pipe nipple in the cup hole, add a coupling or elbow, and screw the cup on the end. Oil holes may be tapped to take a length of small pipe or tubing, straight or bent. As an engine's parts become worn and grease cups require turning down oftener, these extensions will lesson the danger of burning one's fingers.

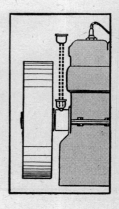

New SHOP IDEAS

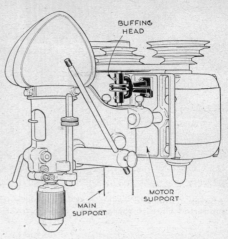

EXTRA DRILL-PRESS SPEEDS are easily obtained by the use of a jackshaft made from an ordinary buffing head. Drill holes in the motor support in order to bolt the buffing head to it, removing the cap of the drill-press column if necessary so that the shaft may extend into the column. If this is impossible, it may be cut short. Mount a step pulley on the shaft and reverse the one on the motor. Both V-belts should be loose enough to shift on the pulleys without undue strain. With this setup, it is possible to obtain very high speeds for shaping and routing, or extremely slow speeds for heavy drilling.—WILLIAM J. PRITCHARD.

A CENTERING GAUGE that will quickly align a shaft under a milling cutter, or level work in the vise of a machine, can be made from a micrometer head and a few pieces of scrap steel. The swivel block at the lower end of the adjusting arm is bored to an accurate fit for the micrometer barrel. Two screws and milled clamping nuts lock all three members rigidly together.

To locate a milling cutter directly above a shaft or a gear blank, for example, the base of the centering tool is placed against the face of the cutter, and the arm and block are locked with the micrometer spindle close to the work and at right angles to the base. The micrometer is then adjusted until the spindle contacts the side of the work, and the reading is carefully noted. With the gauge against the opposite face of the cutter, the micrometer is again adjusted to contact the shaft on that side, the difference in the readings is noted, and the cross-feed screw is adjusted accordingly in either direction in order to center the work.—H. D. CHAPMAN.

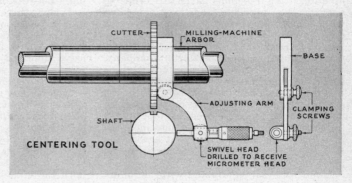

CENTERING TOOL

WOMEN WORKERS play an increasingly important part in the nation's war production, and are making their share of suggestions for speeding Victory jobs. Mrs. Helen Bering, an inspector at the Ternstedt plant of the General Motors Fisher Body Division, suggested a three-in-one gauge for checking dimensions of bearing cups. Formerly three snap gauges were necessary, and it took one hour to check 290 cups. Now one gauge plate makes it possible to check the dimensions of 538 bearing cups an hour. The photos below show both the old and the new gauge setups.

Above, a diamond truing tool in correct position supported close to the point to minimize overhang

A tool-grinding wheel can be dressed by holding an abrasive stick against its rotating surface

TRUING GRINDING WHEELS

MACHINE grinding is the most scientifically accurate method of producing cylindrical, conical, and plane surfaces and of duplicating machine parts. In order to achieve this precision, however, grinding wheels must be perfectly trued. How this may be done is described in an article by E. T. Larson in "Grits and Grinds," a monthly publication of the Norton Company, from which the following pointers and the accompanying illustrations were taken.

All types of abrasive wheels, with the exception of diamond wheels, may be dressed with diamond tools. A dressing tool of this kind consists of one or more stones mounted in a holder, which is traversed across the face of the wheel while the revolving wheel is fed against it.

Mount the tool rigidly and with minimum overhang to avoid chatter, and also be sure that all sources of vibration have been eliminated from the grinding machine itself. The tool should be canted at an angle to the wheel face pointing in the direction of wheel travel. For this "drag angle," a maximum of 10 to 15 deg. and a minimum of 3 deg. are safe margins.

Remember that a diamond dresser is a precision tool. Avoid subjecting it to sudden shocks and blows, turn it frequently in the holder to keep it sharp, and when the diamond has worn badly return it to the manufacturer for resetting.

Before truing is begun, the wheel spindle bearings should be warmed up so that dressing may be done under normal grinding conditions. The dressing operation may be either wet or dry, but it should be the same as that of the grinding. Start truing at the highest point on the face of the wheel, which will usually be at the center, and take light cuts—never more than .001″ for finishing. Let the diamond cool between cuts.

A slow traverse gives a high finish, but if it is too slow, it will cause the wheel to be glazed. A fast traverse produces a free-cutting wheel, but one that is too fast may leave diamond marks that will be transferred to the work. During any one pass, a uniform rate should be maintained.

Cluster-type diamond dressers give better results if traversed faster than the single-point tools. When the diamonds wear down level with the matrix, the dresser can be reconditioned by rolling it up and down and from side to side against the face of a 60- or 80-grit, soft-grade, silicon carbide wheel until the diamonds are again exposed.

In truing for rough grinding, the wheel is fed into the diamond about .001″, and the diamond is traversed at medium speed. Truing for finer finishes requires reduction of the traverse to the slowest speed consistent with the finish desired. The feed should also be lessened, and for very fine finishes, it is advisable to make the last two or three passes without any feed.

Because of high wheel speed, diamond wear may be relatively rapid on a thread-grinding job. The diamond, therefore, must be turned and adjusted frequently. Light truing usually results in less diamond wear, and any temptation to employ a heavy feed, even when a wheel has worn excessively, should be scrupulously put aside.

Truing of thread—grinding wheels should be done with a fairly large stream of lubricant. Three types of diamonds are

Occasional use of an abrasive stick on a metal-bonded diamond wheel will keep the surface clean

A good flow of lubricant is necessary in truing a wheel on a cylindrical grinder as shown above

FOR PRECISION WORK

used, one for each sloping side of the V-face and a third for the "flat" at the apex. The width of the wheel at the apex should be slightly narrower than the width of the flat or root of the thread to be ground so as to permit some radial wheel wear.

All shapes of grinding wheels used for tools and cutters can be dressed with an abrasive stick held in the hand, but for truing newly mounted wheels or for reshaping the face, a diamond tool should be employed.

Metal-bonded diamond wheels for offhand sharpening of cemented carbide-tipped tools should be dressed with the abrasive stick that is supplied by the manufacturer. It scours the metal bond without disturbing the diamond particles, and its occasional use will keep the surface clean and sharp.

If this dressing is neglected until the wheel cuts slowly and heats the tool, the wheel should be dismounted and rubbed by hand on a flat iron plate sprinkled with No. 180 abrasive grain. The entire operation takes only a few minutes and will clean out a wheel that has become severely loaded with steel ground from the shanks of carbide-tipped tools. Resinoid-bonded diamond wheels should be cleaned only with a piece of lump pumice such as that sold by paint shops.

Should it become necessary to grind the periphery of a diamond wheel to restore its face, the truing operation can be done by mounting the wheel on an arbor between centers in a cylindrical grinding machine. Use an indicator to see that it runs true. Rotation should be at the slowest available speed, and grinding is done wet with a soft-grade, medium-grain abrasive wheel.

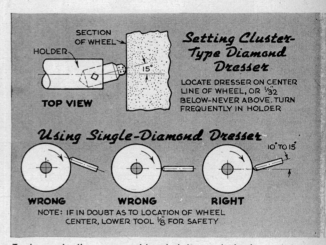

Setting Cluster-Type Diamond Dresser

LOCATE DRESSER ON CENTER LINE OF WHEEL, OR 1/32 BELOW—NEVER ABOVE. TURN FREQUENTLY IN HOLDER

HOLDER

SECTION OF WHEEL

TOP VIEW

15°

Using Single-Diamond Dresser

WRONG   WRONG   RIGHT

10° TO 15°

NOTE: IF IN DOUBT AS TO LOCATION OF WHEEL CENTER, LOWER TOOL 1/8 FOR SAFETY

To dress a badly worn metal-bonded diamond wheel, rub it on an iron plate dusted with abrasive grain

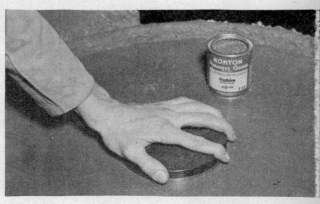

ABC's of Blowtorch Use

NEEDLE VALVE — CLEAN-OUT PLUG

CLEAN-OUT PLUG

GAS GENERATED HERE

FUEL LINE

AIR

PUMP

GASOLINE

WICK

FILLER PLUG

Drawings by William Patrick.

LIKE many another tool, a blowtorch is safe if used with care—dangerous if misused. How a blowtorch works is shown at the left. Air pressure forces gasoline up into the generating passage, which is kept hot enough by the flame of the torch to vaporize the fuel. A needle valve controls the flow of the vapor through a small orifice into the burner, where it draws in air to form a combustible mixture.

Keep the torch out of drafts while gasoline in the drip cup is burning. Pump up air pressure after the torch is lit to obtain the desired flame volume. It is a good idea to release air pressure after shutting off the torch. Empty and rinse out the fuel tank occasionally. For safety, do this in the open air.—J. MODROCH.

USE ONLY UNLEADED GASOLINE. WIPE OFF ANY SPILLED FUEL

KEEP PUMP CLEAN

REMOVE FILLER PLUG FROM BOTTOM-FILL TORCH OR......

REMOVE PUMP FROM TOP-FILL TORCH

KEEP NEEDLE VALVE CLOSED

PUMP UP AIR PRESSURE

DRIP CUP

PLACE HAND OVER NOZZLE; OPEN NEEDLE VALVE TO ALLOW GASOLINE TO FILL DRIP CUP OR....

IF TORCH HAS A PRIMING VALVE, OPEN IT UNTIL DRIP CUP IS FILLED

LIGHT GASOLINE IN DRIP CUP. OPEN NEEDLE VALVE JUST BEFORE CUP BURNS DRY

HOLD MATCH TO NOZZLE IF FLAME FROM CUP DOES NOT IGNITE VAPOR

Starting the Torch

PACKING NUT SHOULD BE LEAKTIGHT, BUT SHOULD NOT BIND VALVE

KEEP PUMP OILED

AFTER TURNING OFF TORCH, BACK OUT NEEDLE VALVE ABOUT 1/8 TURN TO PREVENT JAMMING

Maintenance

Slotted Guard on Wire Gauge Prevents Errors in Measuring

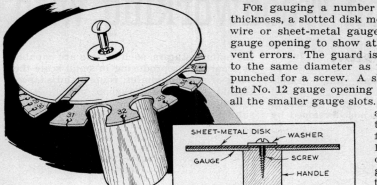

SHEET-METAL DISK — WASHER
GAUGE — SCREW
— HANDLE

FOR gauging a number of parts of the same thickness, a slotted disk mounted over a standard wire or sheet-metal gauge will permit only one gauge opening to show at a time, and thus prevent errors. The guard is cut from sheet metal to the same diameter as the gauge and center-punched for a screw. A slot slightly wider than the No. 12 gauge opening will serve for this and all the smaller gauge slots. As shown, both gauge and guard are screwed to a piece of broomstick for ease of handling. A larger slot can be cut opposite the first for gauge openings Nos. 0 to 11.—RONALD EYRICH.

Flaring Tool for Copper Tubes Can Be Made from Heavy Wire

IN REPLACING gasoline lines or installing other small copper tubing, it is necessary to flare the end in order to make a tight fit with the union nut. A simple emergency tool for this purpose can be made from a piece of heavy wire of smaller diameter than the internal diameter of the tubing. Bent as shown and rotated inside the tubing by means of an ordinary brace, this forms a smooth, even flare. Care should be taken not to make the elbow bend too sharp.—R. E.

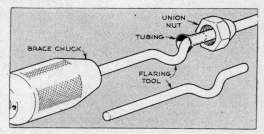

Ordinary Eraser Holds Small Brads Safely for Easy Starting

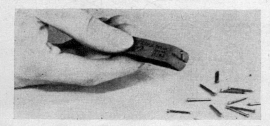

A COMMON long eraser, as shown in the photograph at the left, makes a simple device for protecting your fingers when starting small brads. Both ends should be slit back about ¼" without cutting away any of the rubber. This will provide a flexible grip that will pick up the brads and hold them for starting. As the slit wears, shave the eraser back and deepen the slit so that it enters fresh rubber.

New Production Reamer Speeds Work in Restricted Quarters

A NEW production tool developed by Henry Bernadt, of the General Electric works at Schenectady, N. Y., not only reams holes in places difficult to reach with ordinary tools, but also has an adjustment for compensating wear. The reamer is a steel cylinder with multiple cutting edges on its outer surface that ream to specified tolerances at a single turn. Longitudinal slots permit an expansion of .002" when the tapered arbor is tightened against the washer after the reamer is inserted in the hole. These slots also compensate for cutter wear. By decreasing the thickness of the washer .001", the arbor penetrates deeper, expanding the reamer .0001".

Precision Woodworking with

By EDWIN M. LOVE

SMALL carving motors and flexible shafts are excellent tools for model making, carving, and light grinding. Equipped with special stands developed by the manufacturers, such motors are capable of accurately reproducing in small scale the work of a lathe, jointer, router, and shaper. Should the home-workshop owner desire to build his own accessories, satisfactory substitutes for the manufacturers' stands

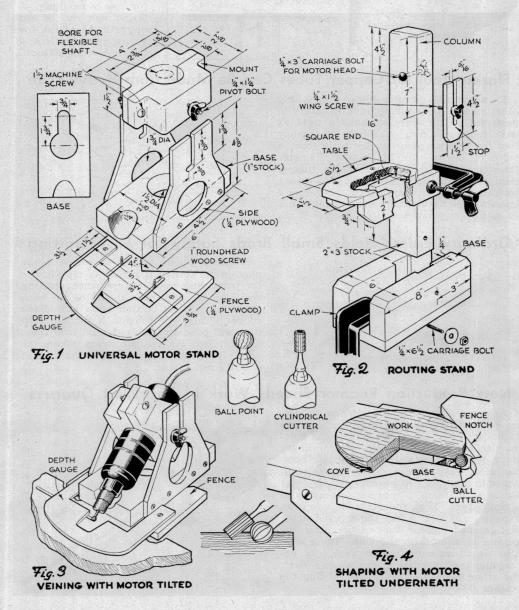

Fig. 1 UNIVERSAL MOTOR STAND

Fig. 2 ROUTING STAND

Fig. 3 VEINING WITH MOTOR TILTED

Fig. 4 SHAPING WITH MOTOR TILTED UNDERNEATH

Small Carving Motors

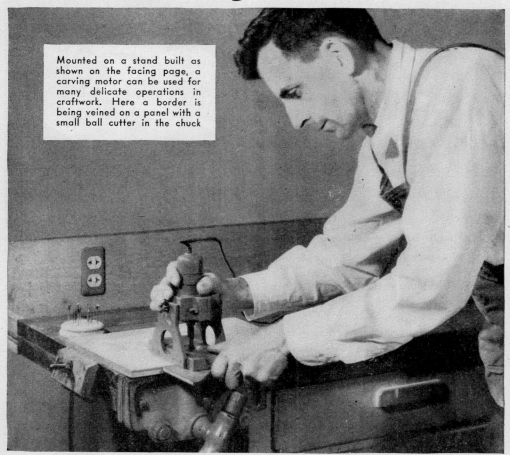

Mounted on a stand built as shown on the facing page, a carving motor can be used for many delicate operations in craftwork. Here a border is being veined on a panel with a small ball cutter in the chuck

can readily be made from sound hardwood.

How are these stands built? A universal stand adaptable to any small carving motor or flexible shaft is shown in Fig. 1 and in the photograph above. Slight alterations, such as a change in the size of the motor-mount hole or in the height of the sides, may be required for your particular carving motor. Make the motor mount from a piece of 2" by 3" stock 4" long. Use an expansion bit for boring the motor hole, setting the cutter by first making test cuts in scrap pieces. Saw the mount into halves and counterbore the pivot-bolt holes at the inner ends so that the boltheads may be sunk flush.

The holes in the sides give visibility, and the L-slots, cut to allow easy entrance of the pivot bolts, provide for clamping the

motor mount at various heights and also for lengthwise adjustments of the base. Bore the base to admit the cutter, extending the hole toward one end to allow tilting of the motor. Gouge a trough at the opposite end to clear the chuck when the motor is used in a tilted position. The fence is straight on one edge and notched on the other. Fasten it to the base with two screws passing through washers or a thin yoke and the adjustment slots. The depth gauge is screwed to the top of the fence.

To increase the usefulness of the mount, make a routing column and table as shown in Fig. 2 of the drawings and in the photo at top left on the following page. The column can be held upright in a vise when in use, but a base that can be clamped to the bench may be built for it. A stop on the

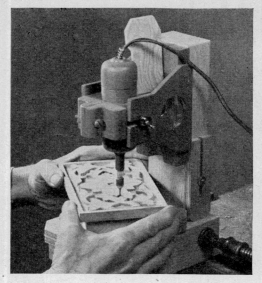

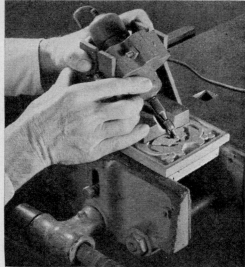

Its motor mount bolted to a column, the carving motor routs out the background of a low-relief carving. The push button is held in by a wedge

Mounted on a universal stand, the motor is tilted to plane down the level of the carving. A ball point cuts best when tilted, if the work permits

side of the column makes it possible to re-place the table at the proper height if it must be removed for adjustment of the work.

Can a small carving motor be used in making full-sized furniture? One job it does easily is veining, which means cutting a shallow, rounded groove in the face of the work to form a border, to separate a light-stained area from one stained dark, or to make a decorative line design. Mount the motor in the universal stand in a vertical position with the tip of a 3/32″ ball cutter projecting below the base by half of the diameter of the cutter. Set the straight edge of the fence to gauge the distance of

the vein from the edge of the work, and mark the starting and stopping points of the lines with a pencil. Start the cut by pressing the fence against the guiding edge and lowering the tool until the base rests on the work. Then push the stand along the edge of the work to the end of the line. A second pass of the cutter without change of setting makes a smoother job.

To cut a border vein on circular work, reverse the fence and use the notched edge as a guide. Veining of intricate designs is best done by using the column and patterns especially cut for the work.

Ball points, in any but small sizes, cut poorly on the ends because of the meeting

Rabbeting a strip with the motor upside down and a cylindrical cutter set in a notch in the fence

Shaping the edge of a disk is done with the motor tilted to bring the side of the cutter into action

of the cutting blades at a dead center. For this reason it is advantageous to tilt the motor in the stand, as in Fig. 3 and in one of the photographs, when the work permits. The cutter, projecting at the end of the base, will be in full view and can be accurately adjusted for depth of cut by varying the tilt of the motor. The fence, fitted with its depth gauge, makes the scoring of lines parallel to the edges easy and rapid. Without the fence, the tilted cutter is efficient for shallow routing when it is not necessary to have vertical sides in the cut.

How is the routing stand used? Bolt the motor stand to the column and set the column upright in the bench vise. Insert the motor mount with the motor shaft parallel to the column. Loosen the column stop and locate the height of the table by resting the work on it and sliding it up until the cutter projects the correct distance below the top of the work. Then clamp the table and set the stop against it.

A small cylindrical cutter with scored teeth works best for routing, but it does not bore well, and therefore a hole should be drilled to depth in the center of each area to be routed. To insert the cutter in the work, loosen the table clamp and swing the front edge of the table down until the work can be placed under the cutter. Raise the table to position against the stop and clamp. Begin routing by feeding the work lightly

against the rotation of the cutter until the blades graze the outline, steadying your hands against the table and manipulating the work with your fingers. The cutter will tend to slip into the routed area instead of gouging into the outline, thus giving positive control. Work as closely into the corners as possible. When the cavity is routed, lower the table and reset it for another. The corners can be carved out with a chisel.

How is intricate veining done? This is easiest with a jigsawed pattern placed over the work and raised above the cutter blades with shims so that the shank will bear against the edge of the pattern and will be guided by it. The pattern must be accurate, for all irregularities will be transferred to the work. If the pattern is an outside one, cut its edges larger by half the diameter of the shank; if it is an inside one, cut the pattern correspondingly smaller. Soap the edges to reduce friction.

What setup is used for operating the motor as a shaper? Insert the desired cutter and set up the motor as for routing without bolting the stand to the column. Clamp the stand upside down, as in Fig. 4 and in two of the photos. Adjust the straight edge of the fence for straight work and the notched edge for round work. When cutting coves, use a ball cutter with the motor tilted to take advantage of side cutting. Make two or three passes on heavy cuts.

Decorative Clock Case Veined with a Carving Motor

MAKE a dual pattern for the front of the clock case with one end an outside template for the panels and the other an inside guide for the border. Cut stock oversize so that the pattern, laid on shims, can be nailed to it in waste wood, and align with a nail thrust through a hole in the center of the pattern and the work. Run the carving motor around all edges; then pry up and reverse the pattern for completing the front. Assemble with glue and, when it is dry, run the top and side border veins.—E. M. L.

HISTORIANS tell us that the first armed vessel to sail under the authority of the Continental Congress was the Marblehead schooner *Hannah* commissioned by George Washington as a privateer. While there are no scale drawings of the *Hannah,* research has given fairly accurate information on her size and general appearance. This weather-vane model follows these specifications, omitting only those details that would be indistinguishable on a mounted vane.

The over-all dimension of the model hull, including the stem, is 12¾". Use 1" or 1⅛" stock, preferably the latter. If light-gauge zinc is not available for the mainsail, any 8" by 8" light sheet metal, or even wood, will be satisfactory. The rigging is 22-gauge copper or galvanized wire fastened to the hull by winding it around partly driven pins that are later driven home.

Make a template for one side of the hull and mark the outline on the stock along with lines for painting and locations of masts, guns, and pivot bearing. Shape the

Manned by soldiers of the Continental Army, the schooner *Hannah* sailed out of Beverly, Mass., on September 5, 1775, with a commission from George Washington as a privateer. Her first prize, the British ship *Unity,* fell to her the next day. Above is a copy of a woodcut of the *Hannah* in the book *Origin of the American Navy,* by Henry E. White, which was published in 1890

hull with square edges; then saw a ¼" slot for the stem-keel-rudder part, as shown by the dotted lines *B-C, C-D,* and *D-E.* The edges are next rounded on both sides, but only to the top of the green stripe at the stern, which is square from this point to the deck. A rounded bow and square stern are important features of the design.

Drill the two ¼" holes in the hull for the masts at a slight angle from the vertical toward the stern; then bore two ¼" holes through the hull for the guns. The bowsprit is glued into a hole drilled into the bow. Use special care in drilling for good alignment fore and aft. Lay out the entire stem-keel-rudder piece on ¼" material to fit the slot sawed in the hull. Glue this piece in place and sand the hull smooth.

The masts and bowsprit are tapered from ¼" dowels, and the main boom, main gaff, fore boom, and fore gaff are tapered from ⅜" dowels. Tapering begins about one third of the way from the base, and can be done with a block plane and then sanded smooth. Give the entire hull a priming coat of flat white and two coats of enamel, coloring the stripes as indicated. The spars and bowsprit are stained brown, and the guns are black. A final coat of spar varnish will provide additional protection from weather.

The mainsail is cut to shape and small holes are punched along three edges for bending it to the mast, boom, and gaff with copper wire. File any burrs caused by punching; then give the sail two coats of flat white and one of glossy white enamel.

Shape the ends of the booms and gaffs to fit the curve of the masts at the angles shown in the drawing. Drill a small hole through the main boom at this end and start the wire around the boom and through the holes at this point, keeping the sail in the center of the boom and the wire pulled taut. Bend the sail to the main gaff in the same manner after most of the rigging has been done, further adjusting the stays if the weight of the sail requires it. Fasten the fore gaff to the fore boom with a brad, lash them together, and tack the end to the deck.

To hold the schooner for rig-

By
Harry D. Hamilton

Mounted where it will receive the full effect of undeflected wind, this model of the historic *Hannah* heads proudly into the breeze. A cotter pin through a hole in the top of the mounting rod will keep the vessel fixed on her mooring

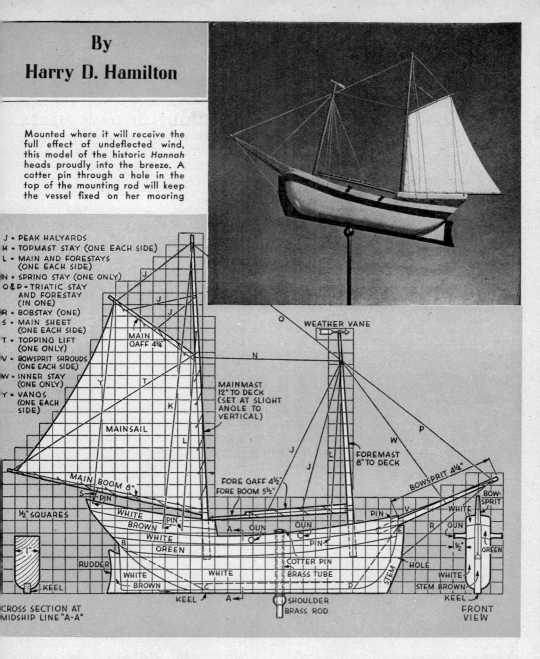

J - PEAK HALYARDS
K - TOPMAST STAY (ONE EACH SIDE)
L - MAIN AND FORESTAYS (ONE EACH SIDE)
N - SPRING STAY (ONE ONLY)
O & P - TRIATIC STAY AND FORESTAY (IN ONE)
R - BOBSTAY (ONE)
S - MAIN SHEET (ONE EACH SIDE)
T - TOPPING LIFT (ONE ONLY)
V - BOWSPRIT SHROUDS (ONE EACH SIDE)
W - INNER STAY (ONE ONLY)
Y - VANGS (ONE EACH SIDE)

ging, set the shaft bearing over a large nail driven through a wide board. Drill small holes in the masts and bowsprit for fastening wires and in the hull for stay and vang pins. Triatic stay O and forestay P are made of one wire which goes through the foremast on a slant. Forepeak halyard J is also one piece of wire, as are the lower J's on the mainmast and the L's and K.

Attach all the rigging wires as shown, leaving ends long enough to be adjusted before final fastening. Adjust all wires for tautness and neatness; then make them fast and drive the pins in carefully. Wire ends can be soldered for strength and neatness.

The weather vane on the foremast is made of a piece of celluloid about 1" long. It adds a touch of authenticity.

Gay Designs Add Sparkle to

BRIGHT NEW THINGS FROM DISCARDED OUT-OF-DATE PIECES WILL GO FAR TOWARD FRESHENING YOUR HOME SURROUNDINGS

WHEN you are digging old pieces of furniture from the attic in the hope of salvaging enough to make that spare room livable, try your skill at freehand decoration. It is surprising what it will do toward rejuvenating a hopelessly outdated bureau, chair, or even bed. With a little alteration in addition to the repainting it is highly possible that you will like a done-over piece so much you will promote it to the best rooms in the house.

While the painted decorations on furniture appear—and are—easy to do, they stem from basic principles of technique, as shown on the facing page in the sampler of Peter Hunt, of Provincetown, Mass. This illustrates several fundamental brush strokes that are used singly and in combinations to make any number of motifs. Fruits, flowers, conventional designs, and even vegetables evolve from these simple strokes. It is fun to do, and it is surprising how many attractive original designs will flow from

your palette when you become acquainted with the freehand use of small, pointed, camel's-hair brushes measuring from 3/8" to 3/4" in length.

Oil paints, available in small tubes and a variety of colors, are used for this fascinating work. The paints can be mixed and blended to make any shade desired, and white can be added to make softer tints. Oil colors are thinned for use with a little turpentine and clear varnish. This makes application easier and drying quicker. Squeeze oil colors first on a palette, which may simply be an old plate or a piece of glass, mix them as desired, and then apply them to the furniture.

Because several colors may be used in combination to make a design, it is necessary to let each dry sufficiently so that it will not mix with the subsequent coat being applied near it or, as in many cases, over it.

Try this new way of decorating old pieces that you have salvaged and rebuilt.

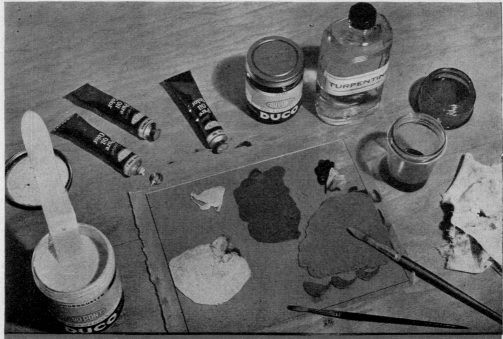

Decorating requires only a few tubes of oil colors, turpentine and clear varnish, and a small palette. Above, a piece of window glass serves as a palette. The gray paper under it provides a neutral background. Keep a glass of turpentine near by for cleaning brushes between colors

Old Furniture

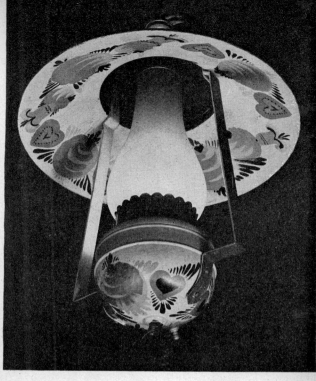

Here is an old oil lamp that was wired, painted white to reflect light, and then decorated in gay colors and hung over a dining-room table. Left, a charming chest decorated with a vegetable motif

Photos and sampler courtesy E. I. du Pont de Nemours & Co.

BASIC DESIGNS TO HELP PERSONALIZE YOUR FURNITURE

paint names and mottos in your own handwriting

Even if you can't draw, study and copy this sampler for decorations that will brighten up your discarded furniture. They require just a few fundamental strokes with a camel's-hair brush and, used singly or in combination, will achieve surprising and fascinating transformations

Folding

TAKES THE DRUDGERY OUT OF WARTIME MARKETING, SAVES GAS AND TIRES

THIS sturdy and attractive shopping cart will help take the drudgery out of transporting purchases home from stores. Its tricycle wheel arrangement makes for ease in crossing curbs and allows the cart to stand alone. A shaped bag, 12″ square and 21″ high, made of waterproofed canvas, will fit the cart and keep a miscellany of small packages safely together. Ties at the back support it upright, and a wire bent to fit inside the seamed top edge holds the bag in shape.

The shopping cart is made almost entirely of dowels. Wheels are of hard yellow pine. Bearings for the large wheels are made of a hardwood such as maple and soaked in oil or hot wax. The maple dowel axle is given the same treatment, which assures squeak-free action for some time.

When not in use, the cart folds to a thickness equal to the diameter of the large wheels and can be tucked away in a closet. Final assembly should be made only after all the parts have been trial-fitted. Use a good grade of waterproof glue for all joints. A first coat of primer paint followed by two coats of enamel will provide a lasting finish.

A hardwood bushing that has been soaked in hot paraffin is driven into each wheel

Two collars are slipped on the front axle and doweled close to the wheel to maintain its central position on the axle

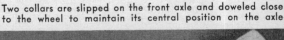
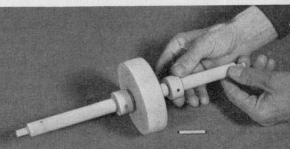

Shopping Cart

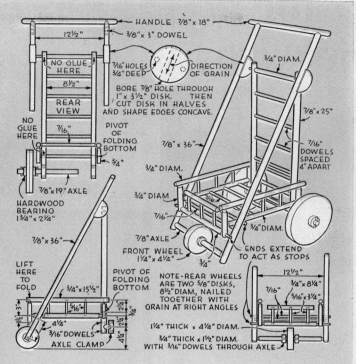

HANDLE 7/8" x 18"

3/8" x 3" DOWEL

12 1/2"

NO GLUE HERE

8 1/2"

7/16" HOLES 3/4" DEEP

DIRECTION OF GRAIN

BORE 7/8" HOLE THROUGH 1" x 3 1/2" DISK. THEN CUT DISK IN HALVES AND SHAPE EDGES CONCAVE.

3/4" DIAM.

REAR VIEW

NO GLUE HERE

7/16"

PIVOT OF FOLDING BOTTOM

3/4"

7/8" x 36"

3/4" DIAM.

7/8" x 25"

7/16" DOWELS SPACED 4" APART

7/8" x 19" AXLE

HARDWOOD BEARING 1 3/4" x 2 1/4"

3/4" DIAM

3/4" DIAM.

7/16"

7/8" x 36"

7/8" AXLE

FRONT WHEEL 1 1/4" x 4 1/4"

3/4"

3/4" DIAM.

ENDS EXTEND TO ACT AS STOPS

LIFT HERE TO FOLD

PIVOT OF FOLDING BOTTOM

3/4" x 15 1/2"

5/16"

4 1/4"

3/16" DOWELS

AXLE CLAMP

NOTE-REAR WHEELS ARE TWO 5/8" DISKS, 8 1/2" DIAM., NAILED TOGETHER WITH GRAIN AT RIGHT ANGLES

1 1/4" THICK x 4 1/4" DIAM.

3/4" THICK x 1 1/2" DIAM. WITH 3/16" DOWELS THROUGH AXLE

12 1/2"

3/4" x 8 1/4"

7/16"

5/16" x 3 1/4"

Benjamin Nielsen designed and built this folding cart to be the last word in accessories for the home shopper who does her own delivering. The color might be natural or enameled

---

SEPTEMBER CHECK LIST   [SHIPSHAPE HOME]

1. If basement is wet, dig outside trench and lay tile drain.
2. Dampproof cellar walls before fall wet weather.
3. Reset loose chimney bricks and capping with cement mortar.
4. Repair and paint storm windows and doors.
5. Install weatherstripping on window and door frames.
6. Enlarge fuel bin if necessary. Put in winter supply.
7. Build a cool, ventilated fruit and vegetable room.
8. Replace all loose or cracked glazing putty.
9. Take out broken window panes and install new ones.
10. Inspect sash cords. Replace any that are frayed.

POPULAR SCIENCE MONTHLY SHOP DATA

Designed for Service...

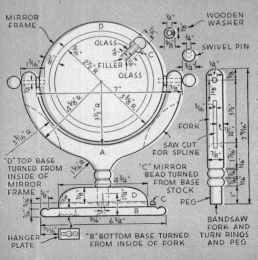

DRESSER AND WALL MIRROR. This double-faced swivel mirror with a walnut frame and base is useful on a dresser or as a shaving mirror on the wall. Cut the bottom of the base from inside the fork, so as not to waste stock, and turn a piece to go on top of it from within the mirror-frame ring. Turn the bead for the inside of the frame from the stock of the bottom of the base, which is then finished in the lathe.

Mount the fork in the lathe and turn the two rings and the peg at the bottom; then slot the fork for splines. Drill swivel-pin holes in line, using a snug filler piece between the prongs.

Turn the frame to the Gothic shape shown in the cross section, making the opening to fit the double-faced mirror to be used. Drill swivel-pin holes on the center line; then glue in the bead over the glass.

Bore carefully through the upper part of the base and into the bottom for the fork peg and

... CRAFTWORK PROJECTS BY

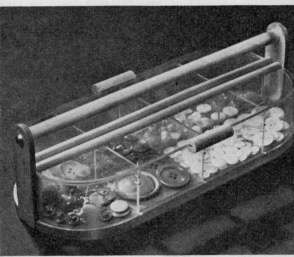

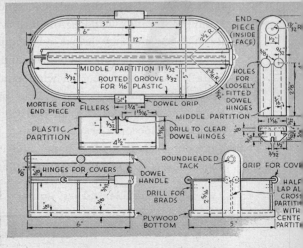

drill a 3/16" hole through the center of the bottom for the wood screw, counterboring for the head. Install the hanger plate with the grain of the bottom. Turn the round-head pins and the washers, and assemble with the washers between the fork and frame. Working time: 6 hours.

PLASTIC BUTTON BOX. The plastic covers, sides, and partitions show at a glance the buttons available. Cut the birch-plywood base, sand smooth, and rout grooves for the sides and partitions. Make two endpieces of maple, using a generous length for ease in handling when cutting slots. Drill holes for the handle and dowel hinges ½" deep, cut the 45-deg. chamfers, shape the tops, and sand. Mortise the base for the endpieces; then groove the hinges and cut to length.

Clamp the three short plastic partitions between two pieces of wood and pass them across a circular saw for half-lap joints. Drill ⅜" holes through a wood jig, as shown, making semicircular cuts in the plastic to clear the hinges. Cut the long partition and saw out half-lap slots.

Assemble the partitions and cement them into the grooves in the base. Fasten the endpieces in place, fitting in the hinges and handle. Bend the plastic sides after immersing them in hot water and fit them into the grooves in the endpieces and base. The dimensions of the sides are 1 15/16" by 13½", and the top corners are rounded to clear the hinges. Brads join the sides to the cross partitions. Cut the plastic covers, leaving a lip on each for slotted dowel grips. Cement these in place to complete the assembly. Working time: 6 hours.

ERNEST R. DEWALT ARE PLANNED TO FILL REAL NEEDS

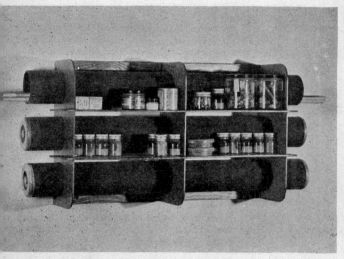

DRAFTSMAN'S SHELF. Scrap pine, three cardboard mailing tubes, and 4 sq. ft. of ⅛" composition board are used for this shelf and tracing holder. Cut three 28" lengths of mailing tube of uniform diameter. Brad the three walls together where the half-lap waste area will occur, and with a circle cutter make holes for the tubes in all three at once. Lap joints are then cut, and the corners are rounded. Drill screw holes in the outside walls and notch the middle wall to fit the saw cuts in the hangers.

Make two shelves, cutting slots as shown, and round the corners. Fit them to the walls, saw out the hangers, and screw the parts together for a trial fit. Remove the hangers to drill and counterbore for the screws.

Stain the wood pieces walnut and varnish them; then paint the tubes black. Between coats, turn the six tube covers, making the inside shoulders a slip fit for the inside of the tubes. Reverse the covers in the chuck, turn the knobs and recesses, and finish with walnut stain and varnish. Working time: 5 hours.

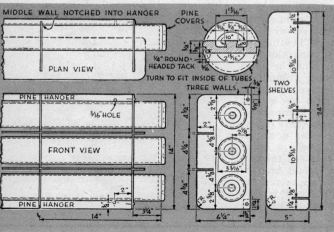

A SEAT AND WASHER combination now on the market not only provides a watertight seal for household faucets, but—as shown in the drawing below—it also eliminates the need for using a separate washer and screw. When installed, it expands and locks tightly in the faucet. Suitable for use in both cold and hot-water taps, the device is available in all of the standard sizes.

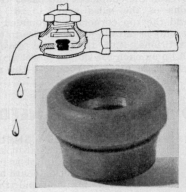

WALL PANELS made of a fiber insulation-board core, sealed with a special compound between two layers of asbestos and cement, are being used in homes under construction for war workers. One panel on each side of the framework replaces the sheathing, building paper, and siding or lath and stucco formerly used in wall construction. The product affords ample insulation and can be used with standard sashes and doors.

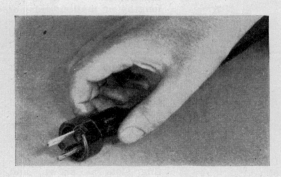

A DRY WALLPAPER CLEANER, shown in use below, literally "erases" dirt from the walls. Consisting of tiny particles of art-eraser gum enclosed in a porous cotton bag, it requires no special skill, but is merely rubbed gently over soiled surfaces. The cleaner will not cake, dry, or smudge, and is safe to use on all types of wallpaper. It can also be used successfully on window shades, white shoes, lamp shades, felt hats, books, pictures, etchings, paintings, Venetian-blind tapes, and the like. It is available in one handy, easy-to-grip size.

CIRCUIT-BREAKER PLUG. Replacing the conventional receptacle plug usually found on the connecting cord of small electric power tools, office machines, home appliances, heating devices, fluorescent light fixtures, and the like, this device breaks the circuit when a short circuit, motor stall, or accidental ground occurs. Protection is provided not only for each individual piece of equipment on a circuit, but also for the circuit itself—that is, faulty operation of one device need not affect others on the same line. To reset the plug after a circuit break, simply pull it out and lower a lever, which will have sprung from between the two prongs, back into place. This circuit breaker will do much to eliminate dangerous fire hazards and costly repair bills, and is also valuable in shops to prevent breakdowns.

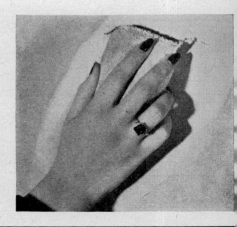

LEAN-TO BASEMENT GREENHOUSE. You can raise flowers and vegetables the year around in this greenhouse, which is easily erected alongside an open basement window. Constructed of red cypress and double-strength glass, it comes semiassembled and can be put up in less than a day. It is available in three, four, and five-section units measuring from 4' 4" to 7'. Entrance is possible through a door at the end or through a cellar window. In winter, heat from the basement provides the proper temperature, but on extremely cold days a small kerosene stove or electric heater can be used.

PLASTIC HINGES are now being used by one aircraft manufacturer on boxes for airplane tools, cases for maps, charts, radios, and the like. Chosen not only because they save essential war metals, but also because they are extremely light in weight and durable, the hinges are said to withstand long, hard wear without denting, chipping, or cracking, and their smooth, lustrous surface is rustproof and dirt resistant. Strips may be cut to any desired length and are easily attached to other materials by means of adhesives, rivets, or screws. They can be made in many colors, and they offer endless possibilities in the designing and manufacturing of light and portable equipment. Such hinges may, in the near future, replace metal ones in a variety of light-duty applications.

HOSE HORSE FOR GARDENS. Simple in construction, the all-wood "horse" shown above holds the hose in such a manner that a spray or stream can be directed on the area desired. By simply adjusting the rear leg, the hose can be placed in any position. The device is covered with a water-repellent wood preservative and comes knocked down, with easy instructions for assembling. It can be set up without the use of screws or nails.

THIS SOIL-TESTING KIT, consisting of about 60 strips of chemically treated paper and a color chart for comparing results, comes conveniently packed in a 3" glass tube. The paper, after being inserted in a slit in the ground made with a knife, changes color according to the condition of the soil. Its hue is then compared with the chart to determine whether the acidity or alkalinity of the soil is such that will need correction.

HAVE you ever repeated a scene until, through its very repetition, your audience laughed uproariously? That's what Hollywood calls a "running gag." Have you ever stopped motion, varied your filming speed, or reversed action by filming a scene upside down? Professional productions, including the newsreels, employ all these ruses to get laughs.

There's no reason why home movies, adopting the same simple technique, can't provide merry as well as informative shots of the family and friends. Laughter is an important morale builder, and it doesn't cost a cent. There's no need, either, to make elaborate setups or produce involved continuities, for with a few twists of the wrist the camera will make your scenes funny. Professional movie makers build comedy from situations and dialogue. But you needn't worry about writing funny lines; just produce situations—some with your people, others with your camera.

Take the running gag, for instance. No trickery is involved in it. You need only straight shots to liven up your little document. Suppose you plan to film a summer picnic at the park. Show your friends pitching horseshoes, playing ball, swimming in the pool as usual, but at intervals make a few shots of Dad on the spring board. Have him walk out on it, then change his mind and return to his easy chair. The first sequence should show the entire routine, from chair to board to chair. No one will laugh at this, for this is Dad's regular ritual.

Then shoot successively shorter scenes of each appearance, until you show only his feet as he stands on the board, with his toes wiggling apprehensively. On his last appearance, return to a medium view, and have him walk out to the end, pose, lose his balance, and splash into the water.

Running gags need not be funny in themselves to get a laugh. Repetition alone becomes hilarious. One of the dignified men at your party, for example, repeatedly tries to light his pipe, only to have the match blow out. Or one of the young ladies attempts to powder her nose, without success because the breeze blows the powder from her compact. For the "payoff", the man takes a pipe, already lighted, from his pocket and calmly proceeds to smoke, while the girl gives up and tosses her compact aside.

One way of giving your movies an

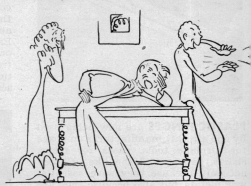

Long a specialist in directing children, Charles Lamont makes frequent use of the laugh-getting methods he describes in this article. They add punch to his latest Universal Studios picture, "Oh, Doctor," starring Abbott and Costello. Stop-motion in the sequence below lets a new child, and finally a dog, be put in the barrel after each climbs out. It looks like magic

Putting Laughs
INTO YOUR
Home Movies

BY CHARLES LAMONT
DIRECTOR, UNIVERSAL STUDIOS

amusing twist is by interrupted action. This is a way of making things happen on the screen that you know can't happen, but which your eyes insist can. It is accomplished by stopping the camera, changing actors or props, and then shooting again.

Using this trick, you can have a lot of film fun with four or five children and a barrel. Set up your camera for a medium shot of an ordinary barrel. Plant the first child inside the barrel and make a shot of him emerging and taking a position alongside it. Stop the camera and put the second child in the barrel. Take him coming out, stop the camera again, and repeat the same procedure until all the children have been taken. You probably will want to title this

one "The Magic Barrel" or some such name, as it will seem that only by some act of legerdemain could so small a barrel hold so many children. It is essential, however, that you set your camera on a tripod or some other steady support, and see that no one disturbs it during the entire time.

The newsreels frequently use stop-motion to emphasize speed. For example, they show people racing out of a subway station to the opening game of the World's Series or scooting across an intersection as a traffic cop waves his arm like a berserk semaphore. This effect is achieved simply by cutting camera speed in half. An occasional flick of the exposure lever makes the scene look like a panic. Even everyday scenes can be made humorous this way.

Set your camera at half speed and make some shots of the youngsters playing about the house. When you project the film on the screen at regular speed, they will seem to be moving at a breakneck rate. Follow this with a normal shot of Mother calling them for their baths; then double the camera speed to slow them down to a snail's crawl as they answer the summons. Many variations of this idea will occur to you.

Don't forget, though, that changes in speed require accommodating changes in exposure. Every change in stop doubles or halves the exposure. If, for instance, you shoot a scene at standard speed at f/8, the diaphragm should be set at f/11 for half

speed, or f/6.5 for double speed. Slow motion heightens interest in many subjects. A calf chases baby across the garden. When the calf is taken at half speed to make its galloping seem faster and the baby in slow motion in order to stress her danger, you have a simple but effective formula for a mirthful sequence.

In the same way, upside-down filming offers many opportunities to provide silly sequences. This is also an old newsreel chestnut. Remember those episodes in which a diver slid feet-first from the water, tumbled upward to land on a high spring board, and walked backward to the platform? All you need do to take such a sequence is to place your camera upside down and make the exposure as the subject

walks out and dives off the board in the usual way.

A simple application of this, to show Junior with extraordinary control over his bike, will make the bike appear to get up off the ground and roll into his hands when he whistles for it. Turn the camera upside down and make a shot of him pushing the bike away. The wheel rolls over and falls on the ground. Now turn the camera over to the normal position and take him standing and whistling as if for the bike. Stop the camera, have someone hand him the bike, and then make a normal shot of him riding away.

When the first shot is cut from the roll and sandwiched top side up between the other two, it will look on the screen as if the bike had come up from the ground at Junior's command.

In trying this stunt with two or more persons, you must have them appear throughout in the correct order from left to right. There's nothing to worry about if you have a 16-mm. camera. When you cut the picture, simply turn the inverted strip end for end with the same side of the film facing you. However, with 8-mm. film it is necessary to reverse the faces of the film when it is turned end for end in order to keep the perforations on the proper side. For this reason, reverse motion cannot be made on 8-mm. film when more than one person ap-

Upside-down shooting will make the tossing away of an armful of bric-a-brac look like a series of humorous catches when the film is projected. Possibilities are limitless

Reverse action, like that above, is taken with the camera upside down. Here the boy really pushes his bicycle away and lets it fall to the ground; but shot upside down, cut from the film, and then turned and spliced, the sequence makes it appear as if the wheel rises at his command. He is photographed normally as he rides off

pears in the scene, since two or more will seem to change places.

All sorts of gags can be brought off by this time-tried stunt of reversed action. For example, dispute your wife's skill as a cook by making egg yolks jump back into their shells, cake batter flow back into the mixing bowl, steaks (if any) leap from the broiler up to her hands. Water soaking Dad's Victory garden can be made to appear to drain back into the hose and leave the earth dry.

Here's another stunt: Have your subject hold an armful of objects such as a vase, a pitcher of water, and one or two other fairly fragile things, and toss them one by one to someone outside the picture. He should use a straight-arm technique, tossing the objects up as well as away from himself and finishing with the palm of his hand open and facing upward. Filmed upside down, this stunt will give every appearance of a series of catches. It will be breath-taking. A similar sequence in which knives are seemingly caught would be especially so.

Did you ever want to stand on the cowcatcher of a train or the front of a street car and film the tracks as the vehicle rolled along? You can do just that, and easily, if you take your position on the rear and shoot at the receding track with the camera upside down. And to "prove" you actually made such a hazardous sequence, have someone grab shots of you climbing on and off the cowcatcher and run these as the introductory and closing scenes. But be sure to reverse the scenic strip!

Jumping offers good reverse-action possibilities. Little Johnny probably can't jump ove·   ·s without falling. Stand him on

top of a fence and, with the camera right side up at a 45-deg. angle to the line of jump, make a shot of him leaping forward. Then have him jump backwards from the same spot on the fence and run backwards from where he lands while you shoot him with the camera inverted. Reverse this last scene, splice the two, and you have an excellent sequence showing Johnny clearing an obstacle higher than his head.

These trick shots are intended to get laughs, not to build up feature productions. Nonstandard camera speeds, upside-down filming, repetition, and stop-motion are methods, not materials, and require none but natural props that are available to everybody.

Subjects are too numerous to name. Divers, hurdlers, long-distance runners, golfers, tennis players, soldiers on parade—slow motion will show their form and add interest to their performances.

Simply pick out your subject, apply the technique you desire, and you'll be producing short subjects the like of which have never before been recorded by your camera.

The END

Accurate weighing with this small beam scale will help the amateur photographer get better results in his home developing and printing

DARKROOM SCALE

BUILT FROM WORKSHOP ODDS AND ENDS

By ROGER MOYER

THIS scale, sensitive to 1 grain and suitable for weighing ingredients in photographic and home-laboratory formulas, can be made from bits of scrap. Its 4-oz. capacity is sufficient for most of the amateur's needs.

The main and supplementary beams of the scale shown were made of scraps of aluminum, but another metal or even plastic will serve.

Turn the brass standard first and fasten it to a temporary wood base until the assembling, testing, and calibrating are completed. Notch the bearings in the top for the knife edge with a file and finish with a scraping cut with a sharp knife. Strive to get the notches as straight and smooth as possible, for upon this the sensitivity of the scale depends.

The knife edges can be ground from a piece of tool steel, or the tang of a file can be hammered to approximate shape, hardened, ground, and then finished on an oilstone. A 2" tang will make the two knife edges with a piece to spare. Adjust them so that they are parallel to each other and at right angles to the beam.

The poise for the main beam is a piece of brass tubing filled with molten lead. This leaves some lead to be drilled out to bring the weight to exactly 1 oz. The poise for the small beam should weigh

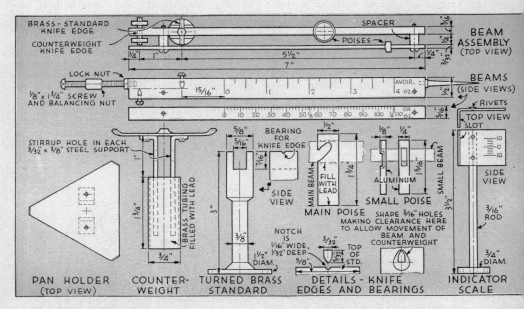

27 11/32 grains, or 1/16 oz. Make it a little oversize of light metal so that it also can be drilled from the bottom to the exact weight. The counterweight is a piece of brass tubing filled with molten lead after the stirrups have been inserted. A pan 4" in diameter and ½" deep can be cut off the bottom of a 10-cent plastic bowl.

In testing and calibrating the scale, it is necessary to have a ¼-oz. and a 1-oz. weight. Assemble the scale in a level position with the pan in place, and set both poises at zero, marked in pencil on the beams. Drill lead out of the bottom of the counterweight cautiously, testing from time to time, until an exact balance is obtained as shown by the indicator at the end of the beam. Now place a 1-oz. weight in the pan and move the large poise out on the beam until it balances. The distance the poise has been moved should be just 1".

The small beam is tested with a ¼-oz. weight in the pan, and the distance the poise is moved to balance the scale should be just 4". The zero marks on the two beams are directly in line. Since the small beam is graduated in 2-grain divisions, and there are 109.375 grains in ¼-oz. avoirdupois, the 110-grain division will be about 1/64" beyond the ¼-oz. division.

Check the scale several times; then mark all the divisions in pencil. Permanent marks are made with a small, sharp chisel, and figures are stamped with dies. A little carbon black will make them readable. Minor variations can be adjusted for by turning the balancing nut to right or left.

If it is desired to calibrate the scale in metric units instead of avoirdupois, use a newly minted nickel, which weighs 5 grams. For weight measurements by grains, use a newly minted cent, which weighs 48 grains. Paper clips may be balanced with a cent, for instance, and counted for use in subdividing the 48-grain measurement.

Fasten the finished scale to the bottom of a box as shown, where it will be ready for use when the pan is placed in position.

TWO-PART JARS (above) in which developers are sold form useful containers for photographic solutions that must be used together, such as hypo and ferrocyanide reducer. The upper compartment will hold 2 oz. of potassium ferrocyanide solution, and the lower one 6 oz. of ordinary hypo. The amber glass of the container protects the solutions from harmful ligʰt action.—JOHN K. KARLOVIC.

A WINDING FORM for the cord of a home-movie projector, shown below, helps prevent tangling and accidental disconnection of the plug when the machine is in use.

The form is 2½" by 12" and can be cut from a scrap of ¼" plywood. Saw a notch near one end to receive the toggle switch and connecting plug. Cut a slot along the same side so that the cord may be taped securely to the winding form as shown in the photograph.

When the projector is not in use, the plug is disconnected and the cord wound on the form inside the notches at both ends. Thus coiled, it is easy to carry.—R. WOODBURY.

CARBON DRAWING PENCILS serve well for spotting glossy prints. The point of the pencil is kept just moist with the tongue or, if much spotting is to be done, on a damp cloth. A special advantage is that spotting done with such a pencil is not affected by repeated ferrotyping. Keep the pencil well sharpened.—WILLIAM SWALLOW.

home
EXPERIMENTS SHOW HOW GASES BEHAVE

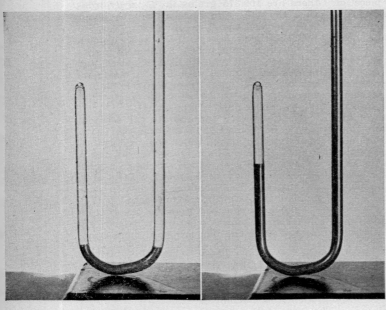

BOYLE'S LAW, which states that the volume of a given quantity of gas is inversely proportional to the pressure upon it, can be demonstrated with a 40" long glass tube bent into a J-shape with the short leg about 6" long. Seal the tip of this leg. Support the tube vertically and pour just enough mercury in it to fill the bottom and rise equally in both legs as at the far left. The air in the short leg is now at normal atmospheric pressure. Pour more mercury into the tube until it stands at a height of about 30", as in the second photo. The air in the short tube is now subjected to the pressure of an extra atmosphere produced by the weight of the mercury. Compare the height of this column of air to that in the first experiment. You will find that it is only half as tall.

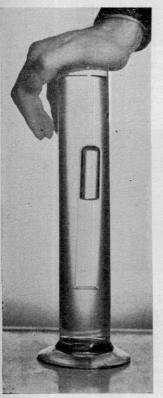

CARTESIAN DIVER. Fill a test tube with just enough water so that it will barely float bottom up in a cylinder or vase filled nearly to the top with water. If you seal the top of the cylinder with the palm of your hand and press down strongly, the test tube will sink. Relax your pressure, and the test tube will rise. The explanation is simple. By compressing the air above the water you transmit the pressure through the entire body of water, which in turn compresses the air in the test tube, reducing its buoyancy.

A MODEL GASWORKS TANK will demonstrate how the big ones that supply your kitchen range store gas under pressure. Punch a hole in the top of a tin can having no bottom and seal in a glass tube drawn to a jet. Into the side of a slightly larger can seal another tube bent as shown below. Attach this with a hose to the jet or a stove burner, fit on a pinch clamp, and fill the can with water. Insert the smaller can, which will sink as air escapes through the jet. When it has sunk, turn on the gas, which will lift the can. Turn off the gas and let the can sink again. Repeat until all the air is expelled; then fill the can with gas, shut off the supply, and light the gas issuing from the jet. It will burn at almost undiminished pressure until the can is empty.

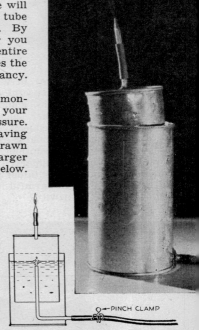

PINCH CLAMP

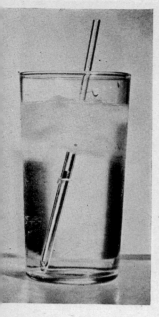

ALL GASES shrink evenly when pressure on them is increased, and they expand evenly when, at a given pressure, their temperature is raised. This law is easily demonstrated. Seal one end of a narrow, 6″ long glass tube; then drop mercury into the tube so that a plug is formed about halfway down. Stand the tube in a tumbler of cracked ice. When the mercury has descended as far as it will, remove the tube and mark the place with thread. Suspend the tube in the steam of a flask of boiling water. When the mercury stops rising, mark this place with thread. Measure the distance between the threads. The distance the air has expanded from 0 deg. C. to 100 deg. C. is 100/273 of its original length. For each degree, the expansion is 1/273 of the volume at 0 deg. C.

WHAT MAKES A SIPHON WORK? Two glasses are half filled with water and connected with rubber tubing full of water as shown below. Raise one glass so that the water in it is above the level in the other glass, and water will start flowing through the siphon and keep on flowing until it is again level in both glasses. The explanation for this is shown in the drawing. The upward pressure on the water in the tube at A is equal to atmospheric pressure (as shown by the arrow) less the weight of the water column AB, while the upward pressure at D is equal to the atmospheric pressure less the weight of the longer column DC. The siphon flows toward the lesser pressure until both columns are the same height.

THE SIPHON AND AIR PRESSURE. Join two small bottles, one of which is partly filled with colored water, with a bent glass tube. The siphon arm which goes into the water-filled bottle is first passed through a cork which seals the bottle. Place the apparatus in a jar which can be tightly closed. If you suck strongly on a glass tube sealed in the cover of the jar, water from the sealed bottle rises in the siphon tube and pours into the open bottle. Let air into the jar, and the water returns to the sealed bottle.

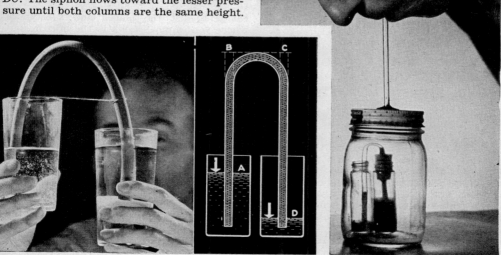

You can make this vital element in your home lab with the gas-collecting apparatus shown above

Oxygen

MAINSTAY OF LIFE

Home Experiments with This Vital Element Help Explain How Fire and Corrosion Act

By KENNETH M. SWEZEY

DO YOU know that iron and steel will burn; that the reaction of cold chemicals may produce fire; that the rusting of iron produces as much heat as the actual burning of the metal? Can you explain the mystery of spontaneous combustion? These are just a few of the facts that can be demonstrated by experiments with oxygen, the most widely distributed and abundant of all the elements.

Where can you find oxygen? It might be easier to list the places and substances where you cannot! Look in the mirror, and behold there a creature made up of 65 percent of this gas by weight! The waters of the sea and the water you drink are nearly 89 percent oxygen. Oxygen makes up about 21 percent of the air you breathe. Oxygen in the earth's crust weighs nearly as much as all the other 91 elements put together—including iron, lead, copper, and all the metallic elements.

Despite its abundance, oxygen was not discovered until a year before the Revolutionary War. Recall that oxygen is a gas without color, taste, or odor, and you can understand how it kept its identity a secret for so long.

Priestley, an English clergyman, made the discovery. He placed some red mercuric oxide on a column of mercury in a glass tube similar to a barometer tube and heated the oxide by focusing the sun's rays on it. The column of mercury was pushed down, showing that a gas had apparently been produced. Priestley thrust a glowing splinter into the gas and found that the splinter burst into flames. Breathing some of the gas himself, the experimenter felt invigorated. A new gas had been found, which was called oxygen by the famous French chemist Lavoisier, who also showed that the gas could be made to combine with other substances.

Today, huge quantities of oxygen are made by the electrolysis of water, and by the fractional distillation of liquid air. When an electric current is passed through water, its molecules are broken into atoms of oxygen and hydrogen, which may then be collected separately. Since the boiling point of nitrogen is lower than the boiling point of oxygen, nitrogen evaporates first when liquid air is allowed to boil. When the nitrogen has all boiled away, oxygen alone remains.

In the home laboratory, oxygen may be made easily by heating a mixture of potassium chlorate or potassium perchlorate with powdered manganese dioxide. Perchlorate, if obtainable, is preferable to ordinary chlorate, as it is a more stable chemical and its release of oxygen is more easily controlled.

Mix together—without grinding—a few grams of the potassium perchlorate with about a third as much manganese dioxide. Place this in a heat-resistant test tube and clamp the tube almost horizontally on a support, as shown in the photograph on page HW 432.

As oxygen dissolves only slightly in water, the gas may be easily collected in a pneumatic trough. Part of a tin can, with a hole punched in the top and a slot cut in the side, will serve as a support for the inverted bottle in which the gas is to be collected. Bent glass tubing, connected by rubber tubing, leads the oxygen under the water in the trough into the mouth of the collecting bottle. The latter should be filled with water. A square of cardboard or glass is held over the top until the bottle is placed on the support with its mouth under the water. As oxygen is generated, it will slowly bubble up into the bottle, gradually replacing the water in the latter.

Heat the test tube gently with an alcohol lamp or Bunsen burner turned low, moving it along the tube to heat the latter evenly. Then increase the heating until gas commences to bubble from the delivery tube. The first bubbles may be allowed to escape, as these are air being driven from the tube. The following ones should be directed to bubble up into the collecting jar. The flow of oxygen can be regulated by controlling the heat.

When the jar is full, slip the cardboard or glass plate under it again and turn the jar upright. Keep the plate in place to prevent the oxygen from diffusing into the air. Before withdrawing the flame from the test tube, be sure to remove the stopper from the tube; otherwise water will be sucked up from the trough and will crack the hot test tube.

Many substances which burn feebly or not

At left below, a small piece of steel wool which has been ignited glows at red heat in ordinary air. When placed in a jar of pure oxygen, however, as at the right, it at once bursts into bright flame. The presence of oxygen increases the rate of combustion to such an extent that an intense heat results

at all in ordinary air will burn brilliantly in the oxygen you have collected. Thrust a glowing splinter of wood into it, and the splinter will burst into bright white flame with almost explosive suddenness. Twist a short length of iron wire around a small wad of fine steel wool and ignite the steel wool in your Bunsen flame. It will merely glow red. Thrust it quickly into your oxygen tank, however, and it bursts into brilliant flame.

When oxygen combines with other substances so rapidly that the heat of this combination produces flame, we call the reaction combustion. But *all* oxidation produces heat, whether the heat is apparent or not. The rusting of iron or steel, for instance, produces as much heat as the burning of the same metal. This form of oxidation is so slow, however, that the heat is dissipated as fast as it is generated.

A simple experiment will prove that rusting produces a rise in temperature. Wrap the bulb of a thermometer with fine steel wool; then moisten the wad of wool with some dilute acetic acid, which will act as a catalyst to speed up the rusting of the metal. For best results, the acid should be at room temperature, and the moist steel wool should be protected from drafts. Rust will quickly appear, and as it does, the mercury in the thermometer will slowly rise.

Spontaneous combustion is the result of

Steel wool, a few drops of dilute acetic acid, and an ordinary thermometer can be used to prove that oxidation does actually produce heat

the accumulation of heat due to slow oxidation of inflammable materials under conditions where this heat cannot be dissipated. The linseed oil in paints, for example, dries into a tough film because of the combination of the oil with oxygen in the air. Heat is generated, but when the oil is spread over a surface, this heat vanishes as fast as it is produced. Throw rags soaked in linseed oil into a pile, however, and you bottle up the heat of oxidation to such an extent that you produce a dangerous fire hazard.

To demonstrate the heat of oxidation of linseed oil, insulate a jar by placing it in a box stuffed with crumpled paper, and place in the jar a rag or bit of cotton waste wet with this oil. Place a thermometer in the midst of the rag, and observe it periodically. The temperature climbs steadily. If left long enough, the rag would probably catch fire.

Rapid oxidation resulting in combustion may be produced by the reaction of cold chemicals. Place a few grains of sodium peroxide on some absorbent cotton. Add a drop or two of warm water. Almost instantly the cotton will burst into flames.

Even the familiar hydrogen peroxide may be made to produce oxygen. Heat, alkalies, and even dirt or powdered glass will cause it to decompose. Powdered manganese dioxide dropped into the liquid will cause the gas to come off rapidly.

Place a little sodium peroxide on a wad of cotton and drop some warm water on it as in the first and second photos below. In an instant the cotton flares up as at the right. Reaction between the sodium peroxide and the water oxidizes the cotton so rapidly that it bursts into flame almost immediately

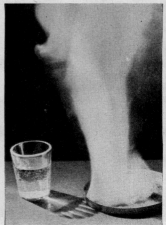

Collapsible Bed Has No Metal Parts

THIS bed is the perfect answer to your extra bed problem. The scarcity of materials is no hindrance to constructing it because the only metal used is in the casters. The chassis is completely separate from any other part of the bed, and can be used with any type of spring and mattress. A further advantage is that the bed can be taken apart for storage or shipment, and easily reassembled.

The standard height for beds is specified in the drawings, but this can be altered to suit personal needs. Simply measure the spring and mattress and make the legs as high as desired. If made of poplar and oak, with turned feet as shown in the drawings, the rails and legs may be painted bone white, and the caps and turned feet stained a warm brown.—J. I. SOWERS.

Except for the bed rails, which should be sound, straight stock, scrap can be used to advantage

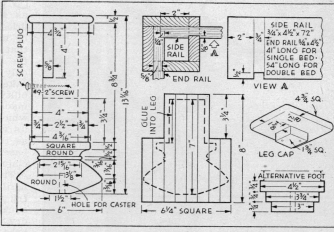

This attractive bed base can be built to fit any type of spring regardless of size. Notice end rails have rabbet and dado but side rails dado only

Microscope Specimens Mounted with Cardboard and Tape

AN EASY way to mount dry microscope specimens permanently is to place each in a cardboard cell secured to a slide with ordinary adhesive tape. The cell must be of the same thickness or slightly thicker than the specimen so that the cover glass will not crush it, and it should be of the same area as the cover glass. An opening may be made in it with a paper punch or cut square with a sharp knife. When specimen and cell are in place, cover with the glass and fasten all to the slide with strips of common adhesive tape. A label may be attached at one end for identification. The tape can be varnished for permanence.—H. F. WHITTAKER.

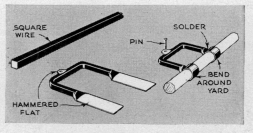

Wire Trusses for Model Yards

TRUSSES to support the lower yards of ship models may be easily made from square copper wire as shown in the drawing above. Hammer the ends of the wire flat, and flatten the middle also so that it can be drilled for an escutcheon pin. The two ends are then bent around the yard as shown and soldered in place. This type of truss will be found entirely suitable for most ship models.—S. P. ROBBINS.

How to

EVEN THOSE WITH BADLY CAKED BRISTLES CAN BE SOFTENED, CLEANED, AND RESHAPED SO AS TO GIVE GOOD SERVICE ONCE MORE.

By ALBERT Q. MAISEL

DON'T throw away that old paintbrush. It may be as hard as a board, bristles may have dried askew, some of them may be missing; but the chances are that there is plenty of life left in the old brush yet. It may need only a cleaning to get out the caked paint and to restore flexibility. If it happens to be a brush made of Chinese hog bristles, which are now scarce, it's worth its weight in gold. Just so long as the bristles are firm in their base, any old brush can be reclaimed.

The first step is to soften the hardened heel in a solvent. Never try to break loose even part of a caked heel while the brush is dry, for you will break valuable bristles in the attempt. Benzine can be used as a solvent, or any good commercial paintbrush cleaner. Use alcohol for old shellac brushes. Put just enough of

Above is a "before and after" photo in the life of a paintbrush. The bristles were all a hardened mass, but the ones on the left side were given a thorough cleaning until they emerged soft and glossy. Compare them with the caked bristles on the right side

NEVER FORCE THE BRUSH INTO TIGHT PLACES

GLUB GLUB

NEVER DROWN THE BRUSH IN THE PAINT CAN

NEVER USE THE BRUSH EDGEWISE

NEVER PAINT A ROUND SURFACE LIKE THIS

THIS IS THE RIGHT WAY

EASILY MADE RACK FOR CLEANING BRUSHES

5/8"X5/8"

NAIL FAST

3/4"

12"

Put Your Old Paintbrushes Back to Work

the fluid in a glass container to cover the bristles but not the setting and ferrule.

Soak for 10 minutes; then knead the brush in water to wash out the loosened paint, repeating both steps until the heel is soft. Most of the paint will come out in the water, and the remaining solvent can be strained through a cloth and stored away for future use.

Now spread the bristles with your fingers and sift fine, dry, hardwood sawdust down into the deepest parts of the brush. Then, under a stream of water in a sink, work the brush back and forth over a washboard or a rack made as shown in the drawing. Five to 10 minutes of this, with the addition of more sawdust as required, will clean the worst caked heel. The sawdust picks up particles of paint and carries them away in the water. Any flakes of dried paint remaining can be removed by working the paintbrush across a stiff fiber scrubbing brush held bristles up in a vise or nailed to a bench top. Be sure the paintbrush bristles point backward as you draw them over the fiber brush.

The soaking-wet, soft bristles will stick out in all directions. Comb them straight with a fine comb and remove any loosened ones by grasping them between the blade of a paring knife and the thumb.

Next, wrap the brush in stiff kraft paper to preserve the fine chisel edge while it is being dried. Perforate the paper for better ventilation and fold it as shown in the drawings. Drying can be done in the hot sun, or over an infrared lamp or an ordinary bulb placed in a box as shown below. A brush of average size will require 45 minutes to one hour to dry, and it should be turned over every 10 minutes during this time. This insures even drying and prevents curling of the bristles.

When thoroughly dry, a brush may need a final combing, and the bristles may be trimmed if they have worn very unevenly. This may be done with a sharp knife or a razor blade. Be careful to cut off no more than absolutely necessary.

Now take a look at the handle, which may be spliced if it is damaged or broken. If the ferrule holding the bristle base to it is loose, it may be tightened. A couple of brads through it into the wood may do the trick, or on some types a wooden wedge may be driven in to make a tight fit.

Take care of the brush once you have it back in shape. Never use force to daub its end into corners, and don't use a brush edgewise. Dip the bristles not more than halfway into the paint. Put the first two coats on rough surfaces with a worn brush, rather than with a new one. Avoid kerosene; it won't evaporate, doesn't mix with paint, and may damage the setting. When left in turpentine, a brush should be suspended so that it won't rest on the bristles. A rack like the one shown below is good.

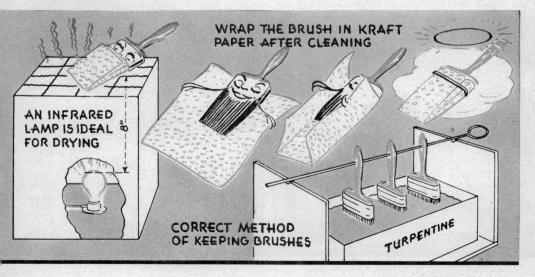

WRAP THE BRUSH IN KRAFT PAPER AFTER CLEANING

AN INFRARED LAMP IS IDEAL FOR DRYING

8"

CORRECT METHOD OF KEEPING BRUSHES

TURPENTINE

Laid face down on a glass in the top of this box, a picture may be projected onto a screen. The hinged lid holds it flat

Set at an angle of 45 deg., the mirror reflects the image of the picture above it through the tube (shown above, right, before assembly) to the lens, which in turn throws it onto the screen. Below, a view of the projector with the top off

WITH an opaque-picture projector, or post-card projector, you can throw enlarged images of drawings, photographs, and magazine clippings on a screen in full color. Besides providing entertainment, such a device is useful in instructing groups of people, copying art work, and lettering.

Dimensions of the box can vary, with the possible exception of the height, which is 8" and correct for a lens of about 9" focal length. For a shorter focal length, the height should be reduced. The distance from lens to mirror to picture must be approximately equal to the focal length of the lens.

The mirror is mounted on a piece of ½" plywood which, in turn, is fastened to a wooden block the upper surface of which is at a 45-deg. angle to the front of the box. A single screw holds the block to the bottom of the box, thus permitting the mirror to be swung slightly to line up the image. Once the mirror is adjusted, the screw is tightened.

The width of the box from front to back may have to be altered, according to the sockets used, to bring the lamp filaments approximately into line with the center of the picture to be projected.

Air space around the lamps protects the wood from heat. An

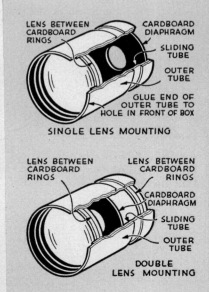

LENS BETWEEN CARDBOARD RINGS
CARDBOARD DIAPHRAGM
SLIDING TUBE
OUTER TUBE
GLUE END OF OUTER TUBE TO HOLE IN FRONT OF BOX

SINGLE LENS MOUNTING

LENS BETWEEN CARDBOARD RINGS
LENS BETWEEN CARDBOARD RINGS
CARDBOARD DIAPHRAGM
SLIDING TUBE
OUTER TUBE

DOUBLE LENS MOUNTING

opening along the bottom of the back and holes in each end provide ventilation. Wire the sockets in parallel, run a cord out through the ventilating slot, and install a through-cord switch a foot or so from the box. The top of the box has a rectangular opening, rabbeted or provided with strips to receive the glass. The glass merely lies in the recess and may be lifted out for cleaning or changing a lamp. Metal hinges or leather strips are used on the hinged lid.

The lens is the most important part of the projector, for upon its performance depends the sharpness of the image. An anastigmat of f/4.5 speed or greater and a focal length of 8″ or more is best. Such a lens may be taken from a view camera or from another projector. An ordinary reading glass 2″ to 4″ in diameter and with a focal length of about 8″ may be used, but image sharpness will be improved with a multiple lens arrangement.

Mount the lens at the end of the tube near the box, and 3″ or so in front of it mount a diaphragm made by cutting a round hole in a cardboard disk. Experiment with hole sizes to determine the best diameter. The smaller the hole, the sharper the image, but illumination decreases as the diameter of the aperture becomes smaller. There is, fortunately, a happy medium. Paint the diaphragm flat black on both surfaces and the edge

of the hole; then cement it to the lens tube.

Two lenses of the reading-glass type, each having a focal length of about 18″, can be combined into a two-lens projection objective, as shown in one sketch. Experimenting will reveal the exact spacing of lens elements. To determine focal length, hold a lens so it throws a sharp image of a distant object on a sheet of paper and measure the distance from lens to paper. The lens mount illustrated was made from a cardboard tube and lid. The lid, with its end cut away, became the outside of the lens mount, and a piece of the tube made the movable inside section.

Cut black paper to mask the sharp section of a projected image and paste it on the glass in the top of the box. Cover the underside of the lid with black cloth to keep light from leaking around the edges.

PICTURE PROJECTOR

GIVES BIG, FULL-COLOR IMAGES FOR ENTERTAINMENT, INSTRUCTION, OR COPYING OF DESIGNS, ART WORK, AND LETTERING ALPHABETS

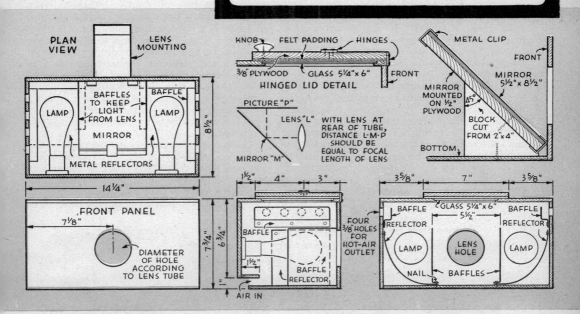

Harnessing Electrons

WHAT HAPPENS IN THE DIODE — SIMPLEST OF

FIRST STEPS IN ELECTRONICS

By JOHN W. CAMPBELL, JR.

IT IS a triumph when the electrical engineer produces a device that can break a circuit in 1/100 second, but the electronics engineer can turn a current on and off 500,000,000 times a second. The electrical engineer's control of electricity depends upon relatively crude, slow-acting mechanisms such as rheostats, fuses, circuit breakers, and solenoids; the electronics engineer controls the electronic flow by means of other electrons forced to work in the confines of electron tubes.

These tubes are used for detecting radio waves, amplifying currents, generating alternating currents of practically any frequency, and rectifying alternating current to direct current. Applied in sound motion pictures in the form of highly sensitive photoelectric cells, they convert the varying light density of a film track into sound. Special electron tubes react to the light of a star a billion billion miles away, probe for a bullet, and control big guns with superhuman accuracy.

We know (Fig. 1) that electrons can be repelled by or attracted to a body by putting an electric charge on that body—that is, by crowding other electrons onto it or by robbing it of electrons. By applying this principle inside vacuum tubes, we gain control of these invisible miracle workers. The simplest vacuum tube consists of an electron-emitting electrode, called the *cathode,* and a target for the electrons, called the *plate.* Triodes (three elements), tetrodes (four elements), and so on are only diodes to which additional control elements have been added.

Since the current that will pass through the tube consists of the electrons emitted by the cathode, it will be limited by the number of electrons we can free from the metal of which the cathode is made. The atoms of the metal exchange outer electrons freely;

these electrons may wander at will among the atoms and, if extra electrons are crowded upon one end of a wire by connection to a battery or generator, an equal number of atomic electrons promptly appears at the other end. But unless outside force is applied, the electrons cannot escape from the wire. This is shown in Fig. 2.

Our problem is to supply the electrons with sufficient extra energy to enable them to break loose from the atoms and escape from the metal altogether. This we can do by heating the metal, since heat causes motion of atoms and some of this motion is imparted to the electrons. How much heat is necessary depends upon the nature of the metal or alloy.

Radiant energy such as light, X rays, or cosmic rays will also free electrons by imparting motion to them. Light striking the sensitive element of your photoelectric meter knocks out electrons that flow through a sensitive galvanometer and move a needle to indicate what exposure you must give a scene in photographing it. Cosmic rays, present everywhere on the earth's surface, are always freeing electrons from matter. A single electron striking a metal target at high speed may blast out a number of other electrons before it finally comes to rest. This method is used in Zworykin's electron multiplier, a special multiple diode that can amplify currents more than a billion times.

When a single atom of radium explodes, it shoots out electrons at tremendous speed, as well as high-power X rays called gamma rays. Both of these knock electrons out of any adjacent atoms, and with such violence that these electrons knock out others in turn, until hundreds or even thousands are freed (Fig. 3).

Thermionic emission—the freeing of electrons by heat—is the simplest method and the one most frequently used. Cathodes in modern tubes are coated with certain alkaline-earth oxides that release electrons at moderate temperatures. The

In this X-ray tube, 400,000 volts are required to drive electrons from the filament across a gap to the target

in Glass

ALL VACUUM TUBES

cathode is usually heated by a filament similar to that in a lamp bulb (Fig. 4). In early tubes and some modern types, the filament itself is the electron-emitting body.

If to the plate of the tube in Fig. 4 we apply a positive charge by connecting it to the positive (electron-deficient) side of a battery or generator, electrons emitted from the cathode will be drawn to it and will constitute a current in any outside circuit we may arrange. But if the cathode is positively charged, electrons driven out by the thermionic effect will promptly be drawn back, and no current will flow.

Here the first characteristic of the vacuum tube appears—it will pass current in one direction only. If alternating current is applied to it, the tube will pass current only on that part of each cycle on which the cathode is negative. The diode tube is therefore first of all a *rectifier*.

This is generally useful; a characteristic not so useful is voltage drop. An electronic tube has terrific internal resistance. After electrons have been freed from the cathode by thermionic or other action, they tend to form an invisible cloud in the space surrounding the cathode. This "space charge" acts to repel the electrons driven out by thermionic action, sending them back into the cathode as fast as they emerge.

A space charge normally forms much closer to the cathode than to the plate, and a very much greater voltage is needed on the plate to overcome the space-charge effect because of the inverse-square law effects in electric repulsion. Thus a space charge of only two volts at .01" from the cathode would block electrons attracted by a plate .1" away charged to 150 volts! It would take more than 200 volts on the plate to pull electrons through that two-volt space charge.

In high-vacuum rectifier tubes designed to handle fairly heavy loads, the plate is put extremely close to the cathode—frequently less than .01" separates the two. The un-

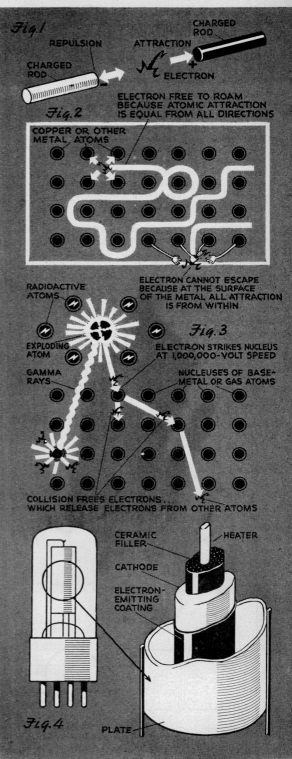

Fig.1

REPULSION · ATTRACTION · CHARGED ROD

CHARGED ROD · ELECTRON

Fig.2

COPPER OR OTHER METAL ATOMS

ELECTRON FREE TO ROAM BECAUSE ATOMIC ATTRACTION IS EQUAL FROM ALL DIRECTIONS

ELECTRON CANNOT ESCAPE BECAUSE AT THE SURFACE OF THE METAL ALL ATTRACTION IS FROM WITHIN

RADIOACTIVE ATOMS

EXPLODING ATOM

GAMMA RAYS

Fig.3

ELECTRON STRIKES NUCLEUS AT 1,000,000-VOLT SPEED

NUCLEUSES OF BASE-METAL OR GAS ATOMS

COLLISION FREES ELECTRONS... WHICH RELEASE ELECTRONS FROM OTHER ATOMS

CERAMIC FILLER · HEATER

CATHODE

ELECTRON-EMITTING COATING

Fig.4

PLATE

avoidable gap reduces it but, in spite of this, the space charge resists the passage of electrons from the cathode until they enter its own region. Once they get this far, it pushes them onward with equal force, which now reinforces the pull of the plate charge.

It would seem that a sufficiently high plate charge would drive as much current as we might wish through the tube, but the accelerating action of the space charge just mentioned, plus such a high plate potential, would drive electrons to hit the plate with such violence that their bombardment would heat it. When hot enough, the plate would begin to emit electrons itself, rectification would cease, excessive current would flow, and the tube would be ruined.

There is, however, one type of tube purposely designed as an inefficient rectifier with the plate several inches or, in large tubes, even a foot or so from the cathode. With such a setup, it takes not hundreds of volts, but hundreds of thousands, to drive electrons through the space-charge blockage, and they hit the plate at a speed as high as 175,000 *miles per second*. Deceleration causes the electrons to radiate extremely short-wave-length electromagnetic energy—called "hard" radiation or X rays.

In a diode having an atmosphere of low-pressure mercury vapor, argon, or neon, electrons flowing from the cathode to the plate are almost certain to bump into a gas atom on the way and knock off a secondary electron. The gas atom, now a positive ion, is attracted toward the cathode, while the dislodged electron heads for the plate. Near the cathode the gas ion picks up another electron and becomes neutral; but it promptly undergoes another collision, and is again a positive ion.

Under such conditions, there will always be many positive ions near the cathode, and their presence will neutralize the negative space charge. The result is that the voltage drop of the gas-filled tube will be very much lower than that of a vacuum tube, actually only a few volts, regardless of the current.

The cathode need supply only a few electrons. Once they start knocking electrons from mercury-vapor atoms, more and more are released until finally a billion or a thousand billion electrons arrive at the plate.

The mercury-vapor rectifier, alone of the electronic devices, is adaptable for heavy duty. It can handle tens of thousands of amperes as readily as it handles milliamperes and can operate at tens of thousands of volts.

Simple Diode Hookup Demonstrates Effect of Space Charge

IF YOU have or can borrow a milliammeter, you can demonstrate with any type of radio tube how electron emission and space charge increase with the temperature of the cathode. Connect the filament or heater to transformer taps of the proper voltage or to the line through a resistor of the correct value, inserting an adjustable rheostat to control the filament temperature and thus the number of electrons emitted.

The milliammeter is connected to the cathode and plate of a heated-cathode tube such as a 117Z6-GT. With a coated-filament tube, connect the meter to the plate and to the center tap of the transformer.

Since no plate-current supply is provided, the cathode, which is losing electrons, will take on a positive charge. The cloud of electrons within the tube gives the plate a negative potential. The more electrons emitted, the greater these opposite charges become. Since the meter is connected across the points of opposite potential, a current of several milliamperes will flow, and this will vary as the number of electrons emitted increases with the temperature of the cathode.

If a high-resistance voltmeter is used instead, the voltage of the space charge can be measured. It is usually one to five volts.

Servicing Your Radio

TONE, volume, and selectivity of midget A.C.-D.C. T.R.F. receivers can be improved by making a few minor changes. Tinny sounds often can be corrected to a certain degree, and a noisy volume control

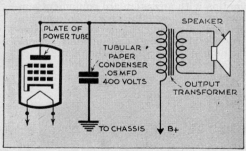

PLATE OF POWER TUBE — TUBULAR PAPER CONDENSER .05 MFD 400 VOLTS — SPEAKER — OUTPUT TRANSFORMER — TO CHASSIS — B+

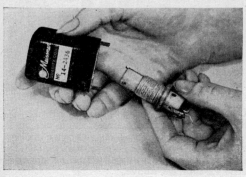

may be replaced with a more suitable one. Old-style glass-bulb tubes will serve for metal ballast tubes that burn out, while new-type coils will greatly improve range and selectivity.

SQUEAKS AND HOWLS or loss of volume when the volume-control knob is moved indicates a faulty control. About 90 percent of the midget A.C.-D.C. T.R.F. sets use a volume control in the form of a metal-encased variable carbon resistor combined with a switch. Replacing this with a 25,000-ohm control will prove satisfactory in most cases even though the one originally contained in the set may have had a resistance of anywhere from 15,000 to as high as 35,000 ohms.

METAL BALLAST TUBES can easily be replaced when they burn out by those having glass bulbs, and the latter will even be found to have some advantage, especially in the matter of heat dissipation. Be sure that the tubes have the same or equivalent code numbers. In a designation such as K55C, the first letter indicates the type of pilot bulb to use (K—brown bead, No. 40; L—blue bead, No. 46; M—white bead, No. 50 or 51). The number is the voltage drop across the tube, and the last letter gives the key to the tube wiring.

TINNY SOUNDS common in some small A.C.-D.C. receivers may be the result of the high notes being accentuated too much. This annoying condition can be corrected to some extent by connecting a .05-mfd. paper tubular condenser of 400 volts working voltage between the plate of the power tube and the chassis. If the set has a condenser in this position, it probably has a lower capacity than .05 mfd. On a 43 power tube, the plate connection is at pin No. 2; on a 25L6, it is at pin No. 3.

SELECTIVITY AND RANGE can be improved greatly by replacing the old R.F. coils with newer types. The best results will be obtained by substituting iron-core coils, but even air-core, litz-wound coils will make a noticeable difference in the performance. Small T.R.F. sets usually are equipped with coils that are not wound with litz wire, are not so well insulated, and are not sealed against moisture, and therefore do not have as high a Q or amplification factor as the newer coils. Either shielded or unshielded coils may be used in making the replacements.

radio ideas

RADIO AMATEURS, no longer able to indulge in their hobby, may find a place for their energy in the War Emergency Radio Service, a new development in radio communications for civilian defense. Junked radio sets and parts, salvaged from attics and cellars, are being rebuilt by amateurs and professionals into two-way stations and operated for the common good. This means of communication bids to set our country ahead of all others in having an independent, foolproof auxiliary that will function regardless of the loss or crippling of all other forms of contact across distances. In the photo at left above volunteers are making sets out of junked parts, while in the other operators stand by at a WERS station. These are OCD photos from the Office of War Information.

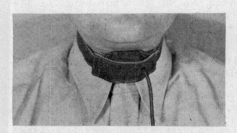

THIS THROAT MICROPHONE strapped around the neck over the larynx picks up words spoken by the wearer and amplifies them in combination with any standard equipment supplied our armed forces in the air, on land and sea, and under water. The device will be particularly useful in planes and in tanks because there is no need to shout, and the mouth is left free of all restrictions which hamper expression, either by voice or muscular reaction.

FLAPS ON A NEW RECORD ALBUM prevent accidental dropping of records when the album is unintentionally held upside down. Placed at the top of all compartments, they also tend to keep dust from sifting into the envelopes and to guard against slipping records between compartments. Both 10″ and 12″ albums are available in this style.

COMMUNICATION RECEIVERS are now being built in separate units, each one on its own specially shaped chassis with fixed resistors and condensers conveniently placed on the outside for rapid servicing, as shown in the 12-tube set above.

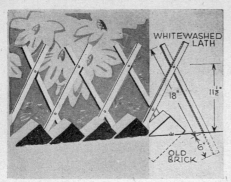

WHITEWASHED LATH

18"

11½"

OLD BRICK

6"

A PICTURESQUE FENCE that will set off a lawn or flower plot to advantage can be made at low cost from ordinary laths. About 7" at the bottom of the laths should be creosoted by standing the bundle in a bucket of creosote compound. Set the laths about 6" deep in the ground, keeping those that slope in the same direction as parallel as possible. Use single nails where the pieces cross.—HI SIBLEY.

OAR RACK. Where several boats are in constant use, the care of oars is a problem that can be much simplified by the use of a rack, such as the one shown below and in the drawing. It goes far toward reducing the loss of oars and damage caused by warping and breakage, permits the oars to be kept in numbered pairs, tells at a glance how many boats are in use, is easily locked when your camp is left alone, and provides a winter storage box.

The top of the rack is entirely enclosed. Oars are inserted with the blades uppermost between partitions. The shafts fit between dowels set in the crosspiece, and the handles rest squarely on the bottom. A hinged board across the bottom can be secured with a padlock. When this is closed, none of the oars can be removed.—MILTON KLEIN.

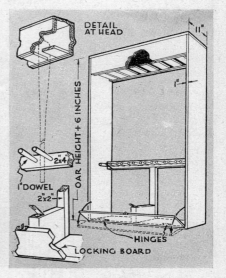

DETAIL AT HEAD

11"

1"

OAR HEIGHT + 6 INCHES

2x4

1" DOWEL

2x2

HINGES

LOCKING BOARD

By E. W. LEHMANN

Head of Department, Agricultural Engineering,
University of Illinois

TO GET along with old machines at a time when the farm labor supply is limited makes it particularly important to avoid breakdowns in the field. Since the mower is used during the fall as well as in the early part of the summer, checking and repairing it now will not only insure its readiness for the first cutting of alfalfa next year, but make a better job of the last this fall.

Toward the end of the season this is, in fact, always a good time to check machinery because the operator knows then whether there is anything wrong with it. If the mower knife is dull or poorly adjusted, it is hard to pull and takes a lot of unnecessary power, and if parts are loose or badly worn, breakdowns are likely to occur.

Check the alignment of the cutter bar— the heart of the mower. With the machine on level ground, block up the front end of the tongue about 2½' and drop the cutter bar so the inner and outer ends rest on the ground. Tie a string to the center of the pitman bearing and hold it tight along the center line of the pitman over the knife head.

Pull the cutter bar back by hand until it is in cutting position; then measure from the line of rivets on the cutter bar to the string. The outer end of a 6' cutter bar should be about 1½" ahead of the inner end—a lead of about ¼" for each foot of length of the cutter bar. Alignment of the bar may be corrected by adjusting the eccentric behind the yoke as shown in one of the drawings. On some machines, it is necessary to drill out or file the old holes in the yoke casting with a rattail file and fit in oversized pins in order to take up slack caused by wear.

The register of the knife is checked by turning the pitman wheel for a complete stroke of the knife. If the knife sections do not stop in the center of the guards at each end of the stroke, the mower will clog and will not cut properly. Some mowers have a provision for adjusting the entire cutter bar in or out. On older makes it may be necessary to lengthen or shorten the pitman, which is a wooden rod with a box bushing on one end and a ball-and-socket knife-head bearing on the other. The length is changed by removing the rivets and replacing the wooden rod with a new one.

Guard alignment may be checked by moving a straightedge along the top of the guard plates after removing the knife. Note

MIDSEASON REPAIRS AND ADJUSTMENTS MAKE MOWING

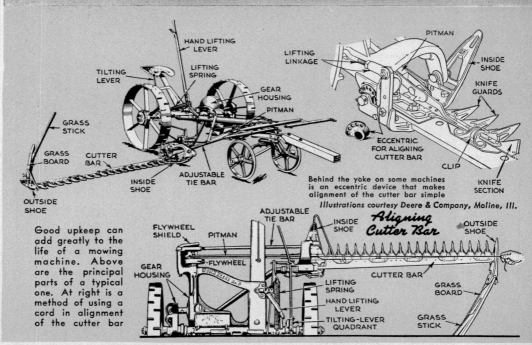

Behind the yoke on some machines is an eccentric device that makes alignment of the cutter bar simple

Illustrations courtesy Deere & Company, Moline, Ill.

Good upkeep can add greatly to the life of a mowing machine. Above are the principal parts of a typical one. At right is a method of using a cord in alignment of the cutter bar

those that are high and those that are low. Drive unaligned guards back into alignment by a blow with a hammer. The plates have serrated edges and, when badly worn, should be replaced. If the greater thickness of a new plate puts it above the others, it may be necessary to lower the entire guard by placing tin shims between it and the cutter bar.

A sharp knife or sickle is essential, an extra knife is desirable as a spare, and knife sections should be available at all times for replacement of those that may be damaged or broken. Check the knife bar to see that it is straight. In grinding the knife sections, maintain the same cutting angle and bevel as on new sections. To replace an old section that has worn much shorter than the others, remove the knife from the

MACHINES EFFICIENT WAR WORKERS

cutter bar, and then hold the edge of the knife bar on the edge of an anvil or piece of railroad iron. Shear the rivets by striking a sharp blow on the edge of the section above each and remove them with a punch. Special riveting sets are convenient, but a good job can be done with a ball-peen hammer.

For best results, adjust the clips after the knife has been straightened and made to register. Begin with the clip next to the inside shoe and, if it is bent up, tap it lightly until it begins to tighten on the knife bar. Examine and adjust all clips in the same manner; then check to see that the knife can be moved freely by hand.

Check the pitman for end play and twist. Excessive lost motion caused by wear in the ball and socket can best be taken up by renewing the knife head and the pitman bearing. Some mower models are equipped with a knife-head correction self-adjusted to take up wear. If a badly worn crankpin in the pitman wheel causes lost motion, remove the crankshaft, saw partly through the worn crankpin, and break it off with a hammer. The small end of the crankpin can then be

driven from the wheel, and a new one installed. While the crankpin is out is a good time to check the condition of the crankshaft bushings, which may need to be renewed.

For ease in operation, see that the lifting spring is at the proper tension to permit the cutter bar to float over the ground without dragging. Check also the tension of the lifting spring to permit easy raising of the cutter bar.

The chief function of the outer and inner shoes is to support the cutter bar and to keep it level. Replace badly worn parts. The proper angle of the grass board and stick is essential to good operation in cutting high grass. The spring tension on the board should be sufficiently flexible to side pressure and yet stiff enough to force the grass away.

In horse-drawn mowers the power to operate the knife is usually transmitted from the wheels by rachets and pawls. Check the pawls and the pawl springs, see that the pawl boxes are clean, and renew badly worn parts or surfaces with a file. *(CONTINUED)*

Provision is made on many machines for adjusting the meshing of drive gears by means of a nut on the end of the countershaft. On some the adjustment is made by means of an adjustable collar or by the use of washers. Replace worn gears and badly worn parts of the clutch mechanism.

To put the mower in the best condition for operation, check all bearings for wear. Flanged bushings can be replaced after driving out the old ones with a piece of shafting slightly smaller than the shaft.

Finally, check the entire machine for loose nuts, worn bolts, broken cotter keys, and weakened or worn parts. There is always danger of breakage where lost motion is present because of loosely fitting parts, and these also impair operating efficiency.

It is generally understood that, while there may be fewer new machines available, the supply of parts will be adequate for the farmer to make his old machines do their work. Careful cleaning, adjusting, repairing, painting, and lubrication will make these old machines last several years longer. It is wise also to check them early enough to get in your order for parts that you may wish to replace during the winter months.

Handy Blackout Flashlight Made by Reversing the Reflector

ANY ordinary flashlight can be adapted at a moment's notice for blackout use. No additional parts or materials are needed for this handy trick. Remove the flashlight lens entirely. Take out, invert, and replace the reflector; then screw on the lens holder. This reduces the light aperture to the small hole that formerly accommodated the bulb, so that only a pale circle of light is emitted, which compares favorably with the illumination of elaborate and expensive blackout flashlights.—RAY JUTILA.

Storm Sash Are Stored on Shelf Installed at End of Garage

SPACE in the garage that would otherwise go to waste can be used for easy storage of storm sash in the summer and screens in the winter. Nail 2 by 4's across the garage from stud to stud to form a shelf above the radiator of your car at a height that will be convenient to reach. Nail on either a board floor as shown, or one of slats, which may be nailed a few inches apart to keep dust from collecting. If many sash are to be stored, cleats under the ends of the 2 by 4's will add support.—WILLIAM FREEMAN.

Sealed-Beam Headlight Unit Makes Powerful Searchlight

WHEN one beam of a sealed-beam headlight burns out, the unit can no longer be used legally on a car, but it can be made into a powerful, portable searchlight that will help greatly on a job that must be completed at night. Nail an upright to a wooden box large enough to contain the storage battery that will provide current for the light; then, on the upper end of the standard, fasten a small bracket to which the sealed-beam unit may be bolted by means of its mounting clips. Such a unit may also be mounted on a tractor or other farm machine and connected to the regular starting and ignition battery.—ROBERT MANN.

Personal Furniture...

FOR THE HOME SECRETARY

Chair, Typewriter Table, and Floor Lamp Are Ideal Projects to Make for the Den or Study

Designed by ERNEST R. DEWALT

MANY American homes have found the typewriter almost indispensable. The machine is used for correspondence, for writing out household accounts, and, by the younger generation, as an aid in the pursuit of schoolwork. To make it still handier, these three projects have been designed—a table of convenient height, a matching chair, and a lamp. They will go far toward simplifying work for the home secretary or student and, when not in use with the typewriter, will serve as occasional furniture.

All of the pieces are simply built, yet each presents interesting points of construction. Birch plywood 13/16″ thick is used for both the table and chair. Sets of legs are made for the table in pairs. Lay out one pair of upper legs inside a pair of lower ones, attach

Turned at right angles to the lower table legs, matched upper legs make neat, invisible joints

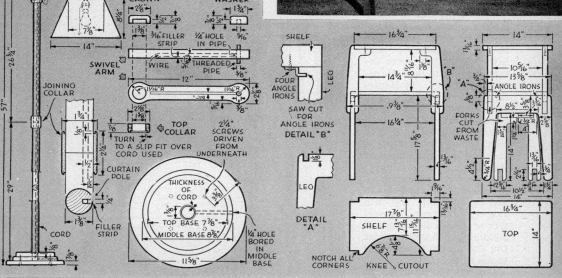

Canvas stretched over dowels forms the seat of this convenient chair, which is sawed out from pieces of birch plywood

the two rear stretchers, as shown in the drawing, allowing space for the thickness of the canvas. Bolt the back to the upper dowel and screw it to the lower one, using washers to keep from twisting and tearing the canvas fabric. Small decorative buttons are turned and screwed to the ends of the stretchers.

The lamp standard is made of a 27″ length and a 29″ length of 1⅜″ curtain pole. Rip out a ¼″ by ½″ channel in each and glue in flush a ¼″ by ¼″ filler strip to make a longitudinal space for the wire. Each piece is then wound in the lathe with white cord, leaving a bare section at each end for fitting. A mahogany turning forms a collar joining the two, and three mahogany disks make the stepped base. Mahogany turnings also form a collar at the upper end and a swivel crown and washer for the lamp arm, as shown in the drawing. The arm itself is cut from mahogany and grooved and filled in for the wire like the standard.

Finishing is similar for all pieces, two coats of clear varnish being applied to all exposed wood except the end grain of the table and chair, which may be painted to harmonize with the canvas chair seat. A shellac or varnish finish is also suitable for the corded sections of the lamp. Average working time: Table, 6 hours; chair, 6½ hours; and lamp, 5½ hours.

a second piece of plywood with nails in what will be waste, and bandsaw them all at the same time. Make the long notches in the upper sets a snug fit for the stock used so that, when the piece is assembled, the glued joints will not show.

The chair legs are also made in pairs and bandsawed at one time, while the back is laid out and sawed from the waste inside one pair of legs. Hardwood dowels ¾″ in diameter are used for the double stretchers at front and back. A strip of olive-drab canvas, 12¼″ wide by 24″ long, forms the seat. It is tacked first at the back of the lower rear stretcher; then it is wound completely around that dowel, up and over the top, and onto the lower front dowel where it is also tacked. Hold a padded iron against the dowels and space the tacks 1″ apart.

Groove the back to fit

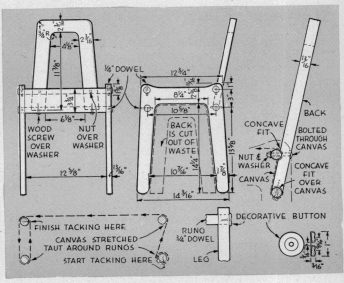

NEW TOOLS FROM OLD HACKSAW BLADES

By C. W. Bertsch

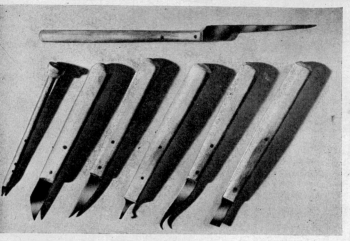

These unique tools, which are of special value to the model builder, can be made from sections of hacksaw blades. The high-quality steel holds a keen edge and will stand up well even under rigorous service

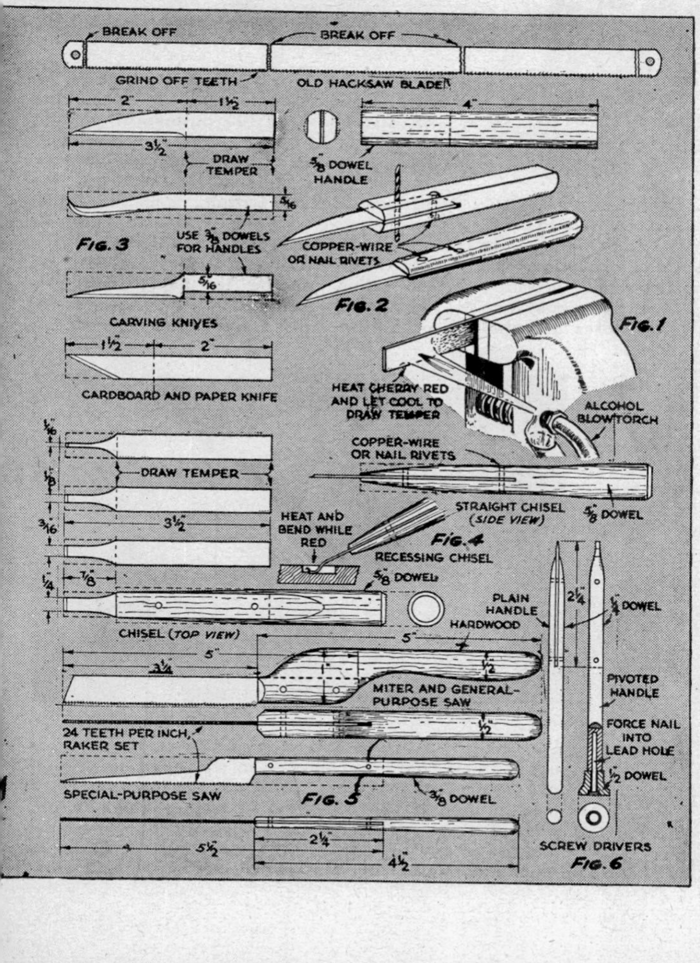

RAZOR-edged knives, chisels, and other tools may easily be made from worn or broken hacksaw blades. Designed to reach hard-to-get-at spots, these tools are particularly suited to model making or other fine work. Blades, nails or copper wire (No. 10 gauge or smaller), and short lengths of dowels are the only materials needed. A 12″ blade is sufficient for three tools.

An all-hard blade, .025″ thick, is best. Break off the required length in a vise and anneal the part to be inserted in the handle, so that it can be drilled. A small alcohol torch generates enough heat for this purpose. Place the part in a vise, heat to a dull red, and let cool (Fig. 1). The vise will prevent the heat from reaching the tempered end. Grind the blade to shape, taking care not to draw the temper by "burning"; then grind the edge.

A dowel serves for the handle. Cut a slot for the blade and drill two holes just large enough for the wires or nails to fit tightly (Fig. 2). Use a small ball-peen hammer to form the rivets. Shape and smooth the handle on a sander or with a file, and put a keen edge on the blade with an oilstone. This knife will hold its edge through hard service.

Illustrated in Fig. 3 are other blade shapes. Excellent chisels for delicate work can also be made in the same manner. To retemper the recessing chisel (Fig. 4), heat it to a cherry red and plunge it into water.

The saws in Fig. 5 should, of course, be made from a new blade. Small screwdrivers, with either plain or jeweler's pivoted handles (Fig. 6), may also prove to be useful additions to your kit of special tools.

BREAK OFF — BREAK OFF

GRIND OFF TEETH — OLD HACKSAW BLADE

2″ 1½″

3½″

DRAW TEMPER

⅝ DOWEL HANDLE

4″

5/16

FIG. 3

USE ⅜ DOWELS FOR HANDLES

COPPER-WIRE OR NAIL RIVETS

FIG. 2

CARVING KNIVES

5/16

1½″ 2″

CARDBOARD AND PAPER KNIFE

HEAT CHERRY RED AND LET COOL TO DRAW TEMPER

ALCOHOL BLOWTORCH

FIG. 1

COPPER-WIRE OR NAIL RIVETS

DRAW TEMPER

3½″

HEAT AND BEND WHILE RED

STRAIGHT CHISEL (SIDE VIEW)

⅝ DOWEL

FIG. 4

RECESSING CHISEL

⅝ DOWEL

CHISEL (TOP VIEW)

PLAIN HANDLE HARDWOOD

2¼ DOWEL

PIVOTED HANDLE

5″

3¼

5′

½″

MITER AND GENERAL-PURPOSE SAW

½″

FORCE NAIL INTO LEAD HOLE

24 TEETH PER INCH, RAKER SET

½″

DOWEL

SPECIAL-PURPOSE SAW

⅜ DOWEL

FIG. 5

5½″ 2¼

4½″

SCREW DRIVERS

FIG. 6

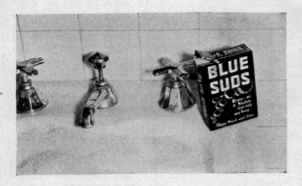

CLOTHES HANGERS are now being made entirely of wood. They have two-part wooden hooks designed to give correct balance when in use. Both inner edges of the hooks are rounded out to fit securely on the closet hanging bar

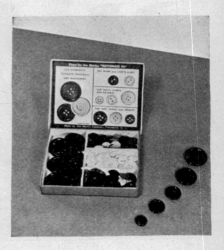

A NEW BUTTON KIT is now added to the list of housekeeping aids. It contains an assortment of 100 buttons of popular colors and sizes particularly suitable for use on men's and children's clothes. The kit is partitioned to separate the various sizes of buttons, and the inside of the cover has an illustrated chart to aid in the selection of just the button you need. Included with the kit is an interesting booklet entitled, "Buttons—Tremendous Trifles," which tells the story of button making and gives helpful tips

BLUE SOAP FLAKES help reduce time required to wash clothes because the bluing is used in combination with soap chips or flakes during the washing operation. The bluing flakes are packaged in a carton similar in shape to those containing regular soap flakes, but about one third the size. Being concentrated, fewer flakes are used

PLASTIC COMES TO AID the seamstress in the form of a triangular scale having a 4" rule on one of its sides and indentations on the other two sides. The notches are in $\frac{1}{4}$", $\frac{1}{8}$", and $\frac{3}{8}$" graduations. The hem marker is simple to use as the notches make it possible either to put pins in the fabric or to mark the hem edge with tailor's chalk

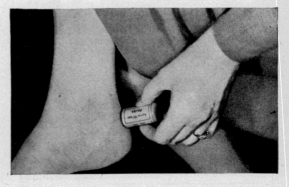

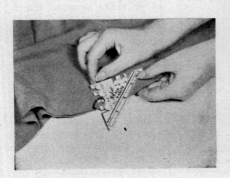

LONGER STOCKING WEAR is said to be the result of using a new coating compound in stick form to prevent any chafing of the fabric. Applied as shown above, it may be used to coat the stocking surface where it rubs against a shoe. The stick is merely rubbed on the heel and toe of the stockings after they are put on. Ordinary laundering washes out the special coating without harm

CERAMIC COOKING UTENSILS now being shown are made with grooved bottoms that expose a greater area to the flame of a stove, causing the inside surface to heat more quickly and more evenly. The items include frying pans, pots, and ramekins for service at the table as well as for cooking. All interior surfaces of these nonporous utensils are glazed to prevent absorption of flavors and to guard against oxidation and other chemical changes that sometimes occur with metal. Exteriors are natural clay, the interiors French brown

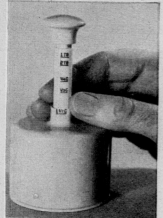

THIS HANDY CUP will help make measuring of shortening accurate and fast. The plunger is marked off in graduations ranging from one tablespoonful to a half cup. It is set at a desired amount and the cup is filled level with the bottom edge. Pushing the plunger empties the cup. The measuring device is entirely of plastic

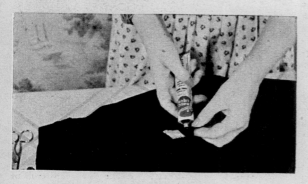

A NEW MAGIC LIQUID is being used to mend holes in cloth goods caused by burns, moths, or accidental tears. First the frayed edges are cut away, a patch is cut to fit, and the liquid spread over the patch and the edges of the hole. Then a piece of lining is placed behind the area, pressed down, and set aside to dry. The liquid also stops stocking runs

PLASTIC FLASHLIGHT CASES are now being made to withstand hard use in emergency situations of cold and heat from 40 deg. below zero to 175 deg. above. The one illustrated has two cells, is prefocused, and has, in addition to its positive "on" and "off" positions, a midway setting that permits operation of the button for fast or slow flashing. An extra emergency bulb is in the bottom cup. Since its case is waterproof, the flashlight will operate under water. It has a hook for fastening to a person's belt or hanging to a projection

Natural wood grain adds to the beauty of these two magazine racks. However, the finish chosen should be one which will harmonize with your entire room

Magazine Racks of Modern Design

By JOSEPH ARONSON

THE problem of where to keep current newspapers and magazines is solved with an attractive rack made of odds and ends. You can modify the proportions somewhat to suit the materials on hand if you have any plywood remnants, but the dimensions listed produce two well-proportioned pieces of furniture.

Both the racks shown were made of ¼" birch plywood. Three panels were glued into slots in each base block. The center slot was cut at right angles and the two outer ones at 100 deg. to the base, all being a tight fit for the panels.

A hole cut in the center panel and trimmed at the upper edge with half-round molding forms a convenient grip. For embellishment, you can wrap leather, cane, or colored twine around the handle. If you find that the wood used has a pleasing grain, an attractive finish can be

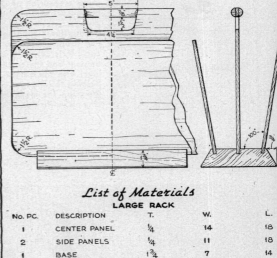

List of Materials

No. PC.	DESCRIPTION	T.	W.	L.
LARGE RACK				
1	CENTER PANEL	¼	14	18
2	SIDE PANELS	¼	11	18
1	BASE	1¾	7	14
2	HANDLE PIECES	½	⅞	5
SMALL RACK				
1	CENTER PANEL	¼	14	14
2	SIDE PANELS	¼	11	14
1	BASE	1¾	7	10
2	HANDLE PIECES	½	⅞	5
NOTE: ALL DIMENSIONS ARE GIVEN IN INCHES				

secured by applying a few thin coats of shellac, being careful to sand well between each coat. Rub the last coat with a hard wax to achieve the final finish.

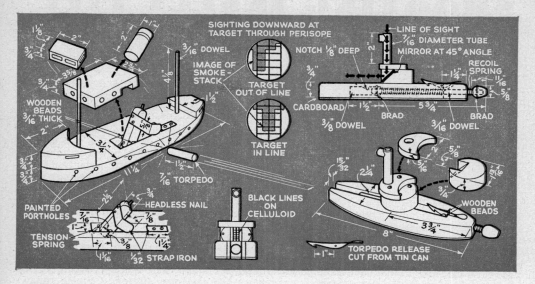

Sub with Periscope Sight "Explodes" Ship

AIM through the periscope sight of this submarine, fire a torpedo, and watch the doomed enemy freighter explode!

The torpedo tube is a slot 15/32" wide, running from the bow to within 1¼" of the stern of the submarine. A hole large enough to take a 3/16" dowel loosely is drilled through the stern. Assemble the torpedo-firing mechanism from a 3/16" dowel, a ⅜" dowel for the torpedo ram, and a cocking knob. The torpedo-release catch pivots on a nail driven across the slot, with two wooden beads for side bearings. Cement a mirror

9/16" square in a slot cut at a 45-deg. angle in the conning-tower base; cover this with a celluloid window marked as shown.

Make the freighter's superstructure from a frame of ¼" strips with a cardboard top. Use a 2" section of broomstick for the funnel. The exploding mechanism is a wooden bar, loosely pivoted on a nail and operated by a tension spring. A headless nail holds the bar under a projecting strip of metal. A second strip extends from the bar down the port side, where it constitutes a target for the torpedo.—MYRON FLEISHMAN.

SHOOTING INSECT LIFE WITH YOUR CAMERA

ONE of the least explored fields of photography lies within a few yards of the spot where you read these lines. Whether you live in town or country, in the mountains or by the sea, insects can always be found; and most of them furnish unrealized opportunities for taking striking and distinctive photographs.

During these late-summer days the insect parade is at its peak. Subjects for your lens are everywhere if you make your back yard a studio.

The two chief requisites of any good insect picture are: first, it must record the insect large enough to show detail; and second, the subject must be in perfect focus. Consequently the camera you use for insect photography must be capable of taking close close-ups, and it must have some method of insuring a perfectly sharp image.

My own preference is a 3¼" by 4¼" film-pack camera equipped with a ground-glass back and a double-extension bellows. Such a camera permits accurate focusing and, when its 15-cm. Tessar lens is replaced with a lens having a 1" focal length, magnifica-

tions up to a dozen diameters are possible.

For your initial shots, the larger insects, such as butterflies, moths, katydids, and praying mantes, offer the best chances for success. They are more likely to stay motionless while their pictures are being taken. Slow-moving creatures like walking sticks also co-operate well. Butterflies and moths make passive and unblemished subjects while their wings are drying just after they have emerged from their cocoons. By collecting cocoons during the winter, a supply of large, beautifully patterned moths, such as the Luna, Polyphemus, and Cecropia, can be provided for spring camera work.

Most insects, however, are lively creatures, and inducing them to pose is an important part of insect photography. A few amateurs stalk their quarry, edging close when the specimen alights. Coupled range finders are needed for this. However, one enthusiast has a slender rod fitted to his camera and, focusing for the length of the rod, snaps the shutter when the tip is even with the foliage on which an insect rests.

Simpler, and still more effective, is to

Photography

Portrait of a cicada—a 16-second exposure with a 1" focal-length lens stopped at f/16 and two photofloods. White cardboard behind the damsel fly reflected light for the silhouette, made in 1 second with a Tessar 15-cm. lens stopped at f/32

By
EDWIN
WAY
TEALE

Just after emerging from its chrysalis, this great spangled fritillary butterfly poses on a sprig of spiraea. This is a 1/5-second exposure with a Tessar lens stopped at f/32 and two photofloods to provide the lighting

Awaiting prey, an ambush bug clings to buddleia for a 16-second exposure (lower left). A 1" focal-length lens at f/16 was used with photofloods. At right, below, a 1/10-second shot in brilliant sunshine of a short-horned grasshopper with a Tessar lens at f/32

focus on a plant, either outdoors or on a table indoors, and then place a captured butterfly or other insect in a natural and effective position on the foliage. Inasmuch as the section of the plant on which the insect clings is already in focus, the picture can be snapped the moment the insect is at rest. For close close-ups, focusing must be done on the insect itself.

To reduce the natural liveliness of your subjects, you can employ any one of several methods. For instance, you can place a captured insect in a jar containing a wad of cotton batting soaked in ammonia. The fumes dull its senses and it clings more or less motionless when placed on a leaf or twig. Ether can also be used. The difficulty with such methods is that the insect may become so deadened it loses its lifelike appearance.

By taking advantage of the nature and habits of different insect subjects, it is possible to catch them during their periods of quiet. Butterflies are active during daylight and inactive at night, and moths, as a rule, follow the reverse procedure. So by taking butterfly pictures after twilight and moth pictures at midday, you find your subjects most quiet.

Capitalizing on the fact that chilling decreases the activity of insects, I once obtained a sequence of pictures showing the rise and fall of a wasp colony. All of the pictures, made over a period of several months, were snapped soon after dawn while the insects were still sluggish from the night chill. Similarly, the placing of an insect in a refrigerator for 10 or 15 minutes before taking a picture of it will diminish its activity so that it will cling where you place it and yet appear natural. In handling insects, particularly butterflies and moths, use tweezers, or lift them by their legs with your fingers. This will prevent damaging them or rubbing off their delicate wing scales.

When taking most insect pictures, it pays to stop the aperture of your camera to the limit. The old rule is, the smaller the stop, the greater the depth of focus. At f/32 the depth of focus is greater than at f/4.5. The closer you work to your subject, the less the depth of focus, and you need all you can get—especially when you enlarge, and still more

The praying mantis snares a katydid: a Proxar auxiliary on a Tessar, f/32, and photofloods. Right, a backlighted snowy tree cricket: f/32, the Tessar rear element alone

Quiet at dawn, paper-making wasps, right, cling to their nest, while a Polyphemus moth unfolds its wings below on emerging from the cocoon—both taken in daylight at f/32 with a Proxar on a Tessar lens, the wasps at one second, the moth at two

when you enlarge only a small portion of the negative. Using the camera on a tripod is virtually a necessity.

Starting with the largest insects, you can work to the more difficult ones, the real Lilliputians of their world. For butterflies and katydids, a Tessar 15-cm., f/4.5 lens is satisfactory. With the bellows extended to the limit, it records an insect almost full size on the negative. A 50-percent increase —pictures that show the subject 1½ times natural size—is obtained by slipping an auxiliary Proxar wide-angle lens on the Tessar. This permits a closer picture of the subject. A double-size image can be obtained by removing the Proxar and screwing out the front element of the Tessar. With only the rear element in use, the depth of focus, even with the diaphragm stopped down to the limit, will be almost paper thin. This makes extra care in focusing imperative.

For the smaller insects, and for recording the amazingly odd faces of many species, I remove the Tessar entirely and replace it with a 1″ focal-length lens originally made for a 16-mm. movie camera. This little ob-

jective is set in a wooden mount designed to slip snugly into the opening left by the removal of the Tessar and its Compur shutter. When the bellows is extended as far as it will go, the small lens throws an image 12 times natural size on the ground glass. This equipment is used only with photofloods or other artificial illumination. As the lens has no shutter, exposures are controlled by switching the lights on and off. With two photoflood bulbs 8″ from the subject, the exposure is 16 seconds with superspeed film.

Insects should be freshly killed in cyanide before portraits of their faces are made. The heat of the lamps will stimulate anesthetized subjects, and they may move during an exposure. A few tiny insects, such as the ¼″ ambush bug, have the habit of remaining perfectly still while awaiting their prey, making it possible to record magnified pictures of living insects.

Filmy creatures, like the lacewing fly and the Luna moth, take on added beauty when recorded indoors with back lighting. Some insects and the plants to which they cling make unusual silhouettes when a photoflood is directed on white cardboard behind them. Supersensitive panchromatic film is most satisfactory for insect photography. Its high-speed emulsion permits shorter exposures with the diaphragm stopped down, and its sensitiveness to all colors, including red, is valuable in recording patterns. As an aid to enlarging small portions of a negative, a fine-grain developer should be employed. Use glossy paper to show maximum detail.

All-Around Lighting for Stills Obtained with a Single Bulb

This inquiring pup was lighted from front and side as in the shots above to get the combined effect at left

WHEN equipment is limited, a method of using a single bulb to get the effect of multiple lighting will prove useful in shooting still subjects such as table-top setups. The lighting is done from one angle at a time, separate exposures being made on the same film. Use a sturdy tripod and time each exposure for the lighted portions, as the shadowed areas will be illuminated when the bulb is shifted for the other exposures. You can control the effect or intensity of light for each angle of illumination by the length of the exposure or the distance of the bulb from the subject. Watch carefully where light from two angles may fall on the same spot, or you may overexpose. You can also light large interiors by this method if you move from place to place with the bulb, turning the light off each time instead of closing the shutter.—LOUIS HOCHMAN.

GLASS CASTER CUPS, such as are used to protect rugs from heavy furniture, are convenient for holding solutions when you are reducing local areas on prints or bleaching vignettes. If you are using two or more solutions, the cups should be labeled.

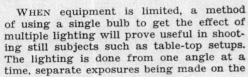

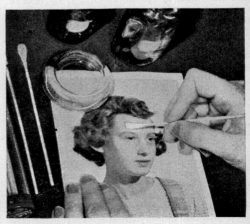

A CUT-FILM HOLDER will afford uniform test strips that save you time and paper in making trial exposures for enlargements. Insert unexposed paper in the sheath, fasten the holder on the enlarger easel, and draw out the slide at carefully timed intervals to spaces marked along the frame, as shown above. Developing the strip print will give you the nearest correct exposure for that negative.—JOHN K. KARLOVIC.

INDICATORS for your darkroom scale will give more accurate readings when you measure small amounts. They can be made from stiff copper wire and soldered directly to the yokes of the pans, as shown in the photo at the right. The hands of the indicators are hammered and filed to shape. A touch of luminous paint will make it easy to balance the scale pans even in the dark.—LOUIS SONKOY.

GLOSSY PRINTS can be tinted with regular photographic water colors if the surface of the print is first rubbed carefully with the open end of a freshly cut potato. The water colors will then flow on smoothly instead of drawing away into droplets on the surface. The print can be ferrotyped again to restore its glossy surface. As the potato dries, cut off thin slices each time you use it.—H. W.

BLOTTER LINT on photographic prints that have been dried between blotters adheres tightly to the emulsion and is often difficult to remove. A dry chamois cloth makes an excellent wiper for this job. Rub gently so as not to press the lint particles into the emulsion. The chamois should be washed frequently and wrung thoroughly dry before it is used again.

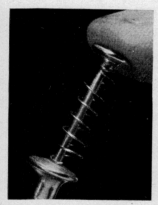

CABLE RELEASES that have lost their tension need not be thrown away. Obtain a small compression spring for a few cents at any hardware store. Work the spring over the head of the plunger so that it fits around the shaft between the head and the base as shown at the left. This will restore your cable release and make it useful once more.—S. ADELMAN.

A SPRING COUNTERBALANCE makes easier work of adjusting an enlarger to obtain the size image desired. Buy a spring sash balance having an 8 to 10-lb. pull at a hardware store. Wedge the balance firmly in the top of the enlarger shaft and attach the tape to the enlarger head to "float" its weight, as shown below.—R. E. WHALLON.

TAGS FOR LABELS on your darkroom bottles are more serviceable than pasted labels since they do not wash off or become stained. Also, they can be changed easily with each fresh solution or new data. Cut them from shipping tags and attach to the neck of the bottle with string or rubber bands as at the left. Tags of different shapes will aid in identifying bottles in the dark.—L. H.

This pair of eggs is laid in a nest of straw to begin the hatching period

These two squabs are just a week old and have only a thin covering of fuzz

After another week they still have little fuzz, but are growing rapidly

Three weeks of life produces added weight in addition to real feathers

The squabs are feathered and ready for eating four weeks after hatching

ONE luxury food everyone may enjoy without ration stamps is home-raised squab. The flesh of this delicacy contains more body-building soluble protein and less connective tissue than does the adult pigeon. In addition, it is an excellent source of vitamin G, is rich in phosphorus, and has a fine texture and a delicious flavor.

Of the many breeds of pigeons, only a few are generally used for squab production. They include the prolific King, the slightly smaller Carneau, the giant Homer, the French Mountain, Swiss Mondane, Hungarian, Maltese, and Runt. The first

FAST-GROWING SQUABS PROVIDE

four are recommended by professional squab raisers because the squabs provide generous servings, some weighing 1½ lb.

Part of an outbuilding may be used for raising squabs, or a coop may be built. The house should include a protected pen, where the birds will be safe against wind and rain, and a screened yard. It should face south if the climate is cold, and it should be on soil that drains well. An open-shed pigeon house 6' high in the rear and 7' to 8' high in front, with an 18" projection on the front as protection against storms, is easily built. The depth of the house depends upon the number of pigeons to be mated. A pen 8' by 12' will hold 25 pairs easily. Houses are generally built of wood and are much like poultry houses. In very cold regions, enough heat to keep the house dry and comfortable (about 40 deg. F.) will

Pigeon nests are built in two sections because the hen often lays another pair of eggs before the two squabs occupying the adjoining nest have grown to maturity

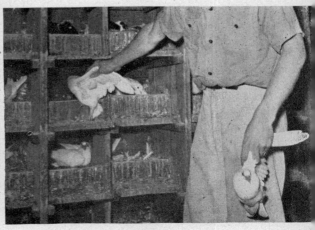

help to increase the production of squabs during the wintertime.

Double nests are essential. Nest compartments may be 15" high, 12" wide, and 25" long, with a partition at the center and a 5" board in front to keep nesting material from falling out. A 5" landing board should also be provided in front, and each double nest should be partitioned off from its neighbor. Tobacco stems, long-leaf pine needles, straw, and hay will make satisfactory nesting materials for the birds.

The outside yard should be about 20' long mated pair. Nest boxes may be closed with a wire or wood screen for use as mating coops.

Good couples should produce 12 or more squabs a year. The hen usually lays one egg, skips a day, then lays again, and 17 or 18 days later the two eggs hatch. The parents build their nest together and alternate in sitting on the eggs. Often the hen lays another setting of eggs when the young are two to three weeks old, leaving their feeding largely to the male. It is for this reason that double nests are provided. Both par-

Meat Miracle

A DELICIOUS PROTEIN FOOD TO SUPPLEMENT FAMILY RATIONS

and as wide as the pen. If available, 1" wire mesh is suitable to inclose it, but laths or similar pieces will serve. The sides should be 7' high. Be sure to extend the wire 12" into the ground to keep out rats.

Select your breeding stock with care, going to a reliable breeder who keeps records of production and the weights of squabs, and will guarantee the sex and age of his birds. Purchase either young pigeons that are nearly ready for breeding or young mated pairs. With care, you can start breeding birds when they are six to eight months old and continue breeding them for five years. Keep only mated birds in the pen.

Once breeding stock is installed, nature may be allowed to take its course in mating, or the mating may be forced. Both methods are satisfactory. To force mating, confine a male and a female bird within a compartment for a week or two, making sure to provide feed and water. Place identification bands bearing the same number on each ents feed their squabs on thick pigeon milk, produced in their crops, shortly after they themselves have been fed.

Retain squabs to be used as breeders in the pen with their parents until they are seven to eight weeks old, or until they learn to eat and care for themselves. For general feeding give whole grains, but no mash or green feed. Farmer's Bulletin No. 684 of the U. S. Department of Agriculture gives precise information on feeding and care.

Given plenty of feed and water, and kept clean and dry, the squabs will grow rapidly. Those for the table should be killed when they are 24 to 30 days old and before they have left the nest. Surplus squabs may be sold, thus reducing the cost. Immediately after killing by severing the jugular vein just below the base of the skull, dry-pick the birds and remove all pin feathers. Cool the picked squabs promptly by immersing for three hours in ice-cold water containing 1 part salt to 32 parts water.

Above are two photos of King pigeons that show rapid growth of squabs of this breed. The bird at the left is a full grown pigeon while the one at the right is a 28-day squab

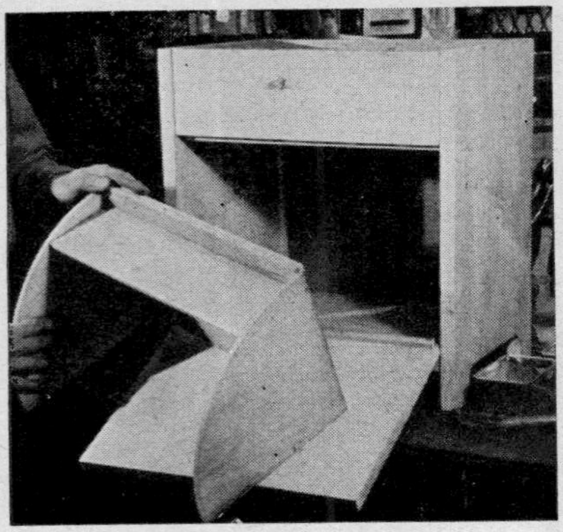

The plywood storage bin is attached to the down-swinging door with glue and set nails

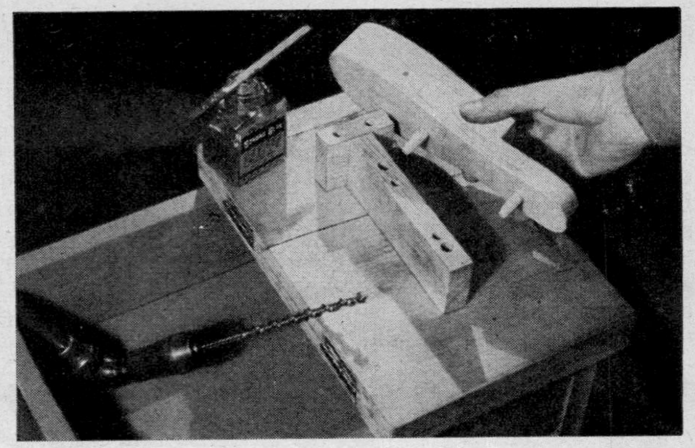

A T-shaped base, nailed to the underside of the hinged lid, raises the footrest to a convenient height for polishing

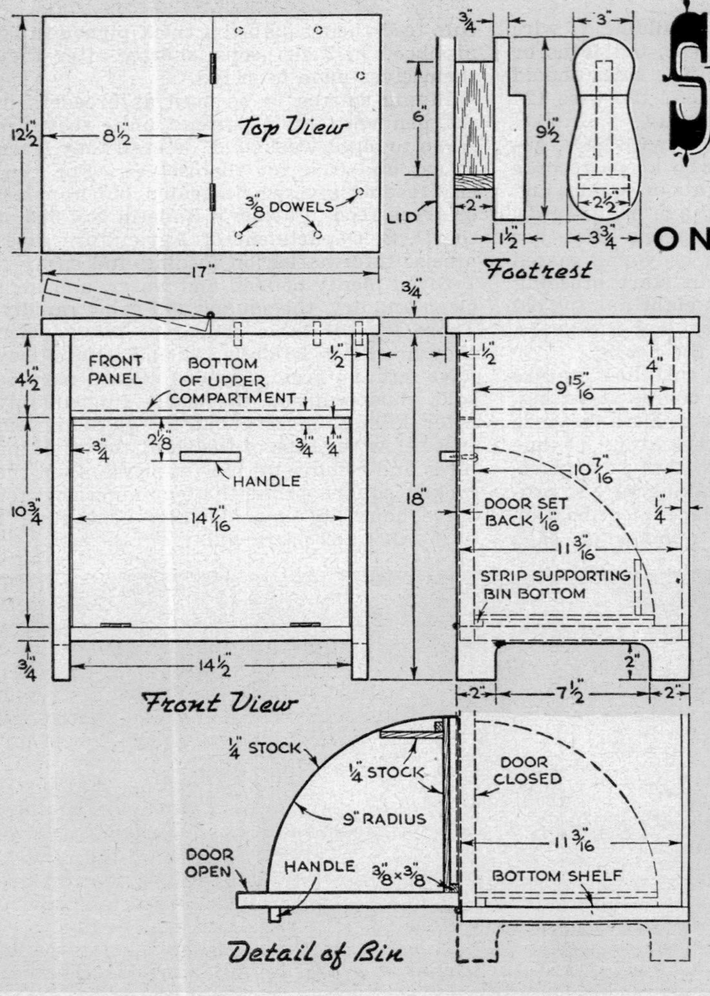

Top View
12½"
8½"
⅜ DOWELS
17"
¾"
6"
9½"
3"
2½"
2"
LID
1½"
3¾"
Footrest
4½"
FRONT PANEL
BOTTOM OF UPPER COMPARTMENT
½"
2⅛
¾"
¾"
¼"
HANDLE
10¾"
14 7/16"
18"
¾"
14½"
Front View
½"
4"
9 15/16"
10 7/16"
DOOR SET BACK 1/16
¼"
11 3/16"
STRIP SUPPORTING BIN BOTTOM
2"
2"
7½"
2"
¼" STOCK
¼" STOCK
9" RADIUS
DOOR OPEN
HANDLE
⅜×⅜"
DOOR CLOSED
11 3/16"
BOTTOM SHELF
Detail of Bin

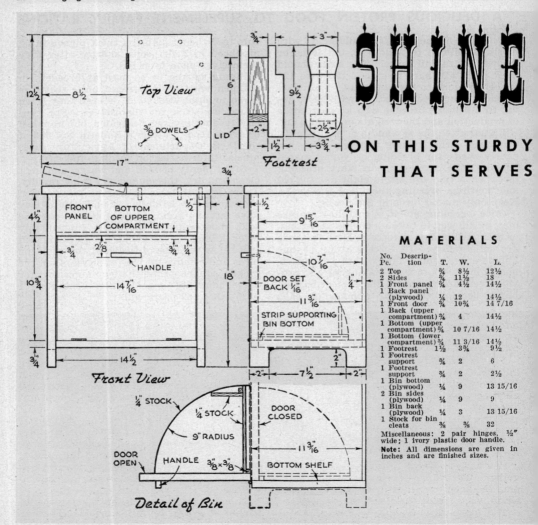

SHINE

ON THIS STURDY ... THAT SERVES

MATERIALS

No. Pc.	Description	T.	W.	L.
2	Top	¾	8½	12½
2	Sides	¾	11½	18
1	Front panel	¾	4½	14½
1	Back panel (plywood)	¼	12	14½
1	Front door	¾	10¾	14 7/16
1	Back (upper compartment)	¾	4	14½
1	Bottom (upper compartment)	¾	10 7/16	14½
1	Bottom (lower compartment)	¾	11 3/16	14½
1	Footrest	1½	3¾	9½
1	Footrest support	¾	2	6
1	Footrest support	¾	2	2½
1	Bin bottom (plywood)	¼	9	13 15/16
2	Bin sides (plywood)	¼	9	9
1	Bin back (plywood)	¼	3	13 15/16
1	Stock for bin cleats	⅜	⅜	32

Miscellaneous: 2 pair hinges, ½" wide; 1 ivory plastic door handle.

Note: All dimensions are given in inches and are finished sizes.

Plastic handle swings open the front door to reveal storage space where brushes and polish may be kept

'EM UP...

SHOE-POLISHING CABINET
THE WHOLE FAMILY

By Vernon B. Case

Here's a cabinet that can take care of the entire family's shoe-polishing needs. Extra cans of polish can be kept under the lid, alongside the footrest

ALTHOUGH a shoe-shine cabinet needs to be practical, it doesn't necessarily have to be an ugly piece of furniture. Here is a cabinet that is thoroughly functional but at the same time has pleasing lines and could even be used as an end or hall table. It provides space for storing brushes, polishing cloths, and bottles or boxes of polish. In addition, it has a convenient footrest that swings into position when the left half of the top is opened.

The cabinet shown was built of white pine and finished in two tones of colored enamel. However, almost any wood that is reasonably easy to work and does not have loose knots will do.

Both of the sides are cut away at the lower ends, as shown, to form short legs. This can be done on a band saw, a jig saw, or even with a small keyhole saw.

Use nails and glue to fasten the parts together. Set the nail heads rather deep and plug the holes over them with plastic composition wood, crack filler, or wooden pegs.

The top is in two sections, one of which swings upward like a trap door. In joining the two top pieces with a pair of hinges, take care to align the upper surface as perfectly as possible. This can best be done by clamping both halves in a vise while attaching the hinges. The fixed portion of the top is held in place by six ⅜" wooden dowels spaced uniformly and secured with glue.

A footrest, raised on 2" strips arranged to form a *T*, is mounted on the lower surface of the hinged lid in such a way that it does not strike the sides of the cabinet when the lid is closed. Attach the strips to the lid with long screws or nails and fasten the footrest to them with glued dowels or countersunk nails.

The front door of the cabinet, hinged at the bottom, swings outward to provide access to the storage compartment fastened to it. The bottom board to which the door is hinged extends to the back of the cabinet, and the rear of the compartment is closed by a piece of ¼" plywood to exclude dust.

To carry the cabinet, simply swing the lid back and grasp the two hinged edges.

NOTE DIRECTION OF GRAIN WHEN CUT FROM LUMBER

IF NATURAL CROOKS ARE AVAILABLE, KNEES CAN BE SLIMMER

METAL KNEES SHOULD HAVE REINFORCING WEB

KNEE OF WATER-PROOF PLYWOOD GLUED TOGETHER

NOTCH ADJOINING MEMBERS INTO KNEE WHERE POSSIBLE

KNEES USED TO TIE TRANSOM TO SIDES AND BOTTOM (SEAT NOT SHOWN)

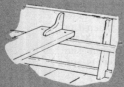

SEAT KNEES FITTED TO ADD CROSS STRENGTH

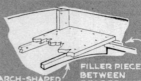

ARCH-SHAPED STRONGBACK

SET FLATHEAD SCREWS OR CLINCHED COPPER NAILS FLUSH. WOODEN PLUGS WEAKEN THIN PLANKING

FLOW MARINE GLUE THINNED WITH ALCOHOL INTO ANY OPENINGS. REFASTEN WITH BRASS SCREWS

FILLER PIECE BETWEEN BEARER AND SIDES

INNER TRANSOM TO STRENGTHEN STERN

DRIVE SCREWS THROUGH PLANK-ING INTO KEEL

INSERT WHITE LEAD BEFORE REFASTENING

REINFORCING WITH OVER-RIBS

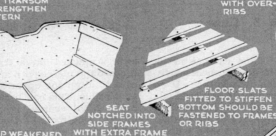

SEAT NOTCHED INTO SIDE FRAMES WITH EXTRA FRAME FITTED

BACK UP WEAKENED SCARF WITH A THIN OAK BUTT BLOCK

FLOOR SLATS FITTED TO STIFFEN BOTTOM SHOULD BE FASTENED TO FRAMES OR RIBS

¾" x 1" KEEL AND ¾ HALF-ROUND OAK STRIPS TO STIFFEN BOTTOM

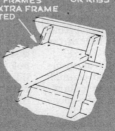

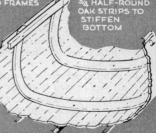

EDGE STRONGBACKS WHERE SEAT IS MERELY FASTENED OVER STRIP OR TO SIDES

KNEES FITTED TO BRACE LEAKING CENTER-BOARD

OAK STRONGBACK PREVENTS SAGGING OF SEAT

BREASTHOOK STRENGTHENS BOW

HW 468

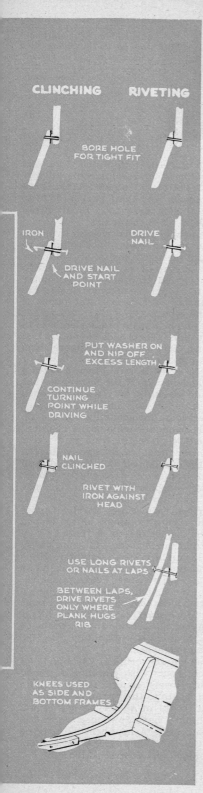

BORE HOLE
FOR TIGHT FIT

IRON   DRIVE
NAIL

DRIVE NAIL
AND START
POINT

PUT WASHER ON
AND NIP OFF
EXCESS LENGTH

CONTINUE
TURNING
POINT WHILE
DRIVING

NAIL
CLINCHED

RIVET WITH
IRON AGAINST
HEAD

USE LONG RIVETS
OR NAILS AT LAPS

BETWEEN LAPS,
DRIVE RIVETS
ONLY WHERE
PLANK HUGS
RIB

KNEES USED
AS SIDE AND
BOTTOM FRAMES

Stitch-in-Time
BOAT REPAIRS

WILL MAKE YOUR CRAFT LAST LONGER

WINTER storage or temporary laying up of a boat is an important period in its life. Mere shelter from the elements is not enough. To keep your boat in good condition, it is important to make small repairs before storing it, while they are still simple and easy to do.

Skiffs and heavily planked small boats usually stay in good condition with a minimum of care, as their stout hulls stand much abuse. Lack of care is likely to result in bothersome leaks rather than in a major failure. However, if such a boat is to be stored outdoors, protection should be given the bottom. Mark leaking spots while it is still in the water. Repairs should be made promptly after the boat is hauled out. While dirt is still damp and easily removed, wash the hull inside and out with a strong soap solution and a stiff broom. Scour off old paint to avoid building up successive layers that will eventually require burning off. If the paint or varnish is badly checked, remove it with a blowtorch or paint remover.

Block up the inverted hull at both ends and amidships above high water, and high enough off the ground to allow free circulation of air. Level the blocking to prevent warping of the hull. An old tarpaulin secured all around, waterproof roofing paper, or untreated canvas covered with closely laid board will afford protection from sun and wind that dry out planking, and keep out rain and melted snow that might run into seams and freeze in cold weather, causing splitting and buckling.

In buckled bottom boards, a common trouble in this type of boat, bore slightly undersized holes for long, flathead screws or galvanized boat nails, staggering the holes between old nails. Use two or three to an end. Be sure to drill sound wood, preferably hardwood of chines or transom liners. Clean out open joints, allow them to dry thoroughly, then work in white lead before refastening the planks. In extreme cases, work a very small amount of soft calking or absorbent cotton in with the paste.

Give special attention to the joints where the last bottom plank and the ends of the above-water planks fasten to the stern transom, as most skiffs leak there when fully loaded. If the transom and sides are unlined, shaped oak pieces should be fitted to give a better hold for plank fastenings. In a skiff with a hardwood keel, drive the fastenings through the planking into the hardwood. If there is no keel, fit one of ¾" by 4" oak to add stiffness.

Hard calking can do more harm than good. Never calk a dried-out boat. Let it swell; then mark leaking seams for attention. Calk the entire seam rather than the leaks only. If a leak is too small to warrant this, taper the ends of the calking, or new leaks may start

Laying deck canvas on the cabin of a 20' motorboat. The owner is filling the canvas with dilute cement before replacing the trim and painting three coats

at these points. Forcing twisted calking mixed with white lead or marine glue into a seam with a putty knife is satisfactory.

The hulls of lightly built boats often work loose and then leak. They can be stiffened by refastening, and by fitting new center seats or refastening old ones to tie the sides tighter. New gunwale strips or half-round, 2" stock, preferably oak, will stiffen the sides, especially if fastenings can be driven through from the inside. When an outboard motor is used, stern stiffness is important. A carefully fitted stern seat and properly shaped knees to tie the side and transom together will give that needed strength.

Light, smooth-planked boats, such as car-top models, require more care if they are to continue giving satisfaction. Winter care is important but should not be carried to extremes, such as storing the boat in a heated basement or other hot, dry room. Storage in an unheated garage or shed, or even in the open under a tarpaulin or boards closely laid over roofing paper, will prevent drying the wood too much. It is essential to block or support these lightly framed boats so as to distribute the weight equally.

Many boats with wide planking have their seams backed by battens for watertightness. If a leak has developed along such a seam, clean out any filler or dirt and work white lead into any large openings, and liquid marine glue thinned with alcohol or gasoline into smaller ones. Drive new fastenings from outside to pull the planking and batten together. As a last resort, tape the seam with muslin ironed over hard canoe glue.

Boats with narrow strip planking usually have the edges of the planking shaped for tighter seams. Nevertheless, permanent tightness depends on the wood not drying out too much. Both the outside and the inside of the boat must be kept well varnished or painted. In the case of a portable model likely to be out of water much of the time, protection from hot sun and drying winds is requisite. These boats are usually well built, but their light weight means lighter construction. Overloading, too fast running in rough water, or use of too powerful a motor will produce a strain, indicated by a tendency to weave or work while running. If allowed to continue, this will result in leaking. Refastening, especially of the ends of bottom and side planking to stem and transom, and along garboards near the keel, will help here too. Small brass screws are best for such repairs.

A common fault is stern weakness, offset by fitting an inner transom—not so much to be watertight in itself as to provide new wood into which to drive fastenings and to stiffen the original transom against motor vibration. It should be fastened inside the regular transom over heavy, wet paint or liquid marine glue.

Seats are important as cross members in lightly built hulls. Their ends should be tied in well with fore-and-aft stringers, and small knees fitted where possible. New floor boards can be fitted to strengthen a bottom having a tendency to work or weave, but they will add strength only when fastened to every frame or rib. The middle board should be left loose for sponging out.

Lapstreak or clinker-built boats, if stored outside, must be protected from rain water or melted snow that might freeze in the seams. As the overlapped planking adds hull stiffness, the frames are often widely spaced. This throws considerable strain on side fastenings, and they become loose.

Copper rivets sometimes stretch under such strain. Old fastenings along lapped edges should be looked to if there is any evidence of play or leaking. In some cases, copper rivets can be drawn up tighter. Have a helper hold an iron against the heads while you strike a small rivet set held against the plain ends of the shanks to tighten the burrs. When short strakes have been used and their ends fitted with scarf joints having sliver ends, a thin oak block behind the scarf with fastenings through the planking into the block will add strength.

Taking up on the original fastenings of round-bottom boats with planking fastened to light but closely spaced ribs will help restore such boats to their original stiffness. As ribs for boats of this type are steam bent, breaks may have developed where the bends are sharpest. A new bent rib may be fastened over a cracked one, with the old one left in place unless it is rotted.

RUSTIC GUN RACK
HAS INGENIOUS HIDDEN COMPARTMENT

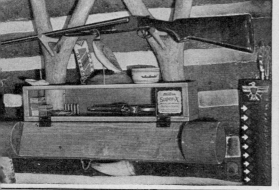

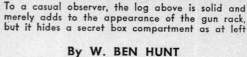

To a casual observer, the log above is solid and merely adds to the appearance of the gun rack, but it hides a secret box compartment as at left

By W. BEN HUNT

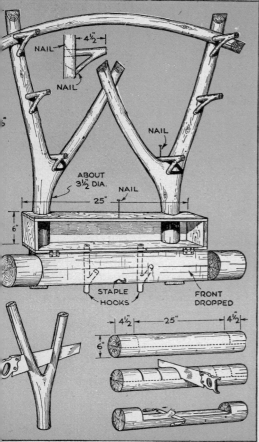

NAIL

4½"

NAIL

NAIL

ABOUT 3½ DIA.

NAIL

25"

6"

STAPLE HOOKS

FRONT DROPPED

4½" 25" 4½"

6"

SYMMETRY was achieved in this rustic rack by the simple process of sawing the large crotch in two lengthwise, as shown in the drawing. Remove the bark from all crotches as well as the log before sawing to be certain the wood is sound. The small crotches are fitted and nailed at a slight angle to keep guns from sliding off.

The log front is held closed by a nail with its head set flush in the shelf and extending down through the staple. The head of the nail is out of sight, yet can be lifted with the fingernail when a slight pressure is applied to the front of the log. Saw the log to the required dimensions, remove the wood with a wide chisel and drawknife, and trim the edges to make a neat fit with the box shelf.

If a dead crotch that is of the right size and will lie flat when cut is not to be had, use a green one that you can force flat. Let it dry in the required position, but be sure to shellac the end and inner crosscuts so as to prevent excessive checking.

Take care in driving all nails to avoid the danger of splitting the stock. It is wise to first drill holes slightly smaller than the nails to be used. The dimensions in the drawing may have to be altered to suit the size of wood used. After the rack is thoroughly dry, finish with stain and varnish.

Decorative Carving with

Free movement for feeding work is possible when the carving motor is mounted rigidly. Below, one hand steadied against the bench top, the little finger can be used as a spring feed control. At bottom, rough cutting with a pear-shaped tool; at right, detailing with a medium ball point

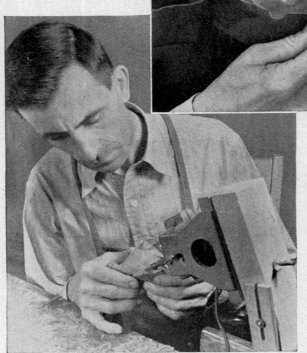

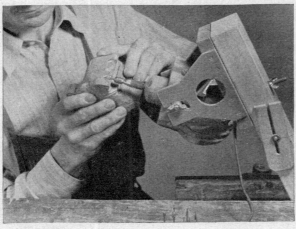

By Edwin M. Love

CARVING with a small motor or a flexible shaft is almost effortless, but extreme care must be exercised, for one false touch with a whirling cutter may mar wood or plastic irreparably. An advantage, however, is elimination of the propensity of hand gouges for splitting the wood, especially when coaxed across bad grain.

What cutters are needed for carving? Although many types are available, comparatively few are really required for most work. The carvings shown in the photographs were made with the five cutters illustrated in the drawing on the facing page. Three different sizes of ball cutters were used, ranging from 1/32" to ⅜" in diameter. Other special cutters will be convenient for certain details, but should be bought only as needed.

How is flat carving done? First, transfer the design to the wood with the aid of carbon paper. Bolt the motor mount to the standard. Rout the background, using a routing or cylindrical cutter and starting the initial operation in predrilled holes. Clamp the work securely; then carve down the various levels of the raised parts of the design with a large ball cutter. Adjust the depth of cuts by tilting the motor in its standard,

Miniature Power Tools

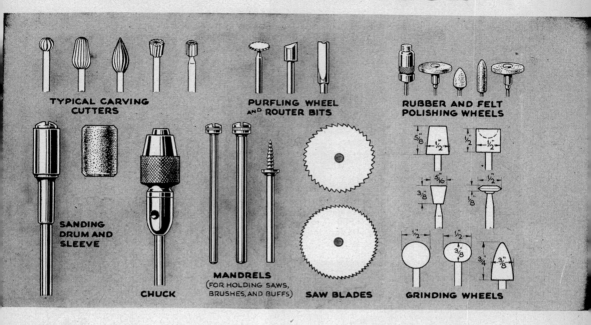

TYPICAL CARVING CUTTERS

PURFLING WHEEL AND ROUTER BITS

RUBBER AND FELT POLISHING WHEELS

SANDING DRUM AND SLEEVE

CHUCK

MANDRELS (FOR HOLDING SAWS, BRUSHES, AND BUFFS)

SAW BLADES

GRINDING WHEELS

and handle the instrument as shown in the photos on page HW 474. When all the levels are established, outline the details of the design with a ball cutter of suitable size. The depth is controlled by the motor mount, but it can be varied slightly by rocking the mount with the fingers of the left hand. After first roughing the work with large cutters, touch up the various details with appropriate smaller cutters.

A general rule for carving is to work uniformly over the whole piece. The future balance of the finished piece can best be judged by this method. Large cutters and long strokes give simplicity and unity of treatment. Radial or concentric lines, and gradual rather than abrupt changes of direction and scale, tend toward better balance.

Carvings done by hand are seldom smoothed with a file or sandpaper, as the carving gouges leave more interesting surfaces. Sometimes the background is stippled with a grounding punch, although the texture left by gouges is usually preferable. However, chisel marks do not appear in mechanical carvings, so a

sanded finish is justifiable, although even strokes of the cutter will produce pleasing textures to be left unsanded.

What is the method for block carving? Transfer the plan and elevation outlines of the design to the block and bandsaw it to shape. Saw the side elevation first, tack the waste pieces back in place, then saw the plan contour. Corners can be trimmed with a coping saw. Fasten the mount and motor

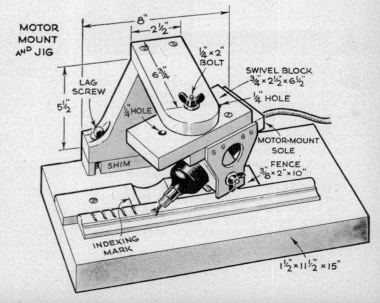

MOTOR MOUNT AND JIG

LAG SCREW

SWIVEL BLOCK 3/4" × 2 1/2" × 6 1/2"

1/4" × 2" BOLT

1/4" HOLE

MOTOR-MOUNT SOLE

FENCE 3/8" × 2" × 10"

SHIM

INDEXING MARK

1 1/2" × 11 1/2" × 15"

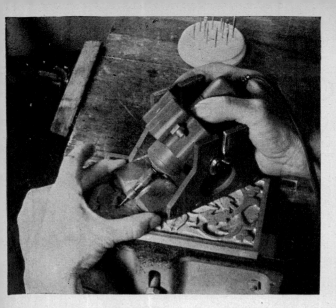

Delicate control of direction is maintained by thumb and finger, while constant depth is maintained by the mount. Rocking the mount slightly will vary the depth

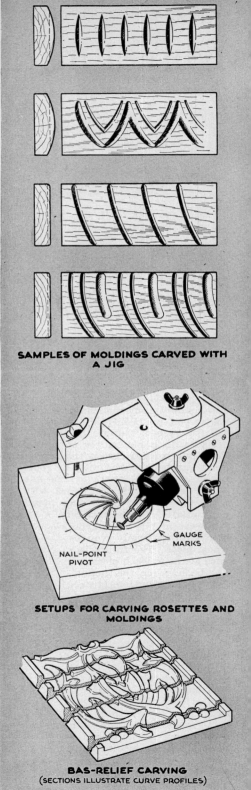

SAMPLES OF MOLDINGS CARVED WITH A JIG

GAUGE MARKS

NAIL-POINT PIVOT

SETUPS FOR CARVING ROSETTES AND MOLDINGS

BAS-RELIEF CARVING
(SECTIONS ILLUSTRATE CURVE PROFILES)

in a vise and round up the piece with a pear-shaped cutter. If the piece is bisymmetrical, one side can be carved first and then used as a guide for doing the other side.

How can moldings be carved? Build a motor mount and jig similar to the one shown in the drawing on page HW 473. In this mount, the motor can be swung from side to side, its arc of movement depending upon which hole the pivot bolt is fastened in and the position of the swivel block on the sole of the motor mount. The position of the fence governs the direction of the cut. The chord of the carving curve is at right angles across the molding when the lengthwise center line of the molding is directly under the pivot center. First make a starting cut; then move the molding forward the desired distance and mark the position of the first cut on the fence. Thereafter, each succeeding cut is moved to the mark and spacing is accurately maintained. The variety of molding carvings possible with this setup is practically unlimited.

Rosettes are carved with this jig by pivoting the blank on a sharpened nail set from underneath into the center of the blank. Radial lines can be brought to the center or else stopped short of the center to form a button.

Can polishing be done with small motors? Sanding drums are available for smoothing wood or plastic, and screw mandrels will hold small sanding and fiber disks and wire brushes. Felt wheels can be used with such polishing agents as tripoli and rouge. Rubber wheels of various shapes, impregnated with special compounds, are useful for removing fine scratches, as well as for polishing small metal and plastic parts.

How is grinding done? A large variety of abrasive wheels may be had for light grinding of surfaces. Such grinding is especially valuable on hardened steel that cannot be filed, and for working in corners and cavities impossible to reach with larger tools. Use light pressure with abrasive wheels, because if the motor slows appreciably, the wheels glaze, wear rapidly, and may mar the work.

Grinding wheels are made of different abrasives suitable for the particular kind of material to be ground. Ordinary aluminum oxide wheels are suitable for average grinding. Silicon carbide is used for materials of low tensile strength, and a pure aluminum oxide for such materials as high-speed steel.

Comical Figure of Baker Tops Off Novel Bread Server

GUESTS will smile when served with bread from this tray, for a jolly little baker stands guard on top of the stack.

Turn the base from a 9¼" maple or birch disk to the section shown. A felt disk cemented to the bottom will hide the holes left by the faceplate screws.

Draw the baker on ½" squares and jigsaw him from ¾" stock. Insert a bit of ¼" dowel for the nose. Color the face pink, the apron, cap, and collar white, the shirt blue, and the hair brown.

Cut the top from ⅝" stock. Paint the top surface white and the edges brown. To simulate bread texture, use a mallet to pound a piece of No. 2 sandpaper on the top after the paint dries. Brush off any loose paint.

Finish the turned tray and the underside of the top with clear lacquer or varnish.—FRANK HEGEMEYER.

Lift the little baker and the top slice comes off, for it is actually a piece of wood that prevents the stack of fresh bread beneath from drying out

At left, turning the crumb trough on the lathe. Transfer the jigsaw patterns by means of squares

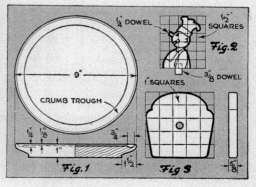

Compact Shining Kit Serves Service Men

SELECTED by a committee of four service men as a prize winner in a Service Men's Gift Contest conducted by POPULAR SCIENCE MONTHLY, this kit for shining shoes rightly lays claim to its ability to serve well.

The entire outfit is contained within a carved and hinged case measuring 1⅝" by 2¼" by 7½". One hinged half is shaped along the edges to fit the fingers; the other is left flat and is padded and covered with velvet or a piece of sheepskin with the wool outside to be used in shining. The unpadded section is carved inside to fit a dauber made from a 1" paint brush cut down to a total length of 2⅝".

A can of shoe polish fits into a carved recess of the lower section; it is allowed to protrude slightly at the sides. The curved top of the can fits neatly into a shallow recess which has been formed in the upper section of the kit.—AXEL E. OGREN.

Polish, dauber, and cloth "shine brush" are all contained in this neatly carved and hinged shoe kit designed for service men

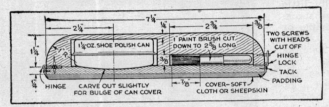

S-Shaped Metal Hook Locks Sea Bag and Acts as Handle

A SAILOR'S sea bag needs to be closed, locked, and carried just as does any other type of hand baggage. The device illustrated at the right does the complete job and, for that reason, was also one of the prize winners in the Service Men's Gift Contest.

The lower end of the hook is rounded to a dull point for ease in threading through the grommets on the top of the sea bag. A hole is drilled through the hook to take a padlock shackle that prevents the grommets from slipping over the end of the hook.

A roundhead rivet is fastened in a hole through the hook, as shown in the drawing, to keep the grommets from slipping past that point to the rest of the hook. When the lower portion of the hook is threaded through the grommets and locked, the upper part is the handle.—HARRY LIEBERMAN.

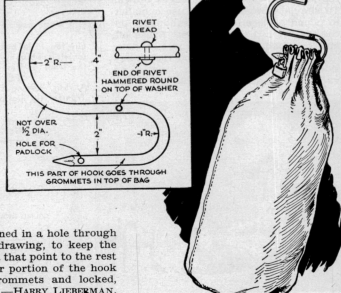

Rustic Garden Bridge Built from Small Logs and Saplings

A PICTURESQUE little bridge for an informal garden can easily be made of small logs and saplings. After selecting the spot for your bridge, brace the end posts with logs and rocks as suggested in the sketch. All the wood should be peeled and seasoned. Creosote the bottom ends of the posts and set them 24" into the ground. The rocks and cross logs hold them steady and add to the rustic effect of the bridge. Trim the arched stringers along their tops with an adze so that they will more readily support the floor.

The height of the handrails is about 24", while the width and length of the bridge is, of course, determined by the location chosen for it. Lag screws are used to hold logs and stringers in place.

It is best to drill the saplings which make up the floor of the bridge before attempting to nail them to the stringers.—H. S.

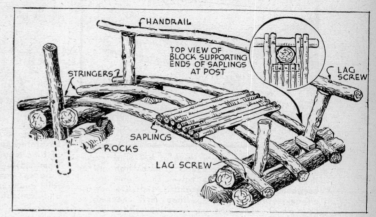

Walnut Shells Form Sprightly Turtles

AN INTERESTING and decorative novelty is a set of turtles varying in sizes and shapes. They are made of walnut shells, pipe cleaners, and short lengths of dowel. The shell is grooved with a rattail file for the legs, head, and tail. Legs are bent from pipe cleaners to the approximate shape shown, the length depending upon the size of the shell. A short length of the same material, bent to a hook shape inside the shell for firmer support, makes the tail.

The turtle's head is whittled from a piece of dowel. Cement all the parts into place, the head being tilted at a slight upward angle, and the legs bent to raise the body ¼". Cut a piece of cardboard to shape to seal the bottom of the shell.—EDWIN DREWITZ.

KEEPING THE HOME

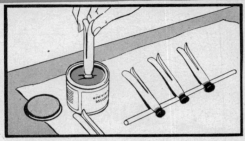

Clothespins that are used to hold dyed materials may transfer the stains to white clothes. If the heads of some pins are dipped in brightly colored enamel, they can easily be set apart for use with dyed wash. Colors also help prevent loss of pins

Pulling out threads when ripping machine stitching is tedious as well as a strain on your finger tips. A pair of household tweezers will allow you to do this with no fatigue and in a fraction of the time

OIL HERE

If a small gas leak on a stove or hot plate occurs at the valve, simply place a drop of light oil on the moving part of the valve. This forms a seal between the tapered plug and its seat. Do not use oil on a tank-gas stove without first checking to be sure it will cause no reaction with this gas

Knitting yarn that is to be stored for any length of time may be kept safe from moths by using old tobacco containers. The faint odor repels moths and does not damage yarn

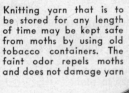

Heavy waxed-paper folding bags in which gelatin powder is sold make ideal leakproof containers for lunch-box pickles. Since the liquid does not evaporate, pickles remain fresh. Use of these bags for any juicy food stops the leakages that may flavor or make soggy the lunch-box contents

Wooden buttons may be protected from grime with a coat or two of colorless nail polish. This polish forms a hard lacquer finish that does not modify the underlying color of the buttons. Painting is done by using the applicator on the bottle cap

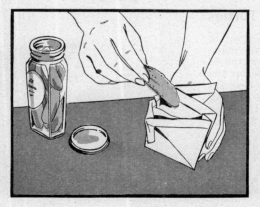

SHIPSHAPE

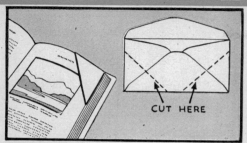

CUT HERE

Useful bookmarks can be easily made by cutting the corners off old envelopes. Such a bookmark can be slipped over a group of pages to block off obsolete data in reference books or catalogues. A strip of cellulose tape will help keep it on

If used in the oven, wooden knobs on pot covers will char and break off. Here is a repair that resists oven heat: Fasten a large glass bead to a pot lid, as shown at right, using a cotter pin to hold it

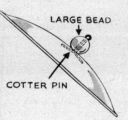

LARGE BEAD

COTTER PIN

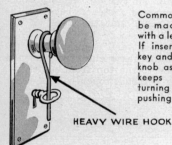

HEAVY WIRE HOOK

Common door locks can be made tamperproof with a length of stiff wire. If inserted through the key and hooked over the knob as shown, the wire keeps marauders from turning the key and pushing it through inside

If an electric plug is hard to pull out, rub both sides of the prongs with a soft-lead pencil. The graphite deposited on the contacts lubricates the parts and permits them to slide in and out easily. Carefully straighten prongs that are misaligned

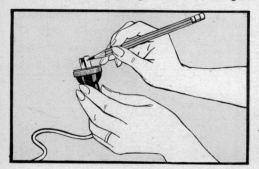

TRAY BOTTOM   RUBBER

Holes in hard-rubber articles such as photo trays can be "soldered" with inner-tube patching rubber. Cut it ¼" larger than the hole and melt it on the area, using an ordinary soldering iron. It will adhere tightly on a dry surface free of oil and rust. Talcum will neutralize surface tackiness

A satisfactory replacement for metal curtain rods and brackets can be made through the use of wood. Saw the brackets from ¾" stock and rout a curved recess in each bracket in order to hold the dowel that serves as the rod. Fasten with wood screws to the casing and finish to match the woodwork

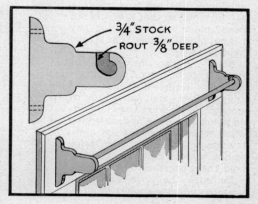

3/4" STOCK
ROUT 3/8" DEEP

SLIDING-DOOR WARDROBE DESIGNED FOR A CHILD'S ROOM

Bette Joan's wardrobe is just like a grownup's except that there are no hinged doors that might pinch her tiny fingers

AS FUNCTIONAL as it is good looking, this wardrobe cabinet will do much to teach a child the fundamentals of neatness. A special feature of it is the door, which slides upward into the top of the cabinet and cannot pinch little fingers. It is also an advantage where space is limited, since it does not swing out into the room.

Dimensions given in the drawing below can be varied according to the size and age of the child. The body of the wardrobe shown was made of ¼" plywood, flathead screws being driven through from the outside edges into quarter-round moldings at all the joints. All screws were slightly countersunk and the holes filled before finishing. The top was made of ½" plywood so that it would not bend under the weight of any heavy object placed on it and bind the door.

Slats for the door were cut from straight unwarped lattice material, rounded on all edges and corners, and sanded down smooth. They were then laid out on a level surface and weighted down with their edges not quite touching each other. Four strips of heavy cloth glued to the back hold them together.

Be sure the door groove is smooth and wide enough to allow

for easy movement. A coating of ordinary floor wax will make for free action. The drawer operates on two ½" square slides screwed to supports fastened between the front bottom panel and the back of the wardrobe.

Finish the cabinet and decorate it as desired. The child's name cut from ¼" plywood and glued to the top front panel will add a pleasing personal touch.—JACK GOSS.

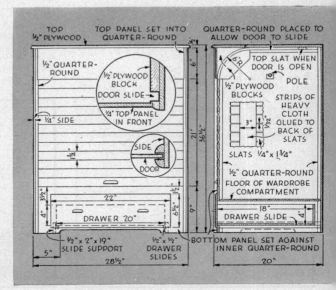

HOW TO SET UP WORK ON A
DIVIDING HEAD

FREQUENTLY the machinist must divide a circle into several parts, as in making a gear, reamer, jig, milling cutter, or similar part on which must be spaced teeth, cutting edges, or holes. Such work is usually done with a dividing head, an accessory mounted on the table of the milling machine that rotates the work through given angles to produce the number of divisions desired.

A dividing head consists of an indexing plate in which are several circles of evenly spaced holes, a crank with a pin that fits into these holes, and gearing that connects the crank to a spindle in a definite ratio, usually 1 to 40. Since the work is mounted on the spindle, one turn of the crank will rotate it 1/40 turn. To cut a 20-tooth gear, for example, the crank would be given two full turns after each cut to locate the next tooth. Thus 40 divided by the number of divisions required gives the number of turns or the fractional part of a turn to be made by the index crank each time.

When this formula does not yield a whole number of turns, but involves a fraction of a turn, the several circles of holes come into full play. A circle is used having a number of holes divisible by the number of divisions required. Thus, counting off 11 holes on the 66-hole circle enables the operator to turn the crank exactly 1/6 turn.

Besides the plain dividing head, which has a spindle that rotates about a horizontal axis, there is the universal dividing head, the spindle of which can be tilted vertically to rotate at various angles, and the helical dividing head. The spindle of the latter can be connected to the lead screw of the milling-machine table, so that the work may be rotated in a fixed ratio to the table movement for milling the flutes of twist drills and the like.

Photographs on the following pages show how a typical job—a blank for a 36-tooth gear—is set up, and how the dividing head is used to space the teeth correctly. These photographs were made from a sound film prepared by the U. S. Office of Education and distributed by Castle Films for training war machinists in school and shop classes.

MACHINISTS FOR WAR WORK

1 Above is a typical setup involving the use of a dividing head. A 36-tooth gear is to be milled from a machined blank. The various steps in setting up the work are explained in the photos that follow

2 Both the dividing head and its tailstock are bolted to the center slot of the table, which is run in close to the column to permit mounting the cutter on a short arbor for maximum rigidity

3 A handbook specifies a No. 3 cutter for gears of from 35 to 54 teeth. Arbor collars used in mounting it must be scrupulously clean; dirt will throw it out of alignment. The cutter is keyed fast

4 With the overarm and outer arbor support locked, the table is traversed until the dividing-head center coincides with a center line on the cutter teeth, and the traverse is locked in this position

5 To cut teeth of uniform depth from end to end, the gear blank must be parallel to the table. Therefore the tailstock center must be adjusted to exactly the same height as the headstock center

6 As spur-gear teeth must be cut parallel to the gear axis, the work mandrel must be parallel to the table feed. Hence both centers are aligned horizontally to a zero mark on the tailstock scale

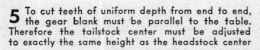

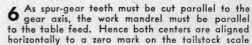

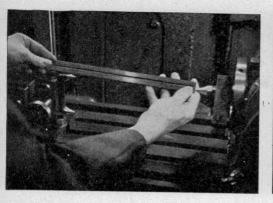

7 The tailstock is backed off a distance equal to the length of the mandrel and bolted fast. Its center can be advanced or retracted like that of a lathe tailstock to permit inserting the work

8 Rebolting the tailstock tighter or looser than it was in its first position may affect its vertical alignment. This is therefore rechecked against the headstock center with a surface gauge

9 A splined sleeve, split lengthwise, is inserted and centered in the bore of the gear blank. As a tapered mandrel is driven into this with a lead hammer, the sleeve expands to grip the blank fast

10 On the larger end of the mandrel, which goes toward the headstock, is bolted a dog. This is held tightly against the driver slot on the spindle by a setscrew to eliminate all backlash

11 The thrust of the cutter, being toward the big end of the mandrel, will only wedge the work tighter. If the thrust were toward the small end, it would loosen the gear blank and spoil the job

12 As the gear ratio of the dividing head is 1 to 40, dividing 40 by the number of teeth to be cut—36—will give 1 1/9 turns as the distance the crank must be rotated for each tooth *(continued)*

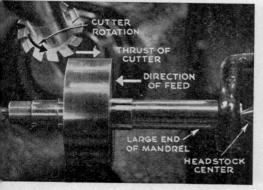

CUTTER
ROTATION

THRUST OF
CUTTER

DIRECTION
OF FEED

LARGE END
OF MANDREL

HEADSTOCK
CENTER

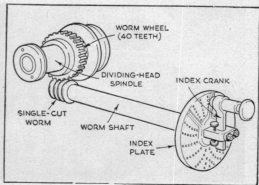

WORM WHEEL
(40 TEETH)

DIVIDING-HEAD
SPINDLE

INDEX CRANK

SINGLE-CUT
WORM

WORM SHAFT

INDEX
PLATE

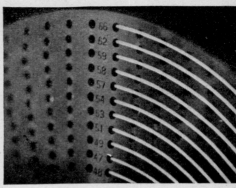

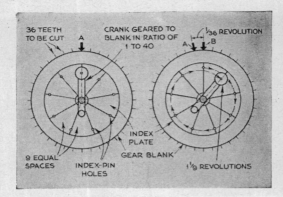

13 Our 36-tooth gear could be cut readily with a nine-space index plate, shown superimposed on the gear in the drawings above. After cutting tooth A as at the left, we would revolve the crank one complete turn plus one division to cut tooth B

14 Instead of nine parts, the index plate has a series of circles on which various numbers o holes are evenly spaced. Each is marked with th number. The 1/9 turn needed can be indexed on an circle having a number of holes divisible by nin

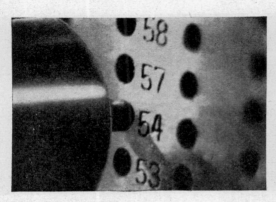

15 In this plate, it is the 54-hole circle that fulfills this condition. The crank handle is adjusted radially until its pin falls into a hole in this circle, and is then locked at this setting

16 Dividing 54 by nine gives six. One sector arm is therefore set up against the crankpin, an the other arm is set flush with the far edge of hole six holes away, not counting the first hol

17 Locked together, both arms can swivel about, always the same distance apart. As each tooth is cut, the crank is turned one revolution and far enough beyond to bring it against the second arm

18 The sector is then swung down against the pi ready for indexing the next tooth. All 36 cut are very lightly nicked. If the first one indexe accurately the second time, the setup is correc

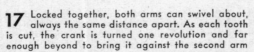

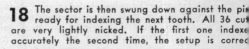

NEW SHOP IDEAS

How the headstock-center knockout bar looks when assembled

A KNOCKOUT BAR for removing the headstock center from your lathe can be turned in the lathe from odd pieces of scrap steel. The drawing and photographs show a bar of a size useful for popular 9" and 10" lathes. The handle projects a few inches beyond the headstock and is knurled for an easy grip, with a turned ornament that adds to the appearance and provides a smooth, rounded end.

The bar is made in two parts, handle and bushing, with the bushing drilled for a tight fit on the handle and, after the two are assembled, drilled again across the diameter for a pin to hold the two pieces firmly together. The bushing is turned to size for an easy fit in the spindle, and a pin is turned on the end of the bushing. With this arrangement both the center and the reducing sleeve can be removed without damage. After the pin takes out the center, another tap causes the bushing to knock out the sleeve, if one is used. The tapered spindle should always be

Drilling the bushing and bar for a pin to lock them rigidly

To knurl, chuck the work and steady it with the tailstock

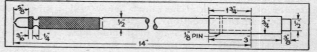

All dimensions for the knockout bar are shown in the drawing

kept clean. Before replacing the center, be sure no dirt particles or chips remain inside, since they may score the spindle and keep it from running true.—C. W. W.

WASHERS AS RADIUS GAUGES solved one machinist's tool-priority problem. Unable to obtain a radius gauge, he turned washers to various sizes to gauge the radii of shaft fillets and other machined parts. For example, a radius of ½" can be gauged with a washer of 1" diameter.—RONALD EYRICH.

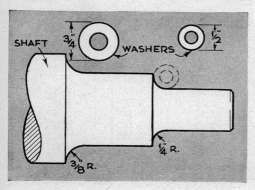

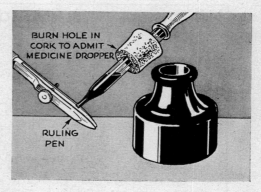

BURN HOLE IN CORK TO ADMIT MEDICINE DROPPER

RULING PEN

RULING PENS CAN BE FILLED from a medicine dropper with more accurate control over the amount of ink than the conventional quill allows. Mounted in a stopper cut to fit the bottle, the dropper can be pushed down as the ink level falls.—R. E.

Centering Work for

By C. W. WOODSON

ACCURATELY located and drilled center holes are required in both ends of work that is to be held between centers in the lathe. Precision in this respect is especially important when several pieces of the same kind are to be machined. These holes, which serve as bearing points for the lathe centers, may be laid out in any of several ways, and they can be drilled in the lathe itself if a centering machine is not available.

When several pieces are to be machined to identical dimensions with the same tool or carriage-stop settings, all the center holes must be drilled and countersunk to the same diameter. When the centerdrilled work is being mounted between the lathe centers, the countersunk holes must be kept free of dirt and chips to assure accurate centering, and the tailstock center must be oiled well to lessen friction.

There is no standard size for center holes, but judgment must be exercised in keeping them reasonably proportionate to the diameter of the work. The chart below will be a help in this direction. It gives several accepted dimensions for the drill, hole, and countersink that have proved to be satisfactory for work of various diameters. One dimension that must be followed precisely, however, is that of the angle of the countersink, which should be 60 deg. for a perfect fit with the lathe center.

Center holes may be located quickly and accurately on round stock with a centerhead and scriber, following the method shown at A in the drawings at the upper right of the facing page. A mark is scribed along the side of the blade held against the end of the stock; then a quarter turn is made with the square, and another mark is scribed at right angles to the first. The intersection of these two lines will indicate the exact point for prick-punching and centerdrilling.

A quick and convenient method of locating the center of stock of any shape is with hermaphrodite calipers, as indicated at B in the drawings. The calipers can be set at half the diameter of the stock or slightly over or under that dimension. This will provide either a point of intersection that will be the center of the piece or several marks that will enclose the center point, as shown in the drawings.

In using a centerpunch, place it accurately on the center you have laid out, as at the left at C, and strike it a sharp blow with the hammer, driving it down far enough to make a hole that will permit the work to be lightly supported between the lathe centers. Revolve the piece in the lathe with one hand, testing for trueness with a piece of chalk. If the chalk marks show high spots, drifting with the centerpunch will draw the hole over to one side. This is done by placing the punch at an angle, as at the right at C, and driving it toward the high side of the

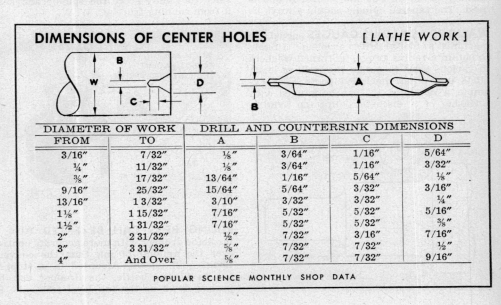

DIMENSIONS OF CENTER HOLES   [LATHE WORK]

DIAMETER OF WORK		DRILL AND COUNTERSINK DIMENSIONS			
FROM	TO	A	B	C	D
3/16"	7/32"	⅛"	3/64"	1/16"	5/64"
¼"	11/32"	⅛"	3/64"	1/16"	3/32"
⅜"	17/32"	13/64"	1/16"	5/64"	⅛"
9/16"	25/32"	15/64"	5/64"	3/32"	3/16"
13/16"	1 3/32"	3/10"	3/32"	3/32"	¼"
1⅛"	1 15/32"	7/16"	5/32"	5/32"	5/16"
1½"	1 31/32"	7/16"	5/32"	5/32"	⅜"
2"	2 31/32"	½"	7/32"	3/16"	7/16"
3"	3 31/32"	⅝"	7/32"	7/32"	½"
4"	And Over	⅝"	7/32"	7/32"	9/16"

POPULAR SCIENCE MONTHLY SHOP DATA

the Lathe

work. The punch is then held vertically and driven in with the hammer to square the sides of the hole, after which the work should be tested again.

A bell centerpunch is convenient for centering a number of small cylindrical pieces. The cup is placed over the squared end of the work as at *D*, automatically locating the punch at the center. It must be held accurately in line with the work, however, or the punch will not be centered properly. Likewise, it cannot be used when the end of the work is cut at an angle.

Punched center holes may be drilled with a combination drill and countersink chucked in the lathe. The work is placed against the tailstock center and held with the left hand while being fed to the drill with the right, as shown at *E* in the drawings. When the hole has been drilled to the proper depth, the work is reversed and the other end drilled. Time can be saved and the countersinking will be sure to be concentric with the hole if a combined drill and countersink (at left at *E*) is used, while the bell-type centerdrill with a double-angle countersink (*E* right) may be used in centerdrilling mandrels and boring bars to reduce the danger of chatter or eccentric work caused by bruising the edge of the center hole.

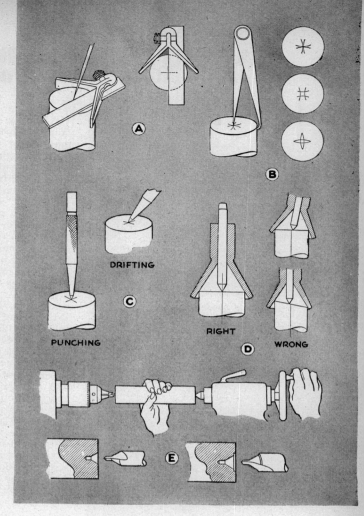

GOOD AND BAD CENTER HOLES   [LATHE WORK]

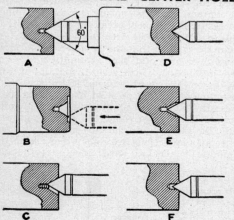

Lathe centers are made to the standard angle of 60 deg., and the countersunk or tapered portion of all center holes must have the same angle for a perfect fit, as shown at **A**.

The type of center hole at **B** is best for mandrels, boring bars, and other tools that are used between centers. The rounded edge keeps the point of the lathe center from striking and burring the edge, and the recess in the end prevents bruising of the hole.

The drawing **C** shows a well-formed center hole rendered useless by failure to remove chips from the hole. Under this condition, accurate work is not possible, and the point of the lathe center will soon wear badly.

At **D** the angle of countersink is too large, and there is no hole to keep the point from receiving all of the bearing pressure. Besides the danger of ruining the lathe center, accurate work is impossible.

A piece of work in which the countersunk hole has been drilled too deep, allowing only the outer edge to rest on the lathe center, is shown at **E**. This will score the lathe center, and accurate work will also be impossible.

The work at **F** has been drilled but not countersunk—bad practice that will cause the lathe center point to heat and wear rapidly.

MAGNETIZER and DEMAGNETIZER
Is Easily Built from Old Loudspeaker Coil

By WALTER E. BURTON

The photograph above shows the first step in making the magnetizer-demagnetizer. The core of a disassembled loudspeaker coil is driven out, leaving a hole 1½" in diameter

A fiber or sheet-metal strip anchors the coil to a base. Note the plug that short-circuits the socket and energizes the coil when pressed

Below, the unit being used to demagnetize a screwdriver. The switch is held down so that current flows steadily, and the tool withdrawn

A SIMPLE magnetizer and demagnetizer operating from a standard 115-volt A.C. line will make strong magnets of files, screwdrivers, hammer heads, and other tools in which magnetic properties are desirable. As a demagnetizer, it will erase all traces of magnetism from lathe bits and other tools that sometimes become magnetized and pick up steel chips.

The unit consists of a solenoid, or a hollow coil of wire, and a momentary-contact switch to control the current. For the unit shown, the 6-volt field coil from an old electrodynamic radio speaker was used without the iron core, which was driven out. Any coil that draws no more than 5 or 6 amp. on the 115-volt line and is of wire heavy enough to carry this current for 30 seconds will do. In testing such a coil, connect it in series with a 10-amp. fuse or an electric iron or heater to avoid blowing the line fuses.

If no coil is available, you can wind your own solenoid with salvaged magnet wire. A satisfactory one can be made of No. 18 enameled copper wire wound in a coil 2⅜" long and 1" deep on a thin-walled fiber tube 1½" in diameter.

A momentary-contact switch that closes the circuit only when depressed is required, as the coil must be energized only 1/120 second—for half a cycle of the 60-cycle current—to magnetize a piece of steel, and only a few seconds to demagnetize one.

To make this switch, cut a piece of broomstick to fit easily inside a surface-mounting lamp socket and to protrude about ½" above the socket. Bend a ½" strip of copper or brass around one end, forcing the ends of the strip into slots in the wood. This will short-circuit the contacts when inserted in the socket.

To the projecting end of the plug, fasten a disk of plastic or wood, or a nonmetallic bottle cap. Slip a short compression spring over the plug against the head. Insert the plug so that the spring rests on the insulated top of the socket. Pressure downward makes contact, and the spring forces the plug up when pressure is released, breaking the contact. Connect this switch in series with the solenoid.

Anchor the coil, so that the hole is horizontal, with a strip of fiber or metal bent around it and screwed fast to a baseboard. If the strip is metal, put a layer of asbestos or cardboard between it and the coil.

To magnetize a piece of steel, insert it in the coil and press the button. A single, swift tap is enough. To demagnetize a tool, hold the button down and draw out the piece while the current is still flowing.

Be sure all connections are soldered or clamped and all terminals, joints, and wires adequately insulated

Contacts are closed in the improvised switch at right when a wooden plug with a metal tip is depressed. A light spring otherwise keeps the plug out of contact

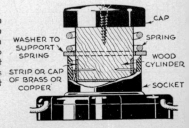

CAP
SPRING
WOOD CYLINDER
SOCKET
WASHER TO SUPPORT SPRING
STRIP OR CAP OF BRASS OR COPPER

ELECTRONIC NAVIGATOR

Guides Ferryboats Through Fog

Launches serving WABC's big island transmitter are guided through fog by the electronic device above. Its coil, located in the bow, is shown below on a table with the amplifier

Current is induced in the electronic-navigator coil by the magnetic flux around power cables under the water

WHEN station WABC, of the Columbia Broadcasting System, erected its 50,000-watt transmitter a few years ago on a tiny island in Long Island Sound a mile off New Rochelle, N. Y., a ferry service was inaugurated for engineers and other members of the staff.

During certain months of the year, however, service was affected when the island and mainland became totally obscured by dense fogs of long duration. In order to insure safe navigation during these periods, CBS engineers devised an electronic navigator to guide the boats by following the power cables under the water.

The flux lines of the magnetic field surrounding the cable induce a current in a specially built coil encased in a wooden box in the bow of the boat. A portable amplifier with a voltage gain of 86 decibels steps up the current gain from the loop, and the output is fed to a volume-indicator meter used as a course indicator. The amplifier is adjusted so that, when the boat is directly over the cable, a maximum deflection of the needle is shown on the meter.

The system is really an induction device basically similar to experiments that perhaps many readers of POPULAR SCIENCE have tried with headphones, microphones, and large loops.

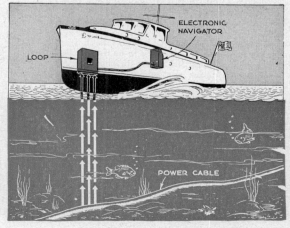

ELECTRONIC NAVIGATOR

LOOP

POWER CABLE

Giant mercury-vapor rectifier tubes, above, supply 500,000 watts to the transmitter of radio station WLW

FIRST STEPS IN ELECTRONICS

Putting Diode Tubes to Work

By JOHN W. CAMPBELL, JR.

MORE than 100 horsepower of electrical energy—1 amp. at 100,000 volts—flows into the giant industrial X-ray tube that spots defects in heavy steel castings. Possibly in the same plant there is an "electric eye," or phototube, that gauges the color of incandescent metal in a Bessemer converter and signals when the blast must be shut off. This tiny diode may draw a current of five millionths of an ampere at 85 volts. Yet both these electronic tubes may be energized from a standard 110-volt or 220-volt A.C. line.

This is possible because A.C. of any given voltage can readily be converted to a higher or a lower voltage by means of a transformer. Typical of the flexibility of A.C. is your radio power-supply transformer, which from the 110-volt line supplies 5 volts for the rectifier-tube filament, 6.3 volts for amplifier-tube heaters, and perhaps 350 volts for plate current.

However, since electrons in electronic tubes can pass only in one direction, such tubes are essentially direct-current devices. Therefore, once A.C. has been converted to the voltage required, it must in most cases be rectified—changed to direct current. We have seen that the electronic tube itself is fundamentally a rectifier. If A.C. is applied to the cathode, the tube will pass current only on that half of each cycle when the cathode is negative. Why not, then, use a special tube to turn A.C. into D.C. for use in the rest of the circuit? This is precisely what is done in A.C. radios and a host of other electronic devices.

The simplest of all rectifier circuits is shown in Fig. 1 on page HW 492 and at *A* in the drawings. This "half-wave" rectifier converts A.C. to D.C. by cutting off one half of the A.C. cycle and passing only the other half, during which current flows in only one direction. In the setup shown in the photograph, a 117Z6-GT tube was used, only one of its two rectifying units being connected.

As the heater of this tube can be connected directly across the line, no filament transformer is needed. If another tube is used, the heater must be connected to trans-

former taps giving the correct voltage. All heater connections are omitted in the diagrams for the sake of clarity.

The output of this half-wave rectifier is 60 pulses of direct current per second, as evidenced by the rapid flickering of an argon bulb connected to it. Such D.C. is perfectly satisfactory in many applications, but for others its pulsations must be smoothed out.

The simplest answer is an 8 to 40-mfd. condenser across the output terminals, as in Fig. 2 and in diagram *B*. The condenser acts as a tiny reservoir, storing current on each impulse, discharging between pulses, and so supplying current when the tube does not. However, the voltage on its plates must drop a little between charges. Although the output current will no longer be discontinuous (unless the condenser is very small or

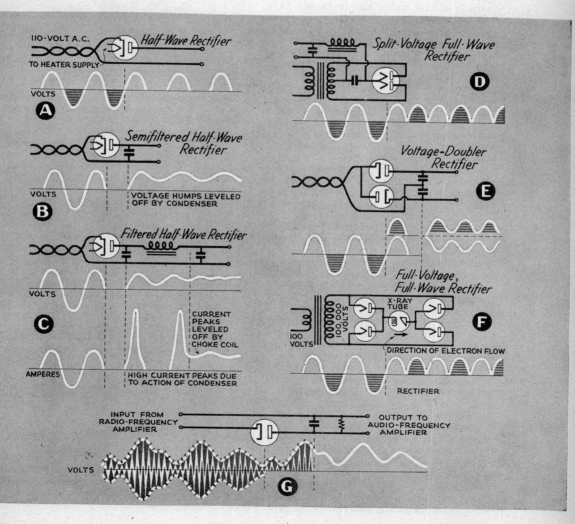

the load very heavy) there will be ripples in the voltage, and consequently in the current. The bigger the condenser and the smaller the load, the less ripple will result.

With the condenser, the argon lamp no longer flickers appreciably. But let us connect a loudspeaker in parallel with the lamp, putting a 2,000-ohm resistor in series with the speaker to avoid overloading the circuit. Being much more sensitive to current irregularities than the lamp, the speaker hums strongly.

Good radio sets have a ripple of about .25 percent—¾ volt in a 300-volt output. The resulting hum is so slight as to be imperceptible. This filtering could be achieved with the circuit of Fig. 2 if the condenser were large enough. But there is a limit to its size in theory as well as in practice.

A 1,000-mfd. condenser, if available, could not be attached to any ordinary rectifier tube without disastrous results. Any discharged condenser offers practically no resistance to the first surge of current; only when the potential on its plates builds up is there any limit to the rate at which current can flow into it. A 1,000-mfd. condenser would act as a dead short-circuit across the tube for a fraction of a second, with the inevitable result that the tube would be ruined.

But we can solve the problem, as shown in Fig. 3 and at C in the drawings, by using two condensers with a choke coil (an inductance) between them. A condenser will draw 1,000 amperes for a millionth of a second and then stop; an inductance has very different ideas. When current increases, the inductance converts the extra energy into magnetic lines of force and chokes off the surge. When current decreases, the lines collapse and augment the current flow. Thus the choke coil holds the current draw of the condensers to a more reasonable value. Furthermore, its storage and discharge of energy also tends to smooth out current ripples.

So far, we have used only one half of the alternating current, getting 60 pulses per second. If we can invert the other half of the cycle somehow, we will get 120 pulses a second and much smoother power. Figure 4 shows how this full-wave rectification can be obtained. Two diodes are needed, but most rectifier tubes of this type have two diode elements—usually two plates with a common cathode, as in drawing D. The 80, 82, and 83 are such types. The 117Z6-GT has two plates and also two cathodes,

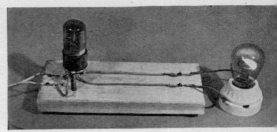

Fig. 1. Only one plate of the argon bulb glows, but with a perceptible flicker, showing that the output although D.C., consists of separate current pulse

Fig. 2. A condenser across the output eliminates the flicker. If a speaker is connected, however, a loud hum tells that current fluctuation is still prese

Fig. 3. The speaker is silent when two condensers ar a choke are used, but the bulb shows current flowin

Fig. 4. A double-diode tube connected to give 2 volts. Resistances protect the bulb and the speak

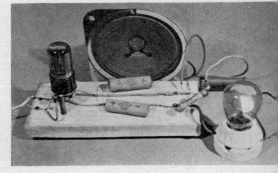

thus permitting it to be used as a full-wave rectifier and also as a voltage-doubler, a different type of full-wave rectifier shown at E.

This voltage-doubler, used in compact radio sets, eliminates the need for a transformer yet produces about 250 volts of plate supply at 120 power impulses a second. The two halves of the A.C. wave are fed to separate condensers, but instead of being in parallel, the two condensers are in series. Since each one is charged to the peak of the A.C. voltage, the resultant is twice this peak voltage. But "110 volts" of A.C. means an *average* value of 110 volts. Between the wave peaks the voltage is zero, and much of the time it is below 50 volts, but the peak value of ordinary household current is 156 volts.

With no load drawn from them, the condensers in diagram E would charge up to the highest voltage given by the rectifiers—156 volts each, minus a little because of voltage drop in the tubes. The result is that the output of the two condensers is 250 to 300 volts. A 10,000-ohm resistance should be used in series with the argon bulb, and one of 25,000 ohms in series with the speaker.

At F in the drawings is a four-diode grid system for full-wave rectification. Remembering that electrons can pass only from cathode to plate, you will see that the current will always flow in the same direction through the load, which is shown as an X-ray tube.

Diagram G shows another interesting half-wave rectifier-filter circuit. This is the same circuit as at B, with a resistance across the output leads. But whereas a condenser of 20 mfd. might be used in B to smooth the current, in G one of a fraction of a microfarad would be used—a condenser so small that the charge on it would be drained out through the resistance in .0001 second. It wouldn't filter out 60-cycle or even 10,000-cycle hum at all, but it is big enough to smooth out perfectly the hum of a 600,000-cycle radio carrier wave. Its output will be free of radio-frequency oscillations, yet will pass on all the audible, lower-frequency signals—voice or music—which were impressed upon the carrier wave in the form of amplitude modulation at the transmitter.

Heavy-Duty Plate-Current Supply for Electronic Experiments

YOU will need a source of rectified plate current for further experiments with electronic tubes. If the old radio you dismantled had a power transformer, this can be used. Shown below is a 350-volt, full-wave rectifier unit using a type 83 mercury-vapor tube, the two plates of which are connected as in diagram D on page HW 491.

Note that the 350-volt secondary winding of the transformer must have a center tap for this hookup, which requires three leads.

This power supply will prove useful in later experiments. If you have no transformer, assemble the circuit shown in Fig. 3

In the photograph, these appear at the extreme right of the transformer. To the left of these are the 5-volt leads which go to the twin filament-cathode, and at the extreme left are the two black primary leads. The tube will carry 225 milliamperes continuously and overloads of 1,000 milliamperes momentarily. Two 16-mfd., 450-volt condensers are used with an ordinary filter choke. The filtered 350-volt output causes no hum on the speaker, but the argon lamp shows that rectified current is flowing. Resistors of 10,000 ohms and 25,000 ohms are used in series with the bulb and speaker respectively.

Never connect this or any other rectifier to the line without a load such as an argon bulb or a 25,000-ohm resistor across the output, as damage to the condensers may otherwise result.

If the tubes you have on hand are not the type mentioned, consult a radio handbook or a manual such as is published by tube manufacturers for others that may be used—the 5Y3-G, 5Y4-G, 5U4-G, 80, and 82 are a few of them. Such receiving-tube manuals include diagrams showing socket connections for various tubes. Consequently they are useful additions to the reference library which every experimenter should have.

radio ideas

CERAMIC BATTERY CASES are replacing those formerly made of rubber for industrial, public-utility, emergency-transmitter, and telephone service. Four clays are blended to produce this vitrified ceramic, which is acidproof, is easy to keep clean, and can be heated to 212 deg. F. and plunged into ice water without contraction. Cases made of the material may be used safely next to other electrical equipment. Since their predominant color is white, they also help to brighten a dark battery room and make a contribution to easier servicing.

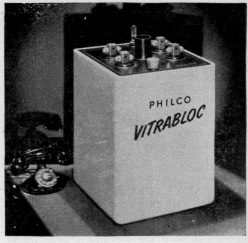

TRANSPARENT PLASTIC COVERS are being supplied to the U. S. Army Signal Corps to prevent dust particles from collecting between the closely spaced plates of small variable condensers required in radio field equipment. The covers are rigid and look something like the transparent containers employed by many manufacturers before the war in the packaging of their products. They are made of a sturdy cellulose acetate material, each being fabricated from a single sheet. When fitted over a condenser, as shown at left, a cover becomes virtually an integral part, often preventing a breakdown of equipment in dusty, sandy areas.

LOCKING A RADIO DIAL in a set position in order to keep it from slipping or jolting out of tune is simple with the new device shown below. This lock is mounted on the panel next to the tuning or tank-condenser dial, and the thumbscrew can be turned down tight without changing the dial setting.

ADJUSTABLE PANEL LIGHTING where variable intensities are required under constantly changing conditions, such as are met in military and aircraft usage, is possible with the new radio panel lamp shown above. Rotation of the shutter permits a gradation of light from full brightness to complete darkness. The lamp is available with a red, green, amber, blue, or opal lens, and also with a polarized lens.

Servicing Your Radio

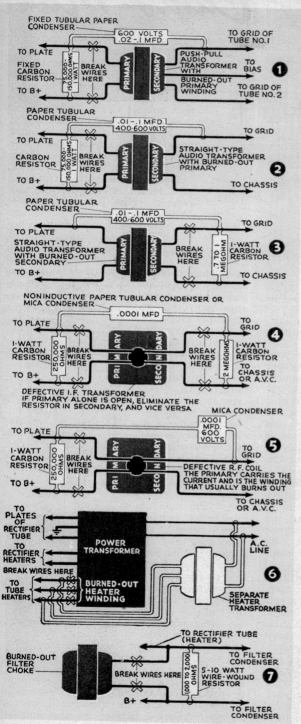

FIXED TUBULAR PAPER CONDENSER
600 VOLTS .02 - .1 MFD
TO GRID OF TUBE NO. 1
TO PLATE
FIXED CARBON RESISTOR
75,000 - 150,000 1 WATT
BREAK WIRES HERE
PUSH-PULL AUDIO TRANSFORMER WITH BURNED-OUT PRIMARY WINDING
TO BIAS
TO GRID OF TUBE NO. 2
TO B+ ❶

PAPER TUBULAR CONDENSER
.01 - .1 MFD. 400-600 VOLTS
TO GRID
TO PLATE
CARBON RESISTOR
75,000 - 150,000 OHMS 1 WATT
BREAK WIRES HERE
STRAIGHT-TYPE AUDIO TRANSFORMER WITH BURNED-OUT PRIMARY
TO B+
TO CHASSIS ❷

PAPER TUBULAR CONDENSER
.01 - .1 MFD 400-600 VOLTS
TO GRID
TO PLATE
STRAIGHT-TYPE AUDIO TRANSFORMER WITH BURNED-OUT SECONDARY
BREAK WIRES HERE
.7 TO 1 MEGOHM
1-WATT CARBON RESISTOR ❸
TO B+
TO CHASSIS

NONINDUCTIVE PAPER TUBULAR CONDENSER OR MICA CONDENSER
.0001 MFD
TO PLATE
TO GRID
1-WATT CARBON RESISTOR
250,000 OHMS
BREAK WIRES HERE
BREAK WIRES HERE
2 MEGOHM
1-WATT CARBON RESISTOR
TO CHASSIS OR A.V.C. ❹
TO B+
DEFECTIVE I.F. TRANSFORMER
IF PRIMARY ALONE IS OPEN, ELIMINATE THE RESISTOR IN SECONDARY, AND VICE VERSA

MICA CONDENSER
.0001 MFD. 600 VOLTS
TO PLATE
TO GRID
1-WATT CARBON RESISTOR
250,000 OHMS
BREAK WIRES HERE
DEFECTIVE R.F. COIL
THE PRIMARY CARRIES THE CURRENT AND IS THE WINDING THAT USUALLY BURNS OUT ❺
TO B+
TO CHASSIS OR A.V.C.

TO PLATES OF RECTIFIER TUBE
TO RECTIFIER HEATERS
BREAK WIRES HERE
POWER TRANSFORMER
A.C. LINE
TO TUBE HEATERS
BURNED-OUT HEATER WINDING
SEPARATE HEATER TRANSFORMER ❻

TO RECTIFIER TUBE (HEATER)
TO FILTER CONDENSER
BURNED-OUT FILTER CHOKE
BREAK WIRES HERE
1,000 TO 2,000 OHMS
5-10 WATT WIRE-WOUND RESISTOR ❼
B+
TO FILTER CONDENSER

BURNED-OUT or damaged parts of a radio receiver can often be put back into service without making an actual repair or replacement should either prove temporarily impracticable. This is especially true of such parts as chokes, power transformers, audio transformers, and coils.

You can often use the damaged part itself as a repair if a section of it is still good; if it is not, a simple change in the circuit sometimes will enables you to do without the part. In the latter instance the over-all sensitivity or power might be slightly impaired, but this will not be enough to keep the receiver from being used.

In audio transformers — both push-pull and straight types — it is usually the primary winding that becomes defective. Simply disconnect this winding and replace it with a condenser-and-resistor network, as shown in Figs. 1 and 2. The value of the resistor will depend on the plate impedance of the tube. If the tube is a low-impedance triode, a 50,000 to 75,000-ohm, 1-watt resistor is generally employed; if it is a high-impedance triode, a 100,000 to 150,000-ohm, 1-watt resistor is best. Low notes are improved by using a high-capacity coupling condenser, but it is best to experiment in order to get the best tone value.

A damaged secondary of an audio transformer is similarly replaced (Fig. 3), but the value of the resistor must be much higher — 750,000 ohms to 1 megohm.

It is possible to eliminate a damaged stage of a receiver having two or more stages of I.F. or R.F. amplification by changing the circuit so that the stage is resistance or impedance coupled, as in Figs. 4 and 5. Volume will, of course, be reduced, but not enough to prevent satisfactory reception of local stations.

Should the heater winding in a power transformer burn out, a separate 2.5-volt or 6.3-volt heater transformer can be inserted in place of the defective section, as in Fig. 6, and the rest of the transformer used as before. A burned-out filter choke can always be replaced by the simple resistor circuit shown in Fig. 7.

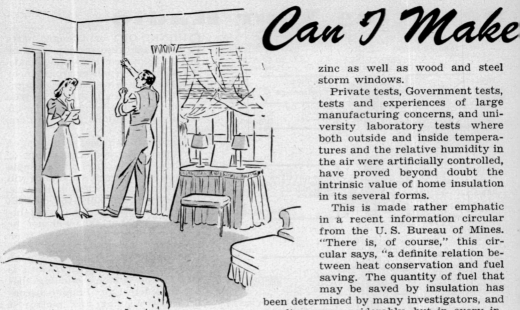

Figure it out for yourself by the square-foot method

By J. HAROLD HAWKINS
Author of *Your House*

IF THE average heating period for your home is seven months a year, with proper insulation you may save up to four months on your fuel bill each winter. This is important information—doubly important now because of the shortage of both fuel oil and coal. But this estimate of your saving must presuppose that you are going to do a thorough job of insulation—not leave cracks at doors, windows, and baseboards for the entrance of cold drafts.

The term insulation, as applied to homes during these times of widespread restrictions in many fields of manufacture, includes loose, batt, and blanket types for wall and ceiling installations; double or storm windows; weatherstripping for windows and doors; and calking compounds for stopping infiltration of cold air around window and door frames. All these are available to home owners in any quantity regardless of the $200 limit set by the Government on home upkeep and repair. This includes metal weatherstrips made of

WEATHER-STRIPPING

zinc as well as wood and steel storm windows.

Private tests, Government tests, tests and experiences of large manufacturing concerns, and university laboratory tests where both outside and inside temperatures and the relative humidity in the air were artificially controlled, have proved beyond doubt the intrinsic value of home insulation in its several forms.

This is made rather emphatic in a recent information circular from the U. S. Bureau of Mines. "There is, of course," this circular says, "a definite relation between heat conservation and fuel saving. The quantity of fuel that may be saved by insulation has been determined by many investigators, and results vary considerably, but in every instance the figures obtained are remarkably large."

And more important still to home owners, it goes on to say, quoting from a Bureau of Standards tabulation: "(it) estimates fuel savings up to 40 percent due to the application of simple heat-loss preventives to walls and roof of an unprotected house, and with suitable weather-stripping and storm sash applied to doors and windows, the total savings were boosted to 60 percent."

CALKING

Because they are lived in, all houses are subject to moisture which, as water vapor, tends to equalize itself with the vapor content of the outdoor air. In winter, outdoor air has a low relative humidity, and water vapor inside the house tends to pass through the walls to be equalized with the outdoor air. This warm vapor passing through a wall will condense as it arrives at a cold surface that is below its dew point.

A small amount of condensation does little or no harm. However, when the relative humidity inside a house is high and the temperature outside is cold, the excessive condensation within an outside wall, with a moisture-resistive barrier on the outside

House Insulation Pay?

surface such as waterproof building paper over the sheathing, may be destructive whether the wall is insulated or not. If loose-fill insulation is introduced from outside, it is a good precaution not to replace the waterproof paper taken off during the process.

Laboratory tests on such a wall have been made to determine safety limits regarding condensation. These tests were made with the indoor temperature at 70 deg., indoor relative humidities varying from 15 to 70 percent, and outside temperature from 20 deg. below zero to 20 deg. above zero. The results of these tests indicate that, on an average, an inside relative humidity of 15 percent is safe at 20 deg. below zero; 18 at 15 deg. below; 22 at 10 below; 27 at 5 below; 33 at zero; 40 at 5 above; 49 at 10 above; 58 at 15 above; and 72 at 20 deg. above zero outdoors.

These limitations of the ratios between inside humidity and outside temperatures are important in any house. They are still more important when an existing wall having a waterproof paper on the outside under the siding is filled with insulation without benefit of a vapor barrier.

Insulation applied between the studding of a wall while it is being built makes it possible to have a vapor barrier between the insulation and the inside surface of the wall. Batts and blankets are available with vaporproof coverings for this purpose. In an existing house, they can be applied over ceilings with the vaporproof side facing the inside of the house, but this is not feasible in the walls. A coat of size and two coats

INSULATION

of oil paint on the surface of the plaster inside a house will help to turn back vapor tending to pass through the wall.

Other usable information regarding insulation in general has been made available by the American Society of Heating and Ventilating Engineers

STORM SASH

and by G. D. Lortz, of the Technical Committee of the National Mineral Wool Association. Certain key figures or ratings have been assigned to 77 different localities in the United States according to the average winter temperatures prevailing there.

A relative figure for practically any locality, including your own home community, can be selected by referring to the list of these 77 cities—given on the following page—and finding one of them that is nearest to your locality, both geographically and from the standpoint of temperatures.

Inasmuch as the major aids in conserving heat are attic-floor insulation, side-wall insulation, and storm sash, these three items are taken into consideration when figuring the fuel oil saving per season to be achieved by the use of any or all of them in an average house of any given size in any locality.

This method of figuring fuel saving is conservative, as the figures given in the table for ceiling, wall, and window treatments have been reduced by 20 percent to allow for variations in weather and for differences in home construction. These computations are also based on an average of 70-percent efficiency of the heating plant, which is good performance.

The method of figuring the fuel saving possible for your own home is a simple matter of arithmetic. For example, suppose your home is in Grand Rapids, Mich. The nearest city on the chart is Detroit, which has a key figure of 6.460. Now figure the square feet of attic-floor area in your house, the wall area, and the window area. Suppose the attic floor totals 800 sq. ft., the walls 1,200 sq. ft., and the windows 240 sq. ft.

On the insulation chart given below the list of cities, the figure for 3″ insulation between ceiling joists is .053. Multiply the key figure representing Grand Rapids (6.460) by the area of the ceiling (800), and then multiply this product by the insulation figure (.053). Thus: $6.460 \times 800 \times .053 = 273$. This

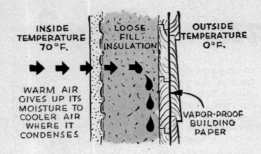

INSIDE TEMPERATURE 70°F.

LOOSE FILL INSULATION

OUTSIDE TEMPERATURE 0°F.

WARM AIR GIVES UP ITS MOISTURE TO COOLER AIR WHERE IT CONDENSES

VAPOR-PROOF BUILDING PAPER

Condensation in the fill could have been avoided here by putting the paper next to the inside wall

represents the number of gallons of fuel oil saved by insulating the ceiling 3" thick.

For the saving to be realized with insulation the full thickness of a wall framed with 2" by 4" studs, multiply 6.460 by 1,200 by .035. The result is 271 gallons saved.

The same method holds for saving by the use of storm sash: $6.460 \times 240 \times .133 = 206$. The total saving in fuel oil if all three of these things are done to this size house in Grand Rapids will be 750 gallons.

If you burn coal, divide 750 by 170 to get 4.4 tons—the total saving in fuel reduced to terms of coal. This computation is based on the fact that an average ton of coal equals 170 gallons of fuel oil burned in domestic heating plants of average efficiency.

The saving in the amount of fuel is easily translated to savings in cost to you by multiplying the gallons or tons by the price you pay in your locality for either fuel.

All window and door openings in a house are likely places for the infiltration of cold air during winter. Loose-fitting sash and window and door frames that are not wind-tight will do much to reduce the possible saving in fuel by the use of insulation and storm windows. To prevent this, the use of weatherstripping around sash and doors is advisable, and the calking of all frames on the outside of the house will add to the fuel saving. Weatherstripping that you can install yourself is available, or you can hire experts to do the job. Calking is no more difficult than puttying, and a calking gun will speed up the job. Calking compounds are available in light and dark colors.

FIGURE YOUR FUEL SAVING FROM THE INFORMATION BELOW

BELOW is a list of representative cities throughout the country along with a key number, or coefficient, by which the area of your insulated space (in square feet) can be multiplied in calculating your fuel saving as explained in the text above. At the end of the table is another set of coefficients for the type of insulation used.

State	City	Coefficient	State	City	Coefficient	State	City	Coefficient
Ala.	Birmingham	2.410	Me.	Eastport	8.476	Ore.	Baker	7.216
	Mobile	1.473		Portland	7.210		Portland	4.442
Ariz.	Phoenix	1.405	Md.	Baltimore	4.525	Pa.	Philadelphia	4.784
Ark.	Fort Smith	3.112	Mass.	Boston	6.003		Pittsburgh	5.183
	Little Rock	2.863	Mich.	Detroit	6.460	S. C.	Charleston	1.721
Calif.	Los Angeles	1.472		Marquette	8.721		Columbia	2.362
	San Francisco	3.244	Minn.	Duluth	9.797	S. D.	Huron	8.174
Colo.	Denver	5.894		Minneapolis	7.883		Rapid City	7.219
Conn.	New Haven	5.918	Miss.	Vicksburg	1.851	Tenn.	Memphis	2.957
D. C.	Washington	4.631	Mo.	Kansas City	5.002		Nashville	3.500
Fla.	Jacksonville	.928		St. Louis	4.539	Tex.	Fort Worth	2.178
Ga.	Atlanta	2.865	Mont.	Havre	8.635		Houston	1.143
	Savannah	1.524		Lincoln	6.053	Utah	Modena	6.637
Idaho	Boise	5.614	Neb.	Omaha	6.154		Salt Lake City	5.601
Ill.	Chicago	6.027	Nevada	Winnemucca	6.330	Vt.	Burlington	7.508
	Springfield	5.405	N. H.	Concord	7.287	Va.	Norfolk	3.342
Ind.	Evansville	4.228	N. J.	Atlantic City	5.173		Richmond	3.819
	Indianapolis	5.321	N. M.	Santa Fe	6.087	Wash.	Seattle	5.107
Iowa	Des Moines	6.409	N. Y.	Buffalo	6.818		Spokane	6.312
	Sioux City	7.052		New York	5.290	W. Va.	Elkins	5.659
Kan.	Dodge City	5.056	N. C.	Raleigh	3.179		Parkersburg	4.807
	Topeka	5.103		Wilmington	2.304	Wis.	Green Bay	7.896
Ky.	Lexington	4.600	N. D.	Bismarck	9.127		Milwaukee	7.152
	Louisville	4.185	Ohio	Cincinnati	5.127	Wyo.	Cheyenne	7.503
La.	New Orleans	1.017		Cleveland	6.150		Lander	8.277
	Shreveport	1.964	Okla.	Oklahoma City	3.625			

INSULATION CHART

Type of insulation	Thickness	Coefficient
Insulation between ceiling joists	2"	.045
" " " "	3"	.053
	4"	.058
Fill insulation inside walls		.035
Double or storm sash		.133

Attractive Rack for Garden Tools Helps Save Extra Steps

CONVENIENCE and an attractive appearance are features of this outdoor rack for garden tools and hose. A rack of this type will save the home gardener many extra steps during the months when tools are most frequently needed. It is not usually desirable to put the rack to year-round use, however, nor to install it where theft of the tools is a possibility.

Design your rack to hold the tools which you use most often; generally this will include a hoe, rake, cultivator, spade, hand trowel, clippers, and hose. If possible, locate the rack in the shade and close to the garden. The overhanging roof adds both weather protection for your tools and a decorative touch to the garden.—MICHELE DE SANTIS.

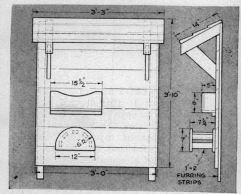

Cut steel nails are used to hold this rack to the brick wall. Expansion plugs can be used on stucco

---

ADJUSTING SCREEN DOORS [SHIPSHAPE HOME]

Screen and storm doors often do not close properly because their spring hinges lack the necessary tension. Hinges are adjustable for tension if they have holes around the collars. Insert a nail in a hole and turn the collar until the stop pin is freed. Replace the pin in a hole farther from the nail and allow the collar to turn back.

If the spring is broken or too weak, replace the hinge or install a screen spring inside the door, maintaining some tension even with the door closed. Be sure to turn the hook openings downward or inward to keep them from catching and tearing clothes.

A spring installed at the top of the door helps if the upper corner is sprung. To remedy the tendency of old doors to bow, install an inexpensive butt hinge at the center.

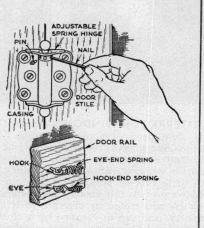

POPULAR SCIENCE MONTHLY SHOP DATA

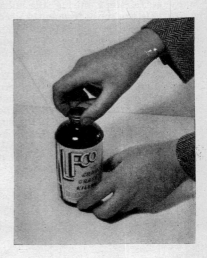

PLASTIC SINK DRAINS are now available to replace metal types. Made of a molded white plastic, the drains will not rust or corrode, and have no plated finish to wear away. The drain assembly consists of three units: a one-piece surface lip and drain, a rubber washer, and a plastic nut shaped to fit a standard wrench. The drain, which is easy to clean, can be quickly installed or removed for the repair of plumbing. An additional advantage is that it will not stain a porcelain sink.

DEAD WEEDS and crab grass are the result if this liquid, properly diluted, is sprayed on lawns. Its makers assert the chemical causes no permanent injury to desirable grasses, and that it contains a nutrient that stimulates lawn growth. It can be used to spot out dandelions. Applied undiluted, it kills all growth on drives or tennis courts.

NONFADING PAINT for exterior trim, doors, and blinds is on the market. The paint (not shown) is made with pigment which is ground so fine that the particles remain in colloidal suspension in the vehicle. Since heavy fillers are not required to give covering power, the paint produces a gloss surface highly resistant to fading and weathering.

SHATTERPROOF WINDOWS made of plastic and wire have been developed to protect workers in shell-loading plants from the danger of glass splinters. Unlike glass, this glazing material can be installed in window frames at the factory and shipped with little risk of breakage. Light in weight, the windows provide fair vision and excellent insulation. They are unaffected by changes in temperature or humidity, and can be cleaned by a cloth dampened with water or kerosene. Such windows are being used in prefabricated troop shelters overseas.

BUILDING BOARD constructed of noncritical asbestos and cement is helping to replace fiber, plywood, and sheet-metal materials that have gone to war. These new boards can be sawed, drilled, or nailed. Being entirely fireproof, they are excellent for making heating or ventilating ducts. Boards come in 4' by 8' size, and in 3/16", ¼", and ⅜" thicknesses.

STARTERS of fluorescent lamps now have long operating lives. Shown above is a manual-reset type with an average rated life of three years. It is designed to lock out dead lamps quickly, eliminating flicker and reducing wear on both the ballast and starter. Below is a glow-type starter built to take hard punishment from a dead lamp and also to show long life in service.

OPAQUE GLASS SHOWER ENCLOSURES, designed to occupy space usually allotted to a bath-tub, are being used in new housing. They are made of thick sheets of colored glass fabricated into a single unit, which can be used as a tub as well as a shower stall although the front is only 1' high. Developed primarily for low-cost war homes, they will fit in an alcove left vacant by the scarcity of bathtubs.

PORCELAIN OR CHINA repairs can be made with the kit pictured at the right. Glass, pottery, plumbing fixtures, and even piano keys may be refinished or cemented. The kit contains a cement compound for filling in any chipped area, and a porcelain glaze, which blends with and covers the repair. The materials are said not to shrink, craze, or crack. After the surface has hardened, it is impervious to the effects of water, alcohol, gasoline, or acids.

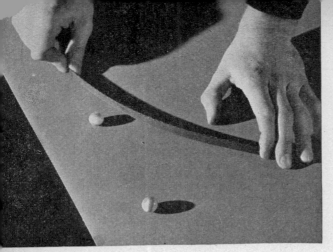

ARTILLERY FIRE. Computing the trajectory or path of a shell is complicated work for an artillery officer, but you can demonstrate the principle on your bridge table with two marbles and a hacksaw blade. Flip the blade as shown above, and the two marbles will shoot off the table, the one closer to the stationary end of the blade a short distance, the other much farther—yet you can tell by the simultaneous clicks that both hit the floor the same instant. This seeming contradiction is due to the constant pull of gravity, which exerts the same force regardless of the motion of the object, even though it may have the speed of a bullet. The instant a bullet leaves the gun, gravity attracts it to the earth. One fired horizontally will hit level ground at the same instant as a bullet dropped simultaneously from the gun muzzle. In order to hit a distant target, artillerymen compensate for this by tilting up the muzzle.

THE MOTION OF A PENDULUM is produced by the constant acceleration of gravity. The time of each swing is directly proportionate to the square root of the length of the pendulum. To prove this, suspend a marble on a string and set it swinging. Time its swings with a watch. You will find that to make it swing in half the time, you must shorten the length of the string not to half, but to one fourth that of the original.

A SUSPENDED ROD is called a compound pendulum, for it acts like a series of weights strung end to end. Suspend a dowel from one end alongside a marble and adjust the string on the latter until both swing at the same rate. The string will be about two thirds the length of the dowel. Mark this point—the *center of oscillation*—on a dowel of like length, insert a pin, and suspend it alongside the others. All three pendulums will swing in unison.

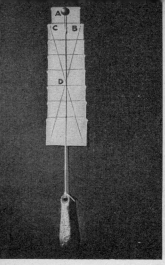
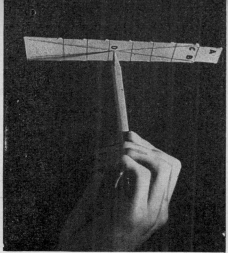
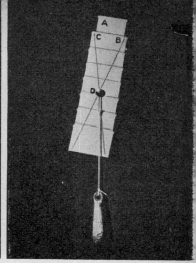

THE LEANING TOWER OF PISA

doesn't fall because its center of gravity is low. To show this, hang a cardboard cutout from a point B near the top. From there hang a weighted cord and mark its line on the model. Rehang from another point C and mark similarly. The intersection D is the center of gravity, as can be shown by hanging the cutout from point A (left, above).

If the lines are accurate, the model can be balanced at D on a pencil, as in the center photo above. If the cutout is pivoted at D and the plumb line also suspended from this point, the model may be tilted until the cord coincides with either pencil line without toppling over, as shown at the right. Because its base is proportionately heavier than that of the model, the Tower of Pisa could lean much further without falling.

WITH "BATTER UP!"

Babe Ruth applied physics to every home run, for a swinging bat is a compound pendulum, and its center of oscillation is also its *center of percussion*. This is the point of most effective drive, and the one which imparts the least jar, with the least likelihood of splitting the bat. It can be located by allowing the bat to swing free 6" from the grip end and synchronizing the swing of a marble with it. The point on the bat opposite the marble is the center of percussion. Tapped there, the bat swings freely; struck elsewhere, it shudders and stings your hand. This same law of physics is applied in many hand tools, such as hammers and axes, and in machinery. For instance, if an ax handle is too long, the center of percussion may not be in its head, but farther up, in the handle. Such an ax shudders, and the handle may break.

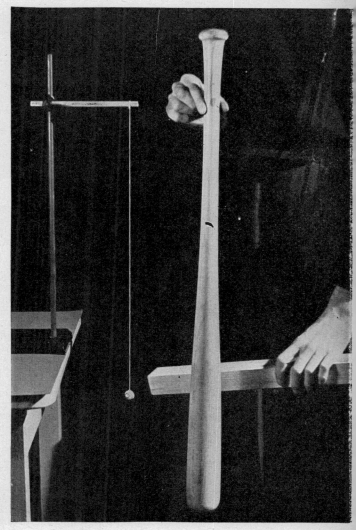

The *Chemistry*

HOW COMMON CHEMICALS CAN

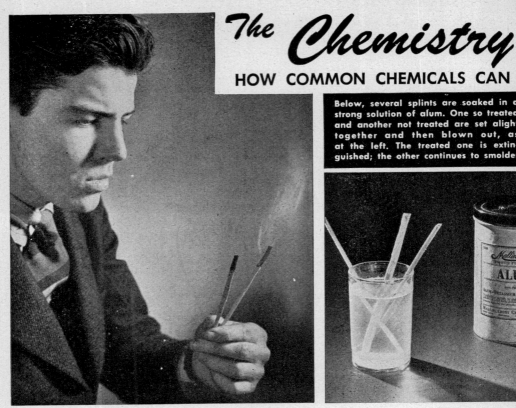

Below, several splints are soaked in a strong solution of alum. One so treated and another not treated are set alight together and then blown out, as at the left. The treated one is extinguished; the other continues to smolder

By Benjamin Taplitz

A SUPPOSEDLY extinguished match, still aflame and carelessly thrown where it falls on or against an inflammable object, may start a fire and cause a catastrophe that could have been avoided by forethought and simple fire-prevention aids. Although some fires start from inexplicable causes, many of them are preventable by chemical means that thwart disaster in the making.

You can easily prove the effects of chemicals in fire retarding by a few simple experiments in your home laboratory. After you have made the tests, you may want to treat certain inflammable objects in your home against the danger of accidental exposure to flame. The method is the same as given in the following experiments.

Take a small piece of unsized cloth—a well-washed and worn handkerchief will do —and tear it in half. Dip one of the pieces into a solution made up of 1 oz. borax crystals and ¾ oz. boric acid crystals dissolved in a pint of water. For a practical application, the cloth should be left in the solution for one hour, but for this experiment one or two minutes will be enough. After dipping

the cloth, allow it to dry out thoroughly.

Now fasten the two pieces of cloth to the ends of an improvised fork made from an old coat hanger, as shown in the photo at right, and hold them above the flames of two candles. The untreated piece of cloth will burn, while the treated piece will merely char. Many chemicals used in safeguarding fabrics against fire work in similar fashion. The cloth may not be kept from charring, but it will not burst into flame and spread the fire.

Although the solution just mentioned is cheap and easily made, the salts are both soluble and will be dissolved out when the fabric is washed. For materials that require repeated washing, a two-solution process is necessary. In one such treatment, a tin salt such as sodium stannate is precipitated directly into the fabric. This is accomplished by first dipping the material in a solution of 3 lb. sodium stannate in 1 gal. water. Follow this by wringing, drying, and then dipping the material in a second bath of

An ordinary piece of cloth blazes merrily, but the other, impregnated with a solution of borax and boric acid, merely chars. This flameproof treatment acts to retard the spreading of fire

# of Fireproofing—

BE USED TO RENDER MANY SUBSTANCES FLAME RESISTANT

1¼ lb. ammonium sulphate dissolved in 1 gal. water. These treatments are suitable for curtains and cloth articles used near candles and lamps, and for party decorations that may be exposed to accidental contact with flame.

For heavy materials, such as awnings and canvas tarpaulins, the following double bath is recommended: First dip the fabric in a solution of 2 lb. ammonium phosphate in 1 gal. water. Allow it to dry; then dip it in a solution of 3 lb. alum in 2 gal. water. If the material is too unwieldy for dipping, the solution may be applied with a spray gun.

A new development in rendering fabrics fire resistant is a solution of ammonium sulphamate. The amazing fire-retarding qualities of this chemical were discovered just in time to make it of tremendous value to the armed forces.

Chemical treatment of the wooden structural members of a frame house will reduce combustibility, and the construction of the walls themselves can be designed to act as a hindrance to fire. For example, the open spaces between the studs should be sealed off from each other to prevent drafts and convection currents that feed a fire. The effect of a convection current on a flame can be demonstrated with a candle and a pickle jar. Light the candle and lower it into the jar, where it will burn feebly. Cover the jar mouth with your hand and the candle will be snuffed out. Now cut a T-shaped strip of metal that will extend down into the jar just clear of the flame. Hang the strip by the bar of the T and relight the candle, which will now burn brightly. The partition creates a convection current that feeds the flame with air, thus supporting combustion.

The chemical treatment of wood to retard combustion is accomplished by putting the wood in an air-lock chamber, removing the moisture from it by creating a near vacuum, and then forcing a treating solution, such as zinc chloride, into the wood under high pressure.

A solution made of 1 part commercial

The photograph above shows the effect of a fire on a piece of wood treated with water glass. The mass of bubbles, each containing a minute amount of inert or noncombustible gases, forms an insulating wall that has a retarding effect upon combustion of the wood

A candle in the jar at left above burns feebly, but a partition inserted in the top of the jar, as shown at right above, creates a convection current, causing the candle to burn brightly

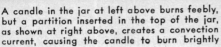

Right, wood shavings heated in a test tube give off combustible gases, which are shown blazing at the tip of a glass nozzle fitted in the cork

water glass to 2 parts water by volume has fire-retarding qualities. For studying the reaction of water glass to fire, paint a piece of wood with three coats of the solution, allowing each coat to dry before applying the next. When the last is thoroughly dry, hold the wood in the flame of a Bunsen burner. The coating swells to a frothy mass which hardens into a thick layer. It is the inert gases in this bubbly mass that insulate the wood against fire.

The chief requirement of a good fire-retarding agent is that it be noninflammable and form a protective coating that persists at high temperatures, or that produces, as a result of contact with high temperature, a noncombustible gas that will render ineffective the volatile, inflammable gas released from the wood. That such a gas is produced can be easily shown. Put a few wood shavings or sawdust in a glass test tube fitted with a stopper from which projects a glass tube drawn to a jet. Heat the tube in a Bunsen flame and, after a minute of heating, hold a lighted match to the smoke from the jet. The gas will burn.

Strange as it may seem, matches are chemically treated for fire resistance—not to keep them from burning, but to prevent afterglow. You may demonstrate this principle with two wooden splints. Soak one for a few minutes in a strong solution of alum. After drying it, hold both the treated and untreated splints in a flame. Both will burn. When you blow out the two flames, however, the treated splint goes out almost immediately, but the other continues to glow for some time.

USEFUL AUTO HINTS

1 A TOOL COMPARTMENT for cars lacking such a space can be made by welding or bolting an angle bracket in the luggage compartment to the bottom of the back of the rear seat. A board is fitted between the seat and the end of the body and is bolted to the bracket. A cross board keeps tools from damaging the taillight.—P.C.S.

2 AN ORDINARY SHOE BAG temporarily fastened to the rear of the front seat with safety pins provides a handy place for carrying articles with which to entertain small children during an auto trip. The pockets are suitable for small toys, dolls, paper and pencils, flexible books that can be rolled, and boxes of cookies.—C.W.C.

3 PORTABLE-RADIO RECEPTION in an automobile may be improved with a few simple connections. Use a standard whip aerial, connecting it with a shielded lead-in to the plug jack on the dash. A 3' piece of single-conductor shielded cable is attached to a microphone plug, with the shield connected to the shank, and fastened at one end to the grid side of the loop aerial. The shield may be fastened to the radio chassis if this will further improve reception. Be sure to keep all the shielding grounded to eliminate ignition noises.—R.S.

4 EMERGENCY BATTERY CONNECTIONS can be made by taping the cable end and turning an ordinary wood screw through the cable into the battery terminal.—J.K.

DRAWINGS BY STEWART ROUSE

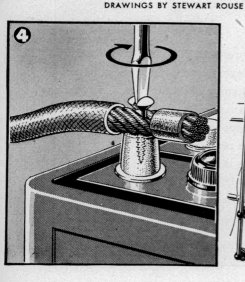

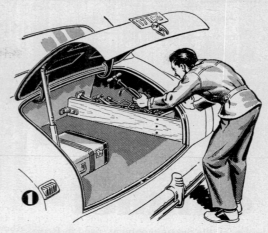

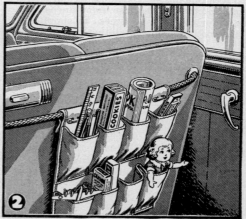

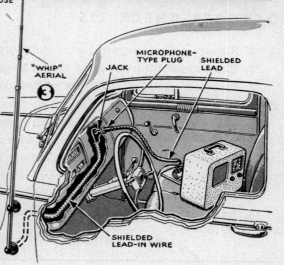

"WHIP" AERIAL

MICROPHONE-TYPE PLUG

JACK

SHIELDED LEAD

SHIELDED LEAD-IN WIRE

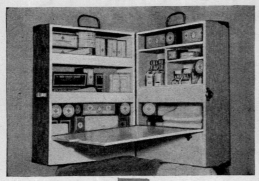

First-Aid Cabinet

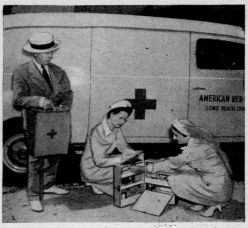

Storage space in this first-aid carrying cabinet is designed to save time in getting at supplies. Above, it is being put to use by a Red Cross unit

THIS portable first-aid cabinet, used in Red Cross and civilian-defense ambulances, is arranged for quick, easy access to supplies and is strong enough to withstand rough handling.

The best method of construction is to build the box complete and then saw it into halves on a circular saw. The side and end joints should be rabbeted to make them both strong and dustproof. Partitions and inside boxes are then made to fit. Finger holes are bored in the fronts of the inside boxes to help in quick handling, and they also make possible a flush front. Hinges, handles, and fasteners are bolted on for strength. For first-aid material, consult the *First-Aid Handbook* published by the American Red Cross.—CHARLES HENRY HUNT.

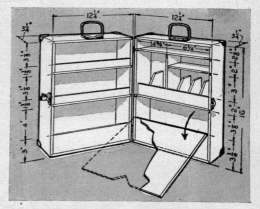

OCTOBER CHECK LIST   [SHIPSHAPE HOME]

1. Remove screens, repair, paint, and store them flat.
2. Clean window frames, metal screen hangers, and paint.
3. Fit storm windows and doors, adjust hangers and hinges.
4. Calk around all windows and door frames.
5. Sweep out eaves troughs and paint inside with protective paint.
6. Scrape out sidewalk cracks and fill with cement mortar.
7. Clean out and repoint cracks in outside masonry walls.
8. Insulate exposed plumbing pipes that might freeze.
9. Insulate warm-air ducts and furnace jacket.
10. Buy a supply of fuses and store near fuse box.

POPULAR SCIENCE MONTHLY SHOP DATA

AUTO *Ideas*

HOW TO MOUNT TIRES

Partially inflate the tube before inserting it to prevent buckling

With your hand, guide the valve through the valve hole in the rim

Push the bead under the valve into the well at the center of the rim

Force the rest of this bead over the flange so it rests in the well

Now pry the top bead opposite the valve over the flange and, with a second tool, work around the rim

Seat the valve correctly, pulling it out by hand and centering it

Holding the valve, inflate until both the beads are properly seated

If there is a centering rib, have it show evenly all the way around

From Goodyear Tire & Rubber Company, Inc.

EMERGENCY AMBULANCE BODIES have been designed by the OCD for use on converted light four-door sedans as supplemental equipment for its medical division. The bodies, which accommodate four stretchers, are built of wooden frame members and plywood panels. Scrap iron is used for lengthening the chassis of the converted cars. In making the ambulances, the sedan bodies are cut off at the rear of the center door posts, the new bodies are bolted to bent iron pieces welded to the chassis, and two additional leaves taken from junked cars are inserted to strengthen each rear spring. The bodies may be used on 1939, 1940, and 1941 Fords, Chevrolets, and Plymouths. That in the photo above is mounted on a 1939 Ford.

TIRE INSPECTION can be speeded in a busy shop by the addition of one or more auxiliary lightweight spreaders. The one below was designed by Charles E. Harris, of Raton, N. M. Its two arms are steel tubing, and the link consists of two pieces of strap iron. Pipe couplings will serve for the other parts. The fulcrum sleeve is adjustable and can be locked at any place by means of a setscrew. To the sliding sleeve is welded a set of bead jaws. Similar jaws are welded to the fixed fitting at the end of the tool.

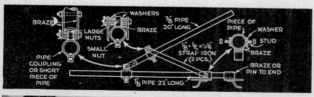

Puncheon Table Adds Rustic Touch to Back-Yard Barbecues

THE most satisfactory tables for outdoor use are heavy ones, and as they are seldom moved about, they might as well be permanently located, provided they are weatherproof. Here is one that will take as much weather as a slate roof—and like it.

If you live in timber country, you can probably buy split logs at a local mill. Elsewhere, you can shape them yourself with a crosscut saw and an adz, which produces an interesting hand-hewn effect.

The table should be about 29" high. Set the supporting posts 18" deep after creosoting the ends for slightly more than this.

Notch the cross members and fasten them with countersunk lag screws.

Puncheons for the table top should also be notched on the undersides and trimmed fairly straight along the edges, but need not fit snugly together. It is better to leave about ¼" between them so that rain and melting snow may drain off. Fasten them with ½" dowels to the cross members.

Set the bench posts to bring the top 18" above the ground. Notch a larger split log for the seat, and secure it to the posts with lag screws, countersinking these well and plugging the holes with dowels.—HI SIBLEY.

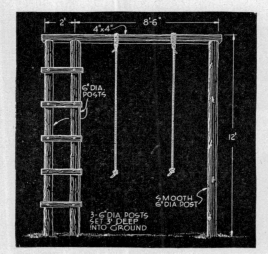

Outdoor Gym Unit Trains Boys

PHYSICAL fitness programs for high-school boys suggested this outdoor gymnasium unit designed especially for developing arm and shoulder muscles.

Three durable posts about 16' long and 6" in diameter are first set securely in concrete. A 4" by 4" piece of lumber to support the combined weights of several husky boys is spiked across the tops of these. The climbing ropes should be at least 1" in diameter to provide a firm grip. The crosspieces that form the ladder are nailed 2' apart so that boys can practice climbing in and out between them as they advance to the top.

Since the post at the other end is designed to be used as a climbing pole, it should be smoothed carefully as insurance against any splinter hazard.—GEORGE A. SMITH.

USEFUL AUTO HINTS

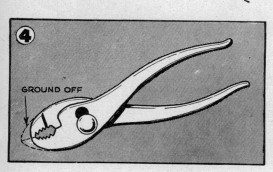

TIRE GAUGE

FILED NOTCH

WIRE

SNAP HOOK

RING

DROP OF SOLDER

Drawings by William Patrick

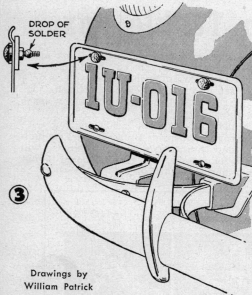

GROUND OFF

1 **A DOOR GUARD FOR CHILDREN** left alone on the back seat of a four-door sedan can be rigged easily with a split ring and a snap hook. Drill the door handle near the end and fit into the hole a ¾″ diameter split ring such as is used to carry keys. Directly above, drill a hole in the window frame for a small, stiff wire. Pull the wire through the hole and the loop of a snap hook. Twist the wire tightly together and solder the end to cover any sharp points. Fasten the snap hook into the ring. The door opens from outside, and adults can unfasten the snap, but it baffles small children.—E. B. A.

2 **YOUR TIRE GAUGE** can readily be adapted to give an accurate pressure check when used in dark places. Simply file a small notch in the indicator at the correct reading for the standard pressure for your tires. The notch can be felt in the dark and does not interfere with the operation of the gauge.—J. R.

3 **REFLECTOR-BUTTON THIEVES,** usually small boys who want the bright buttons for their bicycles, can be thwarted by putting a drop of solder on the bolts that hold the license plates. This is better than crimping the threads, as the solder can be removed at home with a blowtorch or a hot soldering iron.—J. B.

4 **THIS BATTERY TOOL** for loosening terminals can be made by grinding down the nose of a pair of common pliers. The standard nose is too long, interfering with a good grip, while the shorter nose allows closer work and will not mar the battery.—C. L. L

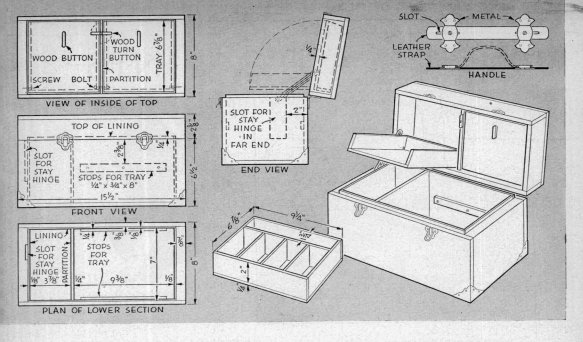

Durable Wooden Tackle Box

SCRAPS of wood from larger projects will do for building this sturdy tackle box. Use 7/8" stock for the ends, 3/8" plywood for the sides, top, and bottom, and 1/4" stock for partitions. A lining of 1/8" composition board extending up 1/4" from the bottom section on the sides and ends creates a watertight joint when the lid is closed.

Make the box 1/8" higher than dimensioned, put marine glue in all the joints, and fasten the sides, top, and bottom together with screws. Then bandsaw the box apart 2⅜" from one side. The two hinged drawers pivot on screws in each side as well as on a bolt set into the center lid partition. One drawer is slightly narrower to allow space for the stay hinge.

Finish the box both inside and out with waterproof varnish. Brass corners, a handle, and catches from an old suitcase will serve for fittings. The handle should lie flat when not in use.—HARRY W. WANNER.

THE SHEET BEND [KNOTS]

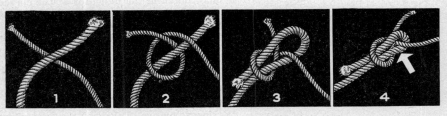

The sheet bend, or weaver's knot as it is sometimes called, is a simple, safe way of joining two ropes or straps together, especially when they are of unequal size. The knot does not slip out of place, yet is very easy to untie.

Hold the larger rope in the left hand and cross it over the smaller rope, holding both at the crossing point with the forefinger and thumb of the left hand (Fig. 1). With the right hand grasp the lower part of the smaller rope and loop it clockwise around its own end (Fig. 2). The end of the larger rope is then threaded through the loop so formed, as in Fig. 3, and the ropes are drawn taut to complete the knot (Fig. 4).

The sheet bend is easily released by pressing down on the bight of the larger rope, which is indicated by an arrow in Fig. 4.

POPULAR SCIENCE MONTHLY SHOP DATA

OLD DUTCH SETTLE
from Early Hudson Valley Days

A TABLE, BENCH, AND STORAGE BOX IN ONE WILL MAKE AN IDEAL PIECE FOR YOUR COUNTRY OR SUBURBAN HOME

By
JOSEPH ARONSON

THE box settle or table settle is an old furniture form. Tudor designs of this type reappeared in American furniture of the 17th and 18th centuries, and in simplified versions the settle still appears in country homes up to the present day. The model illustrated was designed for and used on the covered terrace of a modern American home, doubling as table and bench as the occasion required.

A storage compartment is an authentic part of this piece and accounts for its part-time name of box settle. One other name, Dutch settle, stems from its popularity with the Hollanders who settled in the Hudson Valley. The term "settle" itself has nothing to do with settlers, but is an old word for bench, especially a bench with a high back.

The basic construction of this table settle is elementary, and the materials may be of the average lumber-yard kind. Posts and top stretchers should be selected from the best sections of 2" by 3" pieces of fir or pine, planed and sanded smooth, and then doweled together. Note that the box ends are placed so that their top edges come flush with the **top** of the box lid, and ¾" higher than the

box sides upon which the lid rests. Both ends and sides are fastened to the posts with four dowels at each end.

For the box floor, if ⅜" plywood is not available, ¾" material may be used. Ends and sides of the box are rabbeted to receive the floor, which has its four corners notched out to fit around the posts. The lid should be glued up and reinforced with cleats screwed to the underside. Metal hinges may be used, or dowel pins may be put into the lid from the posts, but be sure to get the dowel centers outside of the back of the box as shown in the drawing.

Material for the top should be selected from clear, straight stock and carefully glued up. Deep cleats, which are screwed on, will help keep the top straight. Pivoting of the top is by means of the turned pins inserted through holes in the cleats into cor-

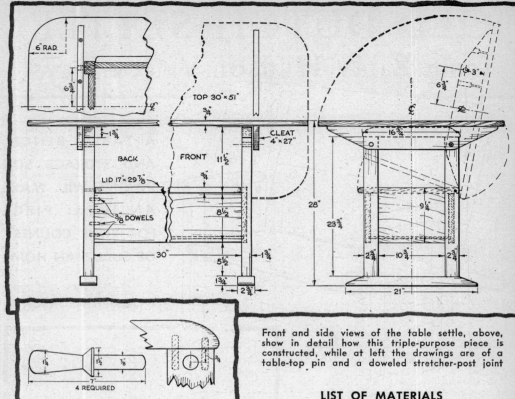

Front and side views of the table settle, above, show in detail how this triple-purpose piece is constructed, while at left the drawings are of a table-top pin and a doweled stretcher-post joint

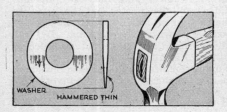

responding holes in the posts. The position of these holes must be exact or the top will either rest at a bad angle when up or not set properly on the arms when down.

Finish the table settle to suit its intended use. If the wood you use has an interesting texture, a pleasing finish can be made to simulate old pine or maple with a water stain of light walnut color, brushed over when dry with shellac and thoroughly sanded to a satin smoothness. On the other hand, a note of strong color is pleasant for porch or terrace furnishings, and some decorators would be tempted to try strong red, blue, or yellow paint.

LIST OF MATERIALS

No. Pc.	Description	T.	W.	L.
4	Posts	1¾	2¾	23¾
2	Stretchers	1¾	1¾	16¾
2	Box ends	¾	9¼	10¾
2	" sides	¾	8½	30
1	" lid	¾	17	29⅞
1	" floor (plywood)	⅜	14¼	30½
2	Feet	1¾	2¾	21
1	Table top	¾	30	51
2	Cleats	¾	4	27
4	Pins turned 7" long from 1½" stock			

Note: All dimensions are given in inches.

Improvised Wedge Made of Washer Locks Hammer Head Firmly

A LOOSE hammer head can be fastened securely and permanently to its handle by the use of a wedge made from an ordinary washer. On an anvil or a block of metal, hammer the washer to a thin edge at one side as shown in the drawing at the left. Drive it into the handle as you would a wedge. The compressed wood tends to expand back into the hole of the washer, locking it firmly.—HARRY S. ALLEN.

FOR THE BOYS IN THE SERVICE

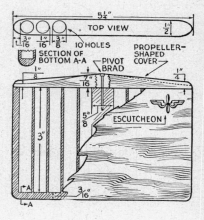

Made from a solid piece of wood, this case will hold 10 cigarettes. Its pivoted lid is held on by a brad and, as a decorative touch, is shaped like an airplane propeller

HAVE you a son or a friend in the Army Air Forces? Here is a simply made cigarette case that will be an acceptable gift. In fact, its airplane-propeller lid lends it a novelty that will make it appreciated by anyone in the services.

Gumwood, mahogany, walnut, or any close-grained wood is suitable for the case. Shape it roughly to the dimensions shown; then bore the ten cigarette holes—holding a half package of cigarettes—to the size in the drawing, which is just large enough to let a cigarette slip in or out. These holes are best made in the drill press, if one is available. Dress the case to shape, sand, and give it a rubbed-varnish finish. The insignia in the corner which decorates the case is taken from an inexpensive pin.—B. M.

Trousers Hanger Clamps Small Glued Parts in Model Making

WHEN small strips of wood or other material are glued up, as in model making, an ordinary trousers hanger will serve to perfection as a clamp. The device works independently of a fixed axis and will clamp equally well whether the outer surfaces of the pieces are parallel or tapered. These hangers are usually faced with felt, which will be a help in keeping tapered sides from slipping under pressure.—R. E.

Craftwork

ATTRACTIVE PHOTOGRAPH FRAME

Designed by ERNEST R. DEWALT

EASEL PICTURE FRAME. This interesting picture frame is made of 1/8" hard, pressed composition board, as shown in the drawing. Heavy cardboard glued up could be substituted for the pressed board. The picture opening is cut in the front mat only, while the 1/2" holes for the rings are drilled 1/16" deep in the front of the mat and in the back of the backing. These holes are lined up to take the rings, which, when in place, hold the mat and backing together.

Make three parallel cuts on the mat on a circular saw for decoration. Cut the easel stand as dimensioned so it will open freely to the proper angle. Rub white paint into the saw cuts, and when it is dry, sand and wax the entire frame. The photo is taped in position on the backing, the mat is arranged over it, and the rings are snapped in place to hold the pieces together. Working time: 3½ hours.

PIVOT CURTAIN BRACKETS OF WOOD. Maple pivot hinges for curtains answer a common household problem in a decorative manner. A pair of brackets and poles swing on dowel pins having beads at top and bottom. The wall mounts are fastened with long screws. Saw out the opening in the mounts, and bore and countersink two screw holes as shown. Fit each bracket in its mount so that it won't bind when swung; then, using a 1/4" auger, bore a hole for the dowel pin through both parts when they are lined up.

Bore a 1/2" hole in the edge of each bracket for a dowel curtain pole. Round and shape the lower part of the bracket, and round the back of the bracket and the front of the wall mount to a 7/16" radius. Turn and drill beads for each dowel pin and the finials for the ends of the curtain poles. The top bead is fixed on the dowel pin with a brad; the bottom bead is removable, but it is a tight fit. Cut the curtain dowel to a length suitable for the width of curtains and size of window. Stain or paint the dowels, finials, and beads any desired color, and varnish or shellac the hinges. Working time: 3½ hours each pair.

DOUBLE WINDOW HANGER. Use maple or some other hardwood for the bracket and circular key, because the joint that holds the weight must have strength. Lay out the

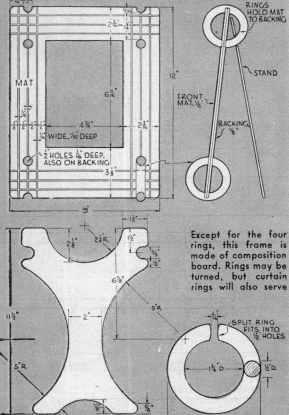

Except for the four rings, this frame is made of composition board. Rings may be turned, but curtain rings will also serve

Ideas for the Home

AND TWO WOOD BRACKETS AND RODS FOR CURTAINS AND DRAPES

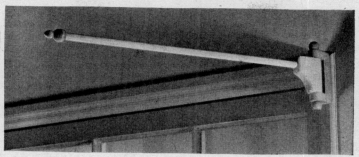

brackets from a center line and make both of them at the same time. Cut out the circles in the base and bore the holes for the two dowel poles. Round the top into the slanting sides and sand smooth. Cut the parallel grooves on a circular saw. Each key is sanded to a slip fit in the curve of its bracket. Bore and countersink each key for a 2⅜″ wood screw. Cut both dowel poles to suit the window dimension. The finish should be such that it will harmonize with the color scheme of decorations in the room.

To install, screw the keys to the woodwork, and then slip the curtain hanger, already assembled, over the keys. The weight of window hangings will prevent slipping of the brackets on the keys. Working time: 3½ hours each pair.

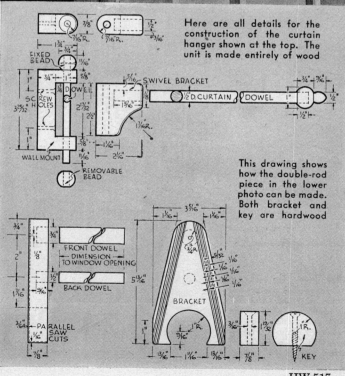

Here are all details for the construction of the curtain hanger shown at the top. The unit is made entirely of wood

This drawing shows how the double-rod piece in the lower photo can be made. Both bracket and key are hardwood

Personal Scrapbook for Mementos from Your Own Hero

ANY family with a member in the service will appreciate a personal scrapbook in which to keep clippings and pictures that are being saved for his return. The covers of this one are made of ¼" plywood, as is also the frame for the cover picture. Saw through the front board 1" from the binding edge and join the two parts with small hinges set flush. Clamp the boards together for accurate alignment and drill two holes for binding posts, countersinking the back for nuts, which are glued in place.

Coat the outside of the back with glue and stretch over it imitation leather, canvas, sailcloth, light corduroy, or other suitable material, allowing ¾" for folding over the edges. Finish the inside face with a piece of stiff paper glued on to cover the edges of the lap.

A different treatment is required for the front. Glue the covering material along one edge only, stretch it into position, and hold it with pins. Center the frame for the picture and draw a sharp knife around the inside of the opening; then remove the frame, the material cut out, and the pins. Next, center the picture in the opening, cover it with a thin sheet of transparent cellulose film, and glue the covering material down. Fold the edges and finish the inside face as was done for the back.

Alternative designs are shown for the frame, which may be glued on or fastened with upholsterers' tacks. Red, white, and blue, olive drab, or Navy blue paint may be used for a finish if the material used for the cover is such that it will take paint readily.—JOHN J. GALLIVAN.

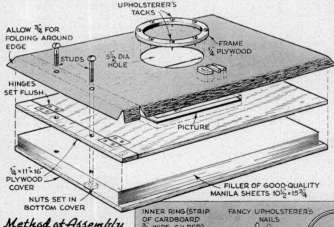

Method of Assembly

Alternative frames for the scrapbook cover are shown at right. Use ¼" plywood except for the truck axle, which may be thinner. Any printing serves as a pattern for letters of 1/16" stock

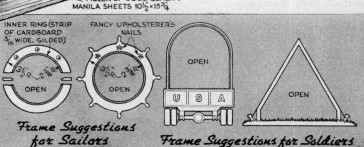

Frame Suggestions for Sailors

Frame Suggestions for Soldiers

from
READERS'
WORKSHOPS

. . . ACTION MODELS
DISPLAY INGENUITY
OF HOME CRAFTSMEN

Capable of firing blank .32's, this deck gun has a 12" long barrel, ¾" recoil, 360-deg. traverse, 60-deg. elevation, and adjustable sights. It was built by Fred Jameson, Jr., of Omaha, and M. C. Gentry, of Detroit

Part of a collection of 50 models built by J. N. Halsted, of Omaha, over a period of 10 years, the two automobiles below depict a phase in the evolution of transportation. At the left is an 1898 Oldsmobile; at right, the same make dated 1903. Each is 9" long

Real oil is pumped by the miniature well above, which is modeled after an old-style, steam-driven rig. A 1/20-hp. motor in the base provides power for a continuous flow through ¼" pipe to a tank and return line. Jae D. Kitchen, of Caro, Mich., the designer, even included floodlights

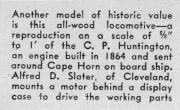

Another model of historic value is this all-wood locomotive—a reproduction on a scale of ⅝" to 1' of the C. P. Huntington, an engine built in 1864 and sent around Cape Horn on board ship. Alfred D. Slater, of Cleveland, mounts a motor behind a display case to drive the working parts

GUMMED STICKERS that take the place of metal paper fasteners in home or office are sold in convenient sheets bound in booklet form. Each booklet contains 500 gummed stickers. The sheets are perforated to tear apart easily and quickly. Being gummed on both sides, they can be used for attaching carbon copies to letters and for mounting photographs, clippings, and souvenirs in your scrapbook or on file cards, labels on bottles, and like purposes

DEHYDRATING IN ANY OVEN is now simple with a new home food drier that can be used to advantage through the growing season and into late fall. Three galvanized-wire racks hold 6½ to 10 lb. of food at one time. The unit measures 11" by 14½" by 17½", which is a convenient fit for most ovens of moderate size. Attached to it is a long, hooklike arm which can be adjusted to hold the oven door ajar for air circulation as drying goes on

DRYING SMALL ARTICLES in the bathroom involves less trouble if the rack shown below is at hand. Hooked over the towel bar, it will still permit use of the latter while itself providing about four times as much additional space for hanging stockings, handkerchiefs, lingerie, and similar light laundry. Made entirely of wood, it can be put up or taken down in a moment, and holds securely in position without any other fastening

THIS HANDY TOOL is made strong enough to open wooden cases and tough corrugated cartons. Besides this, the blade end of it can be used to cut cord and rope. The carton opener, as it is called, is 14" long and 1⅜" wide and has a specially shaped slot in its flat handle which can be used for pulling out nails in wooden cases. The slot is also handy for hanging the opener up when not in use. The blade is of good steel and can be sharpened on an emery wheel or a whetstone

PACKAGED STRING TIES have recently appeared on the market as substitutes for rubber bands. They consist of a stiff paper square with an extra heavy disk to which a length of strong string is fastened. The ties are boxed in the form of a coiled strip having perforations which make it easy to tear off individual ties as needed. Each coil contains 250 ties. Wrapped around papers, envelopes, and small packages, the ties hold securely. They can be saved after use and put into service again and again

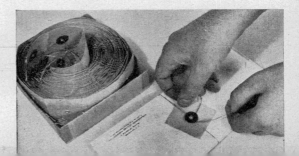

AIDS TO WARTIME
Housekeeping

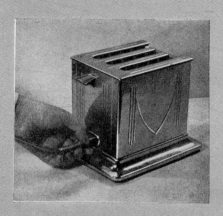

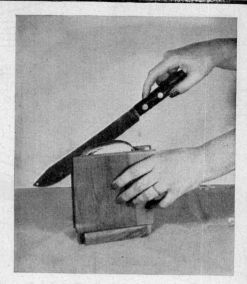

CARE OF YOUR TOASTER is wise practice these days, for in most instances it will be impossible to replace it. Clean crumbs out of the inside frequently with a soft brush. If the toaster has a removable crumb tray, take it out often for cleaning. The chrome-plated outer housing can best be cleaned with a damp, soapy cloth, then rubbed briskly with a dry, soft cloth. Never put the toaster in water. Be extremely careful during all cleaning not to damage the heating elements. After using the appliance, allow it to cool off before you wind the cord loosely around it. This will lessen the risk of short circuits that might come from repeated coiling

RESLICING PRESLICED BREAD is made easy with this wooden gadget designed and hinged like the cover of a book. A slice of bread is placed between the two covers and held upright while a knife is drawn down through it to make two thin slices. The covers permit holding the bread firmly without danger of cutting the hand. Any knife with a sharp blade is used. Besides making thin slices for Melba toast, canapés, and rolled sandwiches, the unit is a help with the last end of a roast or meat loaf

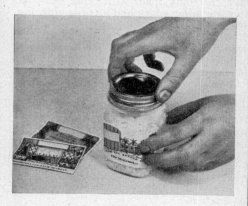

PERSONALIZED LABELS are a new idea in identifying jars for families who raise and put up their foods. The labels are attractively colored and are printed with the name of the purchaser. They come gummed on one side and, measuring 2⅜" by 4", will fit any jelly or canning container. There is a space in which to write the name of the contents and the date. These gay labels will add a bright touch to the fruits of your labor, and they will also be welcome presents for a friend who puts up food

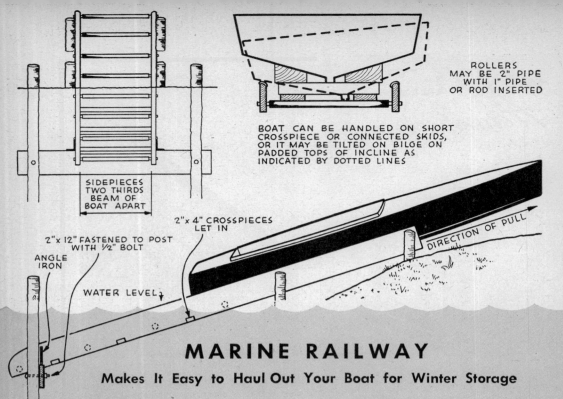

ROLLERS
MAY BE 2" PIPE
WITH 1" PIPE
OR ROD INSERTED

BOAT CAN BE HANDLED ON SHORT
CROSSPIECE OR CONNECTED SKIDS,
OR IT MAY BE TILTED ON BILGE ON
PADDED TOPS OF INCLINE AS
INDICATED BY DOTTED LINES

SIDEPIECES
TWO THIRDS
OF BEAM
OF BOAT APART

2"x 4" CROSSPIECES
LET IN

2"x 12" FASTENED TO POST
WITH 1/2" BOLT

ANGLE
IRON

WATER LEVEL

DIRECTION OF PULL

MARINE RAILWAY

Makes It Easy to Haul Out Your Boat for Winter Storage

THE incline of this easily-built marine railway is made of two planks set on edge. They must reach out to water deep enough to float the boat, and the rise should not be over 4" to 1' of length. Space the planks roughly two thirds the beam of the boat apart, fastening them with crosspieces let into their lower edges and secured with lag screws.

Rollers can be made of pieces of 2" pipe turning on longer 1" pipes or heavy rods which are fixed in the planks about 3' apart. The shape of the bottom of the boat should be taken into consideration in locating the rollers, especially in fixing the distance from them to the top edges of the side planks. Medium-sized boats can lie over slightly until one bilge bears on the top of the adjacent side plank. There will be little pressure when the hull is still water-borne, but above the water the edges of the side planks should be rounded and padded with old hose or canvas, and well greased so as to minimize friction.

Cut notches 2½" wide by 3" deep in the under edges of both side planks about 1' from the ends to be submerged. Fit a plank across two posts, as shown in the drawings, with one bolt only in each end. The posts should be 2' wider apart than the beam of the boat. Drive the posts far enough off shore so that the cross plank can be 2' below the draft of the boat. The single bolt in each end of the cross plank will prevent excessive strain

from developing while the posts are being alternately driven into position.

Float the assembled incline out over its location between the posts. Place rocks on it to submerge it so that the notches slip over the crosspiece, then fasten it there. The easiest way to do this is with strap-iron angles previously bolted on the two side planks just above the notches, each with a hole in its horizontal leg. Spikes can then be driven through these holes into the crosswise plank and bent over to hold the incline down. If necessary, you can submerge in a bathing suit and strike a few blows at a time. This fastening is merely to offset flotation, and can easily be released for hauling the railway ashore after the boat is taken out at the end of the season.

The inshore end of the railway is held securely in place by short posts. Sections can be added to extend it as far as desired. The same incline can even be carried high enough so that a truck can be backed up to the end of it and the boat slid aboard and hauled away for winter storage elsewhere.

No great power is required for hauling because of the rollers, although a block and tackle may prove helpful. Fasten the hauling gear to a heavy line looped completely around the hull and held with lighter lines across the top of the boat. This distributes the strain evenly throughout the hull instead of applying the entire load to a single mooring bitt and cleat.

BOAT HINTS

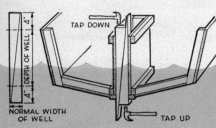

ONE OUTBOARD MOTOR used as shown above saves gas, carries twice as many passengers, and minimizes the danger of a spill in rough weather. The two canoes are held rigid with saplings lashed to the thwarts.

A WARPED TRUNK makes it hard to raise or lower the centerboard. To correct this condition, insert wedges at the center of the well as at the left before the boat is laid up for the winter, and leave them in until spring. Have a helper tap in one wedge while you drive in the other, being careful to expand the slot only slightly beyond its normal width.—H. S.

SMALL-BOAT DRY DOCK. Costing no more than a few dollars, this arrangement makes it easy to lift boats clear of the water for repairs or painting. Small boat yards and clubs, as well as individual boat owners, will find that it pays for itself quickly. The dimensions of the various parts will vary according to the size of the slip and the length of the boats to be accommodated. Those up to 30' in length can be raised in the dock shown at the right.

One man can readily lift a boat by means of the 10' long lever. This is hooked down to the dock at the end of its stroke so that the operator can then remove the pin which has been bearing the load in order to insert it in the new position. All four lifts should be raised to the same height before the first one is raised any further. The fork end of the lever is protected by covering it with sheet metal at the points where wear would otherwise occur.

If such a dock can be located high enough on tidewater, it is possible to make repairs to the bottom of a boat while standing on dry land. Away from tidewater, the top of the slip should be high enough above water level to give sufficient space for one to work conveniently on the bottom of a boat from a dinghy or wherry.—BRUCE MacINTOSH.

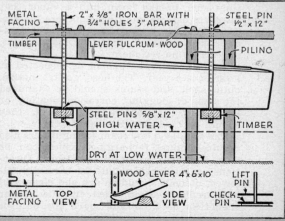

A FIRE extinguisher is a front-line weapon against fire. But, as with other weapons, its effectiveness depends on its ability to do the job for which it was designed, on its upkeep, and on the skill with which it is used.

Only three types are ordinarily found in residences. One, the soda-acid extinguisher, will combat fires fed by ordinary combustibles, such as wood, paper, and textiles, but not those involving inflammable liquids or electrical equipment. Another, the foam type, can smother a gasoline or oil fire, but must not be used on electrical apparatus.

The third—the familiar pump-gun vaporizing-liquid extinguisher—employs a carbon tetrachloride base instead of water and may be used on any kind of fire, but it is rarely made in very large sizes. On coming into contact with heat, the stream from this extinguisher breaks down into a vapor that displaces oxygen and thus smothers the fire. This vapor is a nonconductor, will not damage mechanical or electrical installations, and leaves no residue.

All of these units should be inspected at least once a year. The hose, gasket, nozzle, outer shell, and seams should be examined for signs of clogging, corrosion, denting, or tampering. If repairs are needed, they should be made by the manufacturer.

The soda-acid and foam extinguishers also require annual recharging, which can be done at home, preferably outdoors. Directions on the labels should be carefully followed, utensils should be dry and clean, and only refills recommended by the maker should be used. If you mark the date of maintenance on a tag attached to the handle,

this will serve as your reminder each year.

Despite its designation as a "chemical" extinguisher, the soda-acid unit uses only water to put out a fire. The chemicals provide pressure to throw the stream 30' to 40'. This pressure is supplied by carbon dioxide gas formed by the reaction of sulphuric acid with bicarbonate of soda when the extinguisher is inverted for use.

After the unit has been emptied to take its annual recharge, unscrew the ring-top handle and remove the acid bottle; then wash all interior parts thoroughly with clean water, draining the water through the hose. Dissolve the powdered chemical refill in warm, not hot, water, as directed on the label; pour the solution into the extinguisher to the point marked; and finally replace the acid bottle in its cage. When the cap is screwed back on the shell, make sure that at least four threads are engaged. A small amount of petroleum jelly rubbed on the threads will make this easier and facilitate removal for the next recharge.

The foam extinguisher looks like the soda-acid unit, and its parts are handled the same way when it is recharged. If you have any doubts about the kind you own, the Underwriters' rating on the label will identify it. The soda-acid type is rated A (for use on ordinary combustibles), while the foam is rated both A and B (the B meaning for use on inflammable liquids). Two chemical solutions must be replaced in the foam-type unit—one in the inner chamber and one in the outer. Directions on the label should be followed, and only the materials recommended should be used.

Vaporizing-liquid extinguishers are the easiest of all to service since they need recharging only after use, but the pump action should be tested annually by discharging a portion of the liquid into a clean dry con-

AGAINST FIRE

Extinguishers Must Be Ready for Instant Action . . . Here Is How and When to Service Them

By
DELBERT JOHNSON
Safety Research Institute

tainer. This test liquid can then be poured back through the filler opening. No lubricant should be used on the piston. Because ordinary commercial carbon tetrachloride may corrode and damage the extinguisher, use only the maker's processed refill.

Soda-acid and foam extinguishers located on a porch, in a garage, or in any exposed place should be housed in a tight cabinet that can be heated by a 50-watt bulb to keep the water from freezing—don't try to use an antifreeze chemical. A simple cabinet of 7/8" stock will suffice unless you live in a section where temperatures go below zero, in which case double-wall construction is needed. For this, make the outer walls of 1/2" stock, and arrange a lining of 1/2" wallboard or similar material, leaving a 1/2" air space between the the two walls. The door should also be of double construction, closing into a rabbet and held shut with a spring latch.

Inside dimensions may be as small as practicable just so the extinguisher may be removed quickly. Four 4" iron rods, or similar brackets, set in the sides about 4" above the floor will hold the unit. Under them should be mounted a 3" conduit box and receptacle for the lamp, which will then throw its heat upward and thus keep the entire cabinet warm. During a protracted freeze, or in subzero weather, the lamp should be kept burning continuously.

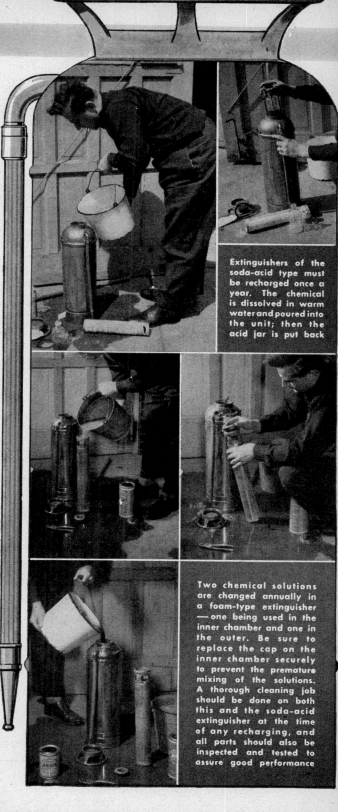

Extinguishers of the soda-acid type must be recharged once a year. The chemical is dissolved in warm water and poured into the unit; then the acid jar is put back

Two chemical solutions are changed annually in a foam-type extinguisher —one being used in the inner chamber and one in the outer. Be sure to replace the cap on the inner chamber securely to prevent the premature mixing of the solutions. A thorough cleaning job should be done on both this and the soda-acid extinguisher at the time of any recharging, and all parts should also be inspected and tested to assure good performance

Dainty Sprinklers Made from Oil Cans

WHEN plants are brought indoors for the winter, you will want one of these sprinklers made from regulation motor-oil cans. The larger one, built from an ordinary quart container with the top left on, holds enough water for several pots. For the opening in the top, score the metal deeply with dividers and tear out the unwanted part with pliers. Punch a hole ¾" from the bottom on the opposite side for soldering on the 9¼" spout, which can be made from a discarded auto gas line, any ¼" tubing, or a strip of tin-can metal rolled up and soldered. Cut a strip of the metal 2" by 15" for the handle, bend it as shown, solder the seam, and solder it to the can in two places.

The smaller sprinkler is made similarly except that only half of a can is used and the top is soldered on. It will be found convenient for small pots or a miniature indoor garden.

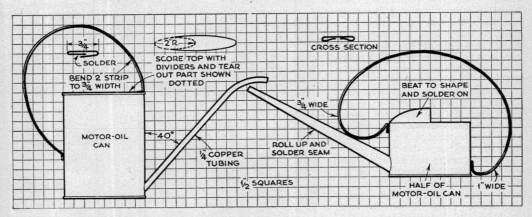

NOVEMBER CHECK LIST   [SHIPSHAPE HOME]

1. Inspect radiators for leaks and repair them with iron cement.
2. Drain a hot-water or steam system and refill with fresh water.
3. Scrape and cement joints in the fire pot of a hot-air furnace.
4. Repair or replace defective furnace grates.
5. Clean soot from the nozzle and burner unit of an oil-heating system.
6. Renew deteriorated smoke pipe from furnace to chimney.
7. Clean out scale and soot in boiler and tubes.
8. Insulate between chimney and wood framing with mineral wool.
9. Cut off water from all outdoor fixtures, such as sill cocks, and drain them.
10. Calk all cracks in the basement where air leaks in.

POPULAR SCIENCE MONTHLY SHOP DATA

ROCKING-HORSE BLOTTER

Is Fun to Carve

By ELMA WALTNER

MEET Hector Hobbyblot, a wooden (but not Trojan) horse whose happiest moments are spent riding hobbyhorse fashion on unblotted ink or in standing stanchly atop a stamp box. A jackknife job, Hector is well within the capabilities of inexperienced carvers.

Use any kind of wood you prefer, so long as it's easily worked. Lay out the profile pattern on a piece of 2" stock, with the grain vertical to give sturdy legs. Then cut out the profile and drill two or three holes between the front and rear legs to help remove extra wood.

The carving is done entirely with a sharp knife. Don't try for fine detail, since the angles and planes add to the attractiveness of the piece as well as making the carving easier. To insure proper proportioning, turn the work often in your hands and rough out the entire figure before finishing any part. Use sandpaper sparingly to preserve planes.

Finish all but the teeth with shellac; they are a gleaming white, with markings added by pen and India ink. Hector's eyes are white map pins painted with black pupils. His crowning glory, his coal-black mane, is achieved by drilling a row of small holes in his neck and gluing in tufts of black yarn.

For a blotter base, cut one piece of stock ¼" by 2" by 4" and one ¾" by 2" by 4" Round off the ends of the thinner piece and mount the figure on it with four small countersunk screws running from the underside to each hoof. Drill the hoofs first to prevent splitting. Shape the lower section of the base to a curve of about 8" radius and attach with two small screws running down from the upper section of the base. Use strips of blotter cut 2" by 6". If you wish, Hector and the upper portion of the base may be mounted on a stamp box.

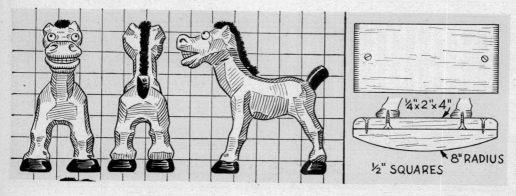

½" SQUARES   ¼"x2"x4"   8" RADIUS

Test Your Skill with This New Double-Deck Skip-Ball Game

IF YOU pull the shooter back just right and release it with a steady hand, your first count may be 200. But if your technique falters, your next count may be a lowly 5. The game is played by shooting balls against the hurdle with just the proper impetus to drop them between the high-scoring dowels. Your turn at play consists of five shots.

The dowel nearest the player, in the bottom row, is numbered 1. The next nine dowels are numbered, in order, 2, 3, 4, 5, 10, 20, 30, 40, 50. Each number refers to the space in which a ball may rest between it and the next dowel behind it. Dowel No. 50 is ⅜″ from the end of the box. The upper three dowels have two scoring spaces, the

forward one counting 200, and the rear space 100. Scoring here takes practice and skill. The five balls are wood, ⅝″ in diameter.

The model of the game shown in the photograph is attractively painted in five colors. The cardboard bottom and both removable backstops are blue. The sidepieces, the two backboards, and the hurdle are red. Bright yellow covers the guide tracks, front endpiece, shooter dowel, and 10 lower dowels in the scoring area. The top scoring dowels and the ram on the end of the shooting dowel are green. Scoring numbers are lettered in black on the upper surfaces of the scoring dowels.—MYRON FLEISHMAN.

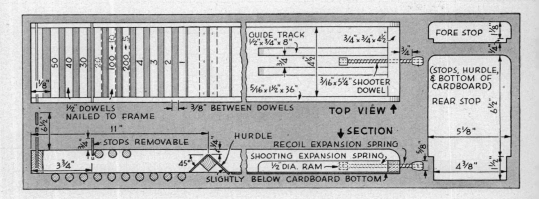

how to get
Better Light from Your Home Lamps

POOR

GOOD

MANY a small electric lamp looks attractive in the store, but when you sit down to read or work by one, you may find that it is better to look at than to see by. Often the lamp is too stubby and the shade too small for proper lighting. Instead of discarding the lamp or putting up with poor light, specialists at the General Electric lighting research laboratories advise, simply make an extension base and use a shade with better proportions. These two steps will result in a substantial increase in the circle of useful light.

The extension base shown in the lower photo is a heavy mailing tube fitted with a turned-wood footing and filled with pebbles for weight. It has a cover recessed about ½" to hold the bottom of the lamp. A small notch in the lip permits the cord to come out. An attractive extension base may also be turned wholly of wood in a design harmonizing with the lamp and bored all the way through for a wire entering at the bottom.

Lighting experts say that a single-socket table lamp, with its recommended 100-watt bulb, should afford comfortable seeing within a 24" radius of the base. Whether or not this coverage is achieved, however, depends upon dimensions A, B, and C in the drawing. A squat, tightly shaded lamp has a relatively small useful light circle.

If B is lengthened to from 13" to 17" by an extension base and C is increased by a larger shade, the maximum useful dispersal can thereby be obtained. A should be as small as practicable, with the lower edge of the shade, viewed at eye level, covering at least part of the socket.

To obtain efficient reflection of light, use a shade that is lined with white. It is also desirable to select one that is fairly dense so as to reduce direct transmission of light to the eyes.

Poor lighting from a small lamp can be corrected very easily by adding an extension base and by replacing the shade. The extension shown above is made principally from a mailing tube

How raising the lamp and increasing the shade diameter give better light dispersal is illustrated at the right

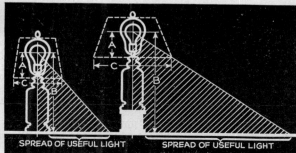

SPREAD OF USEFUL LIGHT   SPREAD OF USEFUL LIGHT

This original negative was made with paper in the camera instead of film. An extra-thin grade of single-weight paper was used here

Filmless Photography

SHOOTING NEGATIVES ON ENLARGING PAPER IS GOOD FUN AND WILL BRING REAL RESULTS

EXPERT photographers desiring to produce highly artistic and dramatic photographs have long used the paper-negative process. This consists of making a positive print from a film and retouching it, and then making a negative paper print from the positive for further retouching, after which a finished photograph is finally secured by a print or enlargement made from the paper negative.

Without going through all these steps, and without using film at all, you can get just as fine results. You can make your first negative on enlarging paper in your own camera, and work directly on that, printing your final positive from this lone negative. It is a simple process and is a lot of fun. Enlarging paper is much cheaper than film, and by using it instead of film, you eliminate expensive waste on questionable shots and can also make a lot of pictures you might otherwise pass up because of the cost.

And not to be overlooked is the opportunity to do really thorough and artistic jobs of retouching. Working on a paper negative, the camera enthusiast has a chance to try many effects, rubbing out those that prove least desirable, altering high lights and shadows, and finally bringing the nega-

PHOTOGRAPHY

Either contact prints or enlargements may be made from the paper negative, which may be retouched for special effects

By KONRAD CRAMER

with Your Own Camera

tive to perfection, confident that erasures, pencil marks, and the like will not show up on the finished print.

Probably still more satisfying is the fact that you can know the results of your picture taking within a few minutes of snapping the shutter, for the whole photograph is unfolded for you as you develop the paper negative. As soon as it is dry, if the shot was a good one, you can begin retouching the paper negative to bring out desired effects, and then print your positive photograph from this negative.

To use this type of direct paper negative, cut the enlarging paper to fit in the back of your camera. Loading is similar to that of plate or film-pack cameras, but only one paper negative can be loaded at a time. If you have a roll-film camera, cut the paper for single negatives and load as you would

for the other types. It is not always necessary to do the loading in a darkroom, but a subdued red-orange light is essential.

For best results in taking these pictures, use single-weight, soft paper and expose it under strong light. The larger-size cameras, $3\frac{1}{4}''$ by $4\frac{1}{4}''$ and up, are ideal for this method. For my own purposes, I use lightweight paper in an 8" by 10" studio camera with which I can get a negative that requires no enlarging. Add to your equipment two or three photoflood lights, and you can make portraits of unusual quality if you can find a model who will hold still for 10 to 15 seconds. This exposure is usually necessary to get a good paper negative. If a comfortable pose is selected, most people can sit still that long with little trouble.

Still life is ideal material for direct paper negatives. Landscapes, with or without

Dramatic silhouettes with high lights and deep shadows for both figures and background, as shown in the photograph above, are created by retouching both sides of a paper negative before it is contact-printed or enlarged as desired

Portraiture of distinction is possible on paper negatives if the subject will hold a pose for as long as 13 seconds

figures in the foreground, are also good. Sometimes you will find that the negative itself has great pictorial charm. In such a case, there is nothing to hinder you from mounting and exhibiting a negative.

The paper negative can be retouched on both sides, using a ground glass and light when working on the back. Light tones, modulations, and additions may be added by building up the wanted values with any soft pencil or crayon and then shading with a stump. Large areas may be handled with a bit of chamois and powdered crayon. Dark tones and accents in the final print can be produced by lightening parts of the negative with local reducer or by carefully rubbing them down with powdered pumice. Major blemishes and faulty backgrounds can thus be corrected.

Some photographers using this process content themselves with only a slight softening of the image, caused by the printing light having to penetrate the paper instead of transparent film, plus a few slight retouching corrections. It seems best to go easy in the beginning so that most of the original character of a photograph is retained. Overworked paper negatives may take on the final appearance of a poor drawing, a result that is to be avoided.

Paper negatives can be enlarged or contact prints made from them. Extra-thin paper should be used in the smaller cameras as it gives a very pleasing texture effect when enlarged. The general effect of the enlargement is diffused, in contrast to the sharp definition of contact prints, yet the enlargement often has simplicity and distinction.

The writer made an 8" by 10" cardboard camera, using an ordinary magnifying glass as a lens, two cartons telescoping into each other, and a piece of ground glass which is interchangeable with a printing frame. If you make up such a camera for yourself, you'll be set for some inexpensive and distinctive photography, for paper negatives afford many ways in which to achieve a controlled artistic effect.

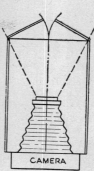

CAMERA

NIGHT AND DAY can be dramatically portrayed in the same picture by using a simple duplicator attachment. Build a box that can be secured to the front of your camera, fitting it with two vertical doors. Aim at a scene that will afford interesting day and night contrast and take, say, a day-light picture with one door closed. Leave the camera untouched until nightfall; then open this door and close the other to make a second exposure on the same film. With a film-pack camera, just block off half the film with cardboard inside the camera, and reverse it between shots.—LOUIS HOCHMAN.

PORTABLE FLOODLIGHTS. Good indoor pictures require adequate lighting, particularly if color film is used. Shown at right is a compact case, only 8" by 11" by 16½", which holds six photofloods, complete with reflectors and extension cords. The case divides into two three-lamp banks of No. 1 photofloods which can be used separately on the floor or on tables or can be hung from picture molding.

As shown in the drawing, the cases are made from thin wood and the reflectors are ordinary white enameled oven pans, fastened to cleats inside each case. Sufficient air space should be allowed so that the cases won't get too hot. Air holes are cut behind the pans to provide ventilation.

In using the outfit, remember that six No. 1 photofloods will load a 15-amp. circuit to capacity. The 18-gauge extension cords should always be plugged into wall outlets, never into lamp sockets.—PAUL KOMROFF.

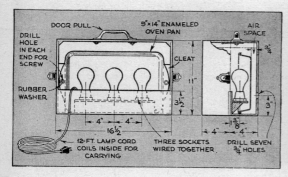

DOOR PULL — 9"x14" ENAMELED OVEN PAN — AIR SPACE

DRILL HOLE IN EACH END FOR SCREW

RUBBER WASHER

CLEAT

¾

11"

3½"

3"

16½"

4" — 4"

4" — 4"

1⅜"

¾"

— 12-FT. LAMP CORD COILS INSIDE FOR CARRYING

THREE SOCKETS WIRED TOGETHER

DRILL SEVEN ¾ HOLES.

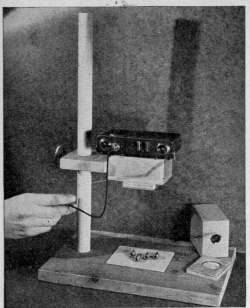

DUMMY CAMERA

Focuses Copying and Close-up Shots

AN INGENIOUS copying and close-up outfit, especially suitable for roll-film cameras which lack ground-glass focusing, may be built of wood scraps, a ground glass, and two lenses.

The principle is simple. A vertically sliding camera holder contains a supplementary lens, while a cardboard dummy camera has a lens of the same focal length as the camera lens. The dummy camera, which has ground glass instead of film, is used while adjusting the camera holder to sharp focus, after which the real camera is put in position and the picture snapped.

Design the camera holder so that the camera will always assume the same position when laid on it. The supplementary lens may be a regular copying or portrait attachment, or one of the clipped-edge lenses now available at low cost.

Make the dummy camera out of cardboard, proportioned so that its lens, when the dummy is in the camera holder, occupies precisely the position which the real camera lens would occupy. The lens in the dummy need not be of high optical quality, provided that its focal length approximates that of the camera lens. Mount a piece of ground glass in the dummy at the plane of sharp focus for objects more than 200' distant. The camera field may be located on the ground glass in this manner: Put a piece of ground glass (rough side down) on the film aperture of your camera, focus at infinity, and then put the camera in the stand. Adjust the height until a sheet of newspaper tacked to the easel is in sharp focus and note the area covered. Then put the dummy in place of the camera and mark the same field on the ground glass.

To take a picture, focus with the dummy camera and supplementary lens in the holder. Replace the dummy with the real camera, which should be focused for infinity and stopped down to f/16 or f/32, and make the exposure.—ERVIN WALTERS.

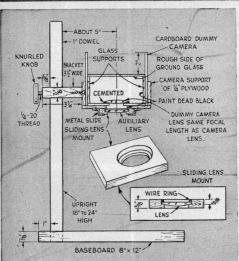

The cardboard dummy camera, below left, uses a lens with a focal length equal to that of the lens in the real camera. Note that the field limits are indicated on the ground glass. The other pictures below show how the supplementary lens and dummy are inserted in the holder. Different auxiliary lenses may be used

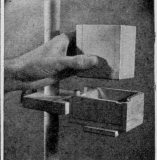

LETTER ALBUMS which combine space for six snapshots and two 4¾" by 8" writing surfaces are now on the market. Excellent for sending photos to service men, the folded letters protect pictures in transit, and may be used on receipt as pocket albums.

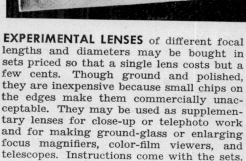

EXPERIMENTAL LENSES of different focal lengths and diameters may be bought in sets priced so that a single lens costs but a few cents. Though ground and polished, they are inexpensive because small chips on the edges make them commercially unacceptable. They may be used as supplementary lenses for close-up or telephoto work and for making ground-glass or enlarging focus magnifiers, color-film viewers, and telescopes. Instructions come with the sets.

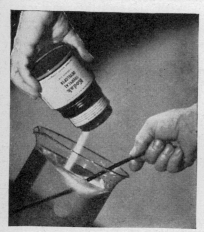

PORTABLE DARKROOM equipment, compactly arranged in an easily carried case, is now being made for the armed forces. Similar models are planned for postwar civilian use. Besides chemicals, paper, trays, and a daylight developing tank, the case holds a timer, safelight, thermometer, easel, and an enlarger that can be powered by a car battery. It also has space for a camera, flash synchronizer, and filters.

HOT-WEATHER DEVELOPMENT of films is said to be easier and safer with certain new chemical solutions. Films can be processed in temperatures that range up to 100 deg. F. without risk of softened emulsion or reticulation. The temperature-resistant solutions include developers, hardeners, and fixers. Photographers working in hot weather in temperate zones, those in the tropics, or those using makeshift field darkrooms will find the chemicals of special value.

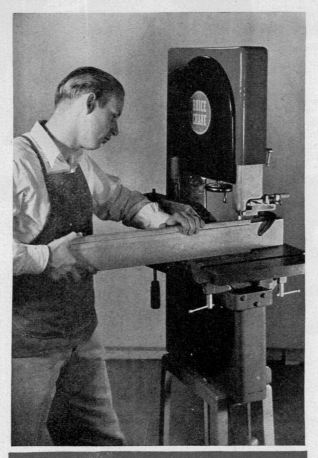

Ripping a cabinet-rail tenon. The length is gauged by a stop block clamped near the end of a straight fence that is long enough to hold the work steady

Special Jigs and Attachments
ADAPT
Your Bandsaw
TO MANY USES

By EDWIN M. LOVE

HOMEMADE attachments and jigs will greatly extend the uses to which a small bandsaw can be put. They make possible accurate cutting of tenons, automatic sawing of irregular curves, thinning of stock for bending around forms, and other types of jobs.

What is a setup for cutting tenons? First cut the cheeks, or sides, of the tenons. To guide the work, clamp a piece of straight square stock to the table for a fence parallel to the line of sawing. This fence must be high enough to support the work accurately with the face side in a vertical plane. The distance from the fence to the saw blade is such that the kerf will be made in waste wood with its far side forming the tenon cheek. This distance should be established by making trial cuts in scrap wood. Clamp a block to the fence where it will stop the forward motion of the work when the cheek is cut to length.

With this setting, saw one cheek of all like tenons, sliding the face side against the fence. If the pieces have parallel edges, they may be turned end for end, with the face sides kept against the fence. The position of the stop block is shifted if the tenons differ in length.

If the pieces are equal in thickness, their opposite sides may be put against the fence when the other cheeks are sawed, but if the thickness of the stock varies, such reversal will make the tenons either too thick or too thin. In this case, the fence should be reset to keep the face sides of the pieces against it. Shifting of the fence can be avoided if it is first set to cut the cheek opposite the face side. Then a shim of proper thickness may be inserted between the fence and work for sawing the face cheeks.

To cut the shoulders, as shown in one photo and in the sketch, clamp a stop block to the table at right angles to the blade. Also clamp on a length block to locate the tenon ends. Rest the piece to be cut on edge, rock the upper edge toward the stop block, and slide the lower edge forward until the blade severs the waste. As before, use test cuts when setting the blocks, and make allowances for variations in stock thicknesses.

These methods apply only to comparatively short stock cut to exact length. Trim the tenons to width with similar setups, but with the face sides lying on the table. Trim the shoulders freehand or use the miter gauge.

When through tenons are made, cut the pieces roughly to length and use shoulder stops to locate the shoulder cuts for the second tenons after the first ends are cut. This assures accurate shoulder-to-shoulder measurements and correct frame dimensions after assembly. It is a good method to use even when the stock is precut to length. If the bandsaw is equipped with a metal fence, screw a larger auxiliary fence to it so as to give a firm support when wide work is handled.

Of what use is a trough jig? This is a jig in which a piece of square stock can be supported cornerwise with the diagonals vertical and horizontal. The construction is shown in the drawing. Make a center kerf

at one end and notch one side. A typical use of this jig is in scoring the ends of a turning square to give bite for the live center of the lathe. Clamp the jig to the table with the blade in the end kerf and feed the turning square against the saw, cutting about 1/16" deep. Turn up the other diagonal and repeat.

With the same jig clamped to the table so that the blade enters the wider side notch, it is possible to trim off the corners of built-up table legs. This saves turning time in roughing down the bulbs on post-blocked turnings and the like.

How is part of a rail sawed thin? Clamp the work to a heavy squared piece. Notch the inner face where the bend is to begin and make a kerf at the end. The slot can be made with several bandsaw cuts and a sideward motion to break out the waste. The blade is then entered to rip out the required portion. Cut the thin section an extra ½" long to allow wedges to be driven in for tightening. This method of clamping the piece to a heavy squared piece of stock is useful on many jobs since it gives ade-

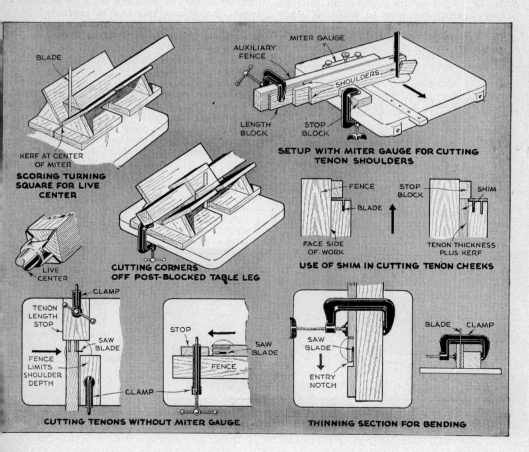

SCORING TURNING SQUARE FOR LIVE CENTER

SETUP WITH MITER GAUGE FOR CUTTING TENON SHOULDERS

CUTTING CORNERS OFF POST-BLOCKED TABLE LEG

USE OF SHIM IN CUTTING TENON CHEEKS

CUTTING TENONS WITHOUT MITER GAUGE

THINNING SECTION FOR BENDING

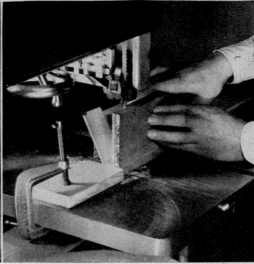

A rail being thinned to allow bending is clamped to a 3″ by 4″ piece permitting freehand guiding

Accurate shoulder cutting is assured with stop and length blocks to control the depths of tenon cuts

quate support when freehand cutting is done.

What can be done to correct saw-blade lead? If the blade doesn't lead true, it can often be improved by holding an oilstone lightly against the side to which it leads while the saw is running, thus reducing slightly the set of the teeth on that side. A little lead is of no consequence in freehand

work, and the fence can be quickly adjusted for ripping to make it parallel to the line of cut, but when a miter gauge is used, difficulties due to wedging may be encountered. Sometimes this can be corrected by loosening the table mounting screws sufficiently to allow the table to be swiveled by light mallet taps on one corner.

How are self-guiding jigs made? The drawings illustrate a basic type. The size depends upon the design to be cut. The lower, or fixed member, has cleats beneath it to locate it on the saw table, and it has a saw kerf to allow entry of the blade. Set a guiding peg in the fixed member in front of the blade, and if the curve to be cut allows, add another peg behind the blade. The

SELF-GUIDING JIG

At the left is a sketch of a jig for sawing several layers of plywood at one time. Before cutting, make sure all pieces are up against the stops. A sliding pin guides the work as it is sawed, thus eliminating layout and producing accurate work at the same time

upper member of the jig is a sliding form with one or more guide slots cut in it. These must be accurately made, with no more than free sliding clearance on the pegs, and they must be long enough for the blade to run free in front of and behind the parts to be cut. Screw on stop blocks, as detailed, and also hardwood bridging strips to stiffen the slit ends of the jig members. Place the stock to be cut against the back and side stops of the sliding member and push forward until stopped by the peg.

Stop Rod Prevents Creeping of Miter Cuts on Circular Saw

MAKE a ¾" hardwood block as long and as high as the face of the miter protractor. Set two countersunk bolts in one side of the block, with nuts set flush on the other side. Let the bolts extend ¾" to go through holes in the miter gauge, where they are attached with two extra nuts. Cut a groove in the bottom of the block for the stop rod. A vertical hole takes a bolt having a hole drilled through its lower end to let the rod slip through. When the wing nut on the upper end of the bolt is tightened, the sliding rod, with a right-angle bend at the end, is locked and holds the work from creeping. If you make rods of various lengths, you can handle many sizes of work.—B. B.

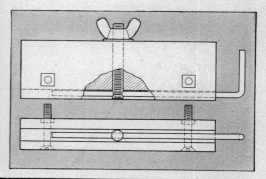

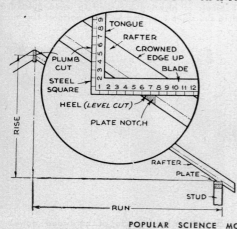

BRACES AND COMMON RAFTERS   [SHIPSHAPE HOME]

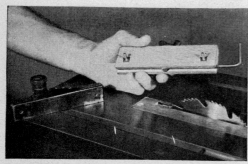

TONGUE
RAFTER
CROWNED EDGE UP
BLADE
PLUMB CUT
STEEL SQUARE
HEEL (LEVEL CUT)
PLATE NOTCH
RISE
RAFTER
PLATE
STUD
RUN

The plumb and level cuts of a common rafter are determined by the rise and run of the roof pitch. The rise is the vertical distance between the plate and a point on the plumb cut which is located by extending a line along the rafter, parallel to its edge, at the depth of the plate notch. The run is the distance from the center to the outside of the plate. This is usually expressed in terms of inches rise per 12" of run. The sketch illustrates 8" in 12".

Lay the square on the stock with the figures coinciding with the crowned edge. A line drawn along the tongue is the guide for the plumb cut, and a line drawn along the blade is a guide for the level or heel cut.

The plate notch is usually cut 1" deep on the plumb for 2" by 4" stock. On wider rafters, cut deep enough to provide a 2" or greater bearing of the heel on the plate.

The same principle applies to cutting butted braces.

POPULAR SCIENCE MONTHLY SHOP DATA

Modern Cabinet Conceals

1 Wood extensions are attached at the sides and back of the machine top with the help of cleats

NEW DRESS PROMOTES IT

By Charles and Bertram Brownold

DUSTED off and rehabilitated, many old-fashioned sewing machines are doing yeoman work to help the family budget. With a new dress to hide ugly Victorian lines, yours may be brought out into the open where it will be easier to get at when there is mending to be done or new clothes to be made. The simple wooden cabinet shown can be made for any drop-head model

2 Use of a plumb line shows the back projects beyond the ironwork

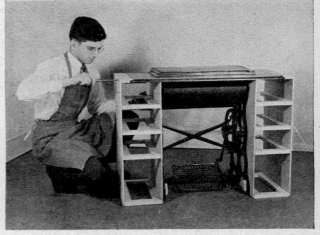

3 Drawer cabinets of plywood attached to rectangular frames are screwed to the sidepieces and wooden parts of the machine

4 Corner blocks lock matching ones on a front panel, while others hold the cabinet to the frame

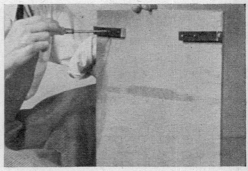

5 Sliding bolts made of hardwood dowels lock the top of this detachable panel to the cabinet

Old Sewing Machine

FROM ATTIC TO PARLOR

and will double as a living-room chest or desk, a dining-room sideboard, or a bedroom dressing table.

Discard the old drawers and attach a 2″ by 3″ piece to each end of the table, as in Fig. 1, rabbeting the inner edge to fit the routed edge of the top. Set the upper surfaces and ends flush and fasten on the underside with thin hardwood cleats, such as those shown in Figs. 1 and 2. The backs of the top drawers that will be installed later

Top and front panel removed and its dropped head lifted, the old machine does a good job of sewing

6 These dowel bolts are screwed to the handles through slots in the panel that permit sliding

7 With its new dress completed, the old-fashioned machine becomes an attractive piece of furniture

are cut down about ½″ to allow them to slide past these cleats.

It may be necessary to attach similar extensions to the front and back if the metal frame projects beyond a plumb line held from the table edges (Fig. 2). On the machine used here, an extension was needed only at the back since all parts at the front were within the plumb line.

For each of the side drawer cabinets shown in Fig. 3, you need two ¼″ plywood panels and four rectangular frames. These frames, of ¾″ by 1½″ stock, must be the same size and accurately squared. They have lap joints glued up under pressure The plywood panels are attached to them

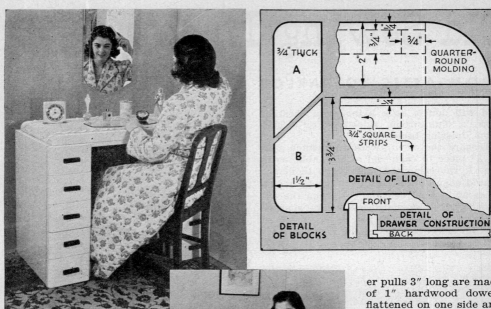

Above, the machine serves as a dressing table when not used for sewing, and at right as a desk. Some details that will aid in construction are shown in drawings at the upper right

with countersunk screws driven in from the outside.

The inner panel of each cabinet is held tightly against the iron frame by fitted hardwood blocks at the bottom, as illustrated in Fig. 4, and at top it is fastened by screws to the woodwork of the machine. Openings should be cut in the plywood to accommodate any projecting parts of the ironwork. The outer panels are about 1" longer than the inner, and their upper ends are fastened with screws to the table-top extensions. One piece of plywood is fastened across the entire back of the machine.

Stock 1" thick is used for the drawer fronts, the sides of which are rounded off as shown in the photographs. The deep bottom drawers—spacious enough to hold both materials and work—have fronts made of two pieces so that when closed each appears to be two drawers. All the fronts are deeper than the drawers themselves, covering the frames upon which the drawers slide, and are wide enough to be flush with the cabinet sides. The bottoms are plywood glued into rabbets ¼" from the lower edges of the fronts, sides, and backs. Draw-er pulls 3" long are made of 1" hardwood dowels flattened on one side and fastened with screws from the inside.

When the machine is not in use, the top is covered by a lid having pegs that fit into holes bored in the table-top extensions. The lid is made of ¼" plywood and quarter-round molding held together by ¾" strips, as shown in a drawing, and on the front is a 1" plywood strip concealing that part of the sewing-machine top between the two drawer cabinets.

The treadle and driving wheel are kept from view by a plywood panel (Fig. 5) that is removable. Hardwood blocks near each lower corner of the panel and on the lower corners of the drawer cabinets hold this removable piece at the bottom (Fig. 4), while sliding hardwood bolts fasten it at the top. These bolts (Fig. 6) are made of 5" lengths of 1" hardwood dowels and are attached to handles on the outside with wood screws extending through slots. The bolts slide into holes bored in the drawer cabinet walls.

Either paint or stain may be used as a finish. Before painting, fill all exposed countersunk screws in the side panels with a hard-drying filler. If a stain is used, it will be necessary to glue a thin veneer panel over each side panel to cover the screw heads. The drawer fronts should be made wide enough to allow for this.

Model Maker's Turning Tools Are Ground from Small Files

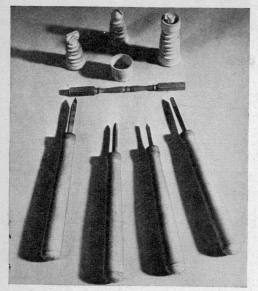

FOUR excellent wood-turning tools, especially suited for model making and other small-scale lathe work, can be ground from two worn-out 6" round files. Break the files in a vise so that the pieces are of about equal length (Fig. 1) and grind them until they are rectangular in shape as shown in Fig. 2. The pointed ends need only be rough-ground (Fig. 3) since they will fit within the handles, but the exposed portions should have all file marks removed. Be sure that the surfaces which will bear on the lathe rest are ground smooth.

The cutting points should be shaped with particular care to secure the angles shown in Fig. 4; use a grinding jig if one is available. Handles can be made from 5/8" birch or maple dowel. Ferrules are not necessary if the handles are drilled out sufficiently before the tools are forced in. Finish the cutting edges on an oilstone to razor keenness. If you wish to make a set of larger tools, pillar files will need less grinding than larger round files.—C. W. BERTSCH.

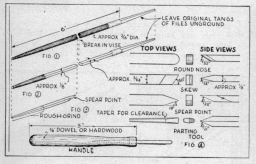

Discarded Razor Transformed into Keen Whittling Knife

A WHITTLING knife that will hold an exceptionally keen edge can be made from an old straight razor. Since the original shaving edge is too thin for its new role, it should be ground back about 1/4". Do not remove more than is necessary to thicken the edge slightly, because many razors are tempered only part way back from the edge. Take care not to "burn" the steel. Grind the entire blade to the shape shown in the drawing at the right, reducing the thickness at the back if desired. Use hardwood or a piece of 3/4" birch dowel for the handle and attach a ferrule of seamless brass or copper tubing. If such tubing is unavailable, a discarded kitchen fork or spoon will probably yield a ferrule. Restore the knife edge to razor sharpness on an oilstone and make a leather or wooden sheath to fit the blade, as shown in the photograph.—C. W. B.

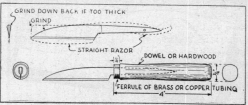

Furniture casters won't stick to a floor and mar its sheen in very hot weather if a thin coating of floor wax is applied to the wheels. In damp weather a little wax put in the sockets of the casters will keep them rust-free and free-turning

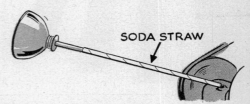

SODA STRAW

If you need to lubricate machine parts so placed that they are hard to reach, and an oil can with a long spout is not available, try using a soda straw on the end of the spout for an extension

NOTCH FILED IN DIAL AT POINT USUALLY DESIRED

Most people prefer to have a furnace-regulating thermostat installed in a spot where it will not be noticeable and yet will serve efficiently. This often means that insufficient light will fall on the dial for accurate setting. Squinting in a dark corner and guesswork regulation of your heat can be avoided, however, by having a small notch filed in the dial face at the temperature or temperatures most frequently desired so that the exact setting can be made by touch alone. A small triangular notch like the one shown above can be made quickly with a three-cornered file

When loose ration points are received in change, a good precaution against their loss is to place them in an envelope pasted on the inside of the ration-book cover—a convenient, safe receptacle

Screw one leg of a spring-type clothespin to the inside of a drawer for keeping letters, bills, and receipts where they can be found when wanted

One way to get a broken key out of a lock is with a piece of jigsaw blade. Push the blade into the lock with the teeth pointing outward, twist it so they will be at right angles to the key, and pull

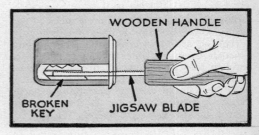

WOODEN HANDLE

BROKEN KEY

JIGSAW BLADE

SHIPSHAPE

If members of your family or office staff absent-mindedly pocket a key that should be left for others to use, put the key on a ring that is too big to go into a pocket

In an emergency, a very satisfactory washer can be made for a faucet by removing the metal from the center of a round typewriter eraser. The hole will fit the screw, and the rubber can then be pared to proper size

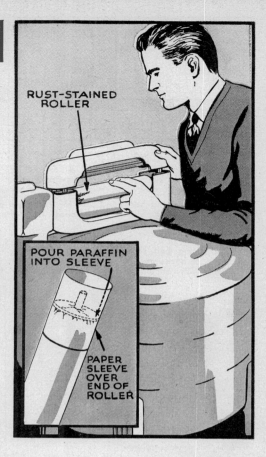

RUST-STAINED ROLLER

POUR PARAFFIN INTO SLEEVE

PAPER SLEEVE OVER END OF ROLLER

SCREWS

1 3/4"

5 1/4"

15 3/4"

1" STOCK

Milk bottles can't be kicked over and broken if they are held in this sturdy wall bracket. Make enough holes for your needs, and slant the back edges of the ends if your house is of clapboard

Friction tape is likely to dry out and lose most of its adhesiveness when removed from an original wrapper. Use an empty shoe-polish can as a handy, airtight container in which tape will keep fresh

Service-worn clothes wringers can be given many a day of extra life if the rust and discoloration that come in time from their iron roller cores are eliminated. These stains result from water that has seeped into the cores through the frayed and loosened rubber at the ends. A repair may be effected by removing the rollers from the wringer and fastening paper collars around the worn ends. The rollers can then be sealed against water and secured against rust if melted paraffin is poured into the collars. Gears and bearings should be cleaned with gasoline and coated with light grease

Bolts may be made to hold in concrete by winding the threads with wire, inserting them in drilled holes, and filling the space left with cement. They are withdrawn and reinserted with a wrench

SHOE POLISH CONTAINER

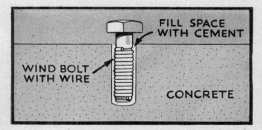

FILL SPACE WITH CEMENT

WIND BOLT WITH WIRE

CONCRETE

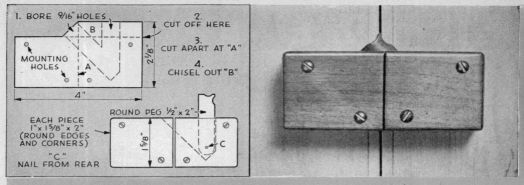

1. BORE 9/16" HOLES
2. CUT OFF HERE
3. CUT APART AT "A"
4. CHISEL OUT "B"

MOUNTING HOLES

2⅛"

4"

EACH PIECE 1" x 1⅝" x 2" (ROUND EDGES AND CORNERS)

"C" NAIL FROM REAR

ROUND PEG ½" x 2"

1⅝"

Mac: entirely of hardwood with the exception of screws, this drop-type latch is designed for use on : home-built cabinet or cupboard. Its pivoted moving part is cut out as shown in the drawing

The sliding bolt shown below, also of wood, is another distinctive latch. The bolt itself is a piece of hardwood dowel, while the remainder of the latch is made up from a block of grained stock. Care should be taken that the grain of the two halves match or form a pleasing contrast

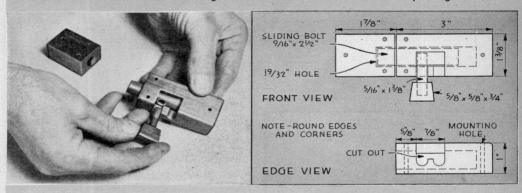

SLIDING BOLT 9/16" x 2½"

1⅞"

3"

1⅜"

19/32" HOLE

FRONT VIEW

5/16" x 1⅜"

5/8" x 5/8" x ¾"

NOTE - ROUND EDGES AND CORNERS

CUT OUT

EDGE VIEW

5/8" 7/8"

MOUNTING HOLE

1"

Wooden Hardware Gives Cabinets

LATCHES AND HINGES MADE FROM NICELY GRAINED STO

By FRANK WHEELOCK

BEAUTIFUL latches and hinges that blend so closely with the grain of your home-built cabinets and cupboards that they seem to grow out of the wood can be made from small bits of matching hardwood. Others that will have as interesting an effect and add to the distinction of a piece may be turned out by the craftsman from contrasting woods. Many designs are possible, from the simplest lines to highly ornamental carvings, and any will be pleasing so long as the fittings are in keeping with the piece on which they are used.

Illustrated are two latches and two hinges for a cabinet door. The dimensions are suitable for many pieces, but the plans are intended primarily to give an idea of what can be done with hardwoods and to form a basis for designs of your own creation.

Care should be taken to have a pleasing flow of grain in adjoining parts, or else the grain of two pieces should be turned so that the contrast will be arresting. The two parts of each of the latches shown may be cut from the same piece of stock to obtain a flowing grain, or a small block can be sawed down the center with the grain for

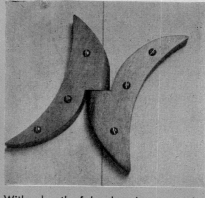

With a length of dowel used as a pin, this wood hinge is strong enough for a cupboard

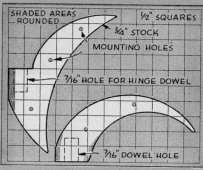

SHADED AREAS ROUNDED
½" SQUARES
¾" STOCK
MOUNTING HOLES
7/16" HOLE FOR HINGE DOWEL
7/16" DOWEL HOLE

Another design for a hinge suitable for a door that has greater width than height

New Character

OR HOME-BUILT PROJECTS

a perfect match. In the latter case,, the inside faces are exposed, and the abutting ends are placed to let the grain coincide.

One of the latches illustrated is of the drop type with the moving part pivoted inside one of the halves. This part may be of dowel, shaped at the top as shown in the drawing. It is raised to unlatch the door and dropped into a slot in the corresponding half to hold it shut. The other latch has a sliding bolt cut from a hardwood dowel, while pieces of hardwood dowel also form the pins of the hinges.

Finishing will depend for the most part on the finish of the piece on which the fit-

tings are used and also on the kind of hardwood from which they are made. In many instances, the finish desired will probably be one that will emphasize the wood grain. It should be put on in any case after a trial fit and before final assembly so that no unfinished corners will show in the exposed moving parts. Before the pieces are permanently assembled, all moving parts and contacting surfaces should be waxed and rubbed well. Parts of this kind that do not show, such as the hinge dowels, will need no finish except a thorough waxing. If it should be decided to use paint, don't paint parts between which there is friction.

CUTTING GEARS on the MILLING MACHINE

ONE of the oldest and most common methods of cutting gears is on the milling machine, which is still extensively used despite the fact that other machines designed specifically for gear cutting can do the job faster. Gear hobbers, shapers, and planers, for instance, can be set up for mass production of various types of gears, such as spur, helical, bevel, spiral, and herringbone gears.

Before using any of these machines, the operator should have a knowledge of the fundamentals and nomenclature of gear-tooth design. Reference to a good handbook will enable him to set the machine to the correct speed and feed for the type of gear to be cut and for the kind of metal of which the gear blank is made. It will also allow him to check on the blueprint to be sure that none of the dimensions are contradictory. In addition, he should check the cutter to be used to make the gear with both the specifications given in the blueprint and the data in the handbook.

Actual setting up of the milling machine for gear cutting and its operation, along with important points in gear design, have been made the subject of one of the series of motion pictures used by the U. S. Office of Education for training machine-tool operators. Frames from this film, which is distributed for the Government by Castle Films, appear on the succeeding pages.

In setting up the milling machine, be sure to place the outer-arbor support as close to the cutter as possible without danger of the gear blank striking the cutter. If the distance between this support and the machine column is too great, the cutter arbor will spring upward under pressure of the cut and result in teeth of uneven depth. For the same reason, a table jack is used to support the gear blank for the fairly heavy roughing cuts. Just how important it is to keep the cutter arbor and the gear-blank mandrel steady can easily be seen when one considers that the clearance of an 8-pitch gear of 36 teeth is only .0195".

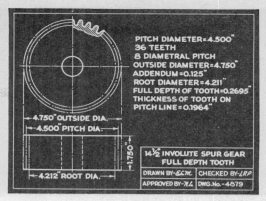

PITCH DIAMETER=4.500"
36 TEETH
8 DIAMETRAL PITCH
OUTSIDE DIAMETER=4.750"
ADDENDUM=0.125"
ROOT DIAMETER=4.211"
FULL DEPTH OF TOOTH=0.2695"
THICKNESS OF TOOTH ON
PITCH LINE=0.1964"

4.750" OUTSIDE DIA.
4.500" PITCH DIA.
4.212" ROOT DIA.
1.750"

14½ INVOLUTE SPUR GEAR
FULL DEPTH TOOTH

| DRAWN BY-EENL | CHECKED BY-LRP |
| APPROVED BY-ML | DWG.No.~4879 |

DIAMETRAL PITCH = $\dfrac{\text{NUMBER OF TEETH}}{\text{PITCH DIAMETER}}$

ADDENDUM
PITCH CIRCLE
DEDENDUM
CLEARANCE
PITCH DIAMETER=4.500
NUMBER OF TEETH=36
DIAMETRAL PITCH=8
PITCH CIRCLE

1 On gears, the pitch circle cuts the working center of the teeth, addendum and dedendum are equal, and clearance is added to give full depth of tooth. Diametral pitch is used in calculations

2 Here is the job. Cut 36 teeth in a gear blank machined to dimensions in the blueprint. The center hole is drilled and reamed so the face will run true when the gear is mounted on the mandrel

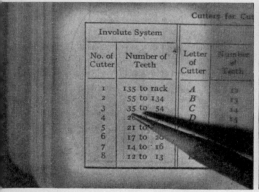

Cutters for Cu—

Involute System

No. of Cutter	Number of Teeth	Letter of Cutter	Number of Teeth
1	135 to rack	A	13
2	55 to 134	B	13
3	35 to 54	C	14
4	26 to	D	15
5	21 to		
6	17 to 20		
7	14 to 16		
8	12 to 13		

3 Since the shape of the teeth is to be involute, refer to the involute-system table of cutters in a handbook. A No. 3 cutter will provide this shape when the number of teeth is from 35 to 54

4 Specifications are stamped on the cutter. Here the diametral pitch (8), the number of teeth (35-54), and the full depth of tooth (D+f=.270") meet the requirements of the blueprint for the job

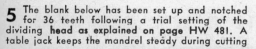

5 The blank below has been set up and notched for 36 teeth following a trial setting of the dividing **head** as explained on page HW 481. A table jack keeps the mandrel steady during cutting

6 One roughing cut and a finishing cut of 1/16" will be sufficient for teeth of this size. To determine the depth of the roughing cut, subtract 1/16" from the full depth of tooth *(continued)*

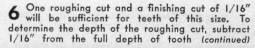

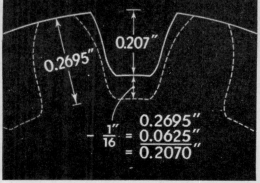

0.2695"
0.207"

$-\dfrac{1"}{16} = \dfrac{\begin{array}{r}0.2695"\\0.0625"\end{array}}{0.2070"}$

7 As the first step in setting the machine for the depth of the roughing cut, the cutter is slowly rotated while the table is raised by hand until the cutter barely scrapes the gear blank

8 At this point, the index dial on the handwheel that moves the table vertically must be set at zero. Each division on the dial represents .001", and a complete revolution raises the table .100"

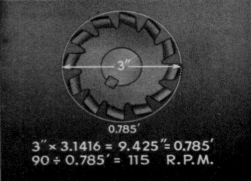

$$3'' \times 3.1416 = 9.425'' = 0.785'$$
$$90 \div 0.785' = 115 \quad \text{R.P.M.}$$

9 Run the table forward so the gear blank will clear the cutter; then raise it .207" for the roughing cut. This is accomplished by two full revolutions plus seven divisions on the index dial

10 Cutter speed is next calculated. Since the gear is cold-rolled steel, a speed of 90' per minute is required at the cutter teeth. Dividing this by the cutter circumference gives 115 r.p.m.

11 On most milling machines, the cutter or arbor speed can be set by a speed selector. Below, the speed dial is set at 116 r.p.m., the nearest speed of this machine to that required for the job

12 Feed, the speed of the table movement, is now determined. The 12 teeth of the cutter will remove 12 chips .002" thick in one revolution, so the feed should be 116 r.p.m. multiplied by .024"

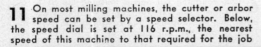

$$12 \times 0.002'' = 0.024'' \text{ PER REVOLUTION}$$
$$116 \times 0.024'' = 2.784'' \text{ PER MINUTE}$$

13 This gives a feed of approximately 2¾" per minute, at which point the feed-selector dial is set. It represents the distance in inches per minute the gear blank will be fed into the cutter

14 With the depth of cut, cutter speed, and feed set, take the first roughing cut, being sure to use an ample supply of cutting fluid; then stop the machine when the cutter just clears the blank

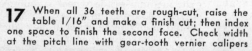

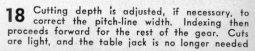

15 Set the table stop dogs to limit its travel at the point where the cutter clears the work. This keeps the cutter from traveling far enough to damage the dividing head and also speeds the job

16 Stop the table at the end of each reverse stroke and index the blank for the next tooth according to the dividing-head setup. Due to backlash, indexing must be continuous in one direction

17 When all 36 teeth are rough-cut, raise the table 1/16" and make a finish cut; then index one space to finish the second face. Check width at the pitch line with gear-tooth vernier calipers

18 Cutting depth is adjusted, if necessary, to correct the pitch-line width. Indexing then proceeds forward for the rest of the gear. Cuts are light, and the table jack is no longer needed

New SHOP IDEAS

BLUEPRINTS remain cleaner and last longer if they are kept off workbenches and left uncreased. One foreman lengthens the life of shop drawings by stapling two shipping tags behind the top edge of each as shown below. The blueprints can then be hung on two screw hooks over the workbench or machine where they are needed. A large number can be stored on two long curtain-rod hooks. If staples are not available, the tags can be attached with glue.—RONALD EYRICH.

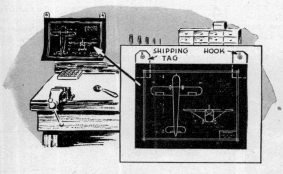

AIR PRESSURE speeds air power to smash the Axis. In the Fisher Body Division of General Motors, an ingenious trick suggested by Russell Dudley, an employee, has cut by 17 percent the time required to install electric wires in horizontal stabilizers. This was formerly done by first pushing through piano wire, which frequently caught at sharp bends in the conduit. Dudley's method is to tie the electric wire to a piece of string, blow the latter through with compressed air as shown below, and then pull the wire through.

IN SOLDERING, a hot iron put down hastily or carelessly may char the bench or table top. If a spring-type paper clip is previously put on the tool just behind the head, such damage will be avoided. Spread the grips of the clamp slightly to afford a broader support.—W. SWALLOW.

Courtesy *Grits and Grinds*, a Norton Company publication.

WORN PIPE WRENCHES can be restored to service by regrinding the teeth on the jaws. This can be done by hand on any bench grinder equipped with a 100 or 120-grit, medium-grade wheel running at 5,000 surface feet per minute. The wheel face should have one sharp and one rounded corner, the sharp one to grind to the root of the teeth and the rounded one to provide clearance when teeth are being ground close to the shank of the jaw. It is usually the teeth on the movable jaw that require sharpening. The angle between teeth is generally 100 deg., and this should be preserved as closely as possible in regrinding. A dull wrench can usually be reconditioned in this way in a few minutes. Teeth can be resharpened several times if care is used, the depth of hardness and the amount of metal removed on each occasion being the only limitations on the life of a wrench so reconditioned. A simple file test will show whether the teeth are still hard; a triangular testing file should just bite enough not to slide over the teeth.

Shop Marking Gauge Has Replaceable Scriber

By C. W. WOODSON

FITTED with a phonograph needle as a scriber, the gauge shown above will be found useful in making extremely accurate layouts on metal. Continued fineness of lines is assured since the needle can be changed when it becomes dull. The gauge is particularly suited to shops where aluminum sheet or steel plate is worked, but it will be a handy accessory also for many operations in home workshops.

Chucked as in Fig. 1, a short piece of 2½" shafting was turned to make the base. A center hole was then drilled in the end for tailstock support, and the handgrip was knurled as shown in Fig. 2. During this operation, the tool should be kept flooded with oil, and the knurls should be sunk deeply enough into the work to make a perfect diamond pattern.

With the knurling complete, and the work still in the chuck, a hole was drilled through and reamed to the diameter of the spindle (Fig. 3). Then a hole for a thumbscrew was drilled and tapped 10-32 in the side of the gauge, and the thumbscrew was turned and threaded on the end of a ⅜" rod. The head was knurled, and the complete screw was finally cut off. An 8" length of drill rod forming the spindle was faced square at each end and drilled to receive the scribing point and a setscrew to hold it securely.

Detailed specifications for the metal-marking gauge

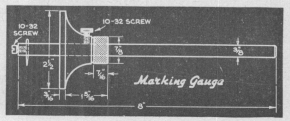

10-32 SCREW · 10-32 SCREW · 2½ · ⅞ · ⅜ · 7/16 · 3/16 · 1 3/16 · *Marking Gauge* · 8"

HW 553

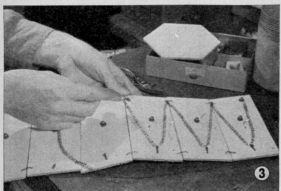
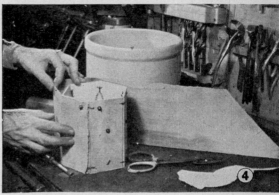

SMALL ELECTRIC

Resistance Furnace

HAS MANY SHOP USES

By Walter E. Burton

TEMPERING small tools, bluing metal parts, melting lead, and baking enameled pieces are just a few of the uses to which this efficient little furnace can be put in the small shop or laboratory.

A resistance coil of the kind used in electric heaters and toasters forms the heating element. Such an element can be purchased at an electrical supply house or salvaged from a discarded appliance. The furnace shown, designed to reach temperatures up to 1,000 deg. F., has one that draws 520 watts. Higher temperatures can be obtained by using a 1,000-watt element, or by making the heating chamber smaller.

Two concrete-asbestos shingles ⅛" by 9½" by 24", either smooth or textured, are needed for the furnace chamber. With a hacksaw, on a jigsaw, or by scoring the material with an awl and breaking it over an edge, cut six rectangles measuring 1¾" by 6". Cut also a hexagonal bottom measuring 1¾" on each side.

A jig such as that shown in Fig. 1 will speed the work of drilling a 1/16" hole ½" from the end and ¼" from the edge at each corner of these pieces. Center a similar hole ½" from one end of each to receive an S-shaped hook for holding the resistance wire. If you intend to use a crucible in the furnace, particularly a metal one, drill a hole in the center of each piece to take a 6-32 screw. Left long enough to project about ⅜" and secured with nuts, these screws will prevent the crucible from touching the element.

Link the rectangles together with small wire loops as shown in Fig. 2, with all the centered holes on the same side.

The coil hooks can be made of iron, copper, or nichrome wire. Insert the lower ones in the holes drilled for them and the upper ones through the links holding the pieces together. Drill a hole near the upper corner of each end rectangle to secure the two ends of the resistance wire. Measure the distance the wire will have to stretch, pull it out to slightly less than this length, and mount it as in Fig. 3.

With the element in position, fasten the two end rectangles together and insert the hexagonal bottom, securing this with some

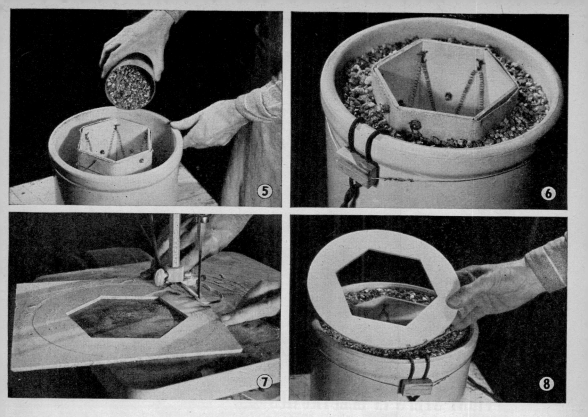

black furnace cement. Wrap a strip of asbestos paper around the outside of the unit as shown in Fig. 4. Tie this with wire.

Expanded mica, rock wool, or similar fireproof insulation material is used to line the furnace body, which may be a 2-gal. crockery jar or a metal can or bucket 8½" in diameter and as deep. Pour enough of the insulating material over the bottom to bring the heating chamber even with the top of the housing as in Fig. 5; then pour more insulation around the sides, tamping it firmly.

The connecting wires should be of the asbestos-covered type, but may be bare for the last 2" inside the crock if well separated. Secure them outside with a grooved wood or fiber block and a wire as shown in Fig. 6.

From the same asbestos shingle material, cut a disk to fit the crock with a hexagonal opening to accommodate the top of the heating chamber, as in Figs. 7 and 8. Add insulating material to within ⅛" of the top and fit this cover in place. A 7" disk of the same material fitted with a metal ring or knob serves as a lid for the furnace.

Work should rest on a platform of fire clay, firebrick, or metal about halfway between top and bottom. Some pieces may be suspended on wires from a rod laid across the top. For accurate temperature control a pyrometer should be used. The finished furnace ready for use is shown at the right.

FIRST STEPS IN ELECTRONICS

Photo courtesy of Westinghouse

How the Vacuum-Tube Grid

By JOHN W. CAMPBELL, JR.

USEFUL though the diode is in its various applications, it was not until Lee De Forest in 1907 inserted that simple third element—the grid—between the cathode and plate that the vacuum tube came into its heritage. That controlling grid has made it the indispensable tool not only of electronics, but also of physics, chemistry, medicine, metallurgy, and astronomy. It has rendered the electron the servant of industry instead of a plaything of the laboratory.

A diode passes current whenever the plate is positive with respect to its electron-emitting cathode. That plate-circuit current can be increased or decreased in just two ways: by controlling the emission of electrons (which in a thermionic-cathode tube can be done by varying the cathode temperature) or by altering the positive potential on the plate. Either method requires comparatively large current changes, such as we can bring about by the use of variable resistors,

as in Fig. 1 in the drawings on page HW 558.

Suppose, however, that we inserted a miniature Venetian blind between the cathode and the plate, along with a microscopic motor that could open or close its slats. If the slats were closed, electrons from the cathode would be unable to reach the plate; no current would pass. With the blind open, only a few electrons would strike the slats; the majority would pass through, and a plate current would flow.

If we could build so tiny a Venetian blind, and a small enough motor to control it, we would be able to control a fairly powerful plate current by means of a small current —the current needed to energize the motor. But although mechanically possible, the method is complicated and impracticable. Instead, the triode tube makes use of an electrostatic equivalent of our Venetian blind—a grid. Its slats are not metal, but electric fields, and they can open and shut smoothly 10,000,000,000 times a second.

The grid is simply a lattice of fine wires

Electrical nerve centers of glass and metal speed the messages of modern warfare. These high-power transmitting tubes, destined for the U. S. Navy, will help to maintain ship-to-shore communication

between cathode and plate, or, in some tubes, an open helix of wire surrounding the cathode. If connected to the cathode and therefore at the same potential, a grid presents to electrons emanating from the cathode the same appearance of an open network as it does to the eye (Fig. 2 on page HW 558) and the full plate current passes.

Suppose, however, that the grid is made more negative than the cathode by applying to it an additional negative potential of, say, -1 volt. Nothing will appear changed to us, but electrons, "seeing" electrically, will behold something like the grid shown in Fig. 3. The wires have been electrically "inflated" to many times their original size, and the space between them through which electrons can pass has been diminished. The electrons on the grid constituting that charge of −1 volt will repel some electrons that would have passed before. Furthermore, a grid negative in respect to the cathode tends to block the strong positive attraction of the plate. Fewer electrons reach the plate, and the plate current is smaller.

If we increase the negative potential on the grid to -2 volts by crowding additional

trol another current powerful enough to fill an auditorium with sound through a loudspeaker, open doors, control heavy machinery, or do other useful work.

A potential as small as .001 volt is detectable in a standard amplifier. A vacuum tube such as the 6F5-G will react to a current of one one-hundred-billionth amp. In a special two-tube circuit, a current of less than one ten-billionth amp. controls a current of 1 amp., which in turn can control 1,000 amp. or more. Special tubes can detect a current consisting of only 30 electrons per second—a flow so infinitesimal as to be meaningless when expressed in amperes.

The reason such sensitivity is possible is that individual electrons fed onto the grid have a cumulative effect. As the grid cannot emit electrons, they cannot escape. Because the grid is already negative, electrons emitted by the cathode are repelled by it and cannot affect it. As the tube is evacuated, there are no gas ions to be attracted by the grid and discharge it. In a theoretically perfect tube, having a perfect vacuum and a fully insulated grid, a current of one electron per hour on the grid would eventually mount to a potential that would block the plate current completely.

But the triode has, in addition to its amazing sensitivity to minute electrical potentials, another important characteristic. It reacts

Controls Electrons

electrons on it, the wires will be inflated still more, as in Fig. 4, and even fewer electrons will reach the plate. Finally, if a sufficient negative potential is applied, the electrostatic fields around the grid wires will completely overlap as in Fig. 5—the "slats" of our electrostatic Venetian blind will be closed—and no current whatever will flow across the tube.

When grid wires are closely spaced, even a charge of a few volts will block the plate current completely. If they are widely spaced, a higher negative potential is necessary.

In the triode, or three-element tube, we thus have a method of controlling the plate current that the diode did not afford. The vastly important advantage of this grid control is that a mere charge—a potential, not a current—will affect the plate circuit. The triode is an ultrasensitive relay, in which an infinitesimal current can con-

The 8012, shown full size at right, is a transmitter tube that delivers 35 watts at 500,000,000 cycles. Below is a slightly larger 300-watt tube

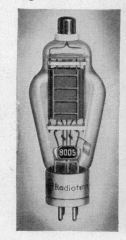

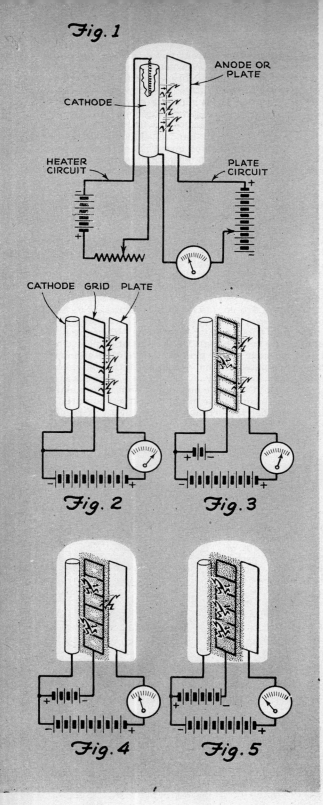

Fig. 1

CATHODE

ANODE OR PLATE

HEATER CIRCUIT

PLATE CIRCUIT

CATHODE GRID PLATE

Fig. 2   Fig. 3

Fig. 4   Fig. 5

This setup shows how grid changes affect the plate current. With a 275-volt power supply, 250 volts can be impressed on the plate and 25 on the grid. A few volts difference on the grid affects the lamp as much as a 100-volt change on the plate, the ratio indicating the amplification. Try varying the potentiometers and also reversing battery polarity. A glow spreads or diminishes on one plate of the neon lamp as the plate current increases or lessens

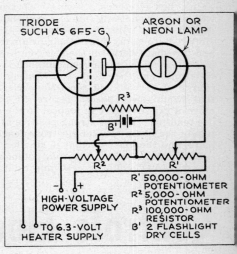

TRIODE SUCH AS 6F5-G

ARGON OR NEON LAMP

R³

B'

R²   R'

HIGH-VOLTAGE POWER SUPPLY

TO 6.3-VOLT HEATER SUPPLY

R' 50,000 - OHM POTENTIOMETER
R² 5,000 - OHM POTENTIOMETER
R³ 100,000 - OHM RESISTOR
B' 2 FLASHLIGHT DRY CELLS

to changes in grid potential at almost the speed of light. Electrons have very little mass, hence very little inertia. They can be moved at tremendous velocities. Electrons can be impressed upon the grid of a vacuum-tube amplifier in a ten-billionth of a second and drained off as quickly. The plate current will respond to such changes in the grid potential faithfully, even though it may take more than a ten-billionth of a second for the electrons comprising that plate current to travel from the cathode to the plate. The plate-current variations would arrive a trifle later than the grid impulses, but all in correct order and properly spaced.

However, to charge and discharge a grid periodically, we must move electrons quickly and in great numbers. Small though their inertia is, pumping them into and out of a grid at high frequencies requires considerable power. The reason for this is that a grid constitutes one plate of a tiny condenser, which in most small amplifier tubes has a capacity of only a few micromicrofarads. Now a certain number of electrons impressed upon a .001-mfd. condenser will produce a charge of, say, 10 volts. But the same number of electrons on a .01-mfd. condenser will charge it to only 1 volt. Therefore, the bigger the grid (that is, the greater its capacity) the more energy is required to pump electrons into and out of it.

A 1-mmfd. condenser will be charged to a potential of 1 volt by a current of 1 micro-microampere flowing for 1 second. To charge this same condenser to the same potential in a millionth of a second takes 1 microampere—a million times the current.

Radio amateurs working with short-wave equipment at frequencies up to 750 megacycles use very small "acorn" tubes in special circuits. At such frequencies, the capacitance even of a straight piece of hook-up wire becomes something to reckon with.

Triode Oscillator Generates Wide Range of Frequencies

WITH the homemade oscillator shown below, you can generate audio frequencies ranging from the lowest to the highest audible to the human ear. The addition of a telegraph key makes the oscillator a useful code-practice set.

By impressing upon the grid of a triode the oscillating current of a resonant circuit,

Mounted on an old radio chassis, the oscillator is powered by a high-voltage supply shown at the right of it. Below, the underside of the chassis

we obtain in the plate circuit a current of the same frequency. Since this same plate current flows in the cathode circuit, which includes the lower half of the inductance L, the varying magnetic field there created will induce a like oscillating current in the remainder of the inductance, thus maintaining the energy in the resonant grid circuit. With the proper values of capacity, inductance, and resistance, any desired frequency can be generated. When the resistance R is adjusted to zero, the circuit oscillates at a frequency given by the formula

$$F = \frac{160}{\sqrt{LC}}$$

where F is the frequency, L the inductance in microhenries, and C the capacitance in microfarads.

With a center-tapped filter choke and a .001 to 1-mfd. condenser, a 1,000,000-ohm potentiometer tunes the circuit to various frequencies. If you have no center-tapped choke, you can use an audio transformer by joining a primary and a secondary lead so that current flows through both in the same direction. The juncture acts as a center tap, and the speaker-lead resistor can be omitted.

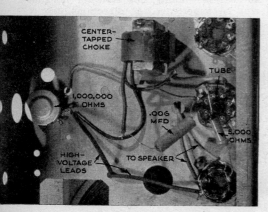

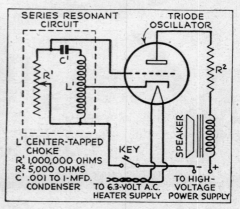

Servicing Your Radio

NOISY VOLUME CONTROLS of either the wire-wound or carbon type often can be repaired simply by removing them from the chassis and cleaning them thoroughly. Soak a piece of clean linen in ordinary noninflammable cleaning fluid and rub the windings and contact arm of a wire-wound control until they are clean. A little more care is necessary with a carbon control. Roll a small piece of absorbent cotton tightly around the end of a toothpick, dip it in the cleaning fluid, and wipe carefully, with a little pressure, along the carbon strip. Be sure also to clean the contact springs on the rotating arm.

SLIPPING IN THE TURNTABLE of a phonograph may cause difficulties that are sometimes incorrectly attributed to the motor. Look first at the rubber washer between the turntable and the motor spindle—the cone-shaped piece marked with an arrow in the photograph at left—for it may be to blame for the turntable failure. Frequently this washer becomes soaked with oil from the motor, and when this is the case, the washer surface is made so slippery that it cannot establish a firm contact with the turntable. Cleaning is rarely effective, and it is much more satisfactory to replace the old washer with a new one.

YOUR HANDS USED ALONE sometimes will serve to locate trouble in a balky receiver. For instance, if reception is weak, touching the grid cap of the converter tube —a tube such as the 6A8 or 2A7—with one finger and chassis with another, as indicated in the photograph, may make it come in louder. This will mean that the secondary of the antenna coil is open or that a corroded connection on the coil is causing an extremely high resistance in the circuit. Even persons shy of electricity need have no fear in making this test, for no shock will be experienced if directions are followed. Don't touch parts below the chassis.

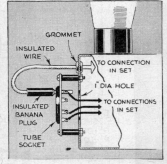

GROMMET
INSULATED WIRE
TO CONNECTION IN SET
1" DIA HOLE
TO CONNECTIONS IN SET
INSULATED BANANA PLUG
TUBE SOCKET

WAVEBAND SWITCHES and other switches in a receiver circuit may be replaced when they break down by using a four to six-prong tube socket and an insulated banana plug, as shown in the photograph at the far left. The socket may be mounted on the back of the chassis, following the directions detailed in the drawing. Two sleeves placed under it will raise it slightly from the chassis so that there will be room for insertion of the plug.

radio ideas

FM POLICE RADIO EQUIPMENT now incorporates "iron-core" or inductive tuning among other new features. The closely controlled movement of an iron core in and out of a small form-wound coil permits easier and more accurate tuning, and reduces the effects of car vibration on tuning adjustments. Likewise new is a "workbench" support which proves convenient when the chassis is inverted for inspection or repair. Test jacks permit direct, simultaneous readings of several functions at one time. All tube sockets and tuning controls are stenciled on the top of the chassis.

A MIDGET RECTIFIER for energizing any electrodynamic speaker having a high-resistance field coil can be made as shown in the accompanying diagram. This will permit substitution of such a speaker in a circuit originally calling for a permanent-magnet speaker. One of the advantages of the midget rectifier is that it is small enough to fit any radio chassis and therefore can be used in a wide range of circuits in which such a speaker is to be supplanted. It will provide the current necessary to operate an electrodynamic speaker if it is equipped with a rectifier tube capable of carrying at least 150 milliamperes, and is a handy expedient when a permanent-magnet speaker is not available.

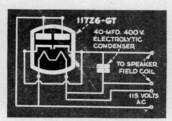

RESISTOR AND CONDENSER CODES   [*ELECTRICAL*]

Small carbon resistors and small mica condensers required in a modern radio set are too small for convenient labeling with numerals, so the Radio Manufacturers Association has adopted a standard code-marking system, a color code. Digits are represented by colors as follows:

0	Black	5	Green
1	Brown	6	Blue
2	Red	7	Violet
3	Orange	8	Gray
4	Yellow	9	White

Two types of markings are used on resistors. The straight-end, tubular-type resistor, with leads coming straight out of the end, is marked with color bands. The band at one end represents the first digit, the next band gives the second digit, and the third band gives the number of zeros. That is, if the bands are brown-green-orange, they are read 1-5-three zeros, or 15,000 ohms. This straight-end type sometimes carries a fourth band, either gold or silver. This band indicates the accuracy of value, gold being the highest.

The second type of resistor —with leads coming out at right angles—uses the body color for the first digit, tip color for the second, and a dot or band at the center for the number of zeros. Thus brown body, green tip, orange band should be interpreted as 1-5-000 or 15,000 ohms.

Condensers use the same type of color coding, but the readings are in micromicrofarads, and the color is applied in small dots with an arrow indicating the order in which they are to be read.

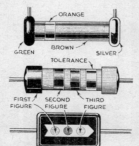

POPULAR SCIENCE MONTHLY SHOP DATA

Dissolved Oxygen Reduces Power Needs and Increases Life of Electron Tubes

THE recent solution of a long-standing electronic mystery promises new radio tubes which will have both longer operating lives and reduced power requirements. Similar improvements are foreseen for other electron tubes.

It is the purpose of a vacuum-tube cathode, of course, to discharge a volley of electrons to the plate. For 40 years scientists have known that an oxide-coated cathode emits electrons more readily than a pure metal one, but they haven't known why. Now Dr. Harvey C. Rentschler, Westinghouse research expert, has an answer.

Atoms of oxygen, he finds, apparently distort the crystal-lattice structure of the cathode and thus enable the electrons to be shot off more easily. Moreover, a method has been discovered by which oxygen can be dissolved within the metal of the cathode, much as salt can be dissolved in water. In previous practice, certain types of cathodes have been made by forming oxides of various metals into a paste and baking the paste on tungsten supports. The procedure developed by Dr. Rentschler consists of heating cathodes of zirconium, titanium, thorium, or caesium in oxygen until a "solid solution" of oxygen is uniformly distributed throughout the metal.

High-voltage vacuum tubes offer a special application of this new technique. Hitherto the cathode of a high-voltage tube has had to be made without an oxide coating because the strong electric field would rip the coating from its support. Oxygen dissolved in the cathode, however, is an integral part of it and can't be pulled off.

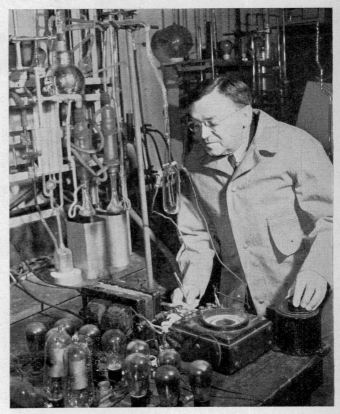

Within the glass tube is a strip of zirconium which Dr. Rentschler is treating with oxygen to improve its electron-emitting characteristics

Below, a photoelectric cell having one of the new cathodes is tested by a spectroscope. Electron emission is caused by both light and heat

How Airplane Wings Get Their Lift

WHAT gives an airplane its lift? Near the beginning of the eighteenth century, a Swiss mathematician, Daniel Bernoulli, discovered a physical principle which accounts for the greater part of the answer. In the course of experimenting with fluids, both liquids and gases, he found that pressure decreases as velocity increases.

The Bernoulli principle explains the increased draft of a chimney when wind blows across its top, the bursting of a house near the path of a tornado, the curve of a ball that is spun as it is thrown. It is also one of the most vital factors in aerodynamics, ac-

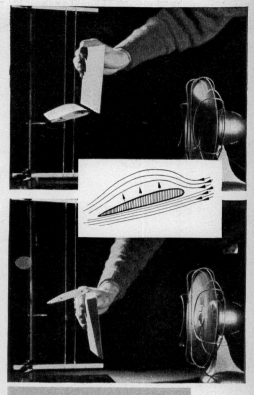

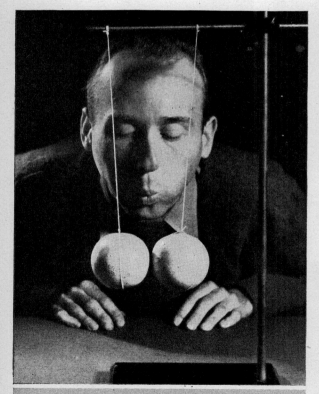

AN AIR STREAM directed in the space between two freely suspended oranges will result in lowered air pressure in this area. The outside air pressure will thereupon force the two oranges together. Suspend the oranges so that they are about 1½" apart when hanging at rest.

MAKE THIS AIRFOIL by covering a cardboard-and-dowel frame with paper. Holes are needed in the paper to enable the airfoil to move freely along the guide wires as pictured in the photographs above. Stops on the wires cause the airfoil to rest normally just a little below the center of the slip stream from the fan. To show that the airfoil gets more lift from the partial vacuum above the wing than from the air stream under it, hold a strip of cardboard under the leading edge so that only the under surface is exposed to the breeze of the fan. The airfoil will rise a little. Then make a second test by holding the cardboard in such a way that the fan blows only above the airfoil, which now rises much higher.

counting for nearly 75 percent of the total lift exerted by an airplane wing. Air passing rapidly over the curved upper surface of a wing reduces pressure there, causing a partial vacuum. The relatively greater pressure beneath the wing then buoys it up. This may sound mysterious, for the idea that lift comes from a partial vacuum above a wing is not the most obvious explanation. But by performing the accompanying simple experiments, you can prove to yourself how the Bernoulli principle plays a part in modern aerodynamics.

A MANOMETER, a device used for measuring gas pressure, can be made by partly filling a bent glass tube with colored water. The level in both sides is normally the same, but when you blow through another tube squarely across one open end of the manometer, the water rises in that leg, showing that the air pressure on that side is reduced. As you blow harder, increasing the speed of the air flow, the water rises higher. Similar manometers are used in determining pressures on the various parts of airplane wing surfaces and on the wings of test models. Atomizers work on the same principle.

CUT TWO DISKS of cardboard about 4″ in diameter. Make a small hole in the center of one and seal the end of a drinking straw over the hole with sealing wax. Push a pin through the center of the other disk. Hold the first disk about ½″ over the other with the pin sticking up into the straw. Blow hard through the straw, and the lower disk will jump up to the other. The harder you blow, the more firmly the disks stick together, since the air rushing between them reduces internal pressure while external pressure remains the same.

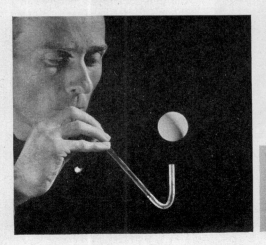

A TABLE-TENNIS BALL bounces up and down if supported on an air stream, but it won't fall to one side. As it tends to do so, the air stream creates a low-pressure area on the opposite side, and atmospheric pressure moves it back.

Magical Tricks
WORKED WITH CHEMISTRY
Simple Home Demonstrations To Mystify Your Friends

By KENNETH M. SWEZEY

ALTHOUGH it may be a far cry from the ancient alchemist's den to the modern laboratory, chemistry is still a science of amazement and seeming magic. Everyone who professes to be a chemist, amateur or otherwise, is expected by his lay friends to be able to conjure up wonders at the slightest notice.

For personal pleasure, and to gratify these friends, every home chemist ought to develop a little "curiosity shop"—a collection of exhibits and fascinating stunts with which he can entertain visitors. Items for this shop can be both permanent displays and tricks that can be performed with the minimum of preparation. A few suggestions follow, but every installment of this home chemistry series contains at least one stunt that could

well be included in your repertory of wonders.

A "silver tree" that can either be "grown" before the spectator's eyes or be set up as a semipermanent exhibit will make a beautiful and instructive feature. Merely dissolve 3 grams silver nitrate in 60 ml. distilled water and pour it into a 2-oz. bottle. Carefully clean and scrape a roll of tin foil about 1½" long and ¼" in diameter, and suspend it from the stopper of the bottle. In a few minutes glittering crystals of pure silver will be deposited over the surface of the tin foil. Being chemically more active than silver, tin drives the silver out of the silver nitrate and replaces it. The crystals of silver keep growing until all the silver in the solution has been replaced. They will remain on the tin-foil core until jarring dislodges them.

A miniature flag that responds as a humidity indicator, and may be changed

Here is a puzzler guaranteed to make spectators gape. A beaker or thin glass containing crystals of ammonium nitrate is set on a damp block of wood. Simply by adding water and stirring vigorously, the beaker can be made to stick tight. As the crystals are dissolved, the beaker becomes intensely cold and the drops under it freeze solid

coating of oil smeared inside the beaker above the solution will allow the water to evaporate eventually of its own accord and keep the chemical from creeping over the top of the beaker. When the crystals are dry, the stunt may be repeated.

You probably know the dinner-table stunt of boiling water on a visiting card with turned-up edges. The match or candle flame used does not burn the card because the water keeps the latter below the temperature of combustion. With care, tinfoil and lead foil may be melted similarly on a card.

The safety lamp, invented by Sir Humphrey Davy to prevent the explosion of free gas in coal mines, makes use of the same principle. In this case a screen of fine wire gauze surrounding the flame prevents igniting of outside gas by limiting the heat that gets through. A model of a safety lamp can be made from metal netting soldered or sewn to form a tube 6" long and 2" in diameter. Fasten on a top of the same material. If copper gauze of 30 or 40 mesh is used, only one layer will be required. Coarser netting, such as ordinary window screen, may require three or four layers. A jar cover forms the base, and a birthday-cake candle the light. Direct a stream of illuminating gas from a small tube toward your safety lamp. The gas will not ignite outside the screening, though it may catch fire within the lamp.

A little ball of steel wool that floats and sinks apparently without rhyme or reason is another good puzzler. Fill a tall tumbler or glass cylinder with a water-clear solution made up of 1 part sulphuric acid and 6 parts water. Compress a little wad of fine steel wool to the size of a marble and drop it into the solution. First it will float because of air trapped in it; then it will sink as the solution penetrates. Suddenly, however, it will rise again, then fall, and go through unpredictable gyrations.

To the chemist, the cause of the rising and sinking is obvious. The iron liberates

from bright blue to pale pink merely by blowing on it, is another stock exhibit that may be made in a few minutes and will always arouse interest. Soak a piece of white cotton goods in a solution of cobalt chloride. While this cloth remains wet, or is even moist from humidity, it will be pink, but as it dries, its color changes to light blue and then to deeper and deeper shades of blue. Mount the cloth on a little flagstaff. Before demonstrating the trick, warm the flag slightly in order to make it the deepest blue. By blowing on it for a minute or so, you can turn it pink as the crystals of cobalt chloride absorb moisture from the breath.

Strips of white paper can be made to turn pink or red when held in what appears to be an empty glass, and then to turn white again when removed. Prepare a supply by soaking strips of blotting or filter paper in phenolphthalein solution and allow them to dry. To work the stunt, moisten a strip in plain water and hold it in a glass that has just been rinsed with household ammonia. In the presence of the ammonia, the phenolphthalein gives its usual reaction to a base, turning pink or red, but returned to fresh air, it loses its color.

A beaker or thin glass containing 60 grams ammonium nitrate will enable you to perform a feat that will get a sure-fire response. Put a dozen drops of water on a wood block and place your beaker in the center of the puddle. Now stir in 60 ml. of water (as cold as you can get it), attempting to dissolve the chemical as quickly as possible. During this process the beaker will become extremely cold and in a minute or two will freeze fast to the block. A thin

As a finale for your home exhibition of chemical magic, put a little potassium thiocyanate in the bottom of a tumbler, some silver nitrate in another, a few drops of potassium ferrocyanide in a third, and ferric chloride and water in a pitcher. Pour this last into the glasses. The first will become red, the second milky white, and the third blue

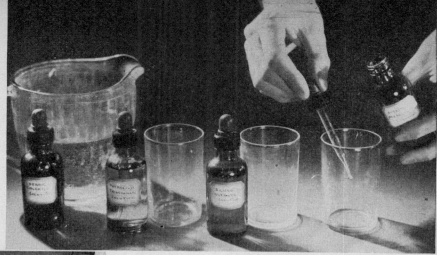

hydrogen from the dilute acid. This clings to the ball and buoys it up, but as some of the gas is lost, the ball drops again. If the ball doesn't rise, fluff out the steel wool; if it doesn't sink, compress it further.

For an astonishing—and patriotic—finale, prepare four little dropper-top bottles, each containing a solution of potassium thiocyanate, silver nitrate, and potassium ferrocyanide, and ferric chloride, dissolving 10 grams of each chemical in 60 ml. water. Into the first of three tumblers put 10 drops of potassium thiocyanate; into the second, 10 drops of silver nitrate; into the third, eight drops of potassium ferrocyanide. These solutions are clear and will not be noticed at the bottoms of the glasses. The ferric chloride solution, however, is yellowish, so about 15 drops of it are put into a tinted or opaque pitcher, together with three glassfuls of plain water.

Pour the solution from the pitcher into the first glass, and it instantly becomes red; pour it into the second, and it becomes white; pour it into the third, and it becomes blue!

Made of ordinary wire gauze or screening, the little lamp above will demonstrate the effectiveness of the miner's safety lamp invented by Sir Humphrey Davy. A jet of illuminating gas directed toward the flame will cause it to flutter, but will not ignite outside the lamp. The wire gauze cuts down the intensity of the heat passing through to prevent combustion

Literally made to grow before the eyes of your friends, the little "silver tree" at right presents a pretty sight. It is a small roll of tin foil in a solution of silver nitrate. Tin is more chemically active than silver, and suspended in the solution it replaces the silver, which is deposited on the roll in glittering crystals as it is freed. This continues until all the silver is used up

GARDEN TOOL SHEDS prefabricated of insulating wallboard for quick assembly are waterproof, fire resistant, and vermin-proof. They consist of seven parts, including four walls, a floor, and a two-part roof. There are three sizes, from 4' by 6' to 10' by 12', and they can be used on the beach as cabanas or as back-yard playhouses for children.

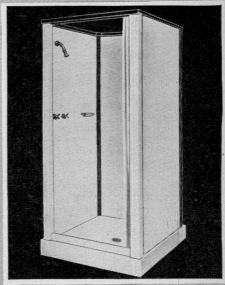

NEW SHOWER CABINETS are made of noncritical materials for quick assembly on the job. The cabinet has less than one pound of metal in it. All walls are made of hard pressed wallboard covered with baked enamel resistant to high temperatures. The receptor is made of green plastic. Complete equipment is included with the cabinets, even to the curtain.

COOKING ON GLASS proves quite practical with this portable grate and grill. It is made of glass that has been fired black, powdered to a fine dust, then molded into the grill and basket grate. A folding frame made of wood is coated with fire-resistant glass to render it safe from flame. The grill surface measures 12" by 19". Any kind of fuel may be used, although charcoal is, of course, ideal for the purpose.

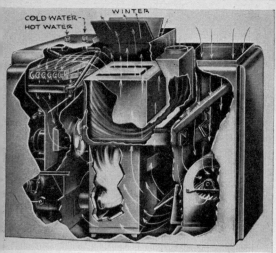

COLD WATER
HOT WATER
WINTER

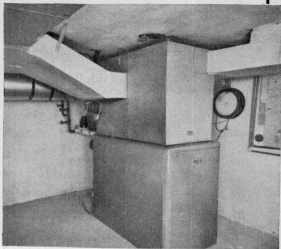

HOME HEATING may be revolutionized by a new furnace recently invented by Corporal Harry Giffords of the Army Air Forces. The automatic unit furnishes hot water the year around, heats and circulates air in cold weather, provides circulation of outside air during hot days, and filters the air at all times. One of the unusual features of the operation of this unit is that it imparts heat from heated air to water, and uses the water so heated to furnish the domestic hot-water supply.

In summer the unit heats air that in turn heats water for storage or for immediate use without interfering with the circulation of cool outside air. An artificial cooling unit can be added if desired. The furnace is said to be economical to operate. Its principle has been suggested for possible use on large postwar air liners.

PRESERVING METAL that is about to rust through and become useless, such as gutters on a house or water buckets, is a simple matter with a new solution. The metal is cleaned of rust and dirt to begin with; then the solution is painted on, leaving a thick coat. This liquid is noninflammable and can be used indoors or outside. Objects treated with the solution should be allowed a week to dry, after which they may, if desired, be painted with any good-quality oil paint.

COMBINATION LADDER. A compact ladder that folds small enough to go into the luggage compartment of a car can be used as a long extension ladder, a small or a large stepladder, or as a support for a scaffold. In the photo above one such ladder is shown extended and another in use as a stepladder. The rails and rungs are of hardwood. Rigidity in all positions is assured by a patented double-lock design.

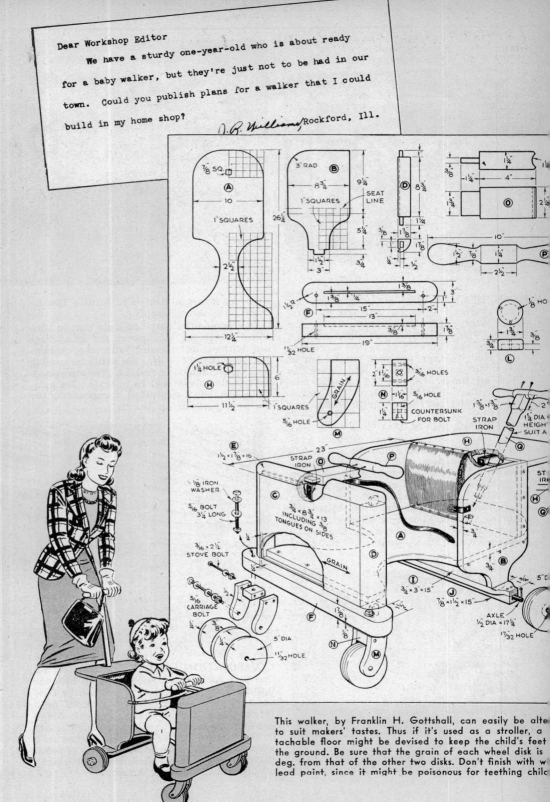

This walker, by Franklin H. Gottshall, can easily be alte to suit makers' tastes. Thus if it's used as a stroller, a tachable floor might be devised to keep the child's feet the ground. Be sure that the grain of each wheel disk is deg. from that of the other two disks. Don't finish with w lead paint, since it might be poisonous for teething chilc

INVISIBLE BREAKS in tires offered for recapping or retreading are now spotted by supersonic vibrations—sound waves beyond the range of the human ear that are also used to record ocean depths and detect submarines. This adaptation, developed by scientists of the Goodyear Tire & Rubber Co., is especially useful in locating separations of the plies or layers of fabric composing a tire. It prevents wasting rubber on a defective tire.

The tire to be tested is demounted, suspended on rollers, and partially immersed in a tank of water. With a high-frequency current through a coil, supersonic vibrations are set up in a nickel rod extending into the tank. These waves, readily transmitted through water, are picked up by a microphone inside the tire. Vibrations pass through

solid portions with full intensity, but air bubbles in any breaks interrupt the waves, causing the microphone to flash a red light.

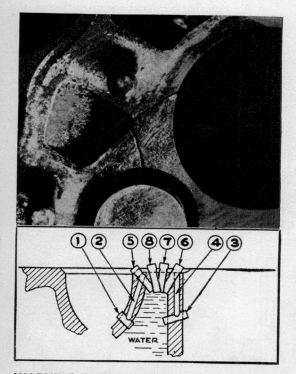

COLD WELDING, or "lacing," has found a place in war work, saving many a cracked motor block that in normal times would have been relegated to the scrap heap. The basis of the method is a new alloy of an extremely low coefficient of expansion and high heat conductivity, which tend to reduce expansion around the crack.

As described in a report prepared by the Society of Automotive Engineers for the Office of Defense Transportation, the crack is channeled and the ends drilled and tapped for pins of the new alloy, which are dipped in a liquid metallic sealing compound and inserted. Depending on the length of the crack, other holes are drilled and tapped at interlocking angles, and more alloy pins are inserted, "lacing" the crack together. The pins are peened and ground down to the original surface, making an almost invisible "weld." The motor block is then flushed with metallic seal and cleaned, and the job is finished. The photograph at left shows a crack at the valve seat of an L-head motor, and the diagram illustrates the method and order of inserting the lacing pins.

WARNING ON ANTIFREEZE made of calcium chloride solution or deodorized kerosene comes from the WPB and U. S. Bureau of Standards. Bureau engineers point out that the use of salt solutions is prohibited in Government vehicles. Salts corrode metal, especially aluminum. Bureau engineers know of no satisfactory corrosion inhibitor. Kerosene eats rubber hose and creates highly in-flammable vapors. It can be detected by its oily feel and light weight, 6¼ to 7 lb. per gal., and salt solutions by their heavy weight, over 10½ lb. per gal. Boiling in an iron skillet—not aluminum—will give a whitish precipitate if salt is present, or a drop or two of silver nitrate added to two spoonfuls of antifreeze will precipitate any salt. Test or don't buy unknown brands.

Easily Made Rope Ladder Is Useful Emergency Equipment

WHEN an emergency strikes, rope ladders are often highly desirable equipment, since they may be quickly put in position and are not hard to use. A feature which makes them especially convenient is that they can be rolled up for compact storage. They are also handy for access to a loft or attic where room does not permit installing a stairway.

These ladders are easily made from strong rope, 18" lengths of oak 1¼" in diameter, and twine. The rope may be used in two pieces or doubled. Unlay the strands at equally spaced intervals 12" to 18" apart, insert the rungs, allowing 1" to protrude, and hold them fast with staples. Bind twine above and below the rungs.

Whip the rope ends by forming a circle of a 15" length of twine, with ends overlapping 2". Hold it against the rope so that one end projects a little beyond the rope end. Wrap the side of the loop which extends beyond the rope back around the rope. When the loop has diminished, hold as shown and pull on the projecting end of twine. Then cut off the loose ends.—WILLIAM H. DAVIS.

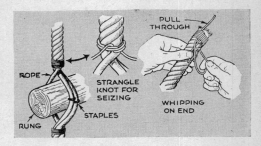

Wrapping an arm and a leg around a rope ladder gives support to the body in climbing. At right are shown details in the construction of a ladder

Perky Halloween Hobgoblins Are Created from Black Walnuts

CAPTIVATING little hobgoblins for Halloween decorations may be made from a few black walnuts and pipe cleaners. Cut off a portion of the tapered end of the walnut so that you may use the exposed cross section for the face. The simplest way to do this is to hold the nut in a vise and cut it with a coping saw. Dig the meat from the two natural eye holes and fill the cavities with wood putty. After the putty has hardened, paint a little pupil on a part of each eye. The natural formation of a black walnut will give the illusion of a nose and mouth. Saw out the hobgoblin's big feet from ½" stock and drill holes in the head, body, and feet. Attach the head and feet to the body with pipe cleaners and glue, allow-

ing the glue to set before painting all but the face with mahogany oil stain. The little fellows will serve to hold nut cups and place cards if their pipe-cleaner arms are bent properly. They may also be placed around the room as Halloween decorations.—E. W.

USEFUL AUTO HINTS

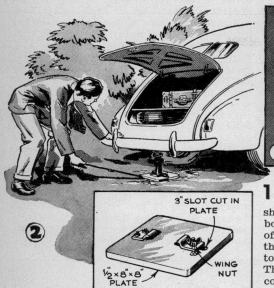

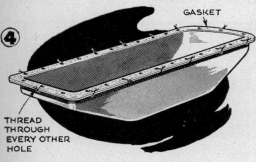

3" SLOT CUT IN PLATE

WING NUT

½"×8"×8" PLATE

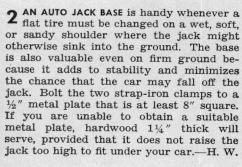

WIRE

CELLULOSE TAPE

6" HOOK-SHAPED BOLT

1"×2"×15" BOARD

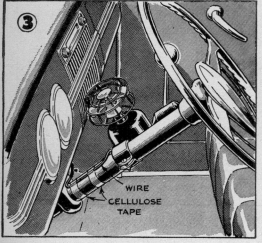

GASKET

THREAD THROUGH EVERY OTHER HOLE

1 **TIRE INSPECTION TOOLS** can be made by inserting two 6″ long screw hooks a short distance from the ends of two boards. If these are hooked over the beads of a casing and the ends of the boards are then pulled away from the tire, it is easy to look for breaks, other injuries, or nails. The tools cost little to make and may be conveniently carried in the car.—A. R.

2 **AN AUTO JACK BASE** is handy whenever a flat tire must be changed on a wet, soft, or sandy shoulder where the jack might otherwise sink into the ground. The base is also valuable even on firm ground because it adds to stability and minimizes the chance that the car may fall off the jack. Bolt the two strap-iron clamps to a ½″ metal plate that is at least 8″ square. If you are unable to obtain a suitable metal plate, hardwood 1¼″ thick will serve, provided that it does not raise the jack too high to fit under your car.—H. W.

3 **CELLULOSE TAPE** is convenient for securing loose or dangling wires about the steering column and dashboard. The tape, which is inconspicuous because of its transparency, both removes a minor accident hazard and reduces the likelihood of short circuits or broken wires. It is also excellent for correcting rattles and squeaks of fittings under the dash.—E. M. G.

4 **GASKETS CAN BE HELD** in place by thread when an oil pan (or any other large part using a gasket) is being reassembled. It is often difficult to insert the bolts through the proper holes even when heavy grease or shellac is used as a binder for the gasket. If ordinary sewing thread is looped through alternate holes, the pan can be bolted on easily. Once the bolts are drawn up tightly, the fine thread will not interfere with a perfect seal.—J. K.

Homemade Brooder Uses Infrared Lamps as Source of Heat

WITH factory-made brooders hard to get, poultrymen may need homemade equipment to increase chick production. Shown below is a simply built brooder of 250-chick capacity which will let you raise "spring" broilers at any season, and which costs only $3 to $7 for materials. It was designed by Professor John E. Nichols, of Pennsylvania State College.

The brooder is made of ⅞" by 10" stock, with legs 2" by 2" by 14". Set the inside cleats 11" from the ground, and nail on them a flooring of 10" stock, 4' long. You will then have two shallow compartments, the lower one giving about 4" ground clearance. Fill the upper compartment with floor litter to serve as insulation, and tack a cloth skirt to the sides. Slats can be nailed across the top so that the brooder may later serve as a roost for older chickens.

On facing inner sides of the lower compartment set two porcelain lamp sockets, and bore a ⅜" hole for the cord. A strip of wood under the upper edge of each socket base will give the lamps a desirable downward tilt. Be sure to use heavy-duty wire in connecting the sockets. The lamps are 150-watt reflector-flood types or 250-watt reflector-drying types, with rated lives of 1,000 and 5,000 hours respectively. These lamps, which project infrared heat rays as well as light, are especially suitable, although ordinary incandescent bulbs can be used if reflector types are unavailable. A thermostat is not needed with the former, since the chicks can find the right heat for their needs, but is desirable with ordinary bulbs.

An even simpler brooder for 200 chicks or less can be built by forming an uncovered enclosure of wood or light sheet metal and suspending one or two reflector bulbs over the area. Start with a lamp about 12" above the brood and raise it with the handy wire shortener as the chicks grow.

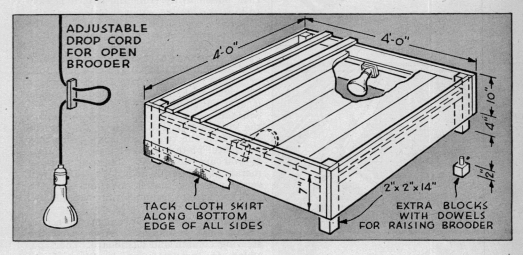

ADJUSTABLE DROP CORD FOR OPEN BROODER

4'-0" 4'-0"

10" 4" 2"

2"x 2"x 14"

TACK CLOTH SKIRT ALONG BOTTOM EDGE OF ALL SIDES

7"

EXTRA BLOCKS WITH DOWELS FOR RAISING BROODER

Wood Supports Keep Chickens from Upsetting Water Pan

CHICKENS perching on the side of a water pan will frequently upset it, particularly when the water level is low. A simple and practical method of preventing this is to use three notched supports as shown in the drawing to the right. Saw kerfs in the tops of three wooden stakes, sharpen the opposite ends, and drive them into the ground in the proper position. It may be necessary to bend the lip of the pan somewhat so that it fits the notches snugly.—JOHN K. KARLOVIC.

NOTCHED SUPPORT

LIP BENT TO FIT NOTCH

PAN

AUTO *Ideas*

OVERSIZE TIRES are now issued to Army motorcycle units for desert use. The tires, which are mounted on 15″ rims, carry only a few pounds of air pressure for travel through sand. Armored Force officers say that they have jumped the motorcycle from the least maneuverable military vehicle in deep sand to the most maneuverable.

The photos above, taken at the Armored Force School, show the new tire undergoing hill-climbing tests and compared to a standard tire. Note the greatly increased road-bearing surface.

PHANTOM RAYS, sun reflections that may make a traffic signal seem to be lighted when the sun is low in the sky, are eliminated in a new type of light shown below. The silvered glass reflector is so shaped as to prevent the reflection of any light except that from the bulb within the signal.

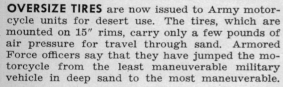

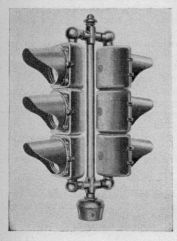

PORTABLE FLUORESCENT lighting units have been developed for use in garages. These utility lamps each contain two fluorescent tubes which are protected from breakage by a clear plastic guard. The lamps may be used on casters under autos or suspended like droplights.

Motor and compressor are mounted on one chassis. A homemade check valve is shown in the sketch to the left; at the upper right, a pressure control

HEAVY-DUTY AIR COMPRESSOR

The throttle of this motor is controlled by a rod from a pressure unit that was made by bolting together two conduit boxes over a rubber diaphragm

On the compressor, below, the throttle control rod is moved by a vacuum overdrive unit, but the type used with the engine would have been satisfactory. The radiator is needed to keep the compressor cool

AIR compressors can't be bought readily today, so when a mining company needed one, Henry Lawrence, of Santa Fe, N. M., built it from two wrecked cars. A motor from one is used to drive a compressor made from the other motor.

To convert the motor to a compressor, Lawrence removed the valve lifters and installed light springs on the valves. This enables both the intake and exhaust valves to feed air to the cylinders, and makes each upward stroke a compression stroke. To filter all the air through the carburetor air cleaner, the exhaust manifold was closed off and an inner wall broken through to the intake manifold.

Studs were screwed into the firing chambers in the cylinder head and lead was poured around them to increase compression. Homemade check valves were screwed into the spark-plug holes. Each was made of a pipe tee, the valve proper consisting of a concave expansion plug such as is used to safeguard engine blocks against freezing. A check valve in the air manifold also keeps air from feeding back.

Two homemade control units govern the machine. The air chambers in the control units are connected with a hot-water tank relief valve set on the air tank. When pressure reaches the point for which this valve is set, the control diaphragms move rods attached to each carburetor. This reduces the engine speed to idling and also cuts off the compressor air intake so that it "coasts." A pinhole in the air line to the control units allows the pressure to bleed out slowly. Then both throttles open and pumping continues.—EUGENE S. HARRIS.

INDEX